ADVANCES IN LIPID RESEARCH

Volume 7

CONTRIBUTORS TO THIS VOLUME

C. W. M. Adams

Neil R. Artman

Fritz Bischoff

Esko A. Nikkilä

George H. Rothblat

Advances in Lipid Research

Volume 7

Edited by

Rodolfo Paoletti

*Institute of Pharmacology
Milan, Italy*

David Kritchevsky

*The Wistar Institute
Philadelphia, Pennsylvania*

 1969

ACADEMIC PRESS • New York and London

ACADEMIC PRESS, INC.
111 Fifth Avenue, New York, New York 10003

United Kingdom Edition published by
ACADEMIC PRESS, INC. (LONDON) LTD.
Berkeley Square House, London W.1

LIBRARY OF CONGRESS CATALOG CARD NUMBER: 63-22330

PRINTED IN THE UNITED STATES OF AMERICA

LIST OF CONTRIBUTORS

Numbers in parentheses indicate the pages on which the authors' contributions begin.

C. W. M. ADAMS, *Guy's Hospital Medical School, London University, and Guy's Hospital, London, Great Britain (1)*

NEIL R. ARTMAN, *The Procter & Gamble Company, Miami Valley Laboratories, Cincinnati, Ohio (245)*

FRITZ BISCHOFF, *Santa Barbara Cottage Hospital Research Institute, Santa Barbara, California (165)*

ESKO A. NIKKILÄ, *Third Department of Medicine, University of Helsinki, Helsinki, Finland (63)*

GEORGE H. ROTHBLAT, *The Wistar Institute of Anatomy and Biology, Philadelphia, Pennsylvania (135)*

PREFACE

The discussions which appear in this volume of *Advances in Lipid Research* illustrate the wide scope of topics which are germane to lipid research. Five completely different areas of interest, all of great current importance, are surveyed in detail.

The first chapter presents a review of lipid histochemistry. The histochemistry of lipids, in both its qualitative and quantitative aspects, is discussed in depth. The second chapter reviews the roles of carbohydrate metabolism and insulin in relation to their control of the metabolism of plasma and liver triglycerides. The increasing body of evidence interrelating carbohydrate and triglyceride metabolism makes the chapter especially pertinent at this time. Tissue culture systems have recently been shown to make an excellent tool for the study of many aspects of lipid metabolism. A thought-provoking review of lipid metabolism in many tissue culture systems is the subject of the third chapter. The fourth contribution deals with a subject not generally associated with lipids, namely, carcinogenesis. However, the work on steroidal carcinogenesis dates back at least three decades. The current chapter reviews the connection between cancer and steroids in its experimental and theoretical aspects. The last chapter deals with a common problem — the possible harmful effects of heating dietary fats. Since heating may affect both the chemical and biological properties of fats, they are discussed together.

June, 1969   RODOLFO PAOLETTI
                                                DAVID KRITCHEVSKY

CONTENTS

LIST OF CONTRIBUTORS   v

PREFACE   vii

CONTENTS OF PREVIOUS VOLUMES   xii

Lipid Histochemistry

C. W. M. Adams

I.	Introduction	1
II.	Histophysical Aspects	2
III.	Histochemical Aspects	9
IV.	Biological and Pathological Applications	36
V.	General Conclusions	44
VI.	Technical Appendix	45
	References	56

Control of Plasma and Liver Triglyceride Kinetics by Carbohydrate Metabolism and Insulin

Esko A. Nikkilä

| I. | Introduction . . . . | 63 |
| II. | General Outline of Triglyceride Fluxes and Their Control | 65 |

  III. Insulin Actions on Triglyceride Metabolism 69
  IV. Triglyceride Metabolism in Diabetes 80
   V. Influence of Exogenous Carbohydrates on
      Triglyceride Metabolism 100
  VI. The Metabolic Error of Endogenous ("Carbohydrate-
      Induced") Hyperglyceridemia 117
      References 124

Lipid Metabolism in Tissue Culture Cells

George H. Rothblat

    I. Introduction 135
   II. Fatty Acids, Triglycerides, and Phospholipids 137
  III. Cholesterol 145
   IV. General Considerations of Lipid Metabolism in
       Tissue Culture Cells 155
       References 161

Carcinogenic Effects of Steroids

Fritz Bischoff

    I. Introduction 165
   II. Cholesterol and Derivatives 168
  III. Neoplasms Induced by Steroid Hormones 190
   IV. Theoretical Considerations 209
    V. The Human Scene 222
   VI. Discussion 231
  VII. Summary 235
       References 237

The Chemical and Biological Properties of Heated and Oxidized Fats

Neil R. Artman

I.	Introduction	245
II.	Auto-oxidation	247
III.	Thermal Reactions in the Absence of Air	261
IV.	Oxidation at High Temperatures	269
V.	Commercial Processing Conditions	289
VI.	Frying	290
VII.	Carcinogenicity Studies	303
VIII.	Metabolic Effects of Heated and Oxidized Fats	306
IX.	Interaction of Heated Fats with Other Dietary Components	309
X.	Analytical Methods	310
XI.	Summary	314
	References	315

AUTHOR INDEX 331
SUBJECT INDEX 355

CONTENTS OF PREVIOUS VOLUMES

Volume 1

The Structural Investigation of Natural Fats
  M. H. Coleman

Physical Structure and Behavior of Lipids and Lipid Enzymes
  A. D. Bangham

Recent Developments in the Mechanism of Fat Absorption
  John M. Johnston

The Clearing Factor Lipase and Its Action in the Transport of Fatty Acids between the Blood and Tissues
  D. S. Robinson

Vitamin E and Lipid Metabolism
  Roslyn B. Alfin-Slater and Rosemary Shull Morris

Atherosclerosis — Spontaneous and Induced
  Thomas B. Clarkson

Chromatographic Investigations in Fatty Acid Biosynthesis
  M. Pascaud

Carnitine and Its Role in Fatty Acid Metabolism
  Irving B. Fritz

Present Status of Research on Catabolism and Excretion of Cholesterol
  Henry Danielsson

The Plant Sulfolipid
  A. A. Benson

AUTHOR INDEX — SUBJECT INDEX

Volume 2

Triglyceride Structure
  R. J. VanderWal

Bacterial Lipids
  M. Kates

Phosphatidylglycerols and Lipoamino Acids
  Marjorie G. Macfarlane

The Brain Phosphoinositides
  J. N. Hawthorne and P. Kemp

The Synthesis of Phosphoglycerides and Some Biochemical
Applications
  L. L. M. van Deenen and G. H. deHaas

The Lipolytic and Esterolytic Activity of Blood and Tissues and
Problems of Atherosclerosis
  T. Zemplényi

Evaluation of Drugs Active against Experimental Atherosclerosis
  Robert Hess

Comparative Evaluation of Lipid Biosynthesis in Vitro and in Vivo
  P. Favarger

AUTHOR INDEX — SUBJECT INDEX

Volume 3

The Metabolism of Polyenoic Fatty Acids
  E. Klenk

The Analysis of Human Serum Lipoprotein Distributions
  Alicia M. Ewing, Norman K. Freeman, and Frank T. Lindgren

Factors Affecting Lipoprotein Metabolism
  Angelo M. Scanu

The Action of Drugs on Phospholipid Metabolism
  G. B. Ansell

Brain Sterol Metabolism
  A. N. Davison

Lipases
  E. D. Wills

AUTHOR INDEX — SUBJECT INDEX

Volume 4

The Role of Lipids in Blood Coagulation
  Aaron J. Marcus

Lipid Responses to Dietary Carbohydrates
  I. Macdonald

Effects of Catecholamines on Lipid Mobilization
  Max Wenke

The Polyunsaturated Fatty Acids of Microorganisms
  Robert Shaw

Lipid Metabolism in the Bacteria
  W. J. Lennarz

Quantitative Methods for the Study of Vitamin D
  Padmanabhan P. Nair

Labeling and Radiopurity of Lipids
  Fred Snyder and Claude Piantadosi

AUTHOR INDEX — SUBJECT INDEX

Volume 5

Fatty Acid Biosynthesis and the Role of the Acyl Carrier Protein
  Philip W. Majerus and P. Roy Vagelos

Comparative Studies on the Physiology of Adipose Tissue
  Daniel Rudman and Mario Di Girolamo

Ethionine Fatty Liver
  Emmanuel Farber

Lipid Metabolism by Macrophages and Its Relationship to Atherosclerosis
  Allan J. Day

Dynamics of Cholesterol in Rats, Studied by the Isotopic Equilibrium
Methods
  F. Chevallier

The Metabolism of Myelin Lipids
  Marion Edmonds Smith

Brain Cholesterol: The Effect of Chemical and Physical Agents
  Jon J. Kabara

The Analysis of Individual Molecular Species of Polar Lipids
  Ossi Renkonen

Phase Diagrams of Triglyceride Systems
  J. B. Rossell

AUTHOR INDEX — SUBJECT INDEX

Volume 6

Practical Methods for Plasma Lipoprotein Analysis
  Frederick T. Hatch and Robert S. Lees

The Lipids of *Mycoplasma*
  Paul F. Smith

Lipid Quinones
  T. Ramasarma

Comparative Pathogenetic Patterns in Atherosclerosis
  Robert W. Wissler and Dragoslava Vesselinovitch

Chemistry and Metabolism of Bile Alcohols and Higher Bile Acids
  Takahiko Hoshita and Taro Kazuno

Hydroxy Fatty Acid Metabolism in Brain
  David M. Bowen and Norman S. Radin

Gas Phase Analytical Methods for the Study of Steroids
  E. C. Horning, C. J. W. Brooks, and W. J. A. Vanden Heuvel

AUTHOR INDEX — SUBJECT INDEX

Lipid Histochemistry

C. W. M. ADAMS

Guy's Hospital Medical School, London University, and Guy's Hospital, London, Great Britain

I. Introduction 1
II. Histophysical Aspects 2
    A. Physical Features of Lipids 2
    B. Lipid Fixation 5
    C. Histophysical Methods 6
III. Histochemical Aspects 9
    A. Chemical Features of Lipids 9
    B. Histochemical Staining Methods 11
    C. Enzymic Digestive Methods 31
    D. Electron Histochemical Methods 32
    E. Lipid Autoradiography 33
    F. Quantitative Lipid Histochemistry 35
IV. Biological and Pathological Applications 36
    A. General Considerations 36
    B. Synopses of Specific Applications 38
V. General Conclusions 44
VI. Technical Appendix 45
    A. Fixation and Microtomy Techniques 45
    B. Slide Histochemical Methods 46
References 56

I. Introduction

Biologists and pathologists have for many years been somewhat exasperated at being confined to structural description of tissues under the microscope. Nevertheless, botanists such as Raspail and the outstanding pathologist of the nineteenth century — Rudolph von Virchow — had endeavored in early days to translate morphological microscopic descriptions into chemical terms. This point is further exemplified by the number of somewhat crude protein tests that were introduced into histology toward the end of the last century (viz., the xanthoproteic and Millon methods).

Since the publication of Lison's *Histochemie Animale* (1936), histochemistry has become a more organized technology than hitherto. At first the techniques were applied to microscopic slides as *qualitative* nonquantitative tests. Subsequently, however, *quantitative* methods were introduced into histochemistry such as techniques for estimating enzymic activity and substances in consecutive histological sections (Linderstrøm-Lang, 1939), ultraviolet absorption estimation of sections (Caspersson, 1940), and, more recently, ultrafine dissection of individual cells and their components (Hydén, 1962). Application of qualitative histochemical methods to electron microscopic preparations has further extended the range of histochemistry's application and, indeed, subcellular fractionation by centrifugal and density gradients can also be regarded as a form of cytological fractionation followed by precise chemical estimation.

The distinction between the terms "histochemistry" and "cytochemistry" is perhaps somewhat nebulous. It is debatable whether there is any value in sharply distinguishing methods that overlap at their boundaries. Moreover, as pointed out by Glick (1967), histochemistry and cytochemistry are only divisions of biochemistry (or histology) and cannot be regarded as separate disciplines. Indeed nothing is gained by "compartmentalization" within a discipline or, for that matter, between disciplines.

The main purpose of this review is to discuss the histochemistry of lipids, both in its direct qualitative application to microscopical sections and with reference to those quantitative methods that are applicable to serially cut tissue sections. Clearly it is impossible to discuss biological and pathological considerations within the context of a technical review. Nevertheless, Section IV is concerned with briefly illustrating some applications of lipid histochemistry and indicating what part they can play in a multidisciplinary approach to biological and pathological problems.

II. Histophysical Aspects

A. PHYSICAL FEATURES OF LIPIDS

Before discussing methods for identifying lipids, it is necessary to mention the different surface properties of lipids. Such varying surface properties clearly would affect the penetration of dyes and reagents toward the center of the lipid mass.

Phospholipids (phosphoglycerides and phosphosphingosides) are equipped with highly polar phosphoryl and basic groups. These groups project toward the water phase when such lipids are in contact with water; they confer hydrophilia and water miscibility on the molecule and thus promote the formation of "myelin buds" (Fig. 1). Bangham (1963) points out that phospholipids are "amphipathic" or "amphiphilic" in nature because the nonpolar paraffin chains of phospholipid would be directed toward the hydrophobic core of a nonpolar lipid, whereas the charged groups would be arrayed on the lipid-water interface. Neutral glycolipids, such as the glycosphingosides cerebroside and ceramide hexosides, would also be expected to be slightly hydrophilic because of their hexose components. Acidic glycolipids — ganglioside and sulfatide — are presumably more polar than the neutral sorts because of their highly charged acidic radicles.

In contrast to these complex polar lipids, simple ester lipids and unconjugated lipids (see Section III,A) are hydrophobic because they contain a predominance of nonpolar groups. Hydrophobic lipids include triglycerides, waxes, and cholesterol esters. These lipids are composed of nonpolar paraffin chains conjugated with glycerol, higher alcohols, or cholesterol. The sterol configuration of cholesterol itself is also relatively nonpolar. Such nonpolar lipids are immiscible with

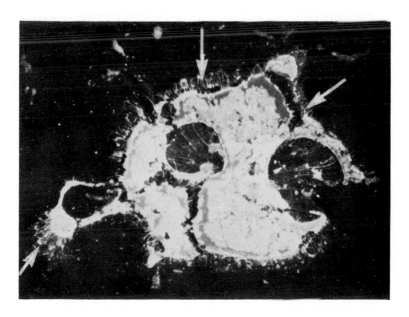

FIG. 1. Myelin buds from surface of polar lipid smear. Dark ground, × 51. (Reproduced by courtesy of the editor of *J. Neurochem.*)

water, develop surface tension at lipid-water interfaces and, hence, assume a globular shape in aqueous media in order to reduce the volume-surface ratio (Dixon, 1958). In tissue fluid or cells these non-polar lipids need to be transported as micelles with phospholipid or in various lipoprotein vehicles (Dixon, 1958; see Rossiter and Strickland, 1960; Fredrickson et al., 1967).

Without penetrating into the question of the physical forms of lipid in normal and pathological tissue (see Dixon, 1958), it is clear that surface molecular features will markedly affect the movement of aqueous reagents and dyes into and out of tissue lipids (Adams, 1958). In this connection, the lipid membrane's permeability to water is inversely related to its cholesterol content (Finkelstein and Cass, 1967).

The melting point of a lipid or a physiological lipid mixture is another factor that influences histochemical reactions, because the close packing of the molecules and paraffin chains in a solid lipid appears to impede the entry of dye substances and reagents. The melting point of simple esterified lipids is inversely related to the number of cis-unsaturated bonds in the attached fatty acid chains. Thus, triolein (18:1) melts at a lower temperature than tristearin (18:0), and cholesteryl oleate (18:1) melts at a higher temperature than cholesteryl linoleate (18:2), etc. However, esters of trans-unsaturated fatty acids usually melt at progressively higher temperatures with increasing number of trans-ethylenes (Adams et al., 1967).

A particularly unfortunate problem in lipid histochemistry is that most lipids are mutually soluble in each other so that small amounts of a particular lipid may be masked in both physical and chemical senses by an excess of a different sort. Furthermore, as outlined above, the physical characteristics of a lipid are profoundly altered when dispersed or bound by protein. Likewise, the dispersion of a hydrophobic lipid in lipoprotein or a macromolecular phospholipid micelle lowers the surface tension of the lipid mass so it loses its characteristic globular physical formation (Dixon, 1958).

In the case of triglycerides, with three fatty acids esterified with the glycerol skeleton, marked physical differences may arise if all the fatty acids are saturated or, conversely, if all are saturated. In general, however, this possibility does not arise under physiological conditions since each of the individual fatty acid species tends to be evenly distributed among the glyceride molecules (Lovern, 1955). Nevertheless, some depot fats may be particularly rich in stearic acid, while the position of certain fatty acids in the triglyceride molecule tends to be constant and nonrandomly determined (Hilditch and Williams, 1964; Brockerhoff et al., 1966).

B. LIPID FIXATION

Before discussing the histological detection of lipids by staining reactions, it is essential to know that the lipids have actually been retained within the tissue section. Fixation with formaldehyde alone may result in some loss of polar lipids; acrolein is reported to be superior as a fixative in this respect (Feustel and Geyer, 1966). Baker (1946, 1958a) observed that the addition of calcium ions to formalin better preserves lipids in tissues, presumably by forming cationic bridges across the polar "head groups" of phospholipids. Wolman and Wiener (1965) went on to show that monovalent cations (Na^+) in high ionic strength tend to solubilize polar lipids, whereas divalent cations (e.g., Ca^{2+}) render such lipids less hydrophilic. Likewise, Elbers *et al.* 1965) recommended the use of various divalent cations for the "tricomplex" stabilization (bridging) of phospholipids for electron microscopic examination. On an empirical basis we have noted that phospholipids are well preserved in frozen sections fixed in calcium-formalin, whereas tissues cut unfixed on the cryostatic microtome retain little phospholipid (Adams, 1965a). By thin layer chromatography, Roozemond (1967) elegantly confirmed that water extracts a large part of the polar lipids from unfixed sections, whereas fixation with calcium-formol minimizes such losses.

Other methods for preserving hydrophilic phospholipids in tissue sections are to cross-link them with osmium tetroxide (Wigglesworth, 1957; Baker, 1958b) or massively to oxidize them with potassium dichromate (Elftman, 1954). However, these latter methods so alter the physical and chemical nature of the phospholipids that, histochemically speaking, they should be eschewed except in certain special circumstances.

In our experience, hydrophobic apolar lipids are well retained within all types of tissue section, except where adipose tissue is cut and large lipid globules escape from the section.

The above discussion is concerned with preservation of lipids in sections cut on the freezing microtome. Similar conclusions would apply to tissues infiltrated with Carbowax and cut on the conventional microtome (Rinehart and Abul-Haj, 1951; Zugibe *et al.*, 1958).

The reader should perhaps be reminded that it is impossible to retain free lipids in conventional histological sections, for the tissue blocks are processed through lipid solvents during dehydration and clearing before embedding in paraffin. In such paraffin sections lipids are only retained if firmly bound to protein or previously massively oxidized with potassium dichromate (Elftman, 1954).

One last aspect of lipid fixation must be examined: To what extent does the fixative chemically alter the tissue lipids? In answer to this problem, Heslinga and Deierkauf (1962) showed that prolonged formalin fixation slowly hydrolyzes phosphoglycerides (lecithins and cephalins) to their water-soluble lyso derivatives. However, cholesterol, phosphoinositides, and all sphingolipids are unaffected. Clearly, it is preferable to work with tissues fixed for relatively short periods in calcium–formalin. In our empirical experience, little phospholipid is lost from tissue blocks stored in fixative for 1-3 months, but storage for a year is undesirable. The presence of altered blood in the tissue may promote iron-catalyzed epoxidation of lipids with formation of chromolipids; this problem is perhaps only a real hazard when tissues are stored for long periods and intermittently exposed to sunlight.

C. HISTOPHYSICAL METHODS

1. *Lipid-Soluble Dyes*

The red Sudan dyes were introduced by Daddi (1896) and Herxheimer (1901) for staining globular lipids in tissues. The most widely used of these dyes is now Oil Red O (Lillie and Ashburn, 1943). These Sudan dyes are soluble in liquid lipid droplets because they are endowed with an organotropic nature. However, Sudan dyes do not satisfactorily display hydrophobic lipids in crystalline state (e.g., solid crystals of tristearin) (see Holczinger and Bálint, 1962; Adams, 1965a). Moreover, the red Sudan dyes do not convincingly stain phospholipids, such as those in myelin, although it must be admitted that with short "differentiation" of the stain a slight color is imparted to phospholipid. Surprisingly, β-lipoprotein is stained by the red Sudan dyes (Walton, 1967), even though its component hydrophobic lipids are in dispersed protein-bound state. However, such sudanophilia is much increased by removal of the apolipoprotein (protein) component by tryptic digestion (Adams and Bayliss, 1967, unpublished observation).

Sudan black has a much wider affinity for lipids than the red Sudan dyes and, in practice, stains all classes of lipids that are in liquid state (i.e., those that contain some unsaturated groups). However, the reaction of Sudan black with phospholipids has been attributed to salt linkage rather than true physical absorption of the dye (Terner *et al.*, 1963). This last view is supported by the fact that phospholipids are stained by Sudan black in a blue-gray shade, in contrast to the black reaction with hydrophobic lipids. Moreover, the complex between

Sudan black and myelin phospholipids is dichroic (bronze) in polarized light (Diezel, 1957a,b, 1958), which suggests that more is involved than simple chemical absorption. It has further been observed that Sudan black reacts *in vitro* with substances of nonlipid nature (Schott and Schoner, 1965), but this is not our experience in applying the dye to tissue sections.

Nile blue sulfate stains hydrophobic unsaturated lipids in a pinkish mauve shade because of physical absorption of the red *oxazone* component of the dye (Lorrain Smith, 1908; Cain, 1947a). In biochemical use this dye is used to titrate free fatty acids, which are thought to bind the blue *oxazine* component. However, unsaturated fatty acids impregnated on paper are stained pink with Cain's (1947a) preparation of Nile blue sulfate (Adams, 1965a). The reason for this discrepancy between "biochemical" and "histochemical" observations is not clear. On paper, phosphoglycerides and sulfatide are stained by the blue *oxazine* of Nile blue; such staining is probably of electrovalent nature and not the result of physical absorption. Sphingolipids on paper are not stained by Nile blue sulfate (Adams, 1965a).

Phosphine 3R is another organotropic dye that is used to demonstrate hydrophobic lipid; its uptake by lipid globules is displayed by its fluorescence in ultraviolet light (Popper, 1944).

2. Birefringence

In contrast to the reaction of Sudan dyes with lipids in liquid state, birefringence in polarized light is exhibited by those tissue lipids that retain some crystalline structure. Solid crystalline lipids develop crystalline anisotropism in polarized light, whereas liquid droplets are usually isotropic (i.e., nonbirefringent). However, certain liquid droplets retain some crystalline structure and exhibit conic focal ("Maltese cross") anisotropism. Crystalline birefringence results from free cholesterol (mp $\simeq$ 150°C) because other lipids usually occur in mixtures that are liquid at physiological temperatures. Cerebrosides are reputed to melt in the range 100°–200°C, but even in the deposits of Gaucher's disease they appear to be mixed with lipids of lower melting point. Triglycerides in adipose tissue are isotropic because the saturated fatty acids are diluted with unsaturated sorts which effectively lower the melting point of the glyceride mixture (see Section II,A).

Conic bifocal (Maltese cross) anisotropism is characteristic of lipids in the mesomorphic (liquid crystalline) state between fully liquid and fully solid forms (thermotropic type), but it may also depend on the presence of water (lyotropic type). Full discussion of the optical features and biological significance of conic focal birefringence is to be found in papers by Friedel (1922) and Weller (1967). In general, cholesterol-phospholipid mixtures appear usually to be responsible for this form of birefringence; it is clearly a fallacy that Maltese crosses indicate the presence of all forms of cholesterol.

It seems almost too obvious to mention that birefringence is not a characteristic that is confined to solid and mesomorphic lipids, for many other crystalline structures show this property. The iron-formalin artifact derived from hemoglobin — so familiar to histologists — is a common example of a birefringent nonlipid substance. The fibrillary structure of amyloid imparts anisotropism to this substance, as does the arrangement of myosin molecules in the A band of the myofilaments of striated muscle. The myelin sheath's birefringence appears to be more a result of the orderly "para-crystalline" arrangement of its constituent polar lipid molecules (Schmidt, 1936) than the presence of free cholesterol in it. Thus, extraction of sections with cold acetone removes the cholesterol from myelin (Adams and Bayliss, 1968a), extinguishes the perchloric acid-naphthoquinone (Adams and Bayliss, 1968b) and Schultz reactions (see Section III,B,1), but does not reverse the birefringence of the sheath (Wolman and Hestrin-Lerner, 1960).

3. Differential Lipid Solubility

The solubility of various lipid species in different solvents has intermittently attracted the interests of histochemists as a tool to discriminate lipid species. Keilig (1944) proposed a battery of solvents for the differential extraction of lipids from tissue sections. However, Edgar and Donker (1957) found that these and similar extractions were unreliable for differentially extracting lipids from sections cut on the freezing microtome. Furthermore, some lipids are so firmly bound to protein that they cannot be extracted or exposed unless the solvent is acidified with hydrochloric acid or the tissue is first treated with proteolytic enzymes (LeBaron and Folch, 1956; Tuqan and Adams, 1961; Adams and Bayliss, 1962; Wolman, 1962; Maggi and Brander, 1963; Maggi et al., 1964). Treatment with soaps or heat and very prolonged solvent extraction have also been used to disrupt lipid from protein (Berenbaum, 1958).

In spite of the above-mentioned reservations, extraction with chloroform-methanol (2:1 v/v) effectively removes free lipids from tissue sections: It is an advantage to extract sections in a wet state or, alternatively, saturate the chloroform-methanol solvent with water

(62:31:6 v/v/v). Protein-bound lipids can usually be extracted by the methods outlined above.

A number of investigators have recommended using acetone for differentially extracting hydrophobic lipids (cholesterol, cholesterol esters, triglycerides, and fatty acids) from frozen tissue sections, while leaving phospholipids intact (Keilig, 1944; Wolfgram and Rose, 1958; Bubis and Wolman, 1962, Dunnigan, 1964).

In a quantitative and chromatographic study of the effect of acetone on lipids in tissue sections, we found that acetone extracts all cholesterol, cholesterol esters, triglycerides, and fatty acids but virtually leaves phospholipids and glycosphingosides intact (Adams and Bayliss, 1968a). Surprisingly, extraction of atherosclerotic plaques with acetone nearly extinguishes all histochemical reactions for phospholipid [osmium tetroxide–potassium chlorate–α-naphthylamine (OTAN), NaOH-OTAN, gold hydroxamic acid, acid hematein, Luxol fast blue, plasmal and, to a lesser extent, Nile blue sulfate oxazine; see methods under Sections III,B and VI,B]. However, extraction of other tissues (e.g., epidermis, renal tubules, arterial media, and the myelin sheath) with acetone leaves such phospholipid staining intact.

The near extinction of OTAN staining of atherosclerotic plaques with acetone was first noted by Elleder and Lojda (1968a). The reason for this discrepancy, as well as our observation of reduced or absent staining with other phospholipid methods, remains quite obscure. Thin-layer chromatography revealed that acetone does not extract phospholipids from sections of arterial tissue (Adams and Bayliss, 1968a). Moreover, phospholipids do not passively "fall out" of the section as a result of possibly losing the "support" of hydrophobic lipids, for rinsing the vessel with chloroform–methanol after acetone extraction failed to reveal any precipitated phospholipid.

III. Histochemical Aspects

A. CHEMICAL FEATURES OF LIPIDS

It is clearly neither the place nor within the author's knowledge to review the structure of lipid species. Nevertheless, it is important to mention briefly the major chemical configurations in the various lipid classes before embarking on a description of histo*chemical* methods for identifying lipids of physiological importance in tissue sections.

1. *Unconjugated Lipids*

Unconjugated lipids are:

(a) Reduced phenanthrenes: cholesterol, desmosterol, and other
    sterols and steroids; or
(b) Free fatty acids.

2. *Conjugated Lipids: Simple Esters*

Conjugated lipids consist of simple esters with fatty acids:

(a) With glycerol—triglycerides, diglycerides, and mono-
    glycerides;
(b) With cholesterol—cholesterol esters; or
(c) With higher alcohols—waxes.

Variants of triglycerides are encountered in which a fatty acid ester
bond ($-CH_2 \cdot OOC \cdot CH_2-$) is replaced by an ether($-CH_2 \cdot O \cdot CH_2-$)
or α,β-unsaturated ether ($-CH_2 \cdot O \cdot CH = CH-$) link.

3. *Conjugated Lipids: Complex Esters or Amides with Fatty Acids*

These lipids are esters of fatty acids with glycerol or amides of fatty
acid with sphingosine, but they also contain a nonlipid moiety such as
phosphorus, various bases or monosaccharides.

a. Phosphoglycerides. Lecithin, cephalins, and phosphoinositides
are *esters* of glycerol with fatty acids and phosphoric acid. The phosphoryl group is also either esterified with a base (choline, ethanol-
amine, serine, and, perhaps, ornithine) or conjugated with inositol.
Variations on this basic structure are encountered when one fatty acid
chain is removed (lyso-phosphoglyceride), when one fatty acid chain is
linked to glycerol by an α,β-unsaturated ether bond ($-CH_2 \cdot O \cdot CH =$
$CH-$; plasmalogen phospholipid), and when one or more fatty acid
chains are linked to glycerol by ether bonds ($-CH_2 \cdot O \cdot CH_2-$). Cardiolipin is an unusual phosphoglyceride in that a glycerol molecule replaces the usual base and links together two phosphatidic acids (see
De Haas *et al.*, 1966).

Other phosphoglycerides of unusual structure or containing unusual components have been identified in bacteria; such lipids are not
relevant to this text.

b. Phosphosphingosides. Sphingomyelin resembles phosphatidylcholine (lecithin), except that the skeleton is sphingosine in lieu of
glycerol and that the fatty acid is linked to the spingosine skeleton by
an amide bond ($-CH_2 \cdot NH \cdot OC \cdot CH_2-$) instead of the ester bond
($-CH_2 \cdot OOC \cdot CH_2-$) in phosphoglycerides. As with lecithin, the base
attached to sphingomyelin's phosphoryl group is choline.

c. Glycosphingosides. These lipids contain a fatty acid chain linked
to sphingosine through an amide bond; this constitutes the ceramide

unit as in sphingomyelin (above). The "nonlipid moiety" consists of one or more monosaccharides or related compounds. *Cerebrosides's* attached monosaccharide is a hexose, usually galactose or glucose. *Gangliosides* contain varying proportions of hexoses, hexosamines, and neuraminic acid: The structure of these lipids is complex and a number of variants and precursors have been identified in recent years (see Svennerholm, 1964; Wherrett *et al.*, 1964; Ledeen *et al.*, 1965). However, for histochemical purposes the above superficial description will suffice.

B. HISTOCHEMICAL STAINING METHODS

1. *Cholesterol and Other Sterols*

The Liebermann–Burchardt reaction was modified for histochemical use by Schultz (1924) and later by Weber *et al.* (1956). Subsequently, Lewis and Lobban (1961) showed that a number of androgens give a direct blue-green color with their modified test and that preliminary oxidation with Fe^{3+} increases the reactivity of cholesterol with their sulfuric acid–ferric chloride reagent. However, these variants of the Liebermann–Burchardt reaction all tend to produce gas bubbles under the section and are somewhat capricious in histochemical practice.

The perchloric acid–naphthoquinone (PAN) method provides a more sensitive method for the detection of cholesterol and related 3-hydroxy $\Delta^{5,7}$ sterols (Figs. 2-5). It also has the advantages that the reaction pigment is rather more stable and the reagents do not distort or "gas" the section as much as does the Schultz reaction. The PAN method depends on the formation of cholesta-3,5-diene by the condensing action of perchloric acid on cholesterol; the diene then reacts with 1,2-naphthoquinone to form a dark blue pigment. Tests on the specificity of the method have been presented and discussed elsewhere (Adams, 1961, 1965a).

Free cholesterol can theoretically be distinguished from esterified cholesterol by treating the section with digitonin. The ester does not react with digitonin, whereas the free sterol is converted into its digitonide. Cholesterol digitonide is not extracted with lipid solvents and can be recognized in the tissues by its birefringence or staining after such treatment, while esterified cholesterol is extracted and disappears from the section (Feigen, 1956). Nevertheless, this digitonin method seems to be of little practical use (Weller, 1966). The digitonin reagent is dissolved in alcohol; this solvent appears to extract cholesterol faster than the digitonide is formed. The result is that the

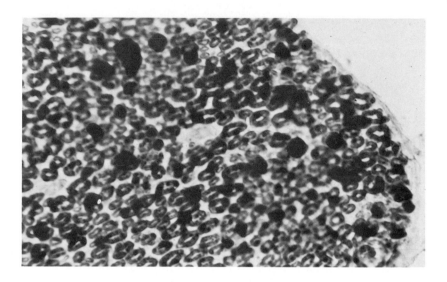

FIG. 2.   Cholesterol in rat sciatic nerve myelin. Perchloric acid–naphthoquinone, × 465. (Reproduced by courtesy of the editor of *Nature*.)

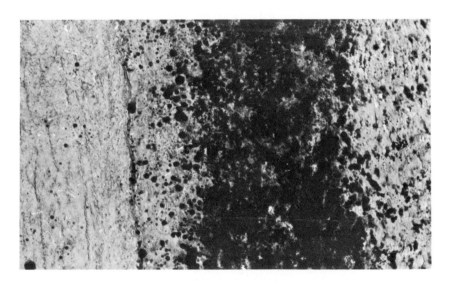

FIG. 3.   Cholesterol in mature human atheromatous plaque (center and right). PAN, × 95. (Reproduced by courtesy of the editor of *Nature*.)

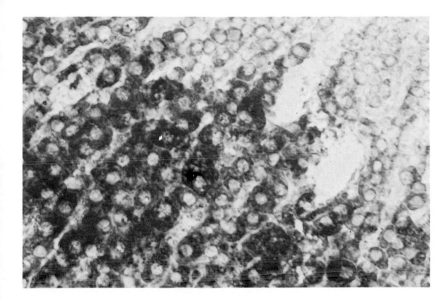

FIG. 4. Cholesterol in the zona fasciculata of rat adrenal; only slight reaction in zona reticularis (top right). PAN, × 385. (Reproduced by courtesy of the editor of *Nature*.)

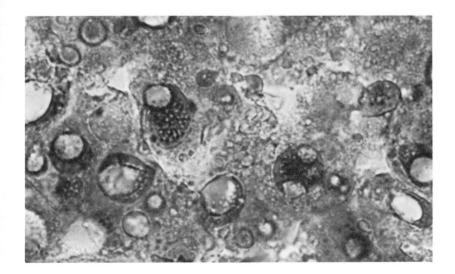

FIG. 5. Cholesterol in liver of cholesterol-fed rabbit. PAN, × 960. (Reproduced by courtesy of the editor of *J. Pathol. Bacteriol.*)

cholesterol digitonide is either lost from the tissue section or precipitated at a distance from the original site of the sterol.

A number of histochemical methods have been introduced for ketosteroids that depend on reactions with hydrazides or hydrazines. By common consent these methods now appear to be nonspecific and result from the presence of aldehyde groups engendered by oxidation of unsaturated groups (Albert and LeBlond, 1947; Wegmann, 1956; Holczinger, 1958; Wolman, 1961; Adams, 1965a). Another method for ketosteroids, depending on the oxidation of the C20-21 α-ketol group with ferric chloride (Khanolkar *et al.*, 1958), also failed to give specific reactions when tested densitometrically *in vitro* against a battery of 22 purified lipids (Adams, 1965a). More recently, Stoward and Adams Smith (1964) have outlined a method in which ketosteroid salicyloyl hydrazones are revealed by their ultraviolet fluorescence. Aldehydes and ketones are first "blocked" by methyl hydrazine; then ketones are specifically unblocked by brief treatment with sulfobenzaldehyde; finally, salicyloyl hydrazones are formed from the unblocked ketones. This last method appears promising, and has been further evaluated by Adams Smith and Stoward (1967).

2. Fatty Acids

A number of metallic methods have been introduced for *free* fatty acids. The earliest of these is lithium-hematoxylin (Fischler, 1904); the lithium ion is captured by the fatty acid to form a lithium soap which in turn acts as a mordant to bind hematoxylin. Holczinger (1959) reviewed these various metal soap methods and recommended a technique in which a copper soap is first formed and is then converted to greenish-black copper rubeanate. In densitometric *in vitro* studies, this method was found to be absolutely specific for free fatty acids (Adams, 1965a). Nevertheless, Holczinger recommends brief treatment of the tissue sections with disodium-EDTA after exposure to Cu^{2+} in order to remove nonspecifically absorbed copper.

3. Unsaturated Groups

There are three main methods for the histochemical detection of unsaturated (ethylene) groups in free or esterified fatty acid chains: oxidation to aldehyde, bromination followed by silver reduction, and reduction of osmium tetroxide. As will be seen the last of these methods is by far the most sensitive.

a. *Oxidation to Aldehyde.* The performic acid-Schiff and peracetic acid-Schiff methods depend on the oxidation of unsaturated bonds to aldehyde, which then reacts with Schiff's reagent (Lillie, 1952, 1954).

Oxidation with air in ultraviolet light has a similar effect and results in the formation of Schiff-stainable aldehydes (Belt and Hayes, 1956): Such atmospheric oxidation of double bonds to aldehyde is also the explanation of the pseudoplasmal reaction (see Section III,B,6). The sensitivity of these oxidation methods is not high, even though densitometric studies *in vitro* show that they are reasonably specific for double bonds (Adams, 1965a). All these methods can be blocked by preliminary bromination of the tissue section.

   b. Bromination Followed by Silver Reduction. Mukherji *et al.* (1960) and Norton *et al.* (1962) introduced methods involving bromination of the unsaturated bonds of fatty acids. In the second stage silver nitrate ejects bromine and silver bromide is formed. In the final stage, silver bromide is converted by a photographic developer into black granular silver. Densitometric studies on 22 lipids *in vitro* showed that only hydrophobic unsaturated lipids are displayed with Norton *et al.*'s method, whereas hydrophilic unsaturated lipids are unreactive (Adams, 1965a). The Δ_5-unsaturated group of cholesterol and desmosterol are stained when the lipids are impregnated on paper. However, cholesterol *crystals* are unreactive in tissue sections.

   c. Reduction of Osmium Tetroxide. The cis-unsaturated groups of lipids reduce osmium tetroxide (OsO_4) to a black compound. The reaction is blocked by preliminary oxidation with performic acid or bromine. The nature of the black reduction compound has been the subject of some speculation (see Griffith, 1965; Adams *et al.*, 1967; and others). Recently, Korn (1966a,b,c, 1967) has conclusively shown that osmium reacts with unsaturated fatty acids to form bridged bis-osmates as previously suggested by Wigglesworth (1957) and Baker (1958b).

$$HC-O\underset{\underset{HC-O}{\diagdown}}{\overset{\overset{O}{\underset{\displaystyle Os}{\parallel}}}{\diagup}}\overset{\displaystyle O-CH}{\underset{\displaystyle O-CH}{}}$$

Lipids were shown to react in this way both *in vitro* and *in vivo*. However, it is not altogether clear whether this diester is the black reaction product seen in tissue sections. Korn (1967) suggested that an osmium–fatty acid monoester may first be formed and then a lower osmium oxide is ejected during formation of the bridged bis-osmate. Possibly this ejected osmium oxide is the black reaction product. However, he noted that the OsO_4–fatty acid ratio is 1:2 in the blackened lipid preparation; thus this observation rather precludes the presence of a lower osmium oxide as a second reaction product.

It has been suggested that osmium marks the position of phospholipid polar groups at the protein-lipid interface in electron micrographs of membrane structures (Stoeckenius, 1961). The notion was proposed that reduced osmium $(OsO_2 \cdot nH_2O)^-$ behaves as an anionic dye and migrates from its site of formation at the fatty acid chain's ethylene bond toward the cations in the phospholipid head groups (Riemersma and Booij, 1962; Riemersma, 1963; Elbers, 1964). However, Korn (1966b, 1967) found that his bis-osmates do not react with phospholipid acidic and basic groups, and we found that various cationic agents do not remove the black complex formed by reducing OsO_4 with polythene (Adams *et al.*, 1967). It is therefore unlikely that the dense (osmiophilic) line in electron micrographs of membrane marks the site of phospholipid polar groups (Korn, 1966c).

Densitometric studies *in vitro* show that OsO_4 is blackened by all cis-unsaturated free or esterified fatty acids and by the double bond in the side chain of desmosterol (Adams, 1965a). However, trans-unsaturated lipids and the $\triangle_5$ double bond in cholesterol do not blacken aqueous OsO_4; the reactivity of the double bond in unsaturated sphingosine has not been established.

A number of investigators have suggested that proteins or mucopolysaccharides reduce OsO_4 (Porter and Kallman, 1953; Bahr, 1954; Wolman, 1957; Rogers, 1959). Nevertheless, proteins and mucopolysaccharides do not manifestly blacken OsO_4 in tissue sections (Adams, 1960, 1965a; Hake, 1965; Adams *et al.*, 1967): thus sections do not react after blockade of lipid ethylene bonds and after extraction with a general solvent for lipids. In our original reports, we noted that bound unreduced osmium could not be demonstrated in such extracted tissue after exposure of the section to ammonium sulfide or thiourea. However, Elleder and Lojda (1968b) subsequently pointed out that bound unreduced osmium can be identified in the hair cortex and epidermis of paraffin-embedded or "lipid-extracted" frozen tissue sections by means of α-naphthylamine (see next section). On repeating their work, we obtained similar results (Adams and Bayliss, 1968, unpub. observations), but we found no evidence to support their view that proteins at these sites may be responsible for binding osmium. Thus, the osmium-α-naphthylamine reaction in paraffin-embedded or frozen sections is diminished by extraction with chloroform-methanol-hydrochloric acid (66:33:1, v/v/v), a solvent which was introduced for disrupting lipids that are firmly bound to protein (LeBaron and Folch, 1956). Moreover, Elleder and Lojda's reaction is nearly extinguished by preliminary blockade of lipid ethylene bonds with bromine. In spite of our objections, it could be argued that hydrochloric acid hydrolyzes protein or that bromine exerts a nonspecific oxidizing effect on protein reducing groups. However, blockade of protein sulfphydryl groups with N-ethylmaleimide in no way alters the reaction of hair cortex and epidermis in paraffin-embedded sections, while destructive nitrosation and coupling of aromatic amino acids with diazonium salts alters the final color but does not extinguish the reaction.

   d. The Marchi Reaction. Marchi (1886) noted that in the presence of potassium dichromate OsO_4 blackens degenerating myelin but not the lipids of normal myelin (Fig. 7). This behavior at first sight seems inexplicable (Lison, 1936; Cain, 1950). However, a clue was provided by George Gomori (1952), who commented that "in some ways OsO_4 behaves like a sudan dye." Gomori's comment implies that OsO_4 would penetrate both hydrophobic and hydrophilic lipids. However, potassium dichromate (or potassium chlorate in the modified Marchi technique) is a highly polar electrolyte and, predictably, it would be unable to penetrate the "high surface tension" interface between hydrophobic lipids and water. By contrast, no such physical barrier would impede dichromate or chlorate's entry into polarized hydrophilic (or amphophilic) lipids. Measurements of the rate of penetration of OsO_4 and $KClO_3$ into smears of hydrophobic and hydrophilic lipids confirmed these predictions (Adams, 1958). Another clue to the mechanism of the Marchi reaction is that OsO_4 acts as a catalyst for the *preferential* oxidation of ethylene bonds and 1,2-glycols by oxidants such as $KClO_3$ (Criegie, 1936; Zelikoff and Taylor, 1950; Milas *et al.,* 1959) or periodate (Hakomori, 1966). It follows that if both $KClO_3$ and OsO_4 penetrate to the double bond of *hydrophilic* lipid molecules $KClO_3$ would be reduced but not OsO_4. In contrast, $KClO_3$ does not enter *hydrophobic* lipids, so here there is no impediment to the reduction and blackening of OsO_4. This hypothesis explains why the *hydrophilic* lipids of normal myelin are unstained with the Marchi method, whereas the *hydrophobic* lipids (cholesterol esters) of degenerating myelin and atheromatous plaques are blackened (Figs. 6 and 7; Adams, 1958, 1960). This interpretation is consistent with the solubility of the "Marchi substance" in acetone (Hurst, 1925; Wolfgram and Rose, 1958).

   This hypothesis can be further tested by showing that OsO_4 plays a carrier role in the oxidation of hydrophilic lipids by $KClO_3$. In fact, hexavalent osmium can be detected in hydrophilic phospholipids, after treatment with the Marchi reagent, by a histochemical adaptation

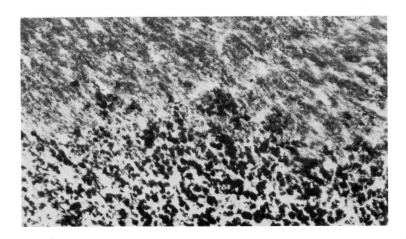

FIG. 6.   Marchi reaction (black in original) in degenerating myelin at edge of plaque of multiple sclerosis; red-brown reaction in surrounding intact myelin (top). OTAN, × 77. (Reproduced by courtesy of the editor of *J. Neurochem.*)

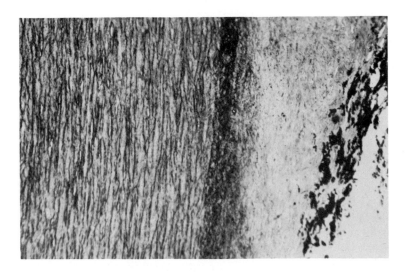

FIG. 7.   Marchi reaction (black in original) in lipophages lying in inner part of human atherosclerotic plaque (right); red-brown reaction (phospholipid) in outer part of plaque and in elastic and smooth muscle of tunica media (left). OTAN, × 40. (Reproduced by courtesy of the editor of *Proc. Roy. Soc. Med.*)

of Wingfield and Yoe's (1956) colorimetric method with α-naphthyl-amine derivatives (Adams, 1958). The presence of hexavalent or un-colored osmium in such hydrophilic lipids suggests that the reaction is "held" at the monoester stage and does not proceed to the formation of OsO_2 or Korn's bisosmates. Presumably further oxidation is ef-fected by $KClO_3$ with regeneration of OsO_4, but we lack positive evi-dence that this is the precise mechanism of the last stage of the reac-tion:

$$HC-O\underset{Os}{\overset{O}{\diagup}}\underset{O}{\overset{VI}{\diagdown}} \atop HC-O\ O \quad + \ \tfrac{2}{3}KClO_3 \longrightarrow \quad {HC=O \atop HC=O} \quad + \ OsO_4 \ + \ \tfrac{2}{3}KCl$$

The reddish-orange reaction of hydrophilic lipids with α-naphthyl-amine after preliminary treatment with the Marchi reagents (OsO_4 + $KClO_3$) is the basis of the OTAN method to be discussed in Section III,B,5.

In summary, OsO_4 in the Marchi reagent blackens hydrophobic, unsaturated lipids such as triglycerides, cholesterol esters, and free fatty acids. However, hydrophilic unsaturated lipids such as phospho-lipids are not blackened by Marchi's reagent because dichromate or perchlorate penetrates into the lipid molecule; such oxidizing agents are reduced in these circumstances in preference to OsO_4.

4. *Triglycerides*

Triglycerides are stained by the red Sudan dyes, Sudan black, and the Marchi method (OTAN black). However, these are not specific tests for triglycerides since other hydrophobic lipids are stained like-wise. Recently, a histochemical technique has been introduced in which triglycerides are specifically hydrolyzed by pancreatic lipase in the presence of calcium ions; released fatty acids are precipitated as calcium soaps and then, in a second stage, the calcium soap is base-exchanged with lead and, finally, the lead soap is converted to black lead sulfide by treatment with ammonium sulfide (Figs. 8 and 9; Ad-ams *et al.*, 1966). Clearly, the specificity of the method depends on the purity of the pancreatic lipase; such purity can be established by chro-matographic study of the digestion products after treating a general lipid mixture with the lipase and by the use of specific lipase inhibi-

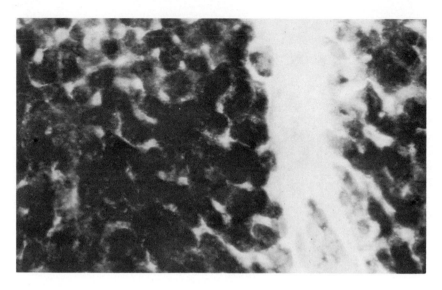

FIG. 8.   Triglycerides in human fatty liver. Lipase–lead sulfide, × 336. (Reproduced by courtesy of the editor of *J. Histochem. Cytochem.*)

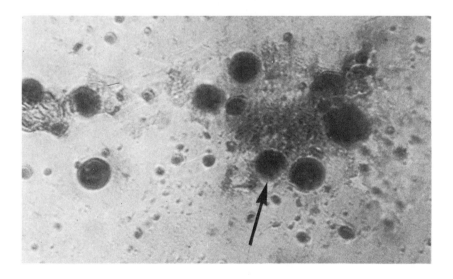

FIG. 9.   Triglycerides in storage cells of bone marrow in familial hyperlipidaemic xanthomatosis. Lipase–lead sulfide, × 960. (Sternal biopsy specimen by courtesy of Dr. Percy Barkhan.)

tors and activators. *In vitro* densitometric studies on lipid spots impregnated on paper revealed that waxes as well as triglycerides react with the method.

5. *Phosphoglycerides*

a. Acid Hematein Method. Chromates were introduced into histology as fixatives in the middle of the last century, possibly because they were extensively used at this time for hardening leather in the tanning process. Weigert, Pal, Kultschitsky, Dietrich, Lorrain Smith, and other workers at the turn of the century noted that myelin that had previously been mordanted with chromate was stained by various sorts of hematoxylin. Subsequently, Baker (1946, 1947) set out an exact schedule for fixation, chromation, staining, and differentiation; this acid hematein method was found to be specific for phospholipids (Baker, 1947; Cain, 1947b). Subsequent work showed that only those phospholipids that contain choline are convincingly stained by acid hematein (Bourgeois and Hack, 1962; Bourgeois and Hubbard, 1965). We have confirmed this observation and found that only a faint reac tion is given by other phospholipids (Adams, 1965a). Choline appears to be essential for the reaction, while the presence of *unsaturated* fatty acid chains only accentuates staining (Adams *et al.*, 1965; see Holczinger, 1964). Bromination does not block the reaction; on the contrary it actually enhances the intensity of acid hematein staining (Adams *et al.*, 1965). The author has previously discussed the mechanism of the reaction, and it is still far from clear (Adams, 1962, 1965a; Adams *et al.*, 1965). The method stains sphingomyelin (see Section III,B,7) as well as phosphatidylcholine (lecithin), so it is not a specific test for phosphoglycerides.

b. The OTAN Method. As discussed in Section III,B,3d, the Marchi reagent (osmium tetroxide–potassium chlorate) only stains hydrophobic unsaturated lipids; the OsO_4 in the mixture being reduced to a black compound. Hydrophilic unsaturated lipids are not directly stained by Marchi's reagent, but bound osmium within them may subsequently be displayed by its orange-brown chelate or complex with α-naphthylamine (Figs. 6, 7, and 10). This reaction is blocked by preliminary oxidation of ethylene bonds with bromine or performic acid (Adams, 1958, 1960). The possible mechanism of osmium binding by hydrophilic lipids and their preferential reduction of potassium chlorate (rather than OsO_4) in Marchi's reagent are discussed in Section III,B,3,d. Phosphoglycerides and sphingomyelin impregnated on paper are stained orange-brown or red-brown with the OTAN method,

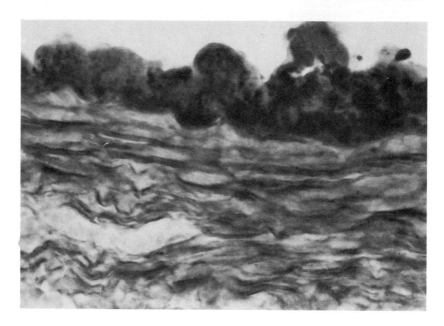

FIG. 10. Phospholipid (orange-brown in original) in early spontaneous atheroma of the sand rat (*Psammomius obesus*). OTAN, × 960. (Specimen provided by courtesy of Professor R. F. Mahler.)

but glycolipids only react faintly (Adams, 1959a, 1962, 1965a). The fatty acids in glycolipids such as cerebrosides tend to be more saturated than those in phosphoglycerides (Deuel, 1951), thus they would contain less groups to react with OTAN. Moreover, cerebroside is moderately "red sudanophilic" (Adams, 1965a), so it is likely to be more hydrophobic than phospholipid.

Theoretically, hydrophobic unsaturated lipid in lipoproteins should be stained orange-brown with OTAN since dispersion within the lipoprotein molecule should render such lipid to some extent hydrophilic. In fact β-lipoprotein impregnated on paper is stained dull red but becomes blacker after digestion with trypsin (Adams and Bayliss, 1967, unpublished observation). Therefore, should the occasion arise, tissue sections can be briefly trypsinized before staining with OTAN, in order to establish whether or not protein-dispersed hydrophobic lipid is present.

Elleder and Lojda (1968a) have criticized this explanation of the OTAN reaction on the grounds that:

(i) Acetone extraction nearly extinguishes the orange-brown reaction of atherosclerotic plaques with OTAN, yet phospholipids are not soluble in acetone (see Section II,C,3).

(ii) In thick sections of brain tissue the expected orange-brown reaction of myelin is replaced by a black color.

(iii) Long exposure of the section to α-naphthylamine (second stage) causes the orange-brown reaction to become black.

(iv) The brown or dark brown reaction of certain lipid globules with OsO_4-$KClO_3$ (first stage) turns black after treatment with α-naphthylamine (second stage).

(v) Lipids that normally stain black with OTAN appear orange-brown if they are only stained for a few seconds with OsO_4 before treating them with α-naphthylamine.

(vi) The red or orange-brown OTAN reaction may indicate a low density of unsaturated (ethylene) groups in the lipid, whereas the black reaction may indicate an abundance of such ethylenes.

These criticisms can be countered by the following arguments:

(i) Acetone essentially extinguishes the staining of atherosclerotic plaques with all phospholipid methods tested (see Section II,C,3); the explanation for this general anomaly remains obscure and requires further investigation.

(ii) In thick sections the orange-brown OTAN reaction might be expected to appear black because of the optical density of a thick layer of pigment.

(iii) Over-reaction with α-naphthylamine might well result in a much darker color than the orange-brown of the standard technique.

(iv) The change in hue from dark brown to black in certain lipid deposits between stages 1 and 2 could be a result of successive reactions with hydrophobic and hydrophilic lipid. Thus, the hydrophobic component of a lipid mixture would reduce a moderate amount of OsO_4 in the first stage (brown reaction), while the osmium bound by the hydrophilic component would form an orange or red chelate with α-naphthylamine in the second stage; the two pigments would optically summate to produce a darker color than that of each individually.

(v) An orange-brown reaction with α-naphthylamine would be expected after brief exposure of a hydrophobic lipid to OsO_4, for it has been predicted that osmium is transiently bound in hexavalent form in all reactions with lipid ethylene bonds (see Section III,B,3,d).

(vi) A red-brown or orange-brown OTAN reaction is seen in typical phospholipid-rich structures such as myelin, hepatic cells, and erythrocytes, whereas a black reaction is always obtained in the purely hydrophobic lipids of white adipose tissue. Moreover, the fatty acids of phospholipids in myelin are more saturated than those in the liver and erythrocytes, yet all three react in a similar orange or reddish hue.

Elleder and Lojda (1968a,b) consider that α-naphthylamine probably reacts with other forms of osmium apart from Os(VI). The reaction between α-naphthylamine and lipoprotein-bound osmium in paraffin sections (see Section III,B,3,c) supports their view. Nevertheless, OsO_4 does not react with α-naphthylamine to form a red or orange-brown pigment: *in vitro* it slowly reacts to produce a violet-colored complex which is not seen in sections stained with OTAN.

In summary, the orange-brown OTAN reaction generally results from unsaturated phospholipids (phosphoglycerides and sphin-gomyelin), but on theoretical grounds hydrophobic lipid dispersed in lipoprotein could react similarly. Mixtures of hydrophilic and hydrophobic unsaturated lipids would be expected to stain more darkly than phospholipid alone; reduction of osmium by hydrophobic lipid in such an intermediate system introduces a complicating factor in interpreting results with the OTAN method.

c. The Gold-Hydroxamic Acid Reaction. Alkaline hydroxylamine reacts with ester bonds to convert them to hydroxamic acids. Such hydroxamates can be identified histochemically (Fig. 11) by their orange ferric complexes (Adams and Davison, 1959), by their reduction of ammoniacal silver nitrate (Gallyas, 1963), or by silver reduction followed by "gold-toning" (i.e., base exchange with gold; Adams *et al.*, 1963). Although theoretically all lipid esters undergo alkaline hydroxylaminolysis, the aqueous conditions in which the histochemical reaction is carried out allow hydrophilic but not hydrophobic lipids to react (see Sections II,A,1 and III,B,3). The only hydrophilic lipids in which the fatty acids are bound by ester bonds are the phosphoglycerides (lecithins, cephalins, phosphoinositides, and cardiolipin); in sphingolipids the fatty acid is bound by an alkali-stable amide bond. Densitometric studies on lipids impregnated on paper showed that only phosphoglycerides were stained among the phospholipids and glycolipids; triglycerides gave faint reactions on paper, presumably because under these conditions they are in a more dispersed state than in tissue lipids (Adams, 1965a). However, the same reservations about lipoprotein dispersal of hydrophobic lipid esters (triglycerides and cholesterol esters) apply to the gold hydroxamic acid method as to the OTAN technique (see preceding section).

The specificity of the ferric and gold-hydroxamic acid methods has been established by the failure of the reaction after preliminary hydrolysis of the ester bond with sodium hydroxide and by showing that

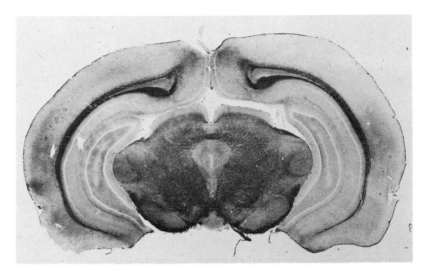

FIG. 11. Phosphoglyceride in myelin of callosal radiation, hippocampal radiation, and in corpus striatum of rat brain. Gold-hydroxamic acid, × 6.

blockade of aldehyde groups did not decrease silver reduction after alkaline hydroxylaminolysis (Adams *et al.*, 1963). Thin-layer chromatography of the reaction products of alkaline hydroxylaminolysis of lecithin showed that only the resulting hydroxamic acid reduced silver and, moreover, such reduction proceeded at a similar rate to that of color production in the histochemical system (Abdulla and Adams, 1966, unpublished observation).

In histochemical use, dispersed lipid in the atherosclerotic plaque is slightly stained with the silver reduction–gold toning sequence without preliminary alkaline hydroxylaminolysis. This nonspecific reaction is not encountered in myelin or in the stratum germinativum of the epidermis; it does not appear to result from "pseudoplasmal" aldehydes because it is not intensified or provoked by preliminary ultraviolet irradiation. Another slight anomaly is that the method does not consistently stain the lipid-rich erythrocyte membrane. However, the occasional staining of erythrocytes with gold hydroxamic acid suggests that this shortcoming is a technical rather than a theoretical deficiency.

In summary, the gold–hydroxamic acid method is a reasonably specific test for hydrophilic lipid esters, in particular phosphoglycerides.

d. Miscellaneous Methods. Böttcher and Boelsma-Van Houte (1964) introduced a method for choline-containing phospholipids (lecithin and sphingomyelin) that depends on the reaction of these lipids with *cis*-aconitic anhydride. The results with this method in arterial tissue seem in general to correspond to those obtained with the OTAN method (see Boelsma-Van Houte and Böttcher, 1967). Since impurities in ordinary glassware impede the *cis*-aconitic anhydride reaction, quartz vessels and slides have to be used.

The phosphomolybdate–stannous chloride method (Landing *et al.*, 1952; Landing and Freiman, 1957) specifically stains choline-containing phospholipids on paper but gives completely erratic results in tissue sections (see Adams, 1965a).

A number of other slide histochemical methods have been introduced or proposed for phospholipids; these include Luxol fast blue, bismuth iodide, hydroquinone-tetrazolium, and mercuric nitrate-diphenylcarbazone. However, densitometric studies on 22 lipids impregnated on paper reveal that none of these methods is even reasonably specific for phospholipids (Adams, 1965a). Even though some of these methods are useful histological stains for lipids, they cannot be regarded as specific *histochemical* methods.

6. *Plasmalogen Phospholipids*

The plasmal reaction was introduced by Feulgen and Voit (1924): It involves the hydrolysis of the α,β-unsaturated bond of plasmalogen phospholipids to the corresponding aldehyde, which is then displayed with Schiff's reagent. The chemical basis of the method is specific in that mercuric chloride does not oxidize fatty acid ethylene bonds to aldehyde (Cain, 1949a,b). However, atmospheric oxidation rapidly converts these ethylenes to aldehydes (pseudoplasmal reaction; see Section III,B,3). For this reason tissues should only be briefly fixed, and a control unhydrolyzed section must be stained with Schiff's reagent to establish the extent of pseudoplasmal–aldehyde formation. Norton and Korey (1962) commented that the α,β-unsaturated ether group of plasmalogen phospholipids is fairly rapidly destroyed by formaldehyde and acrolein; this constitutes another reason for brief tissue fixation.

Densitometric studies of lipids impregnated on paper showed that the plasmal reaction is highly specific for plasmalogens after the blank (pseudoplasmal) reading has been subtracted (Adams, 1965a). After mercuric chloride hydrolysis the plasmal reaction may be blocked by condensing the formed aldehyde with various amines (see Adams, (1965a) or by reducing the aldehyde with borohydride (Jobst and Horváth, 1961).

Norton and his colleagues proposed a new method for plasmalogen phospholipids, in which Hg^{2+} is bound at the α,β-unsaturated bond and is subsequently displayed by its purple chelate with diphenylcarbazone (Norton, 1959; Norton and Korey, 1962). This reaction is theoretically attractive, but unfortunately densitometric studies disclosed that other phosphoglycerides and polyenoic fatty acids are stained as well as plasmalogens (Adams, 1965a). Hg^{2+} is bound by olefin double bonds (Bennett, 1962), so presumably fatty acid ethylenes are responsible for such nonspecific staining with Norton's method.

7. *Glycosphingosides*

a.   Cerebroside. Diezel (1957a,b) adapted the Molisch and Brückner methods for the histochemical demonstration of cerebroside and related compounds. However, we failed to stain cerebroside impregnated on paper with these methods (Adams, 1965a).

Cerebroside, related ceramide hexosides, and protein-bound ganglioside are stained by the periodic acid–Schiff (PAS) method (see review of literature in Adams, 1965a,b). The PAS method was originally devised for staining tissue mucins (McManus, 1946; Lillie, 1947; Hotchkiss, 1948). The adjacent 1,2-hydroxyl groups in hexoses of neutral and weakly acid mucopolysaccharide are oxidized by periodic acid to aldehyde, which in turn is visualized with Schiff's reagent. Cerebroside reacts with PAS because it contains a hexose moiety; this reaction can be distinguished from that resulting from mucopolysaccharides by the solubility of the lipid in neutral or acidified chloroform–methanol (see Wolman, 1962, and Section II,C,3).

Unfortunately, a number of other chemical configurations confer PAS positivity on lipid and protein molecules. Thus, lipid ethylene bonds appear to be oxidized to aldehyde by periodic acid (Adams and Bayliss, 1963; see Wolman, 1956), while atmospheric oxidation of such bonds (pseudoplasmal reaction) results in the formation of Schiff-stainable aldehyde. The inositol ring in phosphoinositides, the 1-hydroxy-2-keto group in α-ketocorticosteroids, and the 1,2-hydroxy group in monoglycerides are all theoretically PAS reactive (Adams *et al.*, 1963; Adams, 1965a). Certain amino acids such as serine and hydroxylysine would be expected to be PAS positive because of their 1-amino-2-hydroxyl or 1-amino-2-hydroxyamino groups (see Hotchkiss, 1948; Hale, 1957).

In order to overcome this nonspecificity of the PAS method, we introduced successive preliminary blockades with chloramine T, performic acid, and 2,4-dinitrophenylhydrazine in order to convert 1-hydroxy-2-amino compounds and ethylene groups to aldehydes. These aldehydes, together with preexisting aldehyde or keto groups, are then blocked with the hydrazine (Fig. 12). A further preliminary step —alkaline hydrolysis—may be used when it is necessary to prevent the possible reaction of 1,2-hydroxyl groups in phosphoinositides, monogalactosyl diglyceride (Steim, 1967), and monoglycerides (Adams and Bayliss, 1963; Adams *et al.*, 1963).

In summary, certain preliminary blockading techniques increase the specificity of the PAS method for the hexose groups in cerebroside, other glycosphingosides, and mucopolysaccharides. With this modified PAS method cerebroside can be distinguished from mucopolysaccharide by its solubility in the relevant lipid solvents.

b. Sulfatide. This sulfuric acid ester of cerebroside is not stained by the standard (Urich, 1962) or modified PAS methods (Adams, 1965a), because one of the hexose 1,2-glycol groups is esterified with sulfate and, hence, rendered inactive. Sulfatide is highly acidic; its pK is presumably as low as that of many sulfated mucopolysaccharides. For this reason it is strongly stained by acidic solutions of Alcian blue (Urich, 1962), colloidal iron (Adams, 1965a), and acriflavine (Hollander, 1963). Nevertheless, this acidic characteristic cannot be

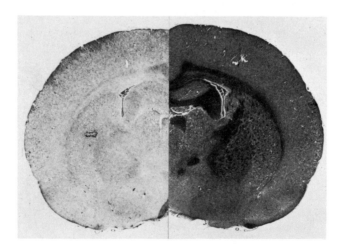

FIG. 12. Cerebroside in myelin of callosal radiation, hippocampal radiation, and corpus striatum of rat brain. Section at left extracted with chloroform–methanol (2:1 v/v). Modified periodic acid-Schiff, × 6. (Reproduced from *Neurohistochemistry* by courtesy of Elsevier Publishing Co.)

used as an identifying histochemical feature unless it can be shown that such basophilia is extinguished by extraction with lipid solvents. Further caution is required, because under some circumstances cholesterol may be present in tissues as a sulfate ester (Moser *et al.*, 1966).

The really distinctive chemical feature of sulfatide is its golden brown metachromasia when stained with an acetic acid–cresyl violet mixture (Peiffer and Hirsch, 1955; Hirsch and Peiffer, 1957). This brown metachromasia is probably a result of the sulfatide–dye complex absorbing light at two different wavelengths (Gregson, 1964). It is widely held that only free deposits of sulfatide develop this brown metachromasia, which has hence come to be regarded as a specific test for the storage products of metachromatic leucodystrophy (sulfatide lipidosis). However, we have recently noticed that sulfatide in CNS myelin is colored brown with cresyl violet when the preparation is mounted in water but reverts to orthochromatic (violet) staining when the section is mounted in glycerine jelly (Adams and Bayliss, 1968b). Nevertheless, peripheral nerve myelin is orthochromatic with cresyl violet both in water and glycerine jelly. The reason for this difference is not clear.

Dayan (1967a) has shown that deposits of sulfatide stained by cresyl violet develop green dichroism when viewed in polarized light. Mast cells, which are sometimes stained equivocally brownish-red with cresyl violet in ordinary light, do not exhibit this specific dichroism in polarized light.

Sulfatide also gives rise to brown metachromasia with Feyrter's (1936) thionin–tartaric acid method, both when the lipid is impregnated on paper and in the deposits of metachromatic leucodystrophy (Adams, 1965a).

c. Gangliosides. These lipids are water soluble; thus, they are not retained in tissue sections unless bound to protein as is reputed — but not proved — in some forms of amaurotic idiocy. Although gangliosides contain hexose, hexosamine, and neuraminic acid, their histochemical detection is not easy. Shear and Pearse's (1963, 1964) histochemical adaptation of Svennerholm's (1957) resorcinol method was at first encouraging, but subsequent studies indicated that this modification is not a reliable histochemical test for ganglioside (Pearse, 1968). Diezel's (1957a,b) histochemical modification of Klenk and Langerbeins' (1941) method for neuraminic acid with Bial's reagent did not work satisfactorily in our hands (see Adams, 1965a). However, Ravetto's (1964) modification of this method does reasonably display ganglioside in amaurotic idiocy, provided that the reagent is applied as a very fine spray (Lake, 1968a; see Section VI, B, method 15).

8. *Phosphosphingosides*

For histochemical purposes, this lipid class is exemplified by sphingomyelin. It differs from phosphoglycerides, not only in containing a sphingosine skeleton but also in the amide ($—CH_2 \cdot NH \cdot OC \cdot CH_2—$) linkage of its fatty acid chain. Amide bonds are resistant to alkaline hydrolysis, so such preliminary treatment before application of a general phospholipid stain should stain only sphingomyelin (Fig. 13). The specificity of the sodium hydroxide-osmium tetroxide-α-naphthylamine (NaOH-OTAN) method for sphingomyelin has been established by histochemical and densitometric studies (Adams and Bayliss, 1963; Adams, 1965a): a similar preliminary alkaline hydrolytic stage has been outlined for the acid hematein method (Adams, 1965a). Phosphoglycerides that contain fatty acids bound by ether (cephalin "B"), α,β-unsaturated ether (plasmalogen), or acetal groups would wholly or partly resist alkaline hydrolysis. The most important of these lipids is plasmalogen, but its unsaturated ether group can be eliminated by preliminary hydrolysis with mercuric chloride (see Section III,B,6). Since acetal phospholipids are degradation products of plasmalogens, preliminary mercuric chloride hydrolysis should also eliminate reaction resulting from these acetal lipids.

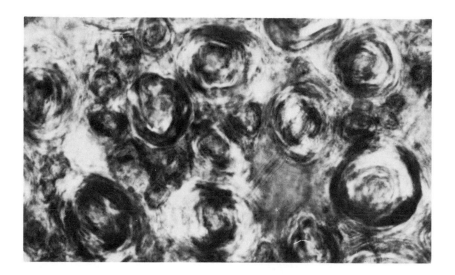

FIG. 13.   Sphingomyelin in rat cord myelin. NaOH-OTAN, phase-contrast, × 2360. (Reproduced from *Neurohistochemistry* by courtesy of Elsevier Publishing Co.)

In summary, the NaOH–OTAN method stains sphingomyelin: preliminary mercuric chloride hydrolysis should exclude interference by plasmalogen and acetal phospholipids.

9. *Lipofuscins*

It is not intended to discuss lipofuscins and ceroid in detail since the histochemistry of these lipid pigments has been extensively reviewed by Pearse (1960) and Wolman (1961, 1964). Ceroid and lipofuscin are probably formed by peroxidation of lipids in intracellular structures, which are then engulfed by lysosomes or phagolysosomes to appear as characteristic intracellular lipofuscin granules (see Adams, 1965c). Lipofuscin can be experimentally produced by a number of quasi-physiological oxidizing agents and be deficiency of the antioxidant α-tocopherol (Granados and Dam, 1950; Hartroft, 1951; Einarson, 1953; Sulkin and Srivanij, 1960; Wolman and Shoshan, 1960; Wolman and Zaidel, 1962).

With increasing degrees of peroxidation and polymerization lipofuscins become less soluble in lipid solvents, more acid-fast with the Ziehl–Neelsen method, more autofluorescent in ultraviolet light, and stain more strongly with the PAS and plasmal methods. The reducing properties of lipofuscin granules for Schmorl's ferric ferricyanide and ammoniacal silver nitrate reagents are variable (see Adams, 1956); strong reduction of these reagents by lipofuscin granules in nerve cells may indicate that melanin is also present (see Lillie *et al.*, 1957). Melanin may be distinguished from lipofuscin by its acetone-resistant staining with Nile blue sulfate (Lillie, 1956; see Section VI).

C. ENZYMIC DIGESTIVE METHODS

Specific lipase has been used for the detection of triglycerides by converting them to insoluble soaps (see Section III,B,4). Enzymes are also used in histochemistry as digestive tools to remove the substance in question. However, before an enzyme can be used for this purpose, its purity has to be firmly established. Thus many commercial sources of neuraminidase are of little histochemical use because they are heavily contaminated with proteolytic enzymes; the interpretation of the results is therefore hazardous (Adams and Bayliss, 1968b).

Boiled snake venom is a well-recognized pure source of phospholipase A. Unfortunately, it is far less active against phosphoglycerides in formalin-fixed tissues than against those in fresh tissue (Adams and Bayliss, 1968b). Because phospholipids are rapidly lost from sections of unfixed tissue, phospholipase A has only a very limited value as a histochemical digestive tool.

In summary, enzymic digestion methods have so far not proved outstandingly valuable in lipid histochemistry.

D. ELECTRON HISTOCHEMICAL METHODS

Thick frozen sections, stained by histochemical methods, can be recut as ultrathin sections for electron microscopy. However, such methods, when applied to lipids, are severely restricted by the solubility of lipids in the preparative solvents used in embedding tissues for electron microscopy. Fixation with formalin, acrolein, or dichromate does not retain lipids during the embedding procedures. Somewhat better results are said to be obtained with calcium-formalin fixation and postchromation (Casley-Smith, 1963, 1967) or glutaraldehyde fixation and "post-osmication" (Idelman, 1965). "Tricomplex fixation" with various divalent cations was proposed by Elbers *et al.* (1965) to prevent phospholipid extraction by "bridging across" the lipid polar head groups. Nevertheless, in practice this method does not seem to retain phospholipids in electron microscopic preparations (Weller, 1965). Fixation with osmium tetroxide or potassium permanganate does not prevent extraction of neutral lipids by the solvents used in embedding for electron microscopy, but it does cause most of the phospholipids to be retained (Korn and Weisman, 1966). (Osmium tetroxide in electron microscopy is discussed further in Section II,B,3.)

Another method for preserving soluble substances for electron microscopy is to cut thin sections from prestained thick sections mounted on a plastic surface (Tranzer, 1965). However, application of this principle to lipid electron histochemistry has not yet led to useful results, mainly because of the massive cellular shattering that occurs during cutting (Weller, 1966).

Because of these various difficulties, electron lipid histochemistry is so far limited to the demonstration of unsaturated groups with osmium tetroxide, copper–azomethine, and OsO_4-thiocarbohydrazide methods (Casley-Smith, 1963, 1967; Jones *et al.*, 1963; Seligman *et al.*, 1966), to the somewhat erratic display of phosphoglyceride with the silver–hydroxamic acid method (see Section II,B,5; Weller *et al.*, 1965), and to the detection of triglycerides at the edge of lipid vacuoles with the lipase–lead sulfide method (see Section III,B,4; Adams *et al.*, 1966).

In summary, present lipid electron histochemical results are not very encouraging; it is unlikely that further advances will be made until a satisfactory method is devised for embedding tissue for electron microscopy without using lipid solvents.

E. LIPID AUTORADIOGRAPHY

Lipid autoradiography may be carried out on conventional calcium–formol-fixed frozen sections, on Carbowax-embedded sections, or by more complex methods for soluble substances that involve freeze-drying the tissue and other techniques (Friedman *et al.*, 1959; Adams *et al.*, 1962, 1964; Schlant and Galambos, 1964; Torvik and Sidman, 1965; Wilske and Ross, 1965; Stumpf and Roth, 1966; Kramsch *et al.*, 1967). The stripping film autoradiographic technique may be applied to frozen sections, but it has been argued that coating with an emulsion of nuclear-sensitive material gives superior results. It has also been suggested that 0.5% trichloroacetic acid should be added to the fixative to precipitate lipoproteins (Kramsch *et al.*, 1967), nevertheless formaldehyde fixation appears to precipitate about 80% of radioactive plasma proteins within the tissue section (Adams and Morgan, 1967, unpublished data).

Autoradiographic techniques have been used to trace the metabolic fate of acetate-H^3 (Torvik and Sidman, 1965), cholesterol-H^3 (Figs. 14 and 15; Adams *et al.*, 1962, 1964; Adams and Morgan, 1966; Kramsch *et al.*, 1967), I^{131}-labeled triolein (Friedman *et al.*, 1959), and cholesterol-4-C^{14} (Schlant and Galambos, 1964).

Tritium is preferred by most autoradiographers, because its short β-particle track of about 1.5 μ allows very precise localization of the labeled substance. Conversely, the long 1.25-mm particle track of P^{32} makes it rather unsuitable for autoradiography. Nevertheless, there is an inherent hazard in tritium autoradiography: a gap of more than 1.5 μ between the section and stripping film will effectively prevent all but the high energy tritium β particles from hitting the nuclear-sensitive coating (see Perry, 1964; Ada *et al.*, 1966). In some respects the "emulsion-dipping" technique overcomes this problem (see above) because the emulsion lodges in closer apposition to the tissue (see Kopriwa and Leblond, 1962). On the other hand, it can be argued that I^{125} is a more suitable isotope to use in lipid autoradiography since its particle track is about 10–15 μ in length. In this case some precision of localization is lost, but the investigator can be certain that he is sampling the middle and bottom layers of a 10μ-thick frozen section instead of only the uppermost 1.5 μ that is allowed with tritium.

Theoretically, doubly labeled lipid autoradiography is feasible. Thus, if two layers of stripping film or emulsion are applied to the sec-

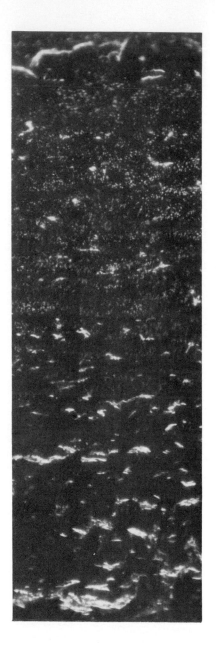 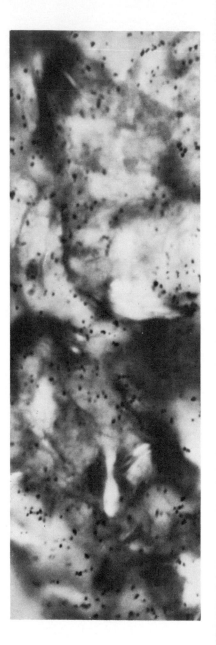

FIG. 14. (*left*) Radioactivity (small white dots) in inner half of normal rabbit aortic wall 4 days after injection of 2 mCi of cholesterol-H³. Autoradiography, dark ground, × 236. (Reproduced by permission of the editor of *J. Atherosclerosis Res.*)

FIG. 15. (*right*) Radioactivity (black dots) in atheromatous plaque of cholesterol-fed rabbit. Autoradiograph, partly polarized light, × 2360. (Reproduced by courtesy of the editor of *Nature*.)

tion (Baserga and Nemeroff, 1962), the lowermost layer could be used to detect H^3 in the cholesterol nucleus, while the uppermost would track C^{14} (particle track 40–60 μ) in the fatty acid chain of a cholesterol ester. However, to the author's knowledge, this technique has not yet been employed in lipid metabolic studies

Kritchevsky *et al.* (1965) reported that 7α-cholesterol-H^3 is metabolically labile in that the tritium label can be transferred to other lipids *in vivo*. If this observation applies to all forms of tritium-labeled cholesterol, it would clearly be useless to use such compounds in tracer studies on the fate of cholesterol in tissues. However, in two separate studies we have found that generally labeled cholesterol-H^3 (Radiochemical Centre, Amersham, Great Britain) does not exchange its tritium label with other plasma lipids *in vivo* over the course of 4-5 days after injection (Adams *et al.*, 1964, 1968).

Autoradiographic results may be quantitated by the laborious process of counting the silver granules within measured areas of tissue with the aid of a graticule inserted in the eyepiece (Fig. 16).

F. QUANTITATIVE LIPID HISTOCHEMISTRY

Up to this point the discussion has centered on "slide" histochemical lipid methods that are essentially nonquantitative. As mentioned in Section I, a number of methods are available for the quantitative estimation of dissected, sectioned, or fractionated tissue samples. It is now relevant to the theme of this chapter to discuss the method introduced by Linderstrøm-Lang (1939), whereby serial cryostat sections are analyzed chemically to establish the cytoarchitectonic distribution of metabolites or enzymes within the tissue. The technique provides for histological "monitoring" during progressive sectioning through the tissue.

Certain tissues lend themselves to cytoarchitectonic lipid analysis. In particular the lipid (and enzyme) constituents of the various layers of the cerebral cortex and subadjacent white matter have already been studied with this technique (Lowry *et al.*, 1954; McDougal *et al.*, 1961, 1964; Derry and Wolfe, 1968). The kidneys and adrenals are examples of other organs that are constructed on a layered histological pattern and would, thus, be amenable to cytoarchitectonic analysis of their constituent lipids, but to the author's knowledge no such study has been made on these organs.

The walls of larger arteries are particularly suitable for layer-by-layer analysis from the inside to the outside of the vessel. After flattening the vessel wall on the chuck of a De La Rue Frigistor thermoelec-

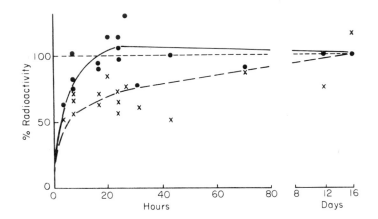

FIG. 16.   Radioactivity in (×) outer and (●) middle thirds of rat aortic wall after injection of 250 μCi cholesterol-H^3; activity expressed as percentage of that in the (---) inner third. Autoradiograph granule count. (Reproduced by courtesy of the editor of *Lancet*.)

tric freezing microtome, some 8-20 consecutive layers can be prepared from human and rabbit aortic wall (Davis *et al.*, 1963; Adams, 1964; Abdulla and Adams, 1965; Adams *et al.*, 1968). As well as enzyme and protein estimations, cholesterol and phospholipid have been determined in such aortic multiple layers (Davis *et al.*, 1963; Adams, 1964). Likewise, quantitative thin-layer chromatography and radio-isotope counting have been performed on grouped layers of human aortic wall (Fig. 17; Abdulla and Adams, 1965; Adams *et al.*, 1968). Variants of the basic Linderstrøm-Lang technique have been introduced for the direct thin-layer chromatography of frozen sections from brain (Strich, 1965) and atherosclerotic plaques (Liadsky and Woolf, 1967). The advantage of such histochromatography is that the sections require no preliminary extraction with solvents and are directly chromatogramed after they have been embedded under the silica gel film; their disadvantage is that at present they are essentially nonquantitative.

IV.   Biological and Pathological Applications

A. General Considerations

1. *Limitations*

The major technical limitations in "slide" histochemistry are the real possibility of diffusion from the section, the essentially nonquan-

titative nature of the techniques, and the less exact chemical characterization that can be achieved than with conventional biochemical
methods. Nevertheless, it should be realized that many of the diffusion problems in histochemistry are also potential hazards in subcellular fractionation techniques.

A certain lack of accuracy in chemical characterization is inherent in
the histochemical method. Biochemists have the advantage that the
substance to be estimated can be first purified by extraction, filtration,
or centrifugation methods, but the histochemist usually has to perform
his tests on intact tissue and often has no opportunity to remove cross-
reacting substances. The disenchantment often expressed when a particular histochemical method turns out to be less "specific" than originally claimed usually reflects the critic's naiveté rather than the
"unreliability" of the technique. Preoccupation with devising
histochemical methods that are "absolutely specific" under all circumstances is about as realistic as the medieval search for the phi-
losopher's stone. This comment, of course, is not to deny the value of
methodological criticism, but such limitations should be balanced
against the advantages when a histochemical procedure is being
evaluated.

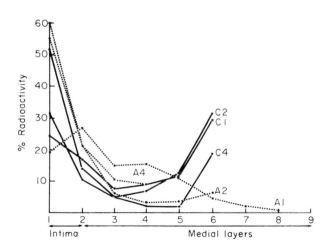

FIG. 17. Radioactivity in multiple layers of aortic wall from normal and cholesterol-
fed rabbits; results for each layer are expressed as percentage of total radioactivity on a
wet weight basis: (– –) control and (· · ·) cholesterol-fed rats. Quantitative histochemical scintillation count. (Reproduced by permission of the editor of *J. Atherosclerosis
Res.*)

2. *Localization vs Quantitation*

"Slide" histochemical methods have an important application in biology and pathology because they allow direct localization of substances or enzymes within normal and abnormal tissues. Furthermore, histochemical slide methods are often a convenient way of screening tissues before embarking on more sophisticated biochemical or cytochemical analyses. In addition to this obviously important advantage of localization, slide methods permit chemical changes to be detected in a minor fraction of a cell population and are relatively quick to perform.

Although slide histochemical methods may be successfully used in isolation from other techniques, the evidence gained with them becomes more valid when linked to results obtained with "conventional" biochemical or quantitative histochemical methods. In this way slide histochemistry can be used as a valuable bridging technique between standard histological and biochemical approaches.

In lipid histochemistry, staining of tissue sections can conveniently be linked with qualitative or quantitative thin-layer chromatography of samples from adjacent tissue (see Section III,F). Likewise, lipid autoradiography may be linked with isotope scintillation counting techniques—although in this instance radioactivity in the autoradiograph slides can be estimated by the tedious and less accurate process of granule counting (see Section III,E).

B. Synopses of Specific Applications

In this section it is proposed to illustrate some examples of the application of lipid histochemistry to specific biological and pathological problems. Since this section is only illustrative, these synopses will be somewhat superficial and mainly derived from work in this laboratory. Moreover, in order to delineate possible future applications a number of speculative suggestions are introduced at certain points in the discussion.

It should be noted that the general application of slide lipid histochemistry to pathology has been extensively reviewed in Wolman's (1964) comprehensive monograph, to which the reader is referred for further information.

1. *Wallerian Degeneration*

The nature of the Marchi substance formed during the secondary stage of demyelination (Fig. 6) has been clarified by histochemical studies on the mechanism of the Marchi method (Adams, 1958; see Section III,B,3). The substance is clearly a hydrophobic lipid containing unsaturated fatty acids and, therefore, could be either triglyceride or esterified cholesterol. It does not react with the lipase–lead sulfide method for triglyceride, but it is stained by the PAN method for cholesterol (Adams, 1966). From this histochemical evidence it can be concluded that the major lipid product of demyelination—as represented by the Marchi substance—is esterified cholesterol. This interpretation is supported by column chromatography of degenerating myelin, which shows that the major fraction reacting with the Marchi reagent is esterified cholesterol (Adams, 1960). This histochemical conclusion is consistent with previous biochemical analyses, which revealed that cholesterol ester is the major lipid breakdown product in both Wallerian degeneration (Johnson *et al.*, 1950) and multiple sclerosis (Cumings, 1953, 1955).

2. *Atherosclerosis*

a. Phospholipids. It has been known for some time that the arterial wall can actively synthesize phospholipids (Zilversmit *et al.*, 1954; Zilversmit and McCandless, 1959; Stein *et al.*, 1963; Newman *et al.*, 1966); the phospholipid that accumulates to the greatest extent is sphingomyelin (Smith, 1960). Histochemical studies reveal that this phospholipid is located in normal and degenerating elastic lamellae (Fig. 7; Adams, 1959b; Adams and Tuqan, 1961; Böttcher and Boelsma-Van Houte, 1964), in the smooth muscle of the tunica media (Adams, 1965e; Adams and Weller, 1966; Boelsma-Van Houte and Böttcher, 1967), and diffusely in the atherosclerotic plaque (but see Section III,B,5b). Apart from endothelium, smooth muscle is the only metabolically active component of the normal arterial wall. By inference, therefore, these smooth muscle cells appear to be responsible for synthesizing most phospholipid of the normal vascular wall. It is not altogether certain whether lipophages in the atherosclerotic intima (Fig. 7) are all modified smooth muscle cells or whether some are macrophages. Nevertheless, both cell types appear to be able to synthesize phospholipid (see Day, 1964; Parker *et al.*, 1966).

b. Lipid Transport. It has been suggested that phospholipid is an important transport vehicle for cholesterol in the arterial wall (see Adams, 1967). With advancing age histoenzymic evidence shows that the middle zone of the human aortic wall undergoes ischaemic atrophy (Adams *et al.*, 1962; Adams, 1967); thus, it would not be unreasonable to suppose that local synthesis of lipotrophic phospholipid is impaired in the senescent larger human artery. As a result of such impaired synthesis, it can be inferred that the outward micellar transport of lipid across the arterial wall would be impeded. The corollary is that lipid would accumulate in the inner arterial wall, as in the atherosclerotic vessel. However, before such an atherogenic mechanism can be entertained, it is necessary to show that cholesterol does in fact filter from inside outward across the normal arterial wall. Such information was obtained by autoradiography of the aorta after intravenous injection of cholesterol-H³ into various species (Figs. 14 and 15; Adams *et al.*, 1962, 1964; Adams and Morgan, 1966). Granule counting of the autoradiograph films for various periods after injection indicated that cholesterol-H³ slowly migrates from the inside to the outside of the aorta (Fig. 16).

In pursuing this problem, we have recently studied the distribution of intravenously injected cholesterol-H³, albumin-I¹²⁵, and β,γ-globulin-I¹²⁵ by scintillation counting of multiple consecutive layers of rabbit aortic wall (see Section III,F; Adams *et al.*, 1968). These quantitative results confirmed that cholesterol is distributed in an inward–outward gradient across both the normal and atheromatous aortic wall (Figs. 14 and 17). Albumin and globulin, however, showed an outward–inward gradient in normal and slightly atheromatous vessels, indicative of diffusion of plasma proteins from outside–inward. In severely atheromatous lesions the gradient for albumin and β-globulin usually matched that for cholesterol (i.e., was inside-outward), suggestive of a direct leak of plasma proteins from the lumen into established severe lesions. These preliminary results are not consistent with the view that plasma proteins (in particular β-lipoprotein) transport cholesterol across the normal and slightly atheromatous arterial wall. It seems more likely that local synthesis of phospholipid or protein within the arterial wall provides the vehicle for trans-mural cholesterol transport.

3. *Lipid Storage Diseases*

Histochemical study of rectal, appendicular or sural nerve biopsies may provide useful knowledge about the accumulated lipids and metabolic derangements in certain storage diseases (Bodian and Lake, 1963; Dayan, 1967b; Lake, 1968b; Sourander and Olsson, 1968; see Adams, 1965d). Such histological and histochemical studies may in themselves be conclusive or indicate the need for histological and chemical study of a brain biopsy (see Blackwood and Cumings, 1966).

Hirsch and Peifer's (1957) cresyl violet method for sulfatide is particularly valuable for detecting deposits of this lipid in peripheral nerves and other organs (Wolfe and Pietra, 1964) in metachromatic leucodystrophy (sulfatide lipidosis). Likewise, certain forms of amaurotic idiocy may be diagnosed from rectal or appendicular biopsies, where the ganglion cells are seen to accumulate ganglioside. This lipid can here be recognized (? in protein-bound form) by its basophilia, strong PAS reaction (Fig. 18), and staining with Bial's reagent (see Section III,B,7c).

The deposits of cerebroside in Gaucher's and Krabbe's disease (Sourander and Olsson, 1968), as well as the accumulation of ceramide di- and trihexosides in Fabry's disease (Lehner and Adams, 1968), may be identified by their strong reaction with the modified PAS method (Fig. 19; see Section III,B,7a; Adams *et al.*, 1963; Adams, 1965a). Deposits of sphingomyelin in Niemann-Pick's disease characteristically react with acid hematein (Wolman, 1964; Lake, 1967; see Sections III,B,5 and III,B,8). Other histochemical studies of lipid storage diseases have been reviewed by Diezel (1957a,b), Wolman (1964), and Adams (1965d).

4. *Pulmonary Physiology and Pathology*

a   Pulmonary "Surfactant." Pulmonary phospholipid synthesis may play an important role in providing a "surfactant" substance (see Section II,A) that promotes alveolar expansion in the fetal lung (Reynolds and Strang, 1966; Taylor and Abrams, 1966). Histochemical studies have demonstrated a film of phospholipid over the pulmonary epithelial surface. Hitherto, it was tacitly assumed that such phospholipid is synthesized by alveolar macrophages, for phospholipid accumulates in these cells in the cholesterol-fed rabbit (Adams, 1962, unpublished observation) and the capacity to synthesize phospholipid is a common feature of the macrophage elements of the reticuloendothelial system (Day, 1964).

However, the bronchiolar epithelium also contains phospholipid (Fig. 20). In a recent study, Niden (1967) demonstrated phosphoglyceride with the hydroxamic acid method (see Section III,B,5) in the nonciliated Clara cells of the infant mouse's bronchiolar epithelium. Niden considered that the alveolar macrophage (large alveolar cell) is predominantly phagocytic, whereas the Clara cell secretes the "surfactant" phospholipid. These bronchiolar cells certainly contain more phospholipid than alveolar macrophages, but the most convincing evidence that Niden presented was the faster incorporation of injected palmitate-H^3 or acetate-H^3 into the Clara cell than into the alveolar macrophages — as detected by autoradiography of the lung.

b.   Paraffin Granuloma. Lipid pneumonias are an ill-understood problem in pathology: It is uncertain how often such lipid is derived

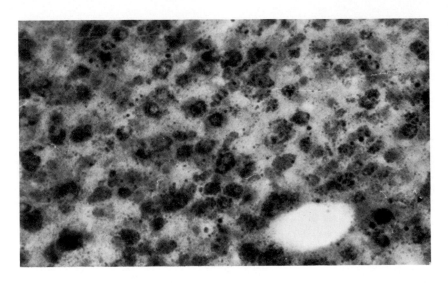

FIG. 18.   Ganglioside (presumed to be protein-bound) in microglia of central white matter in late infantile amaurotic idiocy. Modified periodic acid-Schiff, × 336. (Reproduced from *Neurohistochemistry* by courtesy of Elsevier Publishing Co.)

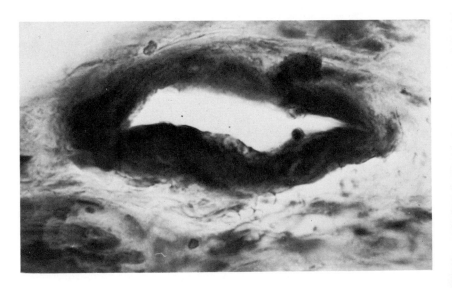

FIG. 19.   Ceramide trihexoside deposits in small artery of oral submucosa in Fabry's disease. Modified periodic acid-Schiff, × 960. (Reproduced by courtesy of the editor of *J. Pathol. Bacteriol.*)

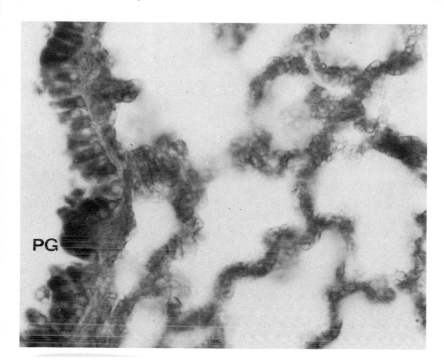

FIG. 20. Phosphoglycerides (PG) in bronchiolar epithelium of adult rabbit lung; slight reaction in alveolar cells. Gold-hydroxamic acid, × 600.

by filtration from the blood and how often by aspiration down the bronchus (see Wolman, 1964).

The following case history illustrates a practical application of lipid histochemistry in the pathology of such pneumonias.[1] A 75-year-old man had suffered from maxillary sinusitis from the age of 30-45 years and from an obscure unresolved lower lobe pneumonitis for about the last 6 years of his life. Microscopy of paraffin-embedded sections of the consolidated lower lobes of the lung (obtained at necropsy) showed areas of organization, in which predominantly extracellular "lipid vacuoles" were distributed between proliferating fibroblasts and macrophages; only occasional "lipid vacuoles" were seen within macrophages. Histochemical examination of frozen sections showed that the "lipid" droplets were stained only by Oil Red O of all the lipid methods used. Sudan black, osmium tetroxide, OTAN, gold-

---

[1]Dr. Patrick Sourander, Pathological Institute, Göteborgs University, Sweden, kindly provided the clinical excerpt and necropsy material.

hydroxamic acid, lipase-lead sulfide, perchloric acid-naphtho-quinone, and PAS were all negative. Clearly this "lipid" was completely saturated, even though it was liquid. Because no *saturated* physiological lipid is liquid at room temperature (see Weast, 1965-1966), the "lipid" droplets seemed possibly to be a saturated mineral (hydrocarbon) oil. Thin-layer and gas-liquid chromatography[2] revealed that the material was in fact a light paraffin oil, with similar characteristics to liquid paraffin B.P.

Review of the clinical history revealed that the patient had treated his constipation with a nightly dose of liquid paraffin for at least the last 10 years of his life. The liquid paraffin in the lung could have been aspirated during sleep from the nightly dose and, in addition, might have been partly derived from the paraffin that was formerly used as a vehicle in ephedrine nasal drops.

In retrospect, it is worth considering whether histochemical examination of the sputum in such cases might reveal the presence of paraffin droplets. The triad of positive "red sudanophilia," negative "black sudanophilia," and negative osmiophilia appear to be absolutely characteristic for liquid paraffin: an essentially similar histochemical staining pattern in paraffin granulomas has been previously reported by Graef (1939) and Wolman (1964).

V. General Conclusions

The physical features of lipids are important determinants of lipid reactions in tissue sections. Water-soluble dyes and reagents would be expected only to penetrate hydrophilic lipids (i.e., those with a polarized surface). Organotropic dyes and reagents preferentially penetrate hydrophobic lipids (i.e., those with a nonpolar surface comprised of paraffin chains). Thus, the histophysical and histochemical reactions of lipids can in part be explained by consideration of these surface (water-lipid phase) phenomena.

Among histophysical methods, lipid-soluble dyes, birefringence, and extraction techniques are commonly employed. In the latter category only the extraction of free lipids with chloroform–methanol and the differential extraction of hydrophobic lipids with acetone appear to be essentially reliable. It should be remembered that much lipid is so firmly bound to protein that it can only be removed after preliminary proteolysis or by acidifying the solvent.

---

[2]Dr. Raymond Baker, Department of Chemical Pathology, Guy's Hospital Medical School, kindly carried out these analyses.

Apart from autoradiography, histochemical lipid methods comprise reasonably specific color reactions for cholesterol, fatty acids, triglycerides, phosphoglycerides, plasmalogens, glycosphingosides, phosphosphingosides, and lipofuscins. It would be extremely unwise to expect that any of these methods can be absolutely specific· histochemical results must be interpreted in a critical but informed fashion.

Slide histochemical methods are valuable aids for localizing lipids at the histological level or for the preliminary "screening" of a tissue. Such methods, however, suffer from the obvious drawback that they are nonquantitative. This defect can in part be remedied by employing quantitative techniques in parallel with slide histochemistry. Quantitative histochemical results can be obtained by estimating tissue sections or microdissected specimens with radioautographic, scintillation-counting, thin-layer chromatographic, and other analytical techniques.

VI. Technical Appendix

A. FIXATION AND MICROTOMY TECHNIQUES

As already discussed in Section II,B, much polar lipid is extracted by water from unfixed frozen (cryostat) sections. For this reason tissues must first be fixed in 1% calcium acetate–10% formalin for an adequate period, before they are cut on a freezing microtome. The most convenient type of freezing microtome is undoubtedly the thermoelectric type (e.g., De La Rue Frigistor). This type of microtome has the great advantage over the carbon dioxide model that the chuck remains at constant temperature so that sections can be cut off the block at practically constant thickness.

Frozen sections are customarily floated out in water before being mounted on slides or transferred to reagent solutions. It is particularly important to remember that a scum of lipid may form over the surface of this water due to the release of globular lipid from the tissue sections. If sections are dragged through this scum, artifactual lipid droplets may appear in the stained preparations. The problem can largely be circumvented by removing the scum with filter paper.

After fixation but before sectioning, tissues may be embedded in gelatin or in water-soluble Carbowax by customary histological techniques. The former procedure better preserves tissue structure in frozen sections, while the latter manoeuvre permits the tissue to be cut at room temperature with conventional microtomes.

Frozen sections of calcium–formol-fixed tissue may be stained by the lipid histochemical methods described below. Such sections, after mounting on glass slides, are also suitable for radioautography with stripping film or liquid emulsion techniques (see Section III,E).

B. SLIDE HISTOCHEMICAL METHODS

The following techniques are described:

1. Perchloric acid-naphthoquinone for cholesterol
2. OsO_4 for unsaturated lipids
3. Bromine-silver nitrate for unsaturated lipids
4. Ultraviolet-Schiff for unsaturated lipids
5. Copper rubeanic acid for free fatty acids
6. Lipase-lead sulfide for triglycerides
7. Acid hematein for choline-containing phospholipids
8. NaOH-acid hematein for sphingomyelin
9. OTAN for phospholipids-hydrophobic lipids
10. NaOH-OTAN for sphingomyelin
11. Gold-hydroxamic acid for phosphoglycerides
12. Plasmal reaction for plasmalogen phospholipids
13. Modified PAS for cerebroside and protein-bound ganglioside
14. Cresyl violet for sulfatide
15. Svennerholm-Bial reagent for ganglioside
16. Nile blue sulfate for phospholipids-hydrophobic lipids
17. Sudan black for all unsaturated lipids
18. Oil Red O for unsaturated hydrophobic lipids.

Method 1. Perchloric Acid-Naphthoquinone Technique for Cholesterol (Adams, 1961, 1965a)

(a) Cut frozen sections from tissues fixed in 1% calcium acetate-10% formalin or in "routine" formalin.

(b) Leave the sections free-floating in calcium-formalin for at least a week (preferably 3-4 weeks) in order to promote preliminary atmospheric oxidation of cholesterol. Then mount the sections on glass slides and dry them in air.

(c) The sections are painted with a thin layer of reagent solution and heated on a hot plate or bottom of an oven at 65°-70°C for 5-10 minutes or until the red color that first appears turns completely blue. Care must be taken not to overheat and burn the sections. The reagent solution is prepared afresh daily by adding 10 mg of 1,2-naphthoquinone-4-sulfonic acid to 10 ml of a mixture of ethanol-perchloric acid (60%)-formalin (= 40% formaldehyde)-water (2:1:0.1:0.9, v/v/v/v).

(d) A drop of perchloric acid (60%) is placed on the reacted section and a cover slip is gently lowered into position.

Cholesterol and related sterols are colored blue. The reaction product is stable for some hours and then turns grayish-black; it is not stable in water, glycerine jelly, or other mounting media.

Method 2. Osmium Tetroxide Technique for Unsaturated Lipids (see Adams, 1959a, 1965a)

(a) Cut frozen sections from tissues fixed in 1% calcium acetate-10% formalin. Mount sections on glass slides or stain them free floating.
(b) Immerse in 1% OsO_4 for 2–18 hours. The container should be stoppered and kept at 4°C. The reduction of OsO_4 is faster at room temperature (Adams et al., 1967), but at this temperature the reagent is more volatile.
(c) Wash in running tap water for 20 minutes and mount in glycerine jelly.

All unsaturated lipids are stained black. Because the reagent is fat soluble, the interior of fat globules is well stained. Saturated lipids and cholesterol do not react.

Method 3. Bromine-Silver Nitrate Technique for Unsaturated Lipids (Norton et al., 1962)

(a) Frozen sections are cut from thin slices of tissue fixed in 1% calcium acetate-10% formalin. Mount sections on glass slides and dry them in air.
(b) Immerse the sections in 2% potassium bromide-0.1 N bromine (1 ml of Br_2 in 390 ml of 2% KBr) or in saturated bromine water for 1 minute.
(c) Wash in water, rinse in 1% sodium bisulfite for 5 minutes, and wash seven times in distilled water.
(d) Treat with 1% silver nitrate in N nitric acid for 18 hours.
(e) Wash seven times in distilled water.
(f) Develop for 10 minutes in Kodak Dektol developer (or equivalent) diluted with water (1:1 v/v).
(g) Wash well in water and mount in glycerine jelly.

Some unsaturated lipids are stained brown-black (see Section III,B,3). Cholesterol reacts when impregnated on paper, but crystals of the sterol in tissues are not stained.

*Method 4. Ultraviolet-Schiff Technique for Unsaturated Lipids
(Modified from Belt and Hayes, 1956)*

(a) Cut unfixed tissues on the cryostat or cut frozen sections from tissues fixed in 1% calcium acetate-10% formalin. Mount sections on glass slides and dry them in air.
(b) Irradiate sections with ultraviolet light for 1-4 hours.
(c) Then proceed as for method 12 stage (c) onward.

Unsaturated lipids appear pink to red because of the formation of pseudoplasmal aldehydes from fatty acid ethylene bonds.

*Method 5. Copper Rubeanic Acid Technique for Fatty Acids
(Holczinger, 1959)*

(a) Cut unfixed tissues on the cryostat, or cut frozen sections from tissues fixed in either 1% calcium acetate-10% formalin or in "routine" formalin. Mount sections on glass slides and dry them in air.
(b) Treat sections with 0.005% cupric acetate for 3-5 hours.
(c) Wash twice for 10 seconds with 0.1% disodium-EDTA at pH 7.1. Then wash for 10 minutes in distilled water.
(d) Immerse sections in 0.1% rubeanic acid in 70% ethanol for 30 minutes. Dissolve the rubeanic acid in ethanol, warm slightly (avoiding a naked flame), and make up to volume with distilled water.
(e) Wash for a few minutes in 70% ethanol and then wash in water. Mount in glycerine jelly, or dehydrate, clear and mount in DPX or balsam.

Fatty acids are stained greenish-black.

*Method 6. Lipase-Lead Sulfide Technique for Triglycerides
(Adams et al., 1966)*

(a) Frozen sections are cut from tissue fixed in 1% calcium acetate-10% formalin or in "routine" formalin.
(b) Incubate free-floating sections in the reaction medium for 2-4 hours at 37°C. The medium is prepared by adding 50 mg of porcine pancreatic lipase to 10 ml of 2% calcium chloride, 15 ml of tris buffer (pH 8.0), and 25 ml of distilled water. [The pancreatic lipase must be shown to be uncontaminated by other lipolytic enzymes. Purity can be established by testing the lipase against the individual spots obtained by previously separating a suit-

able lipid mixture on a thin-layer chromatoplate. The reaction products are then separated in the other dimension of the plate (see Adams *et al.* 1966 for further details). Lipase from California Biochemical Corporation is free of contaminating enzymic activity. Other sources may also be satisfactory but require testing.]

(c) Wash well in several changes of distilled water for 15 minutes.
(d) Treat with 1% lead nitrate for 15 minutes.
(e) Wash well in several changes of distilled water.
(f) Immerse in dilute ammonium sulfide (10 drops/25 ml) for 1 minute.
(g) Wash well, counterstain with Mayer's hemalum, and mount in glycerine jelly.

Triglycerides and waxes are stained brownish-black. Only the surface of large fat droplets is stained because the reagents only slowly penetrate such droplets and because lipolysis only proceeds at the water-fat interface.

A duplicate control section should be processed from stage (d) onward in order to determine the extent of nonspecific lead binding such as that encountered with negatively charged lipid micelles (Rostgaard and Barrnett, 1965). Calcium deposits also give a false positive reaction; they can be eliminated by preliminary treatment of the section with 20% EDTA at pH 6.9 for 30 minutes.

Method 7. Acid Hematein Technique for Choline-Containing Phospholipids (Modified from Baker, 1946, 1947)

Baker's method was originally used on tissue blocks; this slight modification is designed for individual frozen sections cut from tissue fixed in 1% calcium acetate–10% formalin.

(a) Mount frozen sections on glass slides and thoroughly dry them in air.
(b) Treat the sections with 5% potassium dichromate–1% calcium chloride for 18 hours at room temperature and then for a further 18–24 hours at 60°C.
(c) After thoroughly washing with tap water, stain with acid hematein for 5 hours at 37°C. The dye solution should be prepared afresh each day by adding 1 ml of 1% sodium periodate ($NaIO_4$) to 50 ml of 0.1% hematoxylin (BDH reagent grade). Heat to boiling point and then, after cooling, add 1 ml of glacial acetic acid.

(d) Thoroughly wash the sections in tap water and differentiate in 0.25% potassium ferricyanide-0.25% sodium tetraborate for 18 hours at 37°C.

(e) After thorough washing, mount in glycerine jelly.

Lecithin and sphingomyelin are stained blue-black. The reaction of protein-bound phospholipids cannot be prevented by preliminary extraction with pyridine (as recommended by Baker); under these circumstances extraction with chloroform-methanol-hydrochloric acid (66:33:1, v/v/v) may be successful.

Baker's (1946, 1947) original acid hematein method was designed for use on blocks of fixed tissue which were subsequently sectioned. The method outlined above is a modification to use on frozen sections of fixed tissue; results with it are usually as good as with the original method, except in myelin (Adams, 1965a). Bourgeois and Hubbard (1965) described a modification for use on *unfixed* cryostat sections which were fixed after cutting; Lange (1967) reported that this modification is as reliable as the original Baker method. We have found that polar lipids are very poorly preserved in cryostat sections (see Section II,B), but the author has encountered disagreement over this point among some colleagues. We have wondered whether the condensation that forms over a cryostat section when removed from the refrigerated cabinet might be mainly responsible for this extraction of polar lipids. If this were the case, the problem should be circumvented by gently warming the mounted section with a fingertip before removing it from the cryostat cabinet into the laboratory atmosphere. However, we have had no success (i.e., improved staining of cryostat sections) after this manoeuvre.

Method 8. Sodium Hydroxide–Acid Hematein Technique for Sphingomyelin (Adams, 1965a)

(a) Subject frozen sections cut from calcium–formol–fixed tissue to NaOH-hydrolysis as in method 10.

(b) Then proceed as for method 7.

Sphingomyelin (alkali-resistant choline-containing phospholipid) is stained blue-black.

Method 9. Osmium Tetroxide–α-Naphthylamine (OTAN) Technique for Phospholipids (Adams, 1959a, 1960, 1965a)

(a) Cut 10–15 μ frozen sections from tissue fixed in 1% calcium acetate–10% formalin.

(b) Treat free-floating sections for 18 hours (overnight) with a mixture of 1 part 1% osmium tetroxide and 3 parts 1% potassium chlorate. The reaction vessel should be filled to the top and tightly stoppered to prevent vaporization of osmium tetroxide.
(c) Wash the sections in distilled water and then mount them on glass slides.
(d) Treat the sections with a saturated aqueous solution of α-naphthylamine at 37°C for 20 minutes (10–15 minutes for 15 μ sections). The saturated solution of α-naphthylamine is prepared by adding an excess to distilled water, gently warming to 40°C, and then filtering. [α-Naphthylamine may contain the volatile carcinogenic β derivative. For this reason the reagent should not be handled, the solution should be prepared in a fume cupboard (hood), rubber gloves should be used throughout this stage, the reaction vessel should be sealed to prevent vaporization during incubation, and the vessel should be opened in a fume cupboard.]
(e) Wash the sections in distilled water for 5 minutes.
(f) Counterstain the sections with 2% Alcian blue in 2% acetic acid, usually for 15–60 seconds.
(g) Wash in tap water and mount in glycerine jelly.

Unsaturated phospholipids are stained orange-red or orange-brown, while hydrophobic unsaturated lipid esters (triglycerides and cholesterol esters) and unsaturated fatty acids are stained black. Mixtures of hydrophilic and hydrophobic lipids may stain in intermediate shades. However, hydrophobic lipids may be removed by preliminary 2-hour treatment with acetone at 4°C, leaving phospholipids intact (see Section II,C,3; Dunnigan, 1964; Adams and Bayliss, 1968a). For reasons that are not at present understood all phospholipid reactions of atherosclerotic plaques are nearly extinguished by preliminary acetone extraction (see Section II,C,3).

Method 10. NaOH–OTAN Technique for Sphingomyelin (Modified after Adams and Bayliss, 1963; Adams, 1965a)

Before stage (b) of method 9, hydrolyze free-floating sections with 2 N aqueous NaOH at 37°C for 1 hour. The sections are next gently washed in water, rinsed in 1% acetic acid for 1 minute, and again washed with water. Then proceed as for method 9.

Sphingomyelin and other alkali-resistant phospholipids are stained orange-red, while alkali-labile phospholipids (phosphoglycerides) are destroyed by hydrolysis. Cholesterol esters and triglycerides are only

partly hydrolyzed because NaOH is applied in aqueous and not alco-
holic solution. Preliminary acetone extraction may be used to remove
hydrophobic lipids (see method 9).

Method 11. Gold-Hydroxamic Acid Reaction for Phospho-
glycerides (Adams et al., 1963; Adams, 1965a;
Modified after Adams and Davison, 1959 and
Gallyas, 1963)

(a) Cut frozen sections from tissues fixed in 1% calcium
    acetate-10% formalin.
(b) Free-floating sections are hydrolyzed for 20 minutes in a mix-
    ture of equal parts of 12% sodium hydroxide and 5% hydrox-
    ylamine hydrochloride.
(c) After hydroxylaminolysis, the sections are washed with three
    changes of distilled water for 5 minutes each.
(d) Next the sections are treated for 1-2 hours with an aqueous solu-
    tion of 0.2% ammonium nitrate, 0.1% silver nitrate, and 0.025%
    NaOH; the silver reagent should be adjusted to pH 9.5 on the
    glass electrode. The reaction is faster in bright light (sunlight).
(e) After washing in distilled water for 10 minutes, the sections are
    immersed for 5 minutes in 1% acetic acid, washed for 10 min-
    utes in distilled water, and then are toned for 10 minutes with
    0.2% yellow gold chloride.
(f) The sections are next briefly rinsed in distilled water, immersed
    for 5 minutes in 5% sodium thiosulfate, and washed for 10 min-
    utes in distilled water.
(g) The sections are now dried onto slides, dehydrated, cleared,
    and mounted in DPX or Canada balsam. Sections may also be
    mounted in glycerine jelly.

Phosphoglycerides are stained a stable red-purple color. A slight
nonspecific reaction is encountered in some tissues; the extent of such
staining is revealed by omitting stage (b) of the procedure.

Method 12. Plasmal Reaction for Plasmalogen Phospholipids
(Modified after Hayes, 1949)

(a) Frozen sections are cut from tissues that have been briefly fixed
    (3-6 hours) in 1% calcium acetate-10% formalin. The sections
    are mounted on glass slides and rapidly dried.
(b) Hydrolyze the sections with 1-5% mercuric chloride for 10
    minutes.

(c) Wash in three changes of distilled water.
(d) Stain with Schiff's reagent for 20 minutes. (*Do not* reuse the Schiff solution, because it may become contaminated with mercuric chloride.)
(e) Rinse in three changes of acidified bisulfite water (10% $K_2S_2O_5$ in 0.05 N NCl) or in one change of 3 N HCl (see Adams, 1965a).
(f) Wash in running tap water for 20 minutes and then mount in glycerine jelly.

Plasmalogen phospholipids are stained pink to red. The occurrence of pseudoplasmal aldehydes (oxidized ethylene bonds) can be detected by omitting stage (b) (mercuric chloride hydrolysis). Unless the tissues are very fresh, the intensity of pseudoplasmal staining may be very strong and can mask a weak underlying true plasmal reaction.

Method 13. Modified PAS Technique for Cerebroside and Protein-Bound Ganglioside (Adams and Bayliss, 1963; Adams et al., 1963; Adams, 1965a)

(a) Frozen sections are cut from tissues fixed in 1% calcium acetate-10% formalin. Sections are then mounted on glass slides that have been previously coated with chrome-gelatin [see stage (b)]. Prepare these slides by dipping them in a mixture of 0.05% chrome potassium alum and 1% gelatin. Allow the slides to drain and dry them in air.
(b) Optional stage to remove phosphoinositides: hydrolyze sections with 2 N NaOH for 1 hour at 37°C, then wash in water and rinse with 1% acetic acid (see method 10). This manoeuvre must be applied before mounting the sections on slides.
(c) Deaminate with 10% aqueous chloramine T at 37°C for 1 hour.
(d) Wash rapidly in a large volume of water. It is very important to rinse rapidly in order to prevent the tissue section swelling in water and floating off the slide.
(e) Oxidize with performic acid for 10 minutes. Prepare performic acid by adding 4.5 ml. of hydrogen peroxide (30% = 100 volumes) and 0.5 ml of concentrated sulfuric acid to 45 ml of formic acid (Analar or equivalent, 98%). Let the solution mature for 1 hour, and "de-gas" by thoroughly stirring before use; it remains active for 24 hours.
(f) Wash in water.
(g) Treat with saturated 2,4-dinitrophenylhydrazine in N HCl at 4°C for 2 hours.

(h) Wash thoroughly for 10 minutes.
(i) Stain with the standard PAS method (McManus–Lillie type; see Pearse, 1960), but omit the final rinse in bisulfite water.
(j) Briefly rinse sections in 3 N HCl and then wash well in tap water. Mount in glycerine jelly.

Duplicate sections are extracted with chloroform-methanol (2:1 v/v at 20°–25°C for 2–18 hours before stage (b). Pink- to red-stained material that is extracted in sections treated with chloroform–methanol is cerebroside or protein-bound ganglioside. Unextracted stained material is mucopolysaccharide.

Method 14. Cresyl Violet Technique for Sulfatide (Hirsch and Peiffer, 1957; Dayan, 1967a)

(a) Cut frozen sections from tissue fixed in 1% calcium acetate–10% formalin. Mount sections on glass slides and dry them in air.
(b) Stain in 0.02–0.1% cresyl violet in 1% acetic acid for 10–30 minutes.
(c) Wash in tap water.
(d) Examine under water and then mount in glycerine jelly.

Deposits of sulfatide in metachromatic leucodystrophy are stained metachromatically brown. In polarized light these stained deposits exhibit green dichroism (Dayan, 1967a), which distinguishes them from the occasionally troublesome brown-tinted red reaction of mast cell granules.

Myelin stains lilac (orthochromatically) when sections are mounted in glycerine jelly. However, when sections are examined under water, CNS myelin is stained metachromatically brown but peripheral nerve myelin remains orthochromatic violet (Adams and Bayliss, 1968b).

Method 15. Svennerholm-Bial Reagent for Ganglioside (Ravetto, 1964; Lake, 1968a; Modified from Diezel, 1957a,b)

(a) Cut frozen sections from tissue fixed in 1% calcium acetate–10% formalin. Mount on glass slides.
(b) Spray sections with Svennerholm-Bial reagent in a fume cupboard (hood). It is particularly important to use a very fine sprayer, such as Quickfit general-purpose glass spray 7CR (Scientific Supplies). (Previously we obtained negative results with a coarse spray.) The reagent solution is prepared as follows:

Orcinol	200 mg
Copper sulfate (0.1 M)	0.25 ml

| Hydrochloric acid (12 N) | 80 ml |
| Distilled water to | 100 ml |

The solution should be allowed to "mature" for 4 hours before use. It is important that the concentrated hydrochloric acid should be fresh.

(c) Heat the sprayed sections in hydrochloric acid vapor at 70°C for 10 minutes. A thin layer of 12 N hydrochloric acid is poured into the bottom of a polythene Wilson jar; the whole container is brought to 70°C before the slides are inserted.

(d) Rapidly dry sections in air, rinse in xylene, and mount in Canada balsam.

The deposits of ganglioside in Tay-Sachs' disease are stained red, as are the sialomucopolysaccharides in salivary gland acini. This method gives reasonable results which we could not obtain with Diezel's original method.

Method 16. *Nile Blue Sulfate (Modified from Cain, 1947a)*

(a) Cut frozen sections from tissues fixed in 1% calcium acetate-10% formalin. Mount sections on glass slides and dry them in air.

(b) Stain with 1% aqueous Nile blue sulfate at 60°C for 5 minutes, then differentiate in 1% acetic acid at 60°C for 30-60 seconds. Alternatively, stain at room temperature for 30 minutes, and differentiate at this temperature for 2-3 minutes.

(c) Wash and mount in glycerine jelly.

Unsaturated triglycerides, cholesterol esters, and fatty acids are stained by the organotropic pink-mauve oxazone component of Nile blue. Phosphoglycerides, sulfatide, and, possibly, other tissue components are stained by the blue oxazine component. If staining is conducted with 0.05% Nile blue in 1% sulfuric acid, lipofuscins are colored deep blue, while melanins are dark green and myelin is light green; the melanin staining resists extraction with acetone (Lillie, 1956).

Method 17. *Sudan Black B Technique for All Unsaturated Lipids*

(a) Cut frozen sections from tissues fixed in 1% calcium acetate-10% formalin or in "routine" formalin.

(b) Wash sections in water and rinse in 70% alcohol.

(c) Stain for 15 minutes in saturated Sudan black B in 70% alcohol.

(d) Differentiate with 70% alcohol until the dye no longer diffuses out of the section.
(e) Wash well in water and mount in glycerine jelly.

Unsaturated hydrophobic lipids (triglycerides, cholesterol esters, and fatty acids) are stained black, whereas phospholipids are stained blue-black or blue-gray. Some (but not all) phospholipids, stained by Sudan black, exhibit red-bronze dichroism in polarized light (Diezel, 1957a,b; see Adams, 1965a).

Method 18. Oil Red O Technique for Hydrophobic Lipids (Modified after Lillie and Ashburn, 1943)

(a) Cut frozen sections from tissues fixed in 1% calcium acetate-10% formalin or in "routine" formalin.
(b) Wash sections in water and rinse in 70% alcohol.
(c) Stain for 15 minutes in Oil Red O. The dye solution should be prepared 1 hour in advance by mixing 6 parts of stock dye solution with 4 parts of distilled water; it is then filtered immediately before use. The stock solution is saturated Oil Red O in 99% isopropanol.
(d) Differentiate with 70% alcohol until the dye no longer diffuses out of the section.
(e) Wash well in water and mount in glycerine jelly.

Unsaturated hydrophobic lipids (triglycerides, cholesterol esters, and fatty acids) are strongly stained red. Cerebroside and mineral paraffin oil are moderately stained (Adams, 1965a), whereas phospholipids are only lightly tinted with the dye. In tissues, phospholipids give a faint reaction that is quite distinct from the intense staining of hydrophobic globular lipid droplets.

ACKNOWLEDGMENTS

It is a great pleasure to acknowledge the invaluable help of Mrs. O. B. High, without whose assistance this work could not have been started. The author also wishes to acknowledge assistance with the photomicroscopy by Mr. R. S. Morgan. Various aspects of this department's work discussed in this chapter have been supported by the British Heart Foundation, the Multiple Sclerosis Society, Chas. Pfizer Limited, the Tobacco Research Council, the U.S. Public Health Service, and the Wellcome Trust.

References

Abdulla, Y. H., and Adams, C. W. M. (1965). *J. Atherosclerosis Res.* **5**, 504.
Ada, G. L., Humphrey, J. H., Askonas, B. A., McDevitt, H. O., and Nossal, G. J. V. (1966). *Exptl. Cell Res.* **41**, 557.

Adams, C. W. M. (1956). *J. Histochem. Cytochem.* 4, 23.
Adams, C. W. M. (1958). *J. Neurochem.* 2, 178.
Adams, C. W. M. (1959a). *J. Pathol. Bacteriol.* 77, 648.
Adams, C. W. M. (1959b). *Lancet* i, 1075.
Adams, C. W. M. (1960). *J. Histochem. Cytochem.* 8, 262.
Adams, C. W. M. (1961). *Nature* 192, 331.
Adams, C. W. M. (1962). *In* "Neurochemistry" (K. A. C. Elliott, I. H. Page, and J. H. Quastel, eds.), 2nd Ed., pp. 85-112. Thomas, Springfield, Illinois.
Adams, C. W. M. (1964). *Proc. Roy. Soc. Med.* 57, 31.
Adams, C. W. M. (1965a). *In* "Neurohistochemistry" (C. W. M. Adams, ed.), pp. 6-66. Elsevier, Amsterdam.
Adams, C. W. M. (1965b). *In* "Neurohistochemistry" (C. W. M. Adams, ed.), pp. 67-108. Elsevier, Amsterdam.
Adams, C. W. M. (1965c). *In* "Neurohistochemistry" (C. W. M. Adams, ed.), pp. 253-331. Elsevier, Amsterdam.
Adams, C. W. M. (1965d). *In* "Neurohistochemistry" (C. W. M. Adams, ed.), pp. 488-517. Elsevier, Amsterdam.
Adams, C. W. M. (1965e). *Bull. Soc. Roy. Zool.* (Anvers) 37, 21.
Adams, C. W. M. (1966). *Proc. 5th Intern. Congr. Neuropathol.* (F. Lüthy and A. Bischoff, eds.), pp. 328-341. Excerpta Med. Found., Amsterdam.
Adams, C. W. M. (1967). "Vascular Histochemistry." Lloyd-Luke, London.
Adams, C. W. M., and Bayliss, O. B. (1962). *J. Histochem. Cytochem.* 10, 222.
Adams, C. W. M., and Bayliss, O. B. (1963). *J. Pathol. Bacteriol.* 85, 113.
Adams, C. W. M., and Bayliss, O. B. (1968a). *J. Histochem. Cytochem.* 16, 115.
Adams, C. W. M., and Bayliss, O. B. (1968b). *J. Histochem. Cytochem.* 16, 119.
Adams, C. W. M., and Davison, A. N. (1959). *J. Neurochem.* 3, 347.
Adams, C. W. M., and Morgan, R. S. (1966). *Nature* 210, 175.
Adams, C. W. M., and Tuqan, N. A. (1961). *J. Pathol. Bacteriol.* 82, 131.
Adams, C. W. M., and Weller, R. O. (1966). *Acta Zool. Pathol. Antwerp* 39, 27.
Adams, C. W. M., Bayliss, O. B., and Ibrahim, M. Z. M. (1962). *Lancet* i, 890.
Adams, C. W. M., Bayliss, O. B., and Ibrahim, M. Z. M. (1963). *J. Histochem. Cytochem.* 11, 560.
Adams, C. W. M., Bayliss, O. B., Davison, A. N., and Ibrahim, M. Z. M. (1964). *J. Pathol. Bacteriol.* 87, 297.
Adams, C. W. M., Abdulla, Y. H., Bayliss, O. B., and Weller, R. O. (1965). *J. Histochem. Cytochem.* 13, 410.
Adams, C. W. M., Abdulla, Y. H., Bayliss, O. B., and Weller, R. O. (1966). *J. Histochem. Cytochem.* 14, 385.
Adams, C. W. M., Abdulla, Y. H., and Bayliss, O. B. (1967). *Histochemie* 9, 68.
Adams, C. W. M., Virág, S., Morgan, R. S., and Orton, C. C. (1968). *J. Atheroscler. Res.* 8, 679.
Adams Smith, W. N., and Stoward, P. J. (1967). *J. Roy. Microscop. Soc.* 87, 47.
Albert, S., and Leblond, C. P. (1947). *Endocrinology* 39, 386.
Bahr, G. F. (1954). *Exptl. Cell Res.* 7, 457.
Baker, J. R. (1946). *Quart. J. Microscop. Sci.* 87, 441.
Baker, J. R. (1947). *Quart. J. Microscop. Sci.* 88, 463.
Baker, J. R. (1958a). "Principles of Biological Microtechnique." Methuen, London.
Baker, J. R. (1958b). *J. Histochem. Cytochem.* 6, 303.
Bangham, A. D. (1963). *Advan. Lipid Res.* 1, 65.
Baserga, R., and Nemeroff, K. (1962). *J. Histochem. Cytochem.* 10, 628.

Belt, W. D., and Hayes, E. R. (1956). *Stain Technol.* 31, 117.
Bennett, M. A. (1962). *Chem. Rev.* 62, 611.
Berenbaum, M. C. (1958). *Quart. J. Microscop. Sci.* 99, 231.
Blackwood, W., and Cumings, J. N. (1966). *Proc. 5th Intern. Congr. Neuropathol.* (F. Lüthy and A. Bischoff, eds.), pp. 364-371. Excerpta Med. Found., Amsterdam.
Bodian, M., and Lake, B. D. (1963). *Brit. J. Surg.* 50, 702.
Boelsma-Van Houte, E., and Böttcher, C. J. F. (1967). *J. Atheroscler. Res.* 7, 269.
Böttcher, C. J. F., and Boelsma-Van Houte, E. (1964). *J. Atheroscler. Res.* 4, 109.
Bourgeois, C., and Hack, M. H. (1962). *Acta Histochem.* 14, 297.
Bourgeois, C., and Hubbard, B. (1965). *J. Histochem. Cytochem.* 13, 571.
Brockerhoff, H., Hoyle, R. J., and Wolmark, N. (1966). *Biochim. Biophys. Acta* 116, 67.
Bubis, J. J., and Wolman, M. (1962). *Nature* 195, 299.
Cain, A. J. (1947a). *Quart. J. Microscop. Sci.* 88, 383.
Cain, A. J. (1947b). *Quart. J. Microscop. Sci.* 88, 467.
Cain, A. J. (1949a). *Quart. J. Microscop. Sci.* 90, 75.
Cain, A. J. (1949b). *Quart. J. Microscop. Sci.* 90, 411.
Cain, A. J. (1950). *Biol. Rev. Cambridge Phil. Soc.* 25, 73.
Casley-Smith, J. R. (1963). *J. Roy. Microscop. Soc.* 81, 235.
Casley-Smith, J. R. (1967). *J. Roy. Microscop. Soc.* 87, 463.
Caspersson, T. (1940). *J. Roy. Microscop. Soc.* 60, 8.
Criegie, R. (1936). *Ann. Chem.* 522, 75.
Cumings, J. N. (1953). *Brain* 76, 551.
Cumings, J. N. (1955). *Brain* 78, 554.
Daddi, L. (1896). *Arch. Ital. Biol.* 26, 143.
Davis, J. N., Adams, C. W. M., and Bayliss, O. B. (1963). *Lancet* ii, 1254.
Day, A. J. (1964). *J. Atheroscler. Res.* 4, 117.
Dayan, A. D. (1967a). *J. Histochem. Cytochem.* 15, 421.
Dayan, A. D. (1967b). *J. Neurol. Neurosurg. Psychiat.* 30, 311.
De Haas, G. H., Bonsen, P. P. M., and Van Deenen, L. L. M. (1966). *Biochim. Biophys. Acta* 116, 114.
Derry, D. M., and Wolfe, L. S. (1968). *Exptl. Brain Res.* 5, 32.
Deuel, H. J. (1951). "The Lipids. Vol. I: Chemistry." Wiley (Interscience), New York.
Diezel, P. B. (1957a). "Die Stoffwechselstörungen der Sphingolipoide. Eine histochemische Studie an den primaren Lipoidosen." Springer, Berlin.
Diezel, P. B. (1957b). *In* "Cerebral Lipidoses" (J. N. Cumings, ed.), pp. 11-29. Blackwell, Oxford.
Diezel, P. B. (1958). *Acta Histochem. Suppl.* 1, 134.
Dixon, K. C. (1958). *Quart. J. Exptl. Physiol.* 43, 139.
Dunnigan, M. G. (1964). *J. Atheroscler. Res.* 4, 144.
Edgar, G. W. F., and Donker, C. H. M. (1957). *Acta Neurol. Psychiat. Belg.* 5, 451.
Einarson, L. (1953). *J. Neurol. Neurosurg. Psychiat.* 16, 98.
Elbers, P. F. (1964). *In* "Recent Progress in Surface Science" (J. F. Danielli, K. G. A. Parkhurst, and A. C. Riddiford, eds.), pp. 443-503. Academic Press, New York.
Elbers, P. F., Ververgaert, P. H. J. T., and Dimel, R. (1965). *J. Cell Biol.* 24, 23.
Elftman, H. (1954). *J. Histochem. Cytochem.* 2, 1.
Elleder, M., and Lojda, Z. (1968a). *Histochemie* 14, 47.
Elleder, M., and Lojda, Z. (1968b). *Histochemie* 13, 276.
Feigen, I. (1956). *J. Biophys. Biochem. Cytol.* 2, 213.
Feulgen, R., and Voit, K. (1924). *Arch. Ges. Physiol. Pfluegers* 206, 389.
Feustel, E. -M., and Geyer, G. (1966). *Acta Histochem.* 25, 219.

Feyrter, F. (1936). *Arch. Pathol. Anat. Physiol. Virchows* 296, 645.

Finkelstein, A., and Cass, A. (1967). *Nature* 216, 717.

Fischler, F. J. (1904). *Zentr. Allgem. Pathol. Pathol. Anat.* 15, 913.

Fredrickson, D. S., Levy, R. I., and Lees, R. S. (1967). *New Engl. J. Med.* 276, 32, 94, 148, 215, 273.

Friedel, M. G. (1922). *Ann. Phys.* 18, 273.

Friedman, M., Byers, S. O., Felton, L., and Cady, P. (1959). *J. Clin. Invest.* 38, 539.

Gallyas, F. (1963). *J. Neurochem.* 10, 125.

Glick, D. (1967). *J. Histochem. Cytochem.* 15, 299.

Gomori, G. (1952). "Microscopic Histochemistry." Univ. of Chicago Press, Chicago, Illinois.

Graef, I. (1939). *A.M.A. Arch. Pathol.* 28, 613.

Granados, H., and Dam, H. (1950). *Acta Pathol. Microbiol. Scand.* 27, 591.

Gregson, N. A. (1964). Personal communication.

Griffith, W. P. (1965). *Quart. Rev. (London)* 19, 254.

Hake, T. (1965). *Lab. Invest.* 14, 1208.

Hakomori, S.-I. (1966). *J. Lipid Res.* 7, 789.

Hale, A. J. (1957). *Intern. Rev. Cytol.* 6, 193.

Hartroft, W. S. (1951). *Science* 113, 673.

Hayes, E. R. (1949). *Stain Technol.* 24, 19.

Herxheimer, G. (1901). *Deut. Med. Wochschr.* 27, 607.

Heslinga, F. J. M., and Deierkauf, F. A. (1962). *J. Histochem. Cytochem.* 10, 704.

Hilditch, T. P., and Williams, P. N. (1964). "The Chemical Constitution of Natural Fats," 4th Ed. Chapman & Hall, London.

Hirsch, T. V., and Peiffer, J. (1957). *In* "Cerebral Lipidoses" (J. N. Cumings, ed.), pp. 68 70. Blackwell, Oxford.

Holczinger, L. (1958). *Acta Histochem.* 6, 36.

Holczinger, L. (1959). *Acta Histochem.* 8, 167.

Holczinger, L. (1964). *Histochemie* 4, 120.

Holczinger, L., and Bálint, Z. (1962). *Histochemie* 2, 389.

Hollander, H. (1963). *J. Histochem. Cytochem.* 11, 118.

Hotchkiss, R. D. (1948). *Arch. Biochem.* 16, 131.

Hurst, E. W. (1925). *Brain* 48, 1.

Hydén, H. (1962). *Endeavour* 21, 144.

Idelman, S. (1965). *Histochemie* 5, 18.

Jobst, C., and Horváth, A. (1961). *J. Histochem. Cytochem.* 9, 711.

Johnson, A. D., McNabb, A. R., and Rossiter, R. J. (1950). *A.M.A. Arch. Neurol. Psychiat.* 64, 105.

Jones, R., Scott, R. F., Morrison, E. S., Kroms, M., and Thomas, W. A. (1963). *Exptl. Mol. Pathol.* 2, 14.

Keilig, I. (1944). *Arch. Pathol. Anat. Physiol. Virchows* 312, 405.

Khanolkar, V. R., Krishnamurthi, A. S., Bagul, C. D., and Sahasrabudhe, M. B. (1958). *Indian J. Pathol. Bacteriol.* 1, 84.

Klenk, E., and Langerbeins, H. (1941). *Z. Physiol. Chem.* 270, 185.

Kopriwa, B. M., and Leblond, C. P. (1962). *J. Histochem. Cytochem.* 10, 269.

Korn, E. D. (1966a). *Biochim. Biophys. Acta* 116, 317.

Korn, E. D. (1966b). *Biochim. Biophys. Acta* 116, 325.

Korn, E. D. (1966c). *Science* 153, 1491.

Korn, E. D. (1967). *J. Cell Biol.* 34, 627.

Korn, E. D., and Weisman, R. A. (1966). *Biochim. Biophys. Acta* 116, 309.

Kramsch, D. M., Gore, I., and Hollander, W. (1967). *J. Atheroscler. Res.* **7**, 501.
Kritchevsky, D., Werthessen, N. T., Shapiro, I. L., Nair, P. P., and Turner, D. A. (1965). *Nature* **207**, 194.
Lake, B. D. (1967). *J. Roy. Microscop. Soc.* **86**, 417.
Lake, B. D. (1968a). Personal communication.
Lake, B. D. (1968b). *Nature* **217**, 171.
Landing, B. H., and Freiman, D. G. (1957). *Am. J. Pathol.* **33**, 1.
Landing, B. H., Uzman, L. L., and Whipple, A. (1952). *Lab. Invest.* **1**, 456.
Lange, W. (1967). *Acta Histochem* **27**, 321.
LeBaron, F. N., and Folch, J. (1956). *J. Neurochem.* **1**, 101.
Ledeen, R., Salsman, K., Gonatas, J., and Taghavy, A. (1965). *J. Neuropathol. Exptl. Neurol.* **24**, 341.
Lehner, T., and Adams, C. W. M. (1968). *J. Pathol. Bacteriol.* **95**, 411.
Lewis, P. R., and Lobban, M. C. (1961). *J. Histochem. Cytochem.* **9**, 2.
Liadsky, C., and Woolf, N. (1967). *J. Atheroscler. Res.* **7**, 718.
Lillie, R. D. (1947). *J. Lab. Clin. Med.* **32**, 910.
Lillie, R. D. (1952). *Stain Technol.* **27**, 37.
Lillie, R. D. (1954). "Histopathologic Technique and Practical Histochemistry." Mc-Graw-Hill (Blakiston), New York.
Lillie, R. D. (1956). *Stain Technol.* **31**, 151.
Lillie, R. D., and Ashburn, L. L. (1943). *A.M.A. Arch. Pathol.* **36**, 342.
Lillie, R. D., Henson, J. P. G., and Burtner, H. J. (1957). *J. Histochem. Cytochem.* **5**, 311.
Linderstrøm-Lang, K. (1939). *Harvey Lectures Ser.* **34**, 214.
Lison, L. (1936). "Histochemie Animale," 1st Ed. Gauthier-Villars, Paris.
Lorrain, Smith, J. (1908). *J. Pathol. Bacteriol.* **12**, 1.
Lovern, J. A. (1955). "The Chemistry of Lipids of Biochemical Significance." Methuen, London.
Lowry, O. H., Roberts, N. R., Leiner, K. Y., Wu, M. L., Farr, A. L., and Albers, R. (1954). *J. Biol. Chem.* **207**, 39.
McDougal, D. B., Jr., Schulz, D. W., Passonneau, J. V., Clark, J. R., Reynolds, M., and Lowry, O. H. (1961). *J. Gen. Physiol.* **44**, 487.
McDougal, D. B., Jr., Schimke, R. J., Jones, E. M., and Touhill, E. (1964). *J. Gen. Physiol.* **47**, 419.
McManus, J. F. A. (1946). *Nature* **158**, 202.
Maggi, V., and Brander, W. (1963). *Biochem. J.* **89**, 28P.
Maggi, V., Chayen, J., Gahan, P. B., and Brander, W. (1964). *Exptl. Mol. Pathol.* **3**, 413.
Marchi, V. (1886). *Riv. Sper. Freniat.* **12**, 50.
Milas, N. A., Trepagnier, J. H., Noland, J. T., Jr., and Iliopoulos, M. I. (1959). *J. Am. Chem. Soc.* **81**, 4730.
Moser, H. W., Moser, A. B., and Orr, J. C. (1966). *Biochim. Biophys. Acta* **116**, 146.
Mukherji, M., Deb, C., and Sen, P. B. (1960). *J. Histochem. Cytochem.* **8**, 189.
Newman, H. A. I., Day, A. J., and Zilversmit, D. B. (1966). *Circulation Res.* **19**, 132.
Niden, A. H. (1967). *Science* **158**, 1323.
Norton, W. T. (1959). *Nature* **184**, 1144.
Norton, W. T., and Korey, S. R. (1962). *Proc. 4th Intern. Congr. Neuropathol.* (H. Jakob, ed.), Vol. 1, pp. 227–233. Thieme, Stuttgart.
Norton, W. T., Korey, S. R., and Brotz, M. (1962). *J. Histochem. Cytochem.* **10**, 83.
Parker, F., Ormsby, J. W., Peterson, N. F., Odland, G. F., and Williams, R. H. (1966). *Circulation Res.* **19**, 700.
Pearse, A. G. E. (1960). "Histochemistry—Theoretical and Applied," 1st Ed., p. 361. Churchill, London.

Pearse, A. G. E. (1968). "Histochemistry—Theoretical and Applied," 3rd Ed., Vol. 1, pp. 356, 660. Churchill, London.
Peiffer, J., and Hirsch, T. (1955). *Excerpta Med. Sect. VIII* 8, 802.
Perry, R. P. (1964). *In* "Methods in Cell Physiology" (D. M. Prescott, ed.), Vol. 1, pp. 305-363. Academic Press, New York.
Popper, H. (1941). *A.M.A. Arch. Pathol.* 31, 766.
Porter, K. R., and Kallman, F. (1953). *Exptl. Cell Res* 4, 127.
Ravetto, C. (1064). *J. Histochem. Cytochem.* 12, 306.
Reynolds, E. O. R., and Strang, L. B. (1966). *Brit. Med. Bull.* 22, 79.
Riemersma, J. C. (1963). *J. Histochem. Cytochem.* 11, 436.
Riemersma, J. C., and Booij, H. L. (1962). *J. Histochem. Cytochem.* 10, 89.
Rinehart, J. F., and Abul-Haj, S. K. (1951). *A M.A. Arch. Pathol.* 52, 189.
Rogers, G. E. (1959). *J. Ultrastruct. Res.* 2, 309.
Roozemond, R. C. (1967). *J. Histochem. Cytochem.* 15, 526.
Rossiter, R. J., and Strickland, K. P. (1960). *In* "Lipide Metabolism" (K. Bloch ed.), pp. 69-127. Wiley, New York.
Rostgaard, J., and Barrnett, R. J. (1965). *Anat. Record* 152, 325.
Schlant, R. C., and Galambos, J. T. (1964). *Am. J. Pathol.* 44, 877.
Schmidt, W. J. (1936). *Z. Zellforsch. Mikroskop. Anat.* 23, 657.
Schott, H. J., and Schoner, W. (1965). *Histochemie* 5, 154.
Schultz, A. (1924). *Zentr. Allgem. Pathol. Pathol. Anat.* 35, 314.
Seligman, A. M., Wasserkrug, H. L., and Hanker, J. S. (1966) *J. Cell Biol.* 30, 424.
Shear, M., and Pearse, A. G. E. (1963). *Nature* 198, 1273.
Shear, M., and Pearse, A. G. E. (1964). *Nature* 201, 630.
Smith, E. B. (1960). *Lancet* i, 700.
Sourander, P. and Olsson, Y. (1968). *Acta Neuropathol.* 11, 69.
Stein, J. M. (1967). *Biochim. Biophys. Acta* 144, 118.
Stein, Y., Stein, O., and Shapiro, B. (1963). *Biochim. Biophys. Acta* 70, 33.
Stoeckenius, W. (1961). *Proc. European Regional Conf. Electron Microscopy, 1960, Delft* p. 716.
Stoward, P. J., and Adams-Smith, W. N. (1964). *J. Endocrinol.* 30, 273.
Strich, S. J. (1965). *J. Physiol. (London)* 178, 3.
Stumpf, W. E., and Roth, L. J. (1966). *J. Histochem. Cytochem.* 14, 274.
Sulkin, N. M., and Srivanij, P. (1960). *J. Gerontol.* 15, 2.
Svennerholm, L. (1957). *Biochim. Biophys. Acta* 24, 604.
Svennerholm, L. (1964). *J. Lipid Res.* 5, 145.
Taylor, F. B., Jr. and Abrams, M. E. (1966). *Am. J. Med.* 40, 346.
Terner, J. Y., Schnur, J., and Gurland, J. (1963). *Lab. Invest.* 12, 405.
Torvik, A., and Sidman, R. L. (1965). *J. Neurochem.* 12, 555.
Tranzer, J. P. (1965). *J. Microscopie* 4, 319.
Tuqan, N. A., and Adams, C. W. M. (1961). *J. Neurochem.* 6, 327.
Urich, H. (1962). *Proc. 4th Intern. Congr. Neuropathol.* (H. Jakob, ed.), Vol. 1, pp. 42-49. Thieme, Stuttgart.
Walton, K. W. (1967). Personal communication.
Weast, R. C. (1965-1966). "Handbook of Chemistry and Physics," 46th Ed. Chem. Rubber Publ. Co., Cleveland, Ohio.
Weber, A. F., Phillips, M. G., and Bell, J. T. (1956). *J. Histochem. Cytochem.* 4, 308.
Wegmann, R. (1956). *Ann. Histochim.* 1, 116.
Weller, R. O. (1965). Personal communication.
Weller, R. O. (1966). Personal communications.
Weller, R. O. (1967). *J. Pathol. Bacteriol.* 94, 171.

Weller, R. O., Bayliss, O. B., Abdulla, Y. H., and Adams, C. W. M. (1965). *J. Histochem. Cytochem.* **13**, 690.

Wherrett, J. R., Lowden, J. A., and Wolfe, L. S. (1964). *Can. J. Biochem.* **42**, 1057.

Wigglesworth, V. B. (1957). *Proc. Roy. Soc. (London)* **B147**, 185.

Wilske, K. R., and Ross, R. (1965). *J. Histochem. Cytochem.* **13**, 38.

Wingfield, H. C., and Yoe, J. H. (1956). *Anal. Chim. Acta* **14**, 446.

Wolfe, H. J., and Pietra, G. G. (1964). *Am. J. Pathol.* **44**, 921.

Wolfgram, F., and Rose, A. S. (1958). *Neurology* **8**, 839.

Wolman, M. (1956). *Stain Technol.* **31**, 241.

Wolman, M. (1957). *J. Neurochem.* **1**, 270.

Wolman, M. (1961). *Acta Histochem. Suppl.* **2**, 140.

Wolman, M. (1962). *J. Neurochem.* **9**, 59.

Wolman, M. (1964). "Handbuch der Histochemie. Vol. 5: Histochemistry of Lipids in Pathology." Fischer, Stuttgart.

Wolman, M., and Hestrin-Lerner, S. (1960). *J. Neurochem.* **5**, 114.

Wolman, M., and Shoshan, S. (1960). *Histochemie* **2**, 69.

Wolman, M., and Wiener, H. (1965). *Biochim. Biophys. Acta* **102**, 269.

Wolman, M., and Zaidel, L. (1962). *Experientia* **18**, 323.

Zelikoff, M., and Taylor, H. A. (1950). *J. Am. Chem. Soc.* **72**, 5039.

Zilversmit, D. B., and McCandless, E. L. (1959). *J. Lipid Res.* **1**, 118.

Zilversmit, D. B., Shore, M. L., and Ackerman, R. F. (1954). *Circulation* **9**, 581.

Zugibe, F. T., Kopaczyk, K. C., Cape, W. E., and Last, J. H. (1958). *J. Histochem. Cytochem.* **6**, 133.

Control of Plasma and Liver Triglyceride Kinetics by Carbohydrate Metabolism and Insulin

ESKO A. NIKKILÄ

Third Department of Medicine, University of Helsinki, Helsinki, Finland

I.	Introduction	63
II.	General Outline of Triglyceride Fluxes and Their Control	65
III.	Insulin Actions on Triglyceride Metabolism	69
	A. Effect of Insulin on Plasma Triglyceride Concentration	70
	B. Effect of Insulin on Hepatic Fatty Acid Synthesis	70
	C. Effect of Insulin on Synthesis of Liver and Plasma Triglycerides	75
	D. Effect of Insulin on Plasma Triglyceride Outflow	78
IV.	Triglyceride Metabolism in Diabetes	80
	A. Plasma Triglyceride Concentration in Diabetes	80
	B. Hepatic Fatty Acid Synthesis in Diabetes	82
	C. Synthesis and Release of Liver Triglycerides in Diabetes	89
	D. Removal of Triglycerides from Plasma in Diabetes	94
	E. Fatty Acid and Triglyceride Metabolism in Diabetes with Hyperinsulinism	99
V.	Influence of Exogenous Carbohydrates on Triglyceride Metabolism	100
	A. Acute Effects of Glucose on Plasma Triglyceride	101
	B. Long-Term Effects of Dietary Carbohydrate on Triglyceride Kinetics	103
VI.	The Metabolic Error of Endogenous ("Carbohydrate-Induced") Hyperglyceridemia	117
	References	124

I. Introduction

With advanced understanding of the details of metabolic pathways and their regulatory devices the interactions of carbohydrate (glucose) and fat (triglyceride, free fatty acids) metabolism have been revealed to be increasingly intimate. This applies particularly to glucose and free fatty acids (FFA) which exert a homeostatic control of each other's release into the bloodstream and utilization. Plasma triglycerides represent another transport form for fatty acids of both exogenous and endogenous origin, and their formation and fate seem also to be closely related to glucose metabolism. This is best exemplified by the development of hyperglyceridemia, up to a visible lactescence of serum, in connection with uncontrolled diabetes, and on increasing the dietary carbohydrate supply. It is not quite clear why the body requires the two separate systems with different turnover rates for the transport of endogenous fatty acids nor is it known what are the determinants of the relative utilization of these two forms of fatty acids under different energetic and nutritional conditions or in disease states.

Triglyceride metabolism, its regulation and disturbances were still rather neglected areas 10 years ago. Until that time interest was mainly directed to liver triglycerides and the pathogenetic mechanisms of fatty liver while plasma glycerides received major consideration only in connection with gross hyperlipemic states and on following the disappearance of alimentary fat from the blood. In a way, this is surprising since before the discovery of plasma FFA the glycerides were generally held as the principal or sole transport form of fatty acids from stores to utilization. Along with the general clarification of fatty acid fluxes in the body the knowledge of the plasma triglyceride turnover has rapidly expanded. The subject has also gained much practical importance since it has been recognized that hyperglyceridemia is a much more frequent metabolic disorder than believed earlier and that an increased serum glyceride level probably promotes atherogenesis (Hauss and Böhle, 1955; Albrink and Man, 1959; Schrade et al., 1960; Carlson, 1960; Antonis and Bersohn, 1960; Albrink et al., 1961). In fact, moderate endogenous hyperglyceridemia of either dietary or genetic or mixed origin is one of most common metabolic diseases, at least in the western world, its prevalence exceeding even that of diabetes. The recent attempt for a rational classification of hyperlipidemic states on the basis of electrophoretic plasma lipoprotein pattern (Fredrickson and Lees, 1966; Fredrickson et al., 1967) has renewed the interest on pathology of lipoproteins originally raised in the early 1950's by development of ultracentrifugal flotation analysis (Gofman et al., 1950). However, the etiological factors and pathogenetic events of hyperglyceridemias still remain almost unknown, and the different lipoprotein phenotypes are likely to be heterogeneous in this respect. Undoubtedly, many of the gaps of our present knowledge on triglyceride metabolism will be filled within the near future if progress in this important area continues as rapidly as it has in recent years.

This review has been prompted by the numerous observations which show that plasma triglyceride level is much influenced by carbohydrate metabolism. It endeavors to bring together and to discuss the data concerned with the mechanism of this interaction. The subject has not been limited to comprise only the immediate processes of triglyceride influx and efflux, but consideration has also been given to the determinants of these. Accordingly, it has been necessary also to touch on FFA turnover and hepatic fatty acid synthesis although this has extended the field to be covered and made the treatise at least partly superficial. No attempt has been made to prepare a complete list of references,[1] particularly since many of the earlier relevant data are to be found in the more profound and extensive reviews of, e.g., Fredrickson and Gordon (1958), Olson and Vester (1960), Fritz (1961), and Dole and Hamlin (1962).

II. General Outline of Triglyceride Fluxes and Their Control

There is general agreement that the plasma triglyceride at any given time is derived almost solely from only two sources: intestine and liver. In the postabsorptive period when no exogenous fat is ingested, the flow from the gut is small and almost all circulating triglyceride is of hepatic origin. On the other hand, the sites of triglyceride removal are still disputable, and particularly the role of the liver, earlier believed to be important, has recently been challenged (Felts and Mayes, 1965; Mayes and Felts, 1967a).

The kinetic behavior of plasma and liver triglycerides and their component fatty acids and glycerol has been revealed to be a complex one and to show marked species differences at least between rat (Baker and Schotz, 1964, 1967; Nikkilä *et al.*, 1966), man (Farquhar *et al.*, 1965), rabbit (Havel *et al.*, 1962), and dog (Gross *et al.*, 1967). Obviously also the metabolic factors (control points) which determine the plasma triglyceride level and flux rates are not identical in different species, and, accordingly, the results of animal studies cannot be directly extrapolated to man. A simplified kinetic pattern is schematically illustrated in Fig. 1, and the metabolic pathways of triglyceride formation are given in Fig. 2. The fatty acid portion of endogenous

---

[1] The literature which has appeared after June 1968 has not been included except a few publications which have been available to the author as manuscripts or personal communications at the writing of this review.

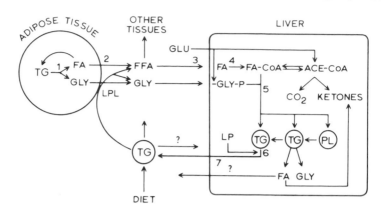

FIG. 1.   A scheme on the formation and fate of liver and plasma triglyceride in a normal fed state. Numbers are described in the text.

plasma triglyceride can be derived either from adipose tissue triglyceride through plasma FFA, from dietary lipid, from other hepatic lipid, from hepatic synthesis (lipogenesis), or from degraded plasma triglyceride through recycling. It should be noted that a (considerable?) part of FFA influx into the liver comes directly from the adipose tissue of splanchnic bed through the portal vein without reaching the systemic circulation. The relative quantitative contribution of each of these fatty acid sources to the liver and plasma triglyceride pool is highly variable depending, among other things, on the species and the nutritional state. Thus, in man, after an overnight fast, the main immediate precursor of plasma triglyceride fatty acids (TGFA) is plasma FFA (Havel, 1961; Friedberg et al., 1961; Eaton et al., 1965); a similar pattern probably also prevails in rabbit (Havel et al., 1962), while in rat only a minor fraction of TGFA comes directly from this pool, the quantitatively most important source being hepatic lipogenesis and phospholipids (Baker and Schotz, 1964, 1967; Nikkilä et al., 1966). It is not known, however, to what extent the fatty acids synthesized in the liver or derived directly from dietary fat are incorporated into endogenous plasma triglyceride in a nonfasting human subject.

The direct pathway of fatty acids from depot triglycerides to plasma glycerides consists of the following major steps: (1) lipolysis of adipose tissue fat, (2) release of FFA into circulation, (3) hepatic uptake of plasma FFA and their absorption to microsomal and mitochondrial membranes, (4) formation of fatty acyl-CoA, (5) esterification to triglyceride (glycerophosphate acyltransferase), (6) coupling of triglyceride to lipoprotein peptide, and (7) secretion of very low density or low density lipoprotein molecules into circulation. The indirect pathway goes from step 4 to non-triglyceride liver lipid esters and to "storage" triglyceride of liver cell sap ("floating fat") from which the fatty acids flow more slowly to step 6. The fatty acids synthesized in the liver are connected to this pathway at step 4, but it is not known whether they are completely mixed to a common acyl-CoA pool and thus share the subsequent fate of fatty acids coming from outside the liver cell.

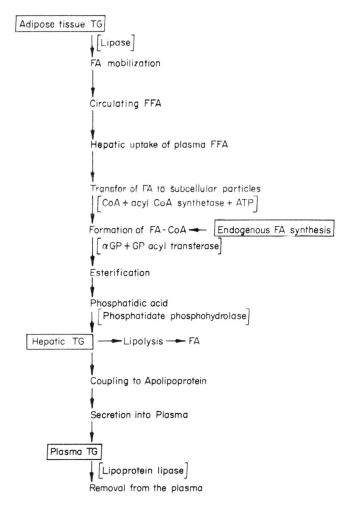

FIG. 2. Metabolic steps in the formation and breakdown of liver and plasma triglycerides.

The most probable control points of hepatic triglyceride secretion are located at steps 2, 5, and 6 of the above scheme. In addition, the activity of hepatic lipogenesis may be an important determinant of triglyceride release from the liver (Windmueller and Spaeth, 1967). In perfused rat liver the amount of triglyceride appearing into the perfusate is proportional to the FFA content of the medium (Gidez et al., 1962; Nestel and Steinberg, 1963). This finding suggests that no rate-limiting reactions are situated between steps 2 and 7 and that the plasma FFA level might be a major determinant of plasma triglyceride influx at least in those species (man, rabbit) in which plasma FFA is the main precursor of plasma TGFA. This view is supported by the following data. Enhancement of plasma FFA level by epinephrine or a lipolytic pituitary polypeptide is followed by a manifold increase of plasma triglyceride concentration in rabbit (Dury, 1957; Rudman et al., 1962), whereas in rat (Shafrir et al., 1960) and dog (Shafrir et al., 1959; Carlson et al., 1965) epinephrine produces only small if any changes of plasma glyceride level. On the other hand, reduction of plasma FFA by nicotinic acid leads rapidly to a decrease of plasma triglyceride level (Carlson and Nye, 1966). It is also known that the hepatic uptake of FFA and absorption of fatty acids by subcellular liver particles (step 3) increase in proportion to FFA concentration (McElroy et al., 1960; Reshef and Shapiro, 1965). Furthermore, in man the plasma TGFA entry rate is correlated to plasma FFA flux and triglyceride concentration (Nestel, 1967).

Even if the plasma FFA level and, ultimately, the release of FFA from adipose tissue will be an important regulatory factor of plasma glyceride concentration, the possibility is not excluded that also other reactions in the above pathway may act as determinants of the hepatic triglyceride output. This is best illustrated by the fasting state, in which the plasma FFA level is high while the triglyceride secretion is low. Another example is the hyperglyceridemia which develops on ethanol administration in spite of a simultaneous decrease of plasma FFA level. Apparently, the esterification reaction (step 5) and the synthesis of lipoprotein peptide (step 6) are the key regulatory loci although there is no definite experimental proof for this view. The esterification may be influenced not only by the activity of the enzymes but also by the availability (rate of production) of glycerol phosphate (Nikkilä and Ojala, 1963a; Tzur et al., 1964). That the capacity for hepatic release of triglycerides has a certain maximum is suggested by the data of Reaven et al. (1965) in man, and this limit may represent the maximal rate of lipoprotein peptide production. The factors directing the flow of fatty acids into the different lipid ester pools of the liver cell are thus far not understood.

The removal of triglycerides from the bloodstream occurs at an exponential rate, which is inversely proportional to the concentration (French and Morris, 1957; Nestel, 1964b) and directly correlated to the size of the fat particle. Thus, the fractional disappearance rate decreases with increasing plasma triglyceride level and fat emulsions are eliminated more rapidly than chylomicrons (Belfrage *et al.*, 1964), larger chylomicrons faster than smaller ones (Quarfordt and Goodman, 1966), and endogenous very low density lipoprotein triglycerides more slowly than chylomicrons. At a certain triglyceride level the removal sites become saturated, and on exceeding this limit the elimination occurs linearly, i.e., with zero-order kinetics (Carlson and Hallberg, 1963). This saturation limit is obviously quite variable in different species.

The dependence of the fractional rate constant from the triglyceride pool size is an important factor to be considered on interpretation of any kinetic studies when comparisons are made between individuals with widely different plasma triglyceride concentrations. Thus, the incorporation of a precursor into plasma triglyceride (often taken as a measure of triglyceride influx) will be estimated higher with larger triglyceride pool size than it will be with smaller, even if the real rates of transfer are identical. An impaired fractional elimination rate of labeled or nonlabeled fat when observed in the presence of hyperglyceridemia indicates only a relative insufficiency of the removal mechanisms but does not establish that the primary cause of increased glyceride concentration is a defective efflux system. This applies also to the term "plasma clearance," which has been recommended for use in preference to disappearance rate as a measure of the efficiency of removal (Ryan and Schwartz, 1965) but actually reflects the same event and is also inversely correlated to plasma triglyceride level.

III. Insulin Actions on Triglyceride Metabolism

In this section, data related to the actions of insulin on fat metabolism in a *normal, nondiabetic* organism or isolated tissue are reviewed. This is done not only to elucidate the possible regulatory role of insulin in the maintenance of a normal triglyceride balance but also, and probably even more, to describe the eventual effects of hyperinsulinemia, which seems to be a fairly frequent abnormality in man. Even if it may appear artificial and often difficult to discuss the effects of insulin, diabetes, and glucose separate from each other this differentiation has been attempted for the sake of clarity because (1) the metabolic consequences of hyperglycemia and hyperinsulinemia are not necessarily identical, particularly if the glucose assimilation in some tissues is inhibited, and (2) the effects of insulin excess may be different from those observed on substitution of insulin deficiency in a diabetic organism.

The subject has been limited to concern only findings in mammals since it seemed too complicated to include also other animals, of which birds, for example, are known to respond to insulin quite "abnormally" (Heald *et al.*, 1965; Lepkovsky *et al.*, 1967) and probably to obey profoundly different principles of regulation of fat metabolism.

A. EFFECT OF INSULIN ON PLASMA TRIGLYCERIDE
   CONCENTRATION

Relatively few data on the effect of insulin administration on serum lipid levels in nondiabetic subjects are available. Jones and Arky (1965) reported that in normal humans a single insulin injection did not change the serum triglyceride level but a prolonged insulin infusion produced a marked fall in all subjects. In pregnant and nonpregnant women, Dannenburg and Burt (1965) found a significant decrease of plasma triglyceride in 3 hours after a single intravenous dose of insulin. Haahti (1959) has described a nondiabetic patient with hyperlipemia, in which insulin treatment effectively reduced all plasma lipids. A similar effect has been more recently observed in hyperglyceridemic cases by Schlierf and Kinsell (1965) using intravenous insulin infusion. In normal rats a single insulin injection rapidly decreases the plasma triglyceride level (Table I).

No data are available on the possible effects of more chronic hyperinsulinism on plasma triglyceride concentration in animals or man.

B. EFFECT OF INSULIN ON HEPATIC FATTY ACID SYNTHESIS

In principle, insulin may influence the hepatic FA synthesis in at least three different ways, viz.: (1) by a direct action on the amount of enzymes concerned with extramitochondrial production of acetyl-CoA and its incorporation into FA (induction or repression of enzyme syntheses, degradation); (2) through depression of FFA and glycerol mobilization accompanied by a decrease of FA, acyl-CoA, acyl carnitine, and glycerophosphate concentrations in the liver cell thus modifying the postulated feedback regulatory devices; and (3) by promoting

Table I

ACUTE EFFECT OF INSULIN[a] ON PLASMA TRIGLYCERIDE CONCENTRATION
AND ON INCORPORATION OF PALMITIC ACID-1-C[14] INTO PLASMA
TRIGLYCERIDES IN FED RATS[b]

Group	Plasma triglyceride (mg/100 ml)	Plasma TG radioactivity (cpm/ml × 10^{-2})	Plasma TG specific activity (cpm/μg)
Saline control	72.3 ± 12.8	654 ± 100	90.4 ± 12.7
Insulin, 15 minutes	78.7 ± 10.3	379 ± 51	40.8 ± 5.3
Insulin, 60 minutes	39.6 ± 6.6	420 ± 89	111.0 ± 19.1

[a] 0.3 unit/kg.
[b] From Nikkilä and Ojala, unpublished results.

hepatic glucose utilization and thus increasing the supply of building material (acetate), necessary cofactors (ATP, NADPH), and enzyme activators (citrate).

Which of these mechanisms is in operation depends much on whether one is dealing with short-term or long-term effects of insulin and whether insulin actions are observed in an insulin-deficient (diabetic, fasting) or normal (fed nondiabetic) organism or tissue. Thus, because of the known inductor activity of insulin on glucokinase (Salas *et al.*, 1963; Sharma *et al.*, 1063) and on key glycolytic enzymes (Weber *et al.*, 1966) it is fully expected that in chronic insulin deficiency the depressed hepatic lipogenesis is restored by insulin at least through the increase of glucose metabolism in the liver [action (3)], but the effect comes as slowly (Renold *et al.*, 1955) as the reappearance of glucokinase (Salas *et al.*, 1963). In this situation the enzyme deficiency masks all possible other effects, particularly the more acute ones of insulin on lipogenesis, and makes a diabetic or starved animal a poor experimental subject for evaluation of the possible direct actions of insulin on FA synthesis. Also, this kind of experiment provides no information on the eventual consequences of chronic insulin excess.

From the viewpoint of the present discussion the main interest is to learn to what extent insulin and particularly hyperinsulinemia will influence hepatic lipogenesis in a nondiabetic organism. Again, it seems worthwhile to try to distinguish short-term and long-term effects. In pioneering studies, Bloch and Kramer (1948) and Brady and Gurin (1950) showed that insulin increases the incorporation of acetate into fatty acids in rat liver slices incubated *in vitro*. This effect is also obtained in the absence of glucose (Medes *et al.*, 1952) but only if the liver is taken from a *fed* animal (Medes *et al.*, 1952; Masri *et al.*,

1952). In the presence of glucose insulin slightly stimulates the lipo-genesis *in vitro* in liver slices from fasted rats also (Masri *et al.*, 1952). These findings were also soon reproduced in a perfusion exper-iment, where addition of insulin to a high glucose medium markedly stimulated the labeling of both phospholipid fatty acids (PLFA) and TGFA from acetate-C^{14} in the liver of fasting rat (Altman *et al.*, 1951). Later, Haft and Miller (1958) reported stimulation of lipogenesis from acetate by insulin in perfused liver taken from fasted rats but not in that removed from fed rats. The effect was parallel to glucose disap-pearance from the medium. Recently, Haft (1967), in a more thorough study, has shown that addition of insulin into medium increases the incorporation of both acetate-H^3 and glucose-C^{14} into total fatty acids in isolated rat liver perfused with physiological glucose concentra-tions irrespective of whether the donor animal is fasted or fed. No effect was obtained if a "fed" liver was perfused with a high glucose medium. In these experiments glucose oxidation was slightly in-creased by insulin but definitely much less than lipogenesis. On the other hand, Williamson *et al.* (1966) in perfusing livers from *fasted* rats could note no other change in the metabolism of glucose-C^{14} upon addition of insulin than a significant increase in total hepatic FA ra-dioactivity. In another similar experiment with a *fed* rat liver insulin added *in vitro* was completely ineffective on glucose oxidation and incorporation into lipids (Boden and Willms, 1966).

While the *in vitro* incubation and perfusion studies have excluded the possibility that the stimulation of hepatic lipogenesis by insulin in a normal animal is entirely secondary to the peripheral actions of the hormone they have missed one probably important additional control mechanism of hepatic FA synthesis present *in vivo*, viz., that exerted by plasma FFA and glycerol and their hepatic metabolites. It is there-fore significant that Goldman and Cahill (1964) were able to show that in fed rats intravenous insulin within 15 minutes caused a sixfold in-crease in the labeling of liver-esterified FA from *in vivo* administered glucose-C^{14}. The effect was not obtained in fasting animals. It might be argued that this result does not necessarily indicate that lipogene-sis from glucose was stimulated by insulin but only that a relatively greater proportion of the endogenously synthesized FA was esterified when the FFA inflow from plasma was reduced by insulin, i.e., the radioactive FA (fatty acyl-CoA) was less diluted by the cold FFA in insulin-treated than in control animals. Since this point is critical for the whole question on insulin and lipogenesis, we took up the study of the acute effect of another antilipolytic agent, nicotinic acid, on the hepatic lipogenesis from glucose and acetate in an experiment fairly similar to that of Goldman and Cahill. It then appeared that in contrast to insulin, nicotinic acid markedly decreased the radioactivity recovered in both liver and plasma triglycerides after administration of acetate-C^{14} or glucose-C^{14} to fed rats. These findings indicate that the results of Goldman and Cahill were not a result of isotope dilution. They also suggest, but do not prove, that the acute stimulating action of insulin on hepatic lipogenesis is not mediated by the decrease of fatty acid or fatty acyl-CoA content of the liver. This tentative conclusion is, in a way, supported by the observation of Bewsher *et al.* (1966) that while insulin effectively counteracts the increase of plasma FFA induced by dichloroisoproterenol it still does not release the inhibition of lipogenesis caused by this agent. Furthermore, anti-insulin serum depresses FA synthesis in hypophysectomized rats without producing any increase of plasma FFA level (Sweeney and Ashmore, 1965).

The investigations cited above seem to provide enough evidence for a statement that insulin is able to rapidly increase the FA synthesis in the liver even when this is basally stimulated by a normal fed state and by endogenous insulin. This action is primarily hepatic although it may be further potentiated *in vivo* by the extrahepatic effects of the hormone, e.g., antilipolysis. The exact mode of this insulin action is as obscure as all the other ones. The prevalent opinion seems still to favor the view that the primary locus of action is outside the metabolic pathways of glucose, notably in the FA synthesis itself. The best argument for this line of thinking is the quantitative difference found between the relative effects of insulin on hepatic glucose utilization and lipogenesis. In fact, it is not established that insulin has any short-term influence on hepatic glucose assimilation at all (Levine and Fritz, 1956; Miller, 1961; Cameron, 1962; Williamson *et al.*, 1966). However, one should take into account that if the insulin effect is limited to stimulation of hexose monophosphate oxidation pathway the overall change of glucose utilization may remain undetectable and anyway NADPH production increases enough to accelerate the FA synthesis (Haft, 1967). On the other hand, it must be recognized that the insulin stimulation of lipogenesis has never been demonstrated in the absence of endogenous (glycogen) or exogenous glucose supply and that the high glucose concentration in the medium perfusing the liver is an effective stimulator of lipogenesis even without insulin (Haft, 1967). Under these circumstances the glucose oxidation is also much increased, presumably as a result of ample substrate presentation for the glycolytic enzymes and maintenance of high glucokinase activity (Ruderman *et al.*, 1967); the lipogenesis is therefore accelerated. Niemeyer *et al.* (1966) have shown that both insulin and glucose are needed for induction of liver glucokinase.

That insulin is not immediately effective on lipogenesis in fasted animals might be simply the result of low activities of hepatic glucokinase (DiPietro and Weinhouse, 1960) and the FA synthesizing enzymes (Gibson and Hubbard, 1960), which are not restored within 1 hour. In perfusion studies, on the other hand, the liver is exposed to glucose and insulin for a few hours which is enough at least for glucokinase to become induced (Blumenthal *et al.*, 1964; Niemeyer *et al.*, 1967) and, therefore, a lipogenic response is obtained also in livers isolated from fasting donors.

One further comment seems to be justified when the mechanism of insulin action on lipogenesis is considered. Always when the FA synthesis is studied in whole tissue, *in vivo* or *in vitro*, the product radioactive FA is almost totally in an esterified form and, thus, the rate of incorporation of any precursor is influenced not only by the rate of FA synthesis itself but also by the rate of esterification and the rate of breakdown of the newly formed lipid esters. If insulin, as will be discussed later (see page 92), inhibits lipolysis of hepatic triglycerides it increases the accumulation of *de novo* synthesized radioactive fatty acids without any actual stimulation of the lipogenesis having occurred. Likewise, insulin might alter the FA esterification rate by decreasing the production of glycerol phosphate (see below), and thus the lipogenesis would be underestimated. To what extent these factors have really influenced the results is unknown.

The *long-term in vivo* effect of hyperinsulinism on hepatic lipogenesis in *normal* nondiabetic animals has received relatively little attention in spite of its obvious importance at least for the discussion on the pathogenesis of human hyperglyceridemias (see Section VI). It must be admitted that chronic endogenous hyperinsulinism is not easy to simulate by experiments where exogenous insulin is administered to otherwise intact animals since the simultaneous over-eating and counterregulatory reactions to hypoglycemia may well mask the insulin actions. In addition, it may be difficult to distinguish the acute and chronic effects of insulin if measurements are made within a few hours from the last injection.

In normal fed rats given insulin for 2 days Stetten and Klein (1945) were unable to detect any increase of hepatic lipogenesis measured with deuterium incorporation, whereas in one rabbit a similar insulin treatment resulted in a definite stimulation of fatty acid synthesis (Stetten and Klein, 1946). On the other hand, Chernick and Chaikoff (1950) observed a tenfold increase in the *in vitro* incorporation of glucose-C^{14} into liver fatty acids in rats given protamine-zinc insulin for 10 days. The finding was confirmed by Milstein and Hausberger (1956), but in both experimental series the possibility is not excluded that the result was a result of an acute insulin effect rather than of a chronic hyperinsulinism. More recently, Salans and Reaven (1966) showed that in liver slices from normal fed rats insulin pretreatment led to a preferential incorporation of glucose-6-C^{14} into triglycerides instead of oxidation. However, when acetate-C^{14} is used as an *in vitro* marker 3 days' insulin administration fails to increase the hepatic lipogenesis in glucose-fed normal rats and does not restore the dietary fat-induced depression of lipogenesis (Hill *et al.*, 1958). Taken together all these results are not liable to an unambiguous interpretation, but it seems possible that a chronic insulin excess stimulates the hepatic utilization of glucose and through this action also increases the production of fatty acids (and possibly also of glycerol phosphate) but that the process of fatty acid synthesis remains primarily uninfluenced. The last postulate is worth reexamination, however, since it has been shown that of the enzymes directly involved in hepatic fatty acid synthesis at least the citrate cleavage enzyme increases many times in activity when normal rats are given large doses of insulin during several days (Kornacker and Lowenstein, 1965b; Lowenstein, 1968). Although this enzyme probably does not form the rate-limiting step in the generation of fatty acids (Foster and Srere, 1968) its activity is closely related to the rate of lipogenesis (Lowenstein, 1968).

When *diabetic* rats are treated with high doses of insulin the activities of liver glucokinase, phosphofructokinase, pyruvate kinase, glucose-6-phosphate dehydrogenase, and citrate cleavage enzyme are increased much above the level of normal fed rat (Weber and Singhal, 1965; Weber and Hird Convery, 1966; Weber *et al.*, 1965b; Kornacker and Lowenstein, 1965b). A similar overshooting occurs in the incorporation of glucose-C^{14} into hepatic fatty acids (Lequin and Steyn-Parvé, 1962). No conclusions can be drawn, however, on the validity of these insulin effects in a nondiabetic state. It may be that the chronic effects of hyperinsulinism on lipogenesis are best observable in animals with experimental or hereditary obesity. These data are presented in Section IV, E.

C. EFFECT OF INSULIN ON SYNTHESIS OF LIVER AND PLASMA TRIGLYCERIDES

One of the most marked and immediate effects of insulin administration *in vivo* is decrease of plasma FFA (Dole, 1956; Gordon and

Cherkes, 1956) and glycerol (Hagen, 1963; Hagen *et al.*, 1963; Mueller and Evans, 1963) levels. The fall of plasma FFA is attributed to anti-lipolytic action of insulin within fat cell (Jungas and Ball, 1963; Mahler *et al.*, 1963, 1964), but an increased reesterification may be a contributing factor. The prevailing opinion at present is that reduced lipolysis is achieved through inhibition of adenyl cyclase (Jungas, 1966) and activation of phosphodiesterase (Schultz *et al.*, 1966) with the resulting decrease of cyclic adenosine monophosphate (AMP) (Butcher *et al.*, 1966). The effect is evidently not dependent on glucose assimilation.

It is believed that insulin reduces the plasma FFA and glycerol turnover and concentration only through a decreased influx, while the efflux rate remains primarily unaffected but decreases secondary to falling plasma FFA (Bierman *et al.*, 1957b; Havel and Carlson, 1963; Csorba *et al.*, 1966; West and Passey, 1967). However, claims for an increased hepatic uptake of FFA as an additional cause of plasma FFA fall have also been presented (Shoemaker *et al.*, 1960). The major view is that insulin does not influence the fractional extraction of FFA by the liver, and, thus, the absolute hepatic uptake of FFA diminishes in parallel with the FFA concentration of the blood perfusing the liver (Armstrong *et al.*, 1961; Fine and Williams, 1960; Spitzer and Mc-Elroy, 1960). In accordance with these earlier studies, Heimberg *et al.* (1966) reported that insulin pretreatment of fed rats did not alter the rate of palmitate uptake in perfused liver. On the other hand, Penhos *et al.* (1968) found that addition of insulin to perfusate caused a decrease of FFA concentration in perfusions of livers from both fed and fasted rats. They held this as an evidence for an increased uptake of FFA from the medium, but it may equally well be ascribed to inhibition of triglyceride breakdown and a concomitant decrease of FFA release. The possible effect of insulin on the hepatic handling of glycerol is not known, but it may be assumed that uptake of glycerol and formation of glycerol phosphate from plasma glycerol are decreased in parallel with glycerol concentration, i.e., the fractional hepatic clearance remains unchanged.

As an outcome of these peripheral actions of insulin, reduced amounts of precursors for hepatic synthesis of triglycerides are presented to the liver from plasma. If not compensated by an increased hepatic lipogenesis and glycerol phosphate production from endogenous sources this process alone presumably leads to a diminished formation of esterified lipids in the liver cell. If the flow of FA into the "triglyceride secreting compartment" is equally reduced the plasma triglyceride production falls secondarily without being directly influenced by insulin. The evidence for this concept is reviewed in the following.

When the esterification of palmitic acid-C^{14} has been studied in rat liver slices no effect has been obtained by addition of insulin or glucose *in vitro* (Rubinstein and Rubenstein, 1966). Similarly, treatment of normal fed rats with insulin does not modify the secretion of triglyceride from their isolated livers perfused *in vitro* with palmitic acid (Heimberg *et al.*, 1966), although a complete inhibition of triglyceride output from perfused rat liver has been reported on addition of insulin *in vitro* (Penhos *et al.*, 1968). The reason for this discrepancy is not clear. In experiments carried out by the writer some years ago (Nikkilä and Ojala, 1966), palmitic acid-1-C^{14} was injected intravenously to anesthetized rats 15 and 60 minutes after a small single dose of insulin and the labeling of liver and plasma triglycerides was followed. No constant difference from controls could be observed in the rate or amount of incorporation of radioactivity, although the specific activity of plasma triglycerides was somewhat increased (Table I) as might be expected in view of the higher specific activity of precursor FFA. Three studies made in human subjects have given essentially compatible results. Jones and Arky (1965) found that a single dose of insulin did not influence plasma triglyceride concentration but slightly suppressed the labeling of plasma triglyceride on constant infusion of palmitic acid-1-C^{14}. When a prolonged infusion of insulin was used also the plasma triglyceride level decreased slowly during the subsequent 24 hours. In a similar study, Nestel (1967) could not observe any constant change in the slope of plasma triglyceride radioactivity–time curve during insulin infusion, but calculation of TGFA influx from the rate of plasma triglyceride labeling and the plasma FFA specific activity showed that the FFA flux and TGFA influx were significantly interrelated both before and during the insulin infusion. Neither, in a third human experiment with the same design, could Csorba *et al.* (1966) influence the rate of appearance of palmitic acid-1-C^{14} into plasma triglyceride by a single dose of intravenous insulin. In contrast to these results, Ogino *et al.* (1965) observed in one normal human subject that insulin decreased the triglyceride radioactivity after injection of palmitic acid-C^{14}.

It seems from all these investigations that none of the individual metabolic steps located on the pathway of flow of plasma FFA into plasma triglyceride is specifically controlled by insulin. The decrease of total plasma FFA flux consequent to the antilipolytic action of this hormone is thus followed by a diminished availability of FA from this particular source to liver and plasma triglyceride synthesis and by a parallel fall of plasma triglyceride inflow. Some additional decrease of FA esterification may take place because of a reduced supply of glycerol phosphate pool from plasma glycerol, and this effect might explain the slightly decreased rate of appearance of plasma FFA carbon into plasma TGFA as observed by Jones and Arky (1965). However, it should be borne in mind that, in some species at least (Baker and Schotz, 1964; Nikkilä *et al.*, 1966), the synthesis of triglycerides from endogenous hepatic precursors may well exceed the flux from plasma FFA and glycerol pools. Although this probably does not occur in man, who has a relatively slow plasma triglyceride turnover, the chronic influences of hyperinsulinemia, particularly in association with hyperglycemia, may well be quite opposite to those observed during the next few hours after an acute insulin load. Thus, the increased lipogenesis may lead to an increased triglyceride synthesis even in face of a reduced plasma FFA flux. Additional data on this point are desirable.

D. Effect of Insulin on Plasma Triglyceride Outflow

Although the acute fall of plasma triglyceride level after insulin may be fully accounted for by a reduced influx, there are several indications that the hormone also influences the removal mechanisms of triglycerides of both dietary and endogenous origin. Since the factors determining the overall disappearance rate of plasma chylomicron or lipoprotein triglycerides are so far poorly understood it is not possible to discuss the subject in any detail. Furthermore, observations related to the effect of insulin excess are relatively few as compared to an increasing number of studies made on triglyceride removal in insulin deficiency (see below).

In 1930 (Rony and Ching, 1930), it was already shown that insulin effectively counteracts or even abolishes alimentary lipemia in fasting dogs. Rony and Ching suggested that the hormone accelerated the removal of fat from the circulation probably through promotion of glucose metabolism. From a more recent date the writer has been able to trace only two studies concerning direct effects of insulin in this respect. Brown and Olivecrona (1966) measured blood and tissue radioactivity 10 minutes after intravenous injection of H^3-palmitate-labeled chylomicrons to normal refed rats. Insulin administration did not influence the disappearance of radioactivity from blood, but it enhanced the uptake by adipose tissue and decreased that by the liver. On the other hand, Heimberg *et al.* (1966) found that insulin pretreatment accelerated the rate of removal of artificial fat emulsion from the blood of fed normal rats. These apparently divergent results may result from difference in the physical state or the dose of fat used, but at any rate they leave the question of the insulin action upon triglyceride efflux unsolved. In view of the results obtained in diabetic state and of those referred to above one is inclined to think that hyperinsulinemia, if anything, facilitates the overall disposal of plasma triglycerides. Whether the locus of this action is in the liver, adipose tissue, or in other removal sites is not known but most evidence points to an activation of the triglyceride uptake in adipose tissue while the hepatic extraction remains unaffected or decreases.

The transport of triglycerides from the plasma to adipose tissue is closely related to the lipoprotein lipase activity of fat cells (Bezman *et al.*, 1962; Markscheid and Shafrir, 1965; Garfinkel *et al.*, 1967). Insulin and glucose when added together to incubated adipose tissue are able to increase the lipoprotein lipase probably through stimulation of *de novo* synthesis of the enzyme protein (Hollenberg, 1959, 1962, Salaman and Robinson, 1966), but it has not been decided so far whether the induction and activation result from an enhanced glucose metabolism or some other factor, e.g., reduced FFA concentration. In the experiments of Salaman and Robinson (1966), insulin without glucose was ineffective when the lipoprotein lipase induction was studied in adipose tissue of starved rats. However, when the tissue is taken from fed rats or from rats that have been made to fast for only a short period in order to maintain the enzymes needed for a new protein synthesis, insulin alone is a much more effective inducer of lipoprotein lipase synthesis than glucose (Nikkilä and Pykälistö, 1968b). Evidence has been recently provided for the view that insulin derepresses the enzyme synthesis by decreasing the FFA concentration within the fat cell (Nikkilä and Pykälistö, 1968b). This hypothesis is further substantiated by the finding that nicotinic acid, parallel to its antilipolytic action, is able to rapidly induce the lipoprotein lipase of adipose tissue in fasted rats *in vivo* but not *in vitro* (Nikkilä and Pykälistö, 1968a). It has also been found that administration of insulin *in vivo* very rapidly increases the enzymic activity in adipose tissue of fed and fasted rats (Nikkilä and Pykälistö, 1968c). Of course, final evidence that the repressor of the enzyme is just FFA is still lacking, and other possibilities such as cyclic AMP must be considered. In this context it may be noted that Jones *et al.* (1966) could not find any change in post-heparin plasma lipoprotein lipase in two normal human subjects after being given insulin.

It seems fairly well established that insulin greatly facilitates the removal of chylomicron and lipoprotein triglycerides at the adipose tissue and that this occurs through (1) derepression of lipoprotein lipase synthesis by a decrease of FFA or some other compound, (2) enhancement of glucose metabolism providing more favorable conditions for a new enzyme protein synthesis, and (3) a possible activation of the lipoprotein lipase on decrease of the inhibitory FFA by antilipolysis and reesterification. How this change at tissue level influences the fractional or absolute removal rates of circulating triglycerides remains to be determined by simultaneous measurements of their plasma clearance and lipoprotein lipase activity under a variety of experimental conditions. It may be relevant for the pathogenesis of different types of hyperlipemia that insulin action on lipoprotein lipase is not necessarily dependent on the facilitation of glucose transport and metabolism in adipose tissue cell.

IV. Triglyceride Metabolism in Diabetes

A. PLASMA TRIGLYCERIDE CONCENTRATION IN DIABETES

The plasma level of triglycerides in *human diabetes* is highly variable and depends at least on the following factors: type of disease, degree of control, age of the patient, previous diet, obesity, and the presence or absence of complications (micro- or macroangiopathy). This high number of influencing variables makes it easy to understand that no uniform pattern of plasma triglyceride in diabetes has evolved. Among the many fairly extensive clinical materials published there is thus far none where the effects of all these factors should have been studied separately from each other. Many reports have recorded only the mean values and standard deviations without giving information on the frequency of hyperglyceridemia. Lack of exact dietary data and pooling of insulin-dependent and insulin-independent diabetics are further disadvantages which often hamper the evaluation and comparison of clinical materials.

The hyperlipemia associated with uncontrolled juvenile-type diabetes and particularly with ketoacidosis was well recognized in the early pre-insulin era (for references, see e.g., Blix, 1926). The increase concerns chiefly triglycerides, which are more or less rapidly restored to normal or even subnormal level on insulin administration (Man and Peters, 1934, 1935; Chaikoff *et al.*, 1936). On continuation of insulin treatment and maintenance of good or even moderate control of glucose metabolism the average plasma triglyceride concentration keeps normal or near normal (Albrink and Man, 1958; Adlersberg and Eisler, 1959; Traisman *et al.*, 1960; Sterky *et al.*, 1963; New *et al.*, 1963;

Schrade *et al.*, 1963) and is not related to the duration of the disease (New *et al.*, 1963). However, there are individual cases that remain hyperlipemic in spite of fairly adequate regulation of diabetes (Albrink *et al.*, 1963; Schrade *et al.*, 1963), but it might well be that these patients should have the same degree of hyperglyceridemia also without diabetes; i.e., they represent a pure coincidence of two common disorders. Of certainly another type is the syndrome of mild diabetes and hyperlipemia described by Adlersberg and Wang (1955). When the control of diabetes is poor the average plasma triglyceride level increases (Albrink and Man, 1958; Adlersberg and Eisler, 1959; Sterky *et al.*, 1963) and shows some degree of correlation to the blood glucose level (Hirsch *et al.*, 1953).

An increase of plasma triglyceride levels occurs if diabetics are given a high-carbohydrate low-fat diet (Blix, 1926; Bierman and Hamlin, 1961; Albrink *et al.*, 1963) this response being obviously identical to that seen in nondiabetics. On high fat diet the triglycerides are markedly lower than during a normal diet (Albrink *et al.*, 1963). An exceptional group, possibly those with the Adlersberg-Wang syndrome, develops hyperlipemia on increasing the fat content of diet (Bagdade *et al.*, 1967; see Section IV, D). Also van Eck (1959) has observed a decrease rather than increase of plasma triglycerides in diabetics on reducing the dietary fat intake.

In diabetics presenting signs of atherosclerosis (coronary or peripheral artery disease) the plasma triglycerides are increased in a high percentage, but there is little difference to corresponding nondiabetic atherosclerotic patients (Albrink *et al.*, 1963). When comparison is made between diabetics over 30 years of age and age-matched healthy control subjects, the former group shows somewhat higher mean plasma triglyceride levels (Albrink *et al.*, 1963; New *et al.*, 1963). In diabetics with small vessel disease variable triglyceride concentrations have been reported, but increases may be partly a result of the diabetic nephrotic syndrome. Obesity associated with insulin-controlled diabetes produces elevated plasma triglyceride levels, and the increase of triglyceride per unit increment of body weight is many times higher than in nondiabetic control subjects (Sailer *et al.*, 1966a).

It is difficult to make any conclusive statements on plasma triglyceride pattern of patients with adult-onset type of diabetes. On comparison to a nondiabetic group matched for age and obesity, Östman (1965) did not find increased levels in untreated adult-type diabetics. In the material of Schrade *et al.* (1963) the plasma triglyceride was elevated in a considerable proportion of older diabetics, particularly if their disease was not well controlled. Sailer *et al.* (1966a) have compared tolbutamide-controlled diabetics and nondiabetics at different levels of relative body weight and noted that the regression of plasma triglyceride concentration versus body weight is much steeper for the diabetic group. It thus seems that a combination of overt adult-type diabetes and obesity is associated with hyperglyceridemia more frequently than either disorder alone and that control of the hyperglycemia by sulfonylurea is not sufficient to combat the hyperlipemia. Since this condition is characterized by hyperinsulinemia rather than insulin deficiency and the sulfonylurea still increases the insulin secretion it is not impossible that high plasma insulin level together with hyperglycemia is the essential pathogenetic factor of hyperglyceridemia in these cases (see discussion in Section VI).

In acute *alloxan diabetes* of rats the plasma triglyceride level is increased far above normal (Schnatz and Williams, 1963; Tarrant and Ashmore, 1965; Brown, 1967). The same applies to pancreatectomized animals (Gibbs and Chaikoff, 1941; Gillman *et al.*, 1958; Chernick and Scow, 1959) and to rats treated with anti-insulin serum (Tarrant *et al.*, 1962; Gross and Carlson, 1968). The liver triglyceride concentration is also clearly increased in these animals. However, in chronic alloxan diabetes the plasma triglyceride returns to normal (Cagan *et al.*, 1956; Rudas, 1967), and this explains why many authors (e.g., Carlson and Östman, 1965; Maruhama, 1965; Bierman *et al.*, 1966) have not been able to demonstrate hyperglyceridemia in alloxan diabetic animals without special dietary arrangements.

B. HEPATIC FATTY ACID SYNTHESIS IN DIABETES

The defect in the hepatic biosynthesis of FA in alloxan-induced diabetes and its correction by the administration of insulin was demonstrated almost 30 years ago (Drury, 1940; Stetten and Boxer, 1944; Chernick *et al.*, 1950; Chernick and Chaikoff, 1950) and has ever since been one of the most thoroughly studied disorders of lipid metabolism. The same lesion was somewhat later demonstrated also in adipose tissue (Hausberger *et al.* 1954). Nobody has thereafter failed to reproduce these observations regardless of whether working with a whole organism *in vivo* or with perfused, sliced, or homogenized livers *in vitro*. However, in spite of extensive and imaginative research, the exact biochemical nature of the diabetic defect in lipogenesis is still somewhat unclear. Until recently progress in this field has probably been much restrained by the use of alloxan diabetic or pancreatectomized animals which, even if good experimental counterparts of human untreated insulin-deficient (juvenile) diabetic, represent a very complex mixture of multiple metabolic disturbances caused by both enzyme deficiencies and disordered feedback regulatory devices. The tangle of causal relationships has begun to clear up only after the introduction of means to induce an acute insulin deficiency (anti-insulin serum, mannoheptulose), which permits the exact localization of different abnormal events on time axis. Valuable instructive information may also be expected from experiments where the effects of insulin lack on glucose and fat metabolism can be separated from each other (nicotinic acid) or mimicked (heparin) by pharmacological means.

The literature related to the control of lipogenesis in diabetes and fasting is extensive, and no attempt is made here to review it in full length. Since the fatty acid synthesis is one of the major sites of fat metabolism which is influenced by diabetes, and, particularly, because investigations of this point in different types of human diabetes should be important but are so far very few, a concise and fairly superficial survey of the most essential features has been found justifiable. The writer does not know of any quite recent comprehensive reviews of this topic, but the earlier knowledge has been excellently presented by Masoro (1962).

Two basic facts on diabetic lipogenesis were clearly established in the early experiments made with liver slices. First, it was shown that the site of the defect is in the FA synthesis itself since the transfer of carbon atoms to FA was impaired in diabetic liver not only from glucose (Chernick and Chaikoff, 1950) but also from fructose (Chernick and Chaikoff, 1951), acetate (Brady and Gurin, 1950; Brady *et al.*, 1951; Felts *et al.*, 1951a), pyruvate (Osborn *et al.*, 1951), lactate (Felts *et al.*, 1951b), and formate (Felts *et al.*, 1951a). Furthermore, the oxidation of glucose was shown to be much less depressed than its conversion to FA (Chernick *et al.*, 1950) and the oxidation of acetate proceeded in a normal way. A second important finding was that the lipogenic defect is not corrected by insulin *in vitro* (Brady and Gurin, 1950; Renold *et al.*, 1955) and that also *in vivo* the reappearance of lipogenic activity is a process of hours (Renold *et al.*, 1955; Williams *et al.*, 1960). It was thus apparent that this characteristic block of diabetic organism was not a direct consequence of insulin absence but secondary to some other metabolic error. This view was essentially corroborated by the demonstration of Baker *et al.*(1952) that in diabetic rat fructose administration alleviates the defective lipogenesis from acetate but not that from glucose. Like insulin fructose failed to produce any effect when added *in vitro*. Proof was thus obtained that mere activation of carbohydrate utilization is enough to reconstitute the FA synthesis and that lipogenesis is not a site of primary insulin action.

The slow reactivation of lipogenesis by insulin differs essentially from the prompt response of adipose tissue lipolysis to the administration of this hormone and shows clearly that in a long-standing diabetes one or several enzymes of FA synthesis are deficient, and time is needed for their resynthesis to occur. In fact more or less decreased activities have been found in a diabetic liver for fatty acid synthetase (Gibson and Hubbard, 1960), acetyl-CoA carboxylase (Wieland *et al.*, 1963a; Wieland and Eger-Neufeldt, 1963), malic enzyme (Shrago *et al.*, 1963), and citrate cleavage enzyme (Kornacker and Lowenstein, 1965b). It has not been established which of these enzymes is rate-limiting in the lipogenesis of diabetic liver, but it is significant that acetyl-CoA carboxylase is reduced approximately to the same extent as total FA synthesizing capacity and that addition of this enzyme to the cofactor supplemented supernatant of diabetic rat liver completely restores the lipogenic activity (Wieland *et al.*, 1963a). Location of the main diabetic lesion of lipogenesis to the acetyl-CoA carboxylase step should also fit well with the current belief that this enzyme represents the key point for regulatory control of lipogenesis (Vagelos, 1964; Numa *et al.*, 1965; Vagelos *et al.*, 1966). The possible importance of citrate cleavage enzyme in the lipogenesis has been emphasized on the basis of its low activity in diabetic liver and reattainment of normal or even supernormal activities by insulin, fructose, and glycerol (Kornacker and Lowenstein, 1965b; Lowenstein, 1968). This view has been strongly opposed, however, by Foster and Srere (1968) in showing that there is no correlation between the rate of lipogenesis and the activity of citrate cleavage enzyme in acute alloxan diabetes or fasting. It may be added that the alleviation of the lipogenic defect by fructose and glycerol in parallel with the reappearance of citrate cleavage enzyme cannot be used as evidence for the specific role of the latter since fructose is known to induce several enzymes in the diabetic liver (Fitch and Chaikoff, 1962) and glycerol administration restores not only the citrate cleavage enzyme but also the acetyl-CoA carboxylase activity (Takeda *et al.*, 1967). It may well be that the citrate cleavage is one of the steps where the flow of precursors into FA is impaired in diabetes, but the essential defect must lie between acetyl-CoA and FA, i.e., beyond the reaction catalyzed by citrate cleavage enzyme.

The mechanism responsible for the diminished concentration of acetyl-CoA carboxylase and of other enzymes of lipogenesis is unknown at present. A repression of enzyme synthesis in preference to

an accelerated destruction is suggested by the finding that actinomy-
cin inhibits the insulin-induced rise of lipogenesis from acetate
(Gellhorn and Benjamin, 1964). A lack of substrate cannot be involved
since the concentration of acetyl-CoA is increased in diabetic liver
(Wieland and Weiss, 1963; Tubbs and Garland, 1964). A general inhibition of protein and enzyme synthesis is also a less plausible explanation since at least the activity of gluconeogenic enzymes is increased
in diabetes (Weber *et al.*, 1965). An essential fact is the release of repression by fructose and glycerol *in vivo* which indicates that some
substance is produced during the metabolization of these compounds
which induces (derepresses) the enzyme synthesis. Since the effect
has been produced only *in vivo* it is not possible to conclude whether
the action is hepatic or extrahepatic, but in view of the knowledge that
both fructose and glycerol are predominantly metabolized in the liver
it should be more natural to prefer the former possibility. That the lipogenic defect of diabetic liver can be repaired without influences
from periphery is also shown by liver perfusion studies where addition of insulin (with glucose) is able to increase the low FA synthesis
(Haft and Miller, 1958; Boden and Willms, 1966; Haft, 1968a,b). One
tempting but so far fully tentative hypothesis is to imply that the fatty
acids or their CoA esters act as repressors of enzyme synthesis. The
role of these metabolites as a feedback regulator of acetyl-CoA carboxylase and of many other enzymes of both glycolysis, hexose monophosphate (HMP) shunt, and lipogenesis has been widely recognized
(see references below). It might be thought that fatty acids not only
inhibit the activity of these enzymes but also repress their synthesis.
Both fructose and glycerol are effective producers of glycerol phosphate, which removes the fatty acids by esterification. It is perhaps
pertinent for this view that the lipolytic agents epinephrine and glucagon are able to inhibit the induction of glucokinase by glucose and
insulin (Pitot *et al.*, 1964; Niemeyer *et al.*, 1966). For a further investigation of the problem it should be helpful to know the exact
timing of the increase of both lipogenesis and the different enzymic
activities on administration of insulin and fructose to diabetic animals.

The impairment of lipogenesis in diabetes is more marked when
studied *in vivo* in a diabetic animal or with liver slices than by using
cofactor supplemented liver supernatant fraction (Wieland and Eger-
Neufeldt, 1963). In fact, nearly normal activities have been reported
by soluble liver preparations obtained from acutely diabetic animals
(Matthes *et al.*, 1960; Shamoian *et al.*, 1964; Brady *et al.*, 1965). This
shows that inhibition of enzymes or shortage of cofactors or both are
superposed on the enzyme deficiency in diabetic liver to suppress the

FA synthesis. This is also clearly evident from observations made in acute anti-insulin serum (AIS) induced diabetes, which forms an excellent opportunity for the study of short-term regulatory disturbances of lipogenesis and other metabolic processes. This agent produces an insulin deficiency within minutes (Moloney and Coval, 1955; Armin *et al.*, 1960) and allows observations at a time when enzyme concentrations are presumably still normal but blood glucose and FFA levels are clearly elevated (Tarrant *et al.*, 1962). The incorporation of glucose-C^{14} into liver fatty acids is markedly depressed both *in vitro* (Mahler and Ashmore, 1962) and *in vivo* (Tarrant *et al.*, 1964) 1 hour after the administration of AIS. Also in perfused livers of AIS-treated rats there is a reduction of lipogenesis from both glucose and acetate, this defect being largely corrected by insulin *in vitro* (Haft, 1968b). Likewise, in liver slices obtained from rats 1–3 hours after the injection of AIS the incorporation of both pyruvate-C^{14} and acetate-C^{14} into FA is decreased (Sweeney and Ashmore, 1965). In cofactor supplemented liver homogenates of AIS-treated rats the FA synthesis is impaired from acetate-C^{14} and acetyl-C^{14}-CoA but not from malonyl-C^{14}-CoA, indicating that a block of lipogenesis lies at the level of acetyl-CoA carboxylase (Kalkhoff and Kipnis, 1966).

Of the various nonenzymic factors which might acutely modulate the fatty acid synthesis much attention has been paid to NADPH, which was once held as the key substance in the diabetic lesion of lipogenesis (Langdon, 1957; Siperstein, 1958; Siperstein and Fagan, 1958). Thereafter it has been well documented that the generation of NADPH proceeds at a normal rate in preparations made from livers of depancreatized and of chronic alloxan diabetic rats (Abraham *et al.*, 1962; Gordon, 1963) while the lipogenesis is severely depressed. Also, in acute AIS diabetes the concentration of NADPH and of other pyridine nucleotides remains unchanged (Kalkhoff *et al.*, 1966).

Another compound of potential significance in the lipogenesis is citrate, which is known to stimulate FA synthesis (Brady and Gurin, 1952) through activation of acetyl-CoA carboxylase (Martin and Vagelos, 1962; Waite and Wakil, 1962; Matsuhashi *et al.*, 1962). Addition of citrate to a supernatant plus microsome preparation of diabetic rat liver increases the incorporation of acetate to FA but still leaves it much below the corresponding normal value (Abraham *et al.*, 1960, 1962). The role of endogenous citrate in the depressed lipogenesis is highly questionable, however, since normal (Brady *et al.*, 1965; Spencer and Lowenstein, 1967) or even increased (Parmeggiani and Bowman, 1963; Kalkhoff *et al.*, 1966) citrate concentrations have been recorded in livers of alloxan diabetic rats.

Since the discovery of inhibition of lipogenesis by both long-chain acyl-CoA (Porter and Long, 1958) and fatty acids themselves (Langdon, 1960), the elevated FFA mobilization has been implicated as a negative feedback control device of FA synthesis (Masoro, 1962; Bortz and Lynen, 1963; Numa *et al.*, 1965). Diabetes fits into this scheme excellently since, particularly, the acetyl-CoA carboxylase is inhibited by these compounds (Bortz and Lynen, 1963; Korchak and Masoro, 1964) and the concentration of both long-chain acyl-CoA (Tubbs and Garland, 1964; Wieland *et al.*, 1965) and FFA (Kalkhoff and Kipnis, 1966) is increased in the liver of diabetic animals. However, several observations may be presented which raise doubts as to the validity of this concept. For example, both FFA and fatty acyl-CoA inhibit the FA synthesis also from malonyl-CoA (Robinson *et al.*, 1963; Korchak and Masoro, 1964; Tubbs and Garland, 1964), while this step is little affected by acute diabetes (Kalkhoff and Kipnis, 1966). Furthermore, the lipogenesis seems to be depressed in AIS-induced diabetes before any increase occurs in hepatic FFA content (Kalkhoff and Kipnis, 1966; Tarrant *et al.*, 1962), and a stimulation of FFA mobilization by epinephrine in a normal rat does not depress the hepatic lipogenesis (Sweeney and Ashmore, 1965). In preliminary experiments the writer has not been able to improve the lipogenic activity in liver of acutely diabetic rats with nicotinic acid in spite of reduction of plasma FFA levels. Ultimately, Fang and Lowenstein (1967) have been able to abolish the palmitoyl-CoA inhibition of lipogenesis by increasing protein concentration to a level which might be physiological within the cell. It may be also relevant to emphasize the highly unspecific nature of fatty acid inhibition of numerous enzymic actions and the detergent-like properties of fatty acid and their CoA esters when added to *in vitro* incubation systems (Taketa and Pogell, 1966). Another intermediate of FA metabolism, long-chain acyl carnitine, has been shown to activate FA synthesis and acetyl-CoA carboxylase (Fritz and Hsu, 1967) and to reverse the inhibition of lipogenesis by palmityl-CoA (Fang and Lowenstein, 1967). The concentration of this compound is also much increased in the liver of alloxan diabetic rats (Bøhmer *et al.*, 1966), and it could thus compensate for the inhibitory actions of acyl-CoA.

Glycerol phosphate is a very effective stimulator of FA synthesis when added *in vitro* to a cofactor supplemented supernatant plus microsome preparation of rat liver (Howard and Lowenstein, 1965). The effect is evidently based on removal of preformed and generated FA and fatty acyl-CoA by esterification and concomitant release of inhibition of the acetyl-CoA carboxylase as well as liberation of free acyl carrier protein (Howard and Lowenstein, 1965). In acute AIS diabetic rat the hepatic content of glycerol phosphate is reduced (Kalkhoff *et al.*, 1966). This change may be thought to result from either a decreased formation or increased utilization, but since the supply of liver glycerol phosphate pool from plasma glycerol, at least, is increased in diabetes it should be more plausible to believe that the increased flow of FFA from the plasma into the liver traps glycerol phosphate for esterification. A similar change of hepatic glycerol phosphate content has been noted in other states of stimulated lipid mobilization, viz., after epinephrine (Tzur *et al.*, 1964) and on fasting (Nikkilä and Ojala, 1963b; Bøhmer, 1967). It seems thus unlikely that reduced glycerol phosphate content could be even a partial cause of the decreased lipogenesis observed in diabetic liver under *in vivo* conditions, but it is not impossible that in some *in vitro* experiments using slices or total homogenates the glycerol phosphate could become a limiting factor for FA synthesis and thus partly explain the smaller lipogenesis of diabetic liver preparation.

Studies of the hepatic FA synthesis in different types of *human diabetes* have not been carried out to the writer's knowledge. As an indirect measure of this, one may eventually use the few data on incorporation of labeled acetate or other precursors into plasma triglycerides but only by the presumption that the secretion process itself is not influenced by the disease (see below). Thus, Hennes and Shreeve (1959) as well as Hennes and Redding (1961) reported a markedly impaired incorporation of acetate-1-C^{14} into plasma TGFA in middle-aged subjects with mild diabetes. Both the fractional incorporation and the plasma TGFA specific activity were much reduced despite a normal blood glucose level. A short-term administration of insulin did not increase the labeling of plasma triglyceride (Shreeve, 1965). On the other hand, transfer of tritium from glucose-1-H^3 or lactic acid-2-H^3 into plasma triglycerides has been found to be essentially similar in obese diabetics and nondiabetics (Ghose *et al.*, 1964; Shreeve, 1965). It is remarkable that all these observations have been made in a few occasional cases only, and, therefore no definite conclusions can be drawn from the reported data. As already stressed above, a thorough investigation of the behavior of hepatic lipogenesis in different types of human diabetes is desirable although it may be accompanied by methodological problems.

It can be *concluded* from the foregoing that the ability of the liver to synthesize fatty acids is much impaired not only in a chronic insulin deficiency diabetes but also immediately after acute depletion of circulating insulin activity. In the former instance the defect is caused by an interplay of several factors, which are ultimately based on the impaired hepatic utilization of glucose (lack of glucokinase) and on the increased FFA flow into the liver. The mechanism of the acute lesion is less clear but, in spite of a lot of opposite evidence, the most plausible explanation seems to be afforded by the presence of excessive amounts of FFA and acyl-CoA in the liver cell cytoplasm, where they inhibit the lipogenesis either by conformation of lipogenic enzymes or by saturating the acyl carrier protein. If the activity of fatty acid synthesis also influences the release of triglycerides from the liver, as postulated by Windmueller and Spaeth (1967), then the defective lipogenesis might explain some of the alterations found in this function of the diabetic liver (see Section IV, C).

C. Synthesis and Release of Liver Triglycerides in Diabetes

Plasma FFA concentration is much increased in uncontrolled insulin-deficient clinical diabetes (Laurell, 1956; Bierman *et al.*, 1957a) and acute alloxan diabetes, but the elevation is of lesser degree or even absent in adult-onset diabetes (Östman, 1965) or in chronic alloxan diabetes (Carlson and Östman, 1965). Also, plasma glycerol levels are increased but in individual cases they are not significantly correlated to plasma FFA concentration (Havel, 1965a; Pelkonen *et al.*, 1967). It is evident that the major cause of both these elevations is an increased lipolysis of adipose tissue triglycerides (Wenkeová and Páv, 1959; Hamosh and Wertheimer, 1960; Carlson and Östman, 1963; Tarrant *et al.*, 1964), but a relatively impaired utilization of both FFA and glycerol may be a contributing factor (Butterfield and Schless, 1959; Östman, 1965; Pelkonen *et al.*, 1967). The lipolytic rate is extremely sensitive to the presence of insulin since administration of anti-insulin serum to rats is followed by an increase of plasma FFA level (Tarrant *et al.*, 1962, 1964) and of adipose tissue FFA release (Tarrant *et al.*, 1964) within less than 1 hour. There is no relationship between the *in vitro* FFA release and glucose utilization of adipose tissue in anti-insulin diabetic rats (Tarrant *et al.*, 1964) or in human diabetics (Carlson and Östman, 1963; Östman, 1965), which shows that a reduced esterification of FA is of less importance for the increased FFA release of diabetes.

The total turnover rates of both plasma FFA (Bierman *et al.*, 1957a; Tarrant *et al.*, 1964; Sailer *et al.*, 1967a; Miller, 1967) and glycerol (Havel, 1965a; Pelkonen *et al.*, 1967) are increased in proportion to the plasma levels in experimental as well as in untreated juvenile human diabetes. In some investigations normal FFA fluxes have been found in diabetes (Ford *et al.*, 1963; Csorba *et al.*, 1966), but this seems to apply only to insulin-treated and mild adult-type cases. The antilipolytic activity of insulin is well retained in diabetes while the glucose utilization defect is restored more slowly (Csorba *et al.*, 1966; Björntorp, 1967), and, accordingly, the glucose and FFA fluxes after insulin are not interrelated (Csorba *et al.*, 1966). This indicates that in spite of the strong insulin dependence of adipose tissue lipase activity the synthesis of this enzyme continues undisturbed also in the absence of insulin, whereas the enzymes of glucose assimilation are heavily repressed. This dissociation of the two effects of insulin at adipose tissue also readily explains the normal FFA turnover of patients with adult obese-type diabetes. In this condition the plasma insulin levels are normal or supernormal, and therefore the lipid mobilization is not increased in spite of defective glucose utilization.

The question on the *hepatic uptake and esterification* of plasma FFA in diabetes seems somewhat difficult to assess since conflicting results have been reported. In a careful *in vivo* study, Spitzer and McElroy (1962) found that the fraction of plasma FFA removed by the liver was unaltered in alloxan diabetic dogs as compared to normal controls. As the portal plasma FFA levels were increased in diabetes the absolute hepatic FFA uptake was elevated in line with this. A similar result was arrived at by Söling *et al.* (1966) when measuring the FFA uptake in isolated perfused liver of chronic alloxan diabetic rats deprived of insulin. On the other hand, Heimberg *et al.* (1966) found that in perfusion the uptake of palmitic acid from the medium is increased in the liver of acutely diabetic rat. In sharp contrast to these results, a decrease of the relative hepatic FFA uptake was demonstrated in diabetic rabbits by Kuhfahl *et al.* (1967) with determination of the FFA difference across the liver and of hepatic plasma flow. This change in the fractional FFA extraction could not, however, compensate for the increase of absolute hepatic uptake caused by elevated plasma FFA concentration. Thus, whatever the relative capacity of the diabetic liver to take up FFA, the absolute rate of flow of FA molecules from plasma is increased when an augmented adipose tissue lipolysis is present.

The conversion of FA to CoA thioesters seems to proceed freely in diabetic liver since increased levels of acyl-CoA have been reported (Tubbs and Garland, 1964; Wieland *et al.*, 1965). Direct assays of glycerol phosphate acyltransferase activity or total triglyceride synthesis capacity of the diabetic liver have not been carried out, but it may be inferred from several indirect observations that these are at least not less than normal. Thus, Heimberg *et al.* (1967) found that the radioactivity of liver triglycerides was similar in diabetic and control rat livers perfused with palmitic acid-C^{14}. In fact, the same group (van Harken *et al.*, 1967) has reported also on decreased radioactivities in perfusion of diabetic liver with radiopalmitate, but since a marked breakdown of liver triglycerides occurs during a prolonged perfusion of livers from diabetic animals it is evident that the residual radioactivity represents a net effect of esterification and lipolysis. In *in vivo* experiments with anesthetized alloxan diabetic rats we have found that the incorporation of injected palmitic acid-C^{14} into liver triglycerides does not differ from values obtained in normal rats (Nikkilä and Ojala, unpublished). That the formation of glyceride ester bonds is uninfluenced by diabetic state is further substantiated by the finding that conversion of both fructose-C^{14} and glucose-C^{14} to glyceride-glycerol is normal in liver slices of pancreatectomized rats deprived of insulin (Chernick and Scow, 1964). It thus seems reasonable to conclude that the hepatic synthesis of triglyceride in diabetes is mainly determined by the plasma FFA and glycerol levels and turnover rates. The possibility of an increased esterification rate, i.e., a relative diversion of FA to esters instead of breakdown, is not excluded by the available data, however.

The fate of liver triglyceride is evidently altered in diabetes. This concerns particularly the *secretion into plasma*, a process which seems to be at least relatively impaired. In livers removed from alloxan diabetic insulin deprived rats and perfused *in vitro* the output of triglyceride into the medium as well as incorporation of palmitic acid-C^{14} into medium triglyceride is severely depressed at all medium FFA levels (Heimberg *et al.*, 1966, 1967; van Harken *et al.*, 1967). This defect of triglyceride release is paralleled by an inhibition of lipoprotein synthesis since also the incorporation of radioactive amino acids into plasma proteins including the major classes of lipoproteins is clearly decreased in perfused livers from acute and chronic alloxan diabetic rats (Wilcox *et al.*, 1968). Curiously, insulin treatment partly corrects the depressed triglyceride release before affecting amino acid incorporation (Wilcox *et al.*, 1968). In good agreement with these data on rats, Sailer *et al.* (1967a) have found that in human insulin-dependent diabetics deprived of insulin for at least 24 hours the relative incorporation of infused radiopalmitate into plasma triglyceride is diminished; i.e., the estimated plasma triglyceride influx is less than predicted from the increased plasma FFA turnover. In this material both the plasma triglyceride turnover rate and concentration were similar in diabetic and control patients. Recent data of Miller (1967) on pancreatectomized dogs have somewhat confused the situation in showing that both relative and absolute amounts of plasma FFA diverted to plasma triglyceride are increased on withdrawal of insulin. In preliminary experiments carried out in our laboratory the absolute plasma triglyceride turnover rate has been found to correlate with plasma triglyceride level in a similar fashion in diabetic and nondiabetic patients. Untreated ketoacidotic patients have high plasma FFA, plasma triglyceride concentration, and triglyceride turnover rate, while under insulin treatment these become normal and parallel to each other (Nikkilä et al., unpublished). This suggests that in uncontrolled clinical diabetes the plasma triglyceride influx is increased, if not completely in line with plasma FFA turnover, at least to some extent. Clearly, this postulate is not applicable to all cases of diabetes since plasma triglyceride level is poorly correlated to plasma FFA concentration and flux, particularly when patients with relatively mild diabetes and with more or less elevated plasma triglyceride are included.

The relative block in the outward transport of triglyceride in the diabetic liver is comparable to the situation in fasting state, where the hepatic triglyceride secretion is much depressed (Laurell, 1959a; Kay and Entenman, 1961; Nikkilä et al., 1966; Mayes and Felts, 1967b) in spite of an increased plasma FFA flux. The biochemical mechanism of the inhibition of triglyceride release may be common for both metabolic states but is unknown for the present. Some possibilities may be speculated upon, however, conforming to the conventional line of thinking that most changes of diabetes and fasting are ultimately due to lack of insulin. First, it might be thought that the primary block is in the synthesis of lipoprotein-protein, but this idea is not well supported by the data of Wilcox et al. (1968) and van Harken et al. (1967) which show that in diabetic liver the amino acid incorporation into perfusate lipoproteins was depressed to a much smaller extent than the release of triglycerides. Another, and probably better, alternative is that the hepatic triglycerides are degraded at an accelerated rate in both diabetes and fasting state; in other words, the intrahepatic lipolysis is activated in the absence of insulin in a manner similar to that in adipose tissue. If cyclic AMP acts as a lipase activator also in the liver this view receives support from the demonstration by Exton et al. (1966) that insulin decreases and anti-insulin serum increases the content of this nucleotide in the liver. Furthermore, during perfusion of livers from alloxan diabetic rats the triglyceride content decreases strongly (van Harken *et al.*, 1967) and the output of FFA is greater than in normal livers (Kyllästinen and Nikkilä, 1968).

This hypothesis on increased lipolysis of intrahepatic triglyceride should explain not only the depression of triglyceride secretion in diabetes and fasting but also the enhanced ketogenesis which seems not be adequately accounted for by the increased presentation of FFA to the liver (Mayes and Felts, 1967b; van Harken *et al.*, 1967; Foster, 1967). That endogenous hepatic TGFA might act as an important precursor for ketone body formation has been suggested by Scow and Chernick (1960) and recently by Heimberg *et al.* (1967). Because of this view it is particularly interesting that Foster (1967) has been able to dissociate the ketogenesis from FA mobilization, FA oxidation, and FA synthesis and to show that insulin promptly depresses the acetoacetate formation by the liver of fasting rats. If the insulin action on hepatic lipase is as rapid as on lipolysis in adipose tissue these findings could be readily explained without assuming a direct effect of insulin on acetoacetate synthesis.

In conclusion it may be stated that the fat accumulation into the liver when it occurs in a diabetic organism is presumably solely the result of an enhanced inflow of FFA and glycerol from the plasma and a concomitant increase of esterification, which is not limited by any deficiency or inhibition of concerned enzymes. The breakdown of hepatic triglycerides is also accelerated, and this fact is mainly responsible for the compensation of increased synthesis and for reaching a new steady state. The output of liver triglycerides into plasma is reduced in proportion to their synthesis, but in absolute terms it may be even markedly increased. Recirculation of triglycerides from plasma to liver is possibly increased, thus still diminishing the net release. The quantitative significance of the impaired secretion of triglycerides for the production of diabetic fatty liver has not been assessed but it may be of less importance, at least in man who has a slow plasma triglyceride flux. Possible changes in the intrahepatic FA fluxes between different triglyceride pools and between triglycerides and phospholipids are also unknown in diabetic liver. When the FFA mobilization from periphery is normal, as in many of the cases with adult-type clinical diabetes or in chronic alloxan diabetes or during insulin treatment the hepatic triglyceride content is not increased. This does not imply that the FA kinetics are normal, however. The boundary between obesity and diabetes is difficult to draw exactly, and, therefore, it is impossible to present a uniform model for the behavior of FA and triglyceride metabolism in cases with overweight and more or less

94

ESKO A. NIKKILÄ

diabetes. Hepatic fat accumulation is fairly common in these patients, but it apparently is more related to the adipose tissue mass in splanchnic bed than to the diabetic state.

D. REMOVAL OF TRIGLYCERIDES FROM PLASMA IN DIABETES

The role of dietary fat in the production of hyperlipemia in more or less controlled human diabetes was intensively discussed in the preinsulin era when the patients were forced to derive much of their calories from fat instead of carbohydrate. Many authors of that time held the view that the degree of lipemia was largely related to the amount of fat in the diet and that blood lipids fell to normal when fat intake was cut down (Allen, 1918; Ervin, 1919; Bang, 1919; Joslin, 1921; Bloor, 1921). Allen (1918) suggested that a pancreatic hormone is necessary for a proper removal of fat from the blood. However, some studies did not support this opinion in indicating that a diabetic, without any insulin substitution, can consume even excessive amounts of fat and still the hyperlipemia is abolished (Marsh and Waller, 1923). Blix (1926), in a most comprehensive treatise of diabetic lipemia, also came to the conclusion that the outflow rate of fat from the blood is not disturbed in human diabetes as evidenced by essentially normal (on a similar diet) oral fat tolerance tests. He recognized, however, the presence of exceptional cases with hyperlipemia of alimentary origin.

In more recent times the question on the disappearance of exogenous fat from the circulation in human diabetes has been reexamined and an impaired removal has been postulated by Hirsch et al. (1953; Hirsch and Carbonaro, 1950), Sandberg et al. (1960), Berkowitz (1962), and others. Of particular interest is the study of Kallio (1967), who on standardized oral fat loading found significantly increased exogenous hyperglyceridemia not only in untreated mild diabetics but also in normal males with a diabetic heredity. Bagdade et al. (1967) have described five diabetic hyperlipemic patients, in which the plasma triglyceride level closely followed dietary intake of fat and most of plasma fat particles behaved like chylomicrons in flotation, polyvinylpyrrolidone flocculation, and starch-block electrophoresis. On this evidence the authors return to the old concept and held that diabetic hyperlipemia can be considered to be dietary fat-induced. The same group had earlier described development of hyperglyceridemia in treated diabetic patients on a low-fat high-carbohydrate regimen (Bierman and Hamlin, 1961). On the other hand, in insulin-controlled diabetics neither Ernest et al. (1962) nor Stone and Connor (1963) could find any dependence between the amount of dietary fat or carbohydrate and serum triglyceride level.

When the disappearance of intravenously administered tracer amounts of triglycerides has been measured in human diabetics the results have been conflicting. Thus, Balodimos *et al.* (1962) found no difference in the removal rate of triolein-I^{131} and tripalmitin-C^{14} emulsions between diabetic and normal subjects. Neither could Bierman and Hamlin (1963) observe any influence of insulin withdrawal or administration in diabetics on the clearing of particulate tripalmitin-C^{14} dissolved in plasma *in vitro*. On the other hand, Bagdade *et al.* (1968) reported recently that in two diabetics disappearance of tripalmitine-C^{14} complexed to plasma low density lipoproteins *in vitro* was delayed when insulin was withheld for one or two days.

Since the fractional removal rate of triglycerides added to plasma pool (by ingestion or intravenously) is inversely proportional to the circulating triglyceride mass (concentration) the interpretation of all disappearance studies must be made with caution if the basal triglyceride level is increased. Since this is often the case in uncontrolled diabetes an apparently defective removal of triglycerides may be found in a situation where the actual removal capacity is intact or even increased. However, a number of observations made in experimental diabetes of animals as well as assays of lipoprotein lipase activity of adipose tissue or postheparin plasma ultimately give strong support to the concept that plasma triglyceride outflow is really impaired in an uncontrolled diabetes and may be an essential factor in the production of hyperglyceridemia.

In pancreatectomized dogs Waddell and Geyer (1957) showed that the clearing of a relatively large dose of fat emulsion (Lipomul) from the plasma was markedly impaired and was normalized by insulin treatment. The finding was confirmed by Kessler (1962), who in both pancreatectomized and alloxan diabetic fasting dogs demonstrated a much decreased rate of clearing (*k* value) of intravenous fat emulsion as compared to insulin-treated diabetic animals. In both of these studies the amount of administered fat (about 750 mg/kg) exceeded the endogenous triglyceride pool so many times that the latter could not influence the result, and, evidently the maximal removal capacity was assayed. Brown (1967) injected smaller amounts (about 100 mg/kg) of H^3-palmitate-labeled lymph chylomicrons to acute alloxan-diabetic rats deprived of insulin and found the clearing to impair progressively when the time from the last insulin increased. However, the endogenous triglyceride pool was much expanded in the insulin-deprived animals, and the prolonged half-life may be a reflection of only this parameter. In an earlier study, Brown and Olivecrona (1966) were unable to note any differences in the chylomicron removal between insulin-treated and insulin-deprived diabetic rats. Also others have reported a decreased disappearance of intravenous chylomicrons (Gries *et al.*, 1967) and of intravenous and oral fat emulsion (Heimberg *et al.*, 1966; Rudas and Reissert, 1967).

The impaired capacity of fat assimilation present in diabetes is probably best revealed from the experiments of Bierman *et al.* (1966) on chronic untreated alloxan diabetic rats. These animals had normal serum triglyceride levels when maintained on fat-free diet but developed a marked hyperglyceridemia on addition of corn oil to make 40% of calories. Rudas (1967) has confirmed this finding in a short-term experiment using both saturated and unsaturated fats. On the other hand, Maruhama (1965) found a decrease of plasma triglycerides on feeding chronic alloxan diabetic rats a high saturated fat diet and only a minor increase on using oil-enriched diet. The reason for the discrepancy between the results of these authors is not readily apparent.

That the triglyceride removal defect of diabetic state particularly concerns adipose tissue is well established in several studies, which have uniformly demonstrated a low recovery of radioactivity in adipose tissue esterified fatty acids of diabetic animals after injection of fatty acid-labeled chylomicrons or fat emulsions (Brown and Olivecrona, 1966; Brown, 1967; Naidoo *et al.*, 1967; Gries *et al.*, 1967). The defect is restored or even overcompensated by administration of insulin. Although poor uptake may be partly a result of isotope dilution in the expanded FA pool of fat cells, or of increased breakdown rate of newly formed adipose tissue triglycerides, or even due to diminished adipose tissue mass it still seems pertinent to assume that a reduced extraction of lipoprotein and chylomicron triglycerides occurs at this tissue site in diabetes.

In contrast to adipose tissue the uptake of triglycerides by heart (Gries *et al.*, 1967) and by skeletal muscle (Naidoo *et al.*, 1967) is increased in alloxan diabetes as is the production of expired $CO_2{}^{14}$ from C^{14}-palmitate-labeled chylomicrons (Naidoo *et al.*, 1967). Also the capacity of the isolated perfused liver to take up fat from emulsion (Heimberg *et al.*, 1958) or chylomicrons (Heimberg *et al.*, 1966) is probably increased in diabetes. In an isolated perfused heart of diabetic rat, Kreisberg (1966), on the other hand, found a diminished utilization of triglycerides. The increased oxidation of triglyceride fatty acids in diabetes as compared to normal animals does not, of course, exclude the possibility of an impaired overall assimilation of fat since only the proportion of oxidized and esterified fatty acid may be changed.

Lipoprotein Lipase

The low uptake of triglycerides by the diabetic adipose tissue is probably caused by a deficiency of lipoprotein lipase (LPL). This view is borne out by all animal studies with direct or indirect assays of the tissue enzyme, while determinations of postheparin plasma LPL in clinical diabetes have given conflicting results.

The low activity was first demonstrated by Meng and Goldfarb (1959) in postheparin plasma of pancreatectomized and alloxan diabetic rats. Administration of insulin restored the activity. Subsequently, Kessler (1962) showed that the post-Lipomul LPL activity was much lower in the plasma of diabetic dogs before insulin administration than after it. In alloxan diabetic rats the LPL activity of adipose tissue is much reduced (Schnatz and Williams, 1962; Kessler, 1963; Brown, 1967), the decrease occurring progressively with time from the last insulin injection and in a significant negative correlation to increase of plasma triglyceride and FFA and blood glucose levels (Schnatz and Williams, 1963). The enzymic activity is also decreased in alloxan subdiabetes when blood glucose levels are still in a normal range and a close correlation exists between the decrease of plasma insulin per glucose ratio, increase of *in vitro* FFA release, and decrease of LPL activity (Pykälistö and Nikkilä, 1968). We have also observed very low activities to be present in streptozotocin diabetes of rats. After mannoheptulose injection into rats the LPL activity of adipose tissue is significantly reduced within 1 hour (Pykälistö and Nikkilä, 1968) but this decrease can be prevented by nicotinic acid (Nikkilä and Pykälistö, 1968c). As pointed out previously, it is probable that the enzyme is very sensitive to the FFA increment produced by lack of insulin. In myocardium the LPL is increased in diabetic rats (Kessler, 1963).

In clinical diabetes no estimations of adipose tissue LPL have been carried out. Persson *et al.* (1966) have reported an inverse correlation between serum triglyceride level and the LPL activity of subcutaneous fat in humans. In postheparin plasma normal LPL activity has been found in several studies of both insulin-dependent and mild adult diabetics irrespective of the presence or absence of hyperglyceridemia (Denborough and Paterson, 1962; Jones *et al.*, 1966; Perry, 1967). Even in patients with severe ketoacidosis, Jones *et al.* (1966) were unable to detect a decreased release of the enzyme into plasma by heparin, and insulin treatment did not change the plasma LPL activity. In contrast to these negative findings, Shigeta *et al.* (1967) reported slightly decreased plasma LPL activities in diabetics, particularly the hyperglyceridemic ones, after dextran sulfate. Similarly, Bagdade *et al.* (1968) observed a significant decrease of postheparin plasma LPL activity following insulin withdrawal in diabetic patients. Again, there is no valid explanation for these divergent results and final solution of the problem cannot occur before direct enzyme assays are carried out on the adipose tissue of diabetic subjects.

CONCLUSIONS

In diabetes with insulin deficiency (untreated juvenile human diabetes and acute experimental diabetes) the plasma triglyceride level is regularly high and is restored to normal with insulin. This hyperglyceridemia is, like hyperglycemia, obviously caused by both an increased entry rate and decreased removal rate of circulating triglyceride pool. The former is mainly if not solely based on an increased inflow of FFA and glycerol into the liver while the impaired elimination might be accounted for by a lipoprotein lipase deficiency. Which of these two basic abnormalities prevails is still a controversial question and may remain such since it has been revealed that both influx and efflux rates of plasma glyceride are controlled by the FFA liberation from adipose tissue. It is known that inhibition of lipolysis by nicotinic acid (Gross and Carlson, 1968) and depletion of fat stores by fasting (Chernick and Scow, 1959) both prevent the development of hyperglyceridemia on acute insulin lack, but neither of these experiments will solve the problem since both procedures influence both the production and elimination of plasma triglycerides (see Fig. 3).

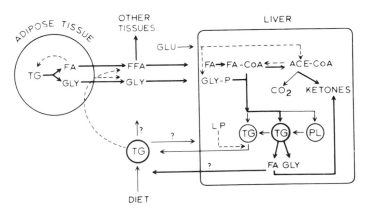

FIG. 3. Alterations in the formation and fate of liver and plasma triglycerides in insulin deficiency. Heavy arrows indicate an increased flow, while the dotted arrows stand for decreased rates.

In addition to the above categories with a "conventional" diabetes there is a possibly heterogeneous group with hyperglyceridemic diabetes in which the metabolic error is so far of unknown nature but evidently not dependent on the absence or excess of endogenous insulin. It has been suggested that the hyperlipemia in these cases is based on an impaired outflow of triglycerides from the blood (fat induction), but the writer knows of several patients with this disorder whose serum triglyceride level can be effectively reduced by a high fat diet and again increased by substituting carbohydrate for fat. Some cases, on the other hand, show a diet-independent hyperlipemia.

E. FATTY ACID AND TRIGLYCERIDE METABOLISM IN DIABETES WITH HYPERINSULINISM

It is important to realize that almost all evidence cited above is derived from diabetic animals with more or less absolute insulin deficiency. These represent the counterpart of human juvenile-type diabetic but obviously have little common features with an overweight human patient whose diabetes is of the adult-onset type. In the latter the basic metabolic abnormality is an impaired peripheral utilization of glucose combined to hyperinsulinism. Since the hepatic assimilation of glucose may be normal or even increased in these cases it is probable that if there is any derangement of fat metabolism the alterations are not similar to those seen in insulin deficiency but may be even opposite in many respects.

The best animal representative of this type of diabetes is the mouse with hereditary obese-hyperglycemic syndrome. Like the obese human with adult-onset diabetes it shows hyperglycemia, hypertrophy of the islet tissue (Bleisch *et al.*, 1952; Gepts *et al.*, 1960), fasting and postprandial hyperinsulinemia (Christophe *et al.*, 1959; Stauffacher *et al.*, 1967; Westman, 1968), and an insulin insensitivity of adipose tissue (Christophe *et al.*, 1961). The fat metabolism of these animals is strikingly abnormal, and it might well be thought that the changes are secondary to the excessive and uncontrolled insulin secretion. Thus, the hepatic fatty acid synthesis from acetate (Bates *et al.*, 1955; Zomzely and Mayer, 1959; Winand *et al.*, 1968), citrate (Howard and Lowenstein, 1965), and glucose (Shigeta and Shreeve, 1964; Jansen *et al.*, 1967) is many times higher in obese mice than in their nonobese littermates and remains elevated also on fasting. The *in vitro* incorporation of fatty acids into liver triglycerides is also increased (Winand *et al.*, 1968). The hyperlipogenesis of obese mice is accounted for by much elevated activities of citrate cleavage enzyme (Kornacker and

Lowenstein, 1964), acetyl-CoA carboxylase, and fatty acid synthetase (Chang *et al.*, 1967). As expected from the high plasma insulin levels, the activity of hepatic glucokinase and of other key glycolytic enzymes is also supernormal (Seidman *et al.*, 1967).

In spite of a decreased glucose utilization the adipose tissue of obese hyperglycemic mice does not show an accelerated lipolysis (Westman and Hellman, 1963) but is even less sensitive to the lipid-mobilizing action of epinephrine and fasting (Marshall and Engel, 1960). This is a further similarity with human hyperinsulinemic diabetes, in which the adipose tissue lipolysis has also been found to be normal (Östman, 1965). The over-all dynamics of fatty acids and triglycerides have not been studied in detail neither in obese mice nor in human diabetes, and therefore it is not possible to decide whether the plasma triglyceride fluxes are altered in these disorders, but one would predict that both the production and utilization of plasma triglycerides are increased.

V. Influence of Exogenous Carbohydrates on Triglyceride Metabolism

It is now generally recognized that triglyceride kinetics whether normal or disordered is not only influenced by exogenous fat but also, and probably even more, by the amount and quality of dietary carbohydrate. In itself this statement is not new, but most of our present knowledge on the details of this interaction stems from the last few years. A wide interest to the subject has arisen, particularly after the suggestion by Ahrens *et al.* (1961) that many hyperglyceridemias are induced by dietary carbohydrate, and the proposal by Yudkin (1964) that dietary sucrose is of importance in the pathogenesis of atherosclerosis. It has been revealed that exogenous carbohydrate not only serves as a precursor of body triglyceride but also that it modifies the fluxes of triglyceride molecules between plasma and different tissue pools through a complex interplay of hormonal, enzymic, and other factors. A recent review in this series (Macdonald, 1966) covers a considerable part of the field and permits the omission of many publications from the present article. Another excellent and detailed collection of pertinent literature has also appeared (McGandy *et al.*, 1967).

Before going into detail it is necessary to make some general comments on the designs used in dietary experiments since these may essentially influence the conclusions and concepts derived from the results. Most of the information on the effect of dietary carbohydrate on different facets of triglyceride metabolism has been obtained from studies in animals, like rabbit, rat, and mouse, which are basally maintained on a chow high in carbohydrate and low in fat. On preparation of special high carbohydrate diets the most usual way has been an exchange of basal chow (starch) to a mixture containing glucose or sucrose as the sole or main source of calories. Another method is to supplement the chow with sugars given in drinking water. This means that the experimental high carbohydrate diets often differ relatively little from the control diet in regard to the quantity of carbohydrates supplied and the possible effects ascribed to the amount of carbohydrate may be actually caused by the different quality of the carbohydrate. Thus, a simultaneous change of both kind and amount makes the evaluation of results often difficult. The same applies to the exchange between dietary carbohydrate and fat. Both dietary constituents have their own influences on triglyceride metabolism and should therefore not be substituted for each other. A lot of knowledge of the effects of dietary carbohydrates is derived from comparisons of fasted and fed or fasted-refed animals. Since fasting actually means living on a pure fat diet, the differences between fasting and fed state can be taken as consequences of carbohydrate lack or supply. In the following the main attempt has been to compare the effects of high and low carbohydrate diets and of the quality of dietary carbohydrate since from the clinical point of view this forms the most pertinent problem.

A. ACUTE EFFECTS OF GLUCOSE ON PLASMA TRIGLYCERIDE

When glucose or sucrose is administered by peroral or intravenous route to previously fasted animals or man the plasma triglyceride level decreases (Havel, 1957; Bragdon *et al.*, 1957; Perry and Corbett, 1964; Dannenburg and Burt, 1965; Swynghedauw *et al.*, 1965; Sailer *et al.*, 1967b; Baker *et al.*, 1968). In rat with a rapid plasma triglyceride turnover rate the nadir is reached in 1 hour (Bragdon *et al.*, 1957; Baker *et al.*, 1968), while at 2 hours a return to the starting level has already occurred (Bragdon *et al.*, 1957), and after 3 hours even a slight increase may be revealed (Nikkilä and Ojala, 1966). In man with a slow triglyceride turnover the low levels persist up to 8–11 hours (Havel, 1957). Glucose ingestion is also able to diminish or even abolish the postalimentary exogenous hyperglyceridemia (Rony and Ching, 1930; Nissen, 1931; Man and Albrink, 1956; Albrink and Man, 1957, 1958; Krut and Barsky, 1964; Nikkilä and Pelkonen, 1966).

It is probable but not proved that this early reduction of plasma triglyceride concentration by glucose is completely accounted for by the
stimulation of insulin secretion, and therefore the discussion on acute
effects of insulin on triglyceride kinetics presented previously (p. 76)
also applies here. In diabetic patients the decrease of plasma triglyceride after intravenous glucose is less than in normal subjects and is
related to the defective decrease of plasma FFA level (Swynghedauw,
1965). Intravenous tolbutamide is also effective in reducing alimentary
hyperglyceridemia (Gebbie and Reid, 1964). One of the probable
ways through which glucose acutely interferes with triglyceride
metabolism is lowering of plasma FFA concentration (Dole, 1956;
Gordon and Cherkes, 1956) and turnover rate. Even if the relative
hepatic uptake and esterification of FFA are increased by glucose
(Bragdon and Gordon, 1958; Laurell, 1959a) the total influx of plasma
FFA (and glycerol) into liver triglycerides and their appearance into
plasma are definitely decreased during an acute glucose load (Miller,
1967; Sailer *et al.*, 1967b). Also, since the endogenous synthesis of
hepatic FA is still depressed during the first few hours after administration of glucose to previously fasted animals (Baker *et al.*,
1968) it follows that the formation of liver and plasma triglyceride
ceases simply as a result of the lack of available precursor material.

Another mechanism, which certainly contributes to the acute decrease of plasma triglyceride with glucose is accelerated removal.
This is shown, e.g., by the rapid onset of the fall of plasma triglyceride
level in humans (Perry and Corbett, 1964; Swynghedauw *et al.*, 1965)
and by the finding that norepinephrine inhibits the effect of glucose
on plasma triglyceride content without affecting the plasma FFA turnover and its conversion into triglyceride (Sailer *et al.*, 1967b). However, studies on the effect of glucose on removal rate of exogenous or
endogenous plasma triglycerides have given somewhat confusing
results. Thus, the disappearance of intravenously injected labeled
chylomicron triglycerides seems to occur at the same rate in fasted
and in acutely glucose-loaded rats (Bragdon and Gordon, 1958; Brown
and Olivecrona, 1966; Schotz *et al.*, 1966). In man, previous administration of glucose can slightly increase the exponential removal rate of
intravenous fat emulsion (Intralipid) (Pelkonen *et al.*, 1967). The initial half-life of endogenous labeled plasma triglycerides has been reported to decrease (Schotz *et al.*, 1966) or remain unaffected by glucose feeding in rats (Laurell, 1959b), while in rabbits Havel *et al.*
(1962) have found a more rapid clearance of very low density (VLD)
lipoprotein triglycerides in refed state as compared to fasting.

If we assume, in accordance with the prevailing opinion of recent years (see Havel, 1965b), that adipose tissue has a central role in the removal of chylomicrons and VLD lipoprotein triglycerides from the circulation and that lipoprotein lipase is essential in this process then it should be fully expected that administration of glucose greatly improves the removal of plasma triglycerides. The uptake of triglyceride from particles or plasma into adipose tissue is in good correlation to the lipoprotein lipase activity (Bezman *et al.*, 1962; Garfinkel *et al.*, 1967) and whether measured by incubation (Bezman *et al.*, 1962; Markscheid and Shafrir, 1965; Garfinkel *et al.*, 1967) or perfusion technique (Rodbell and Scow, 1964) both are always much higher in fed than in fasted state. The proportion of injected labeled triglyceride recovered in adipose tissue is also manifold in fed as compared to fasting animal (Bradgon and Gordon, 1958; Brown and Olivecrona, 1966). However, the time needed for switching from fasted to fed state in this particular metabolic point has not been very much considered. Injection of glucose to previously fasted rats seems not to increase the incorporation of chylomicron TGFA into adipose tissue within 90 minutes (Brown and Olivecrona, 1966) nor does it significantly induce the lipoprotein lipase activity within this time (Garfinkel *et al.*, 1967). Also, since the hepatic uptake of chylomicron triglycerides remains unchanged at least for 90 minutes after infusion of glucose to fasted rats (Brown and Olivecrona, 1966) it is possible that, ultimately, the immediate depression of fasting plasma triglyceride by glucose is mainly caused by a reduced influx rather than by an accelerated efflux. The effect of glucose on alimentary hyperglyceridemia could then be only an apparent phenomenon caused by a simultaneous decrease of endogenous plasma triglycerides but, on the other hand, glucose (and insulin) in these experiments has also enough time to activate the removal mechanisms of adipose tissue. The finding of Albrink and Man (1957) that epinephrine increases the postprandial hyperglyceridemia fits well with the concept on inactivation of lipoprotein lipase by FFA mobilization (see Section IV,D) and indicates that hyperglycemia per se is not the mediating factor in the glucose effect.

B. Long-Term Effects of Dietary Carbohydrate on Triglyceride Kinetics

As pointed out above, the hypoglyceridemic acute effect of glucose lasts only for a few hours, and thereafter the plasma triglyceride not only returns to fasting level but also exceeds it. If the carbohydrate

feeding is continued in the rat for about 20 hours a hyperglyceridemia
of different degrees develops depending on the nature of the fed carbohydrate (Nikkilä and Ojala, 1966). At this time the metabolic state is
different from that prevailing during the very first postfasting hours
and the effects of chronic high carbohydrate diet begin to appear.

The hyperglyceridemic effect of high carbohydrate diet was first
established by the experiments of Watkins *et al.* (1950), Walker *et al.*
(1953), Hatch *et al.* (1955), Ahrens *et al.* (1957), and Nichols *et al.* (1957)
in man, and these observations have been repeatedly confirmed. In a
well-designed and well-performed human study, Antonis and Bersohn (1961) were able to show that the increase of plasma triglyceride
on transfer from a low to a high consumption of carbohydrate is a normal primary response occurring in every subject but that on continuation of this diet the hyperglyceridemia slowly disappears. The maximal levels attained on high carbohydrate diet are extremely variable
individually and they form a continuous spectrum from normal range
to a gross hyperlipemia (Antonis and Bersohn, 1961; Farquhar *et al.*,
1966; Reaven *et al.*, 1967). Young women are far more resistant to this
dietary change than are men and postmenopausal women (Macdonald,
1966). The magnitude of the response also depends on the quality of
carbohydrate as discussed below.

1. *Plasma Triglyceride Fluxes*

On searching for the mechanism of the plasma triglyceride rise by
dietary carbohydrate the first question is, of course, whether the primary event is an increased endogenous production or an impaired
removal of plasma triglycerides. Kinetic studies have uniformly
shown that the turnover rate of plasma triglyceride is accelerated on
increase of dietary carbohydrate supply in both normal and hyperglyceridemic subjects. Thus, Waterhouse *et al.* (1964) on measuring the
fluxes of injected labeled palmitic acid concluded that high carbohydrate feeding increases the rate of transfer of plasma FFA into plasma
triglyceride but decreases the return of TGFA into FFA pool, i.e., the
degradation. Nestel and Hirsch (1965) and Nestel (1966a) used the *in
vivo* labeling of plasma triglyceride with palmitic acid-H^3 and found a
rise in the triglyceride turnover rate to occur in every subject during
10 days on a high carbohydrate regimen. Nestel (1966a) even concluded that dietary carbohydrate is the major determinant of plasma
triglyceride turnover. Reaven *et al.* (1965) assessed the triglyceride
turnover rate by means of tritiated glycerol and demonstrated that in
most subjects increment of dietary carbohydrate stimulated the turn-

over. In experiments so far unpublished we have used a similar technique and found that although the plasma triglyceride turnover rate increases on a high carbohydrate regimen in the majority of cases the extent of this change is highly variable and not well correlated to the increment of plasma triglyceride concentration even if the initial value of the latter is within a fairly narrow range.

It is thus highly probable that the number of triglyceride molecules entering the plasma pool per unit time increases upon addition of carbohydrates to the diet. It might be thought, although without any experimental support, that in each individual the increments of plasma triglyceride production rate and of the amount of carbohydrate consumed are interrelated up to a certain maximum but that the magnitude of the response is individually variable within a wide range. The plasma triglyceride level attained is not solely determined by the rate of entry, however, but may be even more closely related to the efficiency of removal mechanisms. The importance of this factor has been emphasized by Ryan and Schwartz (1965), who showed in one hyperlipemic subject that while the plasma triglyceride turnover rate was increased by a high carbohydrate diet the triglyceride plasma clearance was markedly diminished at the same time. It should be realized that this does not mean a reduced removal rate, expressed in absolute terms, nor does it indicate that dietary carbohydrates inhibit or inactivate the enzyme or other systems responsible for the removal of triglycerides from the plasma. Conversely, a steady state at a higher turnover rate level implies that also the efflux rate must be greater than before, and thus, carbohydrate administration must stimulate the triglyceride uptake by tissues. This thinking agrees well with the known effects of glucose (and insulin) on triglyceride removal and degradation at adipose tissue, at least. The efficiency of removal depends not only on the activity of responsible enzyme(s) but also on the substrate (plasma triglyceride) concentration. If a given carbohydrate load activates the removal enzymes in one subject less than in another then a higher plasma triglyceride concentration will be needed in the former case to reach the same total removal rate as in the latter. In this situation, the absolute number of triglyceride molecules leaving the plasma pool per unit time will be equal in both subjects (and also equal to the entry rate), but the fractional disappearance rate (plasma clearance) is different. Thus, the extent to which the removal enzymes are activated by dietary carbohydrate will determine the steady state level of plasma triglyceride. In the period when plasma triglyceride is in rise the production rate will exceed the removal rate and this difference determines the speed by which the increase occurs.

It has been recently shown by Reaven *et al.* (1967) that the plasma triglyceride turnover rate is in linear correlation to the logarithm of triglyceride concentration, in other words, the higher the initial plasma triglyceride level the greater will be the increment of this level produced by a given constant increase of the entry rate. This is fully expected in view of the earlier knowledge that the disappearance rate of exogenous chylomicron triglycerides is inversely related to the dose (French and Morris, 1957) or to the endogenous pool size (Nestel *et al.*, 1962; Nestel, 1964b). It follows from this kinetic feature that hyperglyceridemic subjects are more sensitive to the increment of dietary carbohydrate than those with low basal plasma triglyceride levels, in whom a much larger increase of triglyceride synthesis rate is needed to produce hyperglyceridemia of an equal degree.

2. *Hepatic Triglyceride Synthesis*

After concluding that the initial cause for the induction of a rise of plasma triglyceride content by dietary carbohydrate is an accelerated influx it remains to be established what metabolic alterations form the ultimate stimulus of triglyceride synthesis. The inhibition of peripheral lipid mobilization caused by an acute glucose load continues also during a prolonged carbohydrate feeding since the fasting plasma FFA levels are lower during a high carbohydrate regimen than on a high fat diet (Stormont and Waterhouse, 1963). Since the relative hepatic uptake apparently is not increased by dietary carbohydrate (Heimberg *et al.*, 1962) the liver receives less precursors for triglyceride synthesis from the plasma.

On the other hand, the esterification of fatty acids in the liver is augmented by carbohydrate feeding. A somewhat higher proportion of *in vivo* injected palmitate-C^{14} is found in esterified lipids of the liver in fed animals than is found in fasted animals (Bragdon and Gordon, 1958; Laurell, 1959b; Havel *et al.*, 1962), but this difference is too small to account for any substantial increase of total production of hepatic and plasma triglyceride. In perfused liver of fed rat about 80% of oleate-C^{14} influx is esterified while only 50% goes into this pathway when the liver is taken from a fasted rat (Mayes and Felts, 1967b). Triglyceride synthesis, measured *in vitro* with a cofactor supplemented rat liver homogenate or microsomal fraction is depressed by fasting but markedly stimulated by a previous high carbohydrate diet compared to chow feeding (Fallon and Kemp, 1968). The mechanism of this stimulation is not clear since the activity of glycerol phosphate acyltransferase does not show corresponding alterations with diet, and under the *in vitro* assay conditions both the substrates and cofactors were present in excess (Fallon and Kemp, 1968). The hepatic concentration of glycerol phosphate is not increased by high glucose diet (Zakim *et al.*, 1967a; Fallon and Kemp, 1968) compared to chow but is decreased by fasting (Nikkilä and Ojala, 1963b; Tzur *et al.*, 1964; Bøhmer, 1967; Fallon and Kemp, 1968). The activity of liver glycerol phosphate dehydrogenase is slightly higher in glucose-fed rats than in chow-fed controls (Tepperman and Tepperman, 1968), but this cannot be the decisive factor. However, there is no doubt that the ample presentation of liver with glucose will result, among other things, in an increased formation of glycerol phosphate, which continuously traps the fatty acids into lipid esters. Glycerol phosphate is undoubtedly one of the factors stimulating the hepatic triglyceride synthesis and, particularly, the formation of plasma triglycerides as demonstrated by the development of hyperglyceridemia in rats fed glycerol (Nikkilä and Ojala, 1964). The concentration of glycerol phosphate does not necessarily reflect its rate of production since also utilization, i.e., turnover rate, is accelerated.

3. Hepatic Fatty Acid Synthesis

Administration of carbohydrates promotes the synthesis of fatty acids from various precursors. Most remarkable hyperlipogenesis is observed on refeeding starved rats with a high-carbohydrate low-fat or fat-free diet, which not only restores the hepatic fatty acid synthesizing capacity to the level of a normally fed rat but overshoots it many times (Tepperman and Tepperman, 1958; Spencer *et al.*, 1964; Allman *et al.*, 1965; Zakim *et al.*, 1967b). Also in previously fed rats a single large dose of glucose is able to increase the incorporation of acetate-C^{14} into fatty acids in liver slices but, as in fasted animals, the effect takes some 6 hours to become manifest (Lyon *et al.*, 1952). The lipogenesis is related to the glycogen content of the liver (Haugaard and Stadie, 1952). After a prolonged feeding of rats with a diet, which contains glucose, fructose, or sucrose as the sole or main carbohydrate the lipogenesis from acetate-C^{14} in liver preparations is increased 2- to 10-fold as compared to chow-fed controls (Christophe and Mayer, 1959; Allman *et al.*, 1965; Alexander *et al.*, 1966; Zakim *et al.*, 1967a; Bar-On and Stein, 1968). Also, under these conditions, the *in vivo* incorporation of acetate-C^{14} into liver lipids is increased (Scheig *et al.*, 1966). When starch is used instead of the sugars the acetate-C^{14} incorporation into both liver and plasma lipids *in vivo* is significantly smaller (Cohen and Teitelbaum, 1968).

It is thus apparent that the simple sugars, possibly with the exception of galactose (Landau *et al.*, 1958), are effective stimulators of hepatic fatty acid synthesis as compared to starch, but it is not established to what extent variations in the total carbohydrate content of the diet (given mainly as starch) are reflected in the activity of lipogenesis. Certainly there is a minimum carbohydrate supply below which lipogenesis will be depressed but when this limit is exceeded does the fatty acid synthesis increase in line with increase of dietary carbohydrate up to some maximal level? This question cannot be answered straightforward since on isocaloric exchange of dietary carbohydrate and fat both changes can influence the hepatic lipogenesis to the same extent. At least in rat, the incorporation of labeled acetate or glucose into liver fatty acids becomes markedly depressed on administration of fat (Masoro et al., 1950; Whitney and Roberts, 1955; Hill et al., 1958; Christophe and Mayer 1959; Bortz et al., 1963; Wieland et al., 1963b). This effect is extremely rapid (Hill et al., 1960) and can be observed with very moderate increases of dietary fat (Hill et al., 1958). The defect may be partly a result of dilution of the de novo synthesized labeled fatty acids by the exogenous ones, but a real inhibition at acetyl-CoA carboxylase step is also involved (Bortz et al., 1963). Since the food protein content does not seem to influence the hepatic lipogenesis (Hill et al., 1958; Cohen and Teitelbaum, 1968) the carbohydrate to fat ratio remains the main dietary determinant of lipogenesis.

All data on the regulation of hepatic fatty acid synthesis by diet are so far derived from animals. Experience from man is limited to measurements of plasma triglyceride, and it should be of utmost importance to complete these by direct assays of the lipogenic activity, in vivo or in vitro or both.

The mode of the stimulating action of dietary sugars on lipogenesis is not completely understood. It has been thought (Lyon et al., 1952, and many other authors) that insulin is largely responsible for the effect and the fact that dietary starch stimulates insulin secretion less than glucose (Swan et al., 1966) is compatible with this concept. However, stimulation of acetate-C^{14} incorporation into fatty acids by a high glucose medium may be observed also in liver slices (Masri et al., 1952) and on in vitro perfusion of livers taken from both fed and fasted rats (Haft, 1967). Furthermore, dietary fructose is at least equally active as glucose on lipogenesis despite its weak action on insulin secretion, and it remains effective also in the absence of insulin (Baker et al., 1952). Therefore, insulin may be one activator of lipogenesis (see above, p. 72), but presentation of the liver with increased hexose concentrations also stimulates the fatty acid synthesis directly.

On chronic glucose feeding as well as during refeeding of starved rats with fat-free high-sucrose diet the incorporation of both labeled acetyl CoA and malonyl CoA into liver fatty acids is increased (Alexander *et al.*, 1966; Allman *et al.*, 1965) indicating that all steps of fatty acid synthesis are stimulated by carbohydrate. The activity of acetyl-CoA carboxylase is increased by refeeding glucose or fructose compared to normal chow (Zakim *et al.*, 1967b). It should be of interest to know whether this increase can be prevented by enhancing the flow of FFA into the liver. Also, many other hepatic enzymes concerned with lipogenesis are induced or "hyperinduced" by dietary hexoses. Thus, glucose-6-phosphate dehydrogenase and 6-phosphogluconate dehydrogenase are elevated up to tenfold the normal "fed" level in refed rats (Tepperman and Tepperman, 1958) and in rats maintained for longer periods on high glucose or high fructose diet (Fitch and Chaikoff, 1960). However, the enzyme induction and onset of lipogenesis are not synchronized and, therefore, cannot be causally related (Tepperman and Tepperman, 1958; Allman *et al.*, 1965). Citrate cleavage enzymic activity of the liver is also increased much above the normal on refeeding starved rats with a diet high in carbohydrate and low in fat but not with a high-fat low-carbohydrate chow (Kornacker and Lowenstein, 1965a). Again, glucose and fructose induce higher activities than complex carbohydrates (Kornacker and Lowenstein, 1965a; Zakim *et al.*, 1967b). When chow-fed rats are placed on a high glucose or high fructose fat-free diet the activity of citrate cleavage enzyme increases 5- to 9-fold over a period of 4 days (Kornacker and Lowenstein, 1965b). As with HMP enzymes, time sequence studies have shown, however, that citrate cleavage enzymic activity and lipogenesis do not change in a parallel fashion under some dietary manipulations (Foster and Srere, 1968). Obviously, therefore, the increase of these enzymes does not form the *primary* event in the stimulation of fatty acid synthesis by dietary sugars, and it may be even secondary to the latter as suggested by Foster and Srere (1968). In spite of this it is possible that high activities of both HMP enzymes and citrate cleavage enzyme are necessary for the long-term maintenance of hyperlipogenesis during high hexose diets. Additional enzymes which behave in a similar manner during carbohydrate feeding are malic enzyme (Shrago *et al.*, 1963) and NADP-malate dehydrogenase (Zakim *et al.*, 1967b).

Since the dietary carbohydrates form the main precursor supply for lipogenesis it is self-evident that the total amount of fatty acids synthesized in a given time increases in parallel with the quantity of ingested sugar until limited by the maximal capacity of regulatory key enzyme(s). If these enzymes are not repressed (as in starvation) some increase of fatty acid formation can certainly occur without any adaptive changes of enzymic activity. For the hepatic lipogenesis from glucose one rate-limiting step is at the glucokinase, and the induction of this enzyme by dietary carbohydrate (Viñuela *et al.*, 1963) conditions the increase of fatty acid synthesis on high glucose diet. However, the incorporation of labeled glucose into hepatic fatty acids can also be increased by fructose feeding without any elevation of glucokinase activity (Zakim *et al.*, 1967b), which demonstrates that the main regulatory point is located between acetyl-CoA and fatty acid. Ultimately, the probable key factors in the stimulation of lipogenesis by carbohydrate obviously are the inhibition of FFA mobilization from periphery and the increased formation of glycerolphosphate. Both decrease the FFA content of the cytoplasma and thus release the acetyl-CoA carboxylase inhibition and liberate binding sites at acyl carrier protein.

4. *Triglyceride Secretion from the Liver*

Kay and Entenman (1961) originally reported that in perfused rat liver there is a net increase of glycerides in the perfusate when the donor animal is fed but not when it is fasted. The finding was confirmed in a similar experiment by Heimberg *et al.* (1962), and recently Mayes and Felts (1967b) have shown that the conversion of labeled oleate into perfusate VLD lipoproteins (triglycerides) is much higher in perfused liver of fed rat than in that taken from a fasted animal. From careful measurements of blood flow and triglyceride gradient across the liver, Carlson and Ekelund (1963) concluded that in fasting *man* the net release of triglycerides from the liver is very low or even zero. By using tritium as label, Windmueller and Spaeth (1967) have demonstrated that in perfused rat liver there is a significant correlation between the rates of fatty acid synthesis and release and that both are parallelly increased in carbohydrate-refed rats compared to chow-fed controls.

Although the rate of hepatic release of triglycerides has not been determined after prolonged feeding of different carbohydrates it seems evident from the studies cited above that the output increases in close relationship to the activity of lipogenesis.

5. *Hepatic Triglyceride Uptake*

The effect of the nutritional state on the overall removal rate of plasma triglycerides as well as on the particular role of adipose tissue in this process has already been discussed above. The hepatic uptake of triglycerides seems to be much less sensitive to dietary changes than is the removal at adipose tissue. Of intravenously injected labeled chylomicrons or endogenous plasma triglycerides a somewhat higher proportion is deposited in the liver of fasted than of fed animals (Bragdon and Gordon, 1958; Havel *et al.*, 1962), but this may well be only a reflection of the impaired uptake by the adipose tissue in fasting state. However, several studies with isolated perfused liver have also shown that the hepatic uptake of triglycerides is accelerated on fasting. Thus, the removal of both fat emulsion (Heimberg *et al.*, 1958, 1962) and of labeled isolated chylomicrons (Heimberg *et al.*, 1962; Morris, 1963a) from the perfusate has been shown to occur more slowly in livers from normal fed rats than from starved animals. Also, since the oxidation and conversion to ketone bodies of chylomicron fatty acids are much greater in fasted than in fed liver (French and Morris, 1958; Morris, 1963a; Ontko and Zilversmit, 1967), the total irreversible removal of esterified fatty acids from the liver-plasma compartment is much less efficient in carbohydrate-fed animal compared to fasted or fat-fed one. It should be of interest to know whether a high hexose diet further impairs the hepatic uptake and utilization of circulating triglycerides from that seen in a chow-fed animal, but data on this are apparently not available.

What may be relevant in this context is the finding of Morris (1963b) that in perfused rat liver the fraction (percentage) of chylomicron triglyceride removed and oxidized decreases on increase of chylomicron concentration of the perfusate. The kinetic behavior of hepatic triglyceride uptake is thus similar to that of the overall removal of fat from the circulation but not to the removal at adipose tissue, which on perfusion takes up chylomicron triglycerides with a constant fractional rate at least within a physiological range of concentration (Rodbell and Scow, 1965). If the liver is held to be responsible for a significant proportion of total triglyceride efflux from the circulation also in fed state, these kinetic circumstances could afford a partial explanation for the expansion of plasma triglyceride pool on high carbohydrate consumption.

6. Differential Effects of Glucose and Fructose

In the earliest studies, where the hyperglyceridemic effect of dietary carbohydrate was discovered, the interchange occurred mainly between fat and starch or glucose and no attention was paid to the possible influence of the quality of carbohydrate fed. However, already at that time Portman and associates (1956) had noticed that in rats maintained on cholesterol–cholic acid-containing diets an isocaloric substitution of glucose, fructose, or sucrose for starch produced an elevation of serum cholesterol and of the triglyceride-carrier S_f20-

400 lipoprotein levels, the response of the latter being particularly prominent with sucrose and fructose. It had also been shown that diets high in fructose or sucrose led to an accumulation of fat into liver (Harper *et al.*, 1953; Marshall and Wormack, 1954). Much earlier, Higgins (1916) had already presented evidence that fructose is converted into lipids to a greater extent than glucose.

The first suggestion on the special hyperglyceridemic effect of dietary sucrose in man emerged from the study of Anderson *et al.* (1963), who, on adding different simple sugars to a low fat basal diet, observed highest serum triglyceride levels with sucrose diet; but no actual isocaloric comparison between starch and other carbohydrates was made. Macdonald and Braithwaite (1964) subsequently found that inclusion of huge amounts of sucrose (500 gm) into the diet of male subjects led to an increase of serum glycerides, while a similar amount of maize starch did not alter their level. The response could not be elicited with glucose or maltose (Macdonald, 1965a). Kuo (1965) compared the effects of dietary starch and sucrose in hyperglyceridemic patients and found markedly higher levels of serum triglycerides during sucrose feeding in all. In normal subjects an induction of hyperglyceridemia succeeded only with a 500-gm but not with a 300-gm daily consumption of sucrose. Kauffman *et al.* (1965, 1966a,b) showed that there are large individual variations in the response of serum triglyceride level to dietary sugars, but when significant differences are found fructose almost always produces higher levels than glucose, sucrose, or starch. On the other hand, there are well-controlled human dietary studies where no difference between the hyperglyceridemic effect of starch and sucrose (Lees, 1965) or starch and glucose (Porte *et al.*, 1966) has been detected. Whether these divergent results are based on individual variations in response, on using different kinds of starch, or on administration of different amounts of total carbohydrate calories is not clear for the present. The mechanism of the postulated sex difference in the response of serum triglycerides to sucrose or fructose (Macdonald, 1965b, 1966) has also remained a mystery.

The hyperglyceridemic effect of fructose as compared to glucose was first described in rats by Nikkilä and Ojala (1965), and this finding has been recently confirmed by others (Zakim *et al.*, 1967b; Bar-On and Stein, 1968). The markedly increased plasma triglyceride levels develop within 18 hours from the start of fructose administration, and they are less when fructose is given without rather than with the basal chow (Nikkilä and Ojala, 1966). Fructose feeding also enhances exogenous hyperglyceridemia in both rats (Nikkilä and Ojala, 1966) and man (Nikkilä and Pelkonen, 1966). Glucose, given in a like manner, increases basal plasma triglyceride levels of rat only slightly (Nikkilä and Ojala, 1965, 1966; Zakim *et al.*, 1967b; Bar-On and Stein, 1968). In these experiments the liver triglyceride concentration was not much increased by the administration of either hexoses, and there was no difference between the effects of fructose and glucose thus showing that it is the flux of plasma triglyceride which is particularly influenced by fructose. It is significant that fructose does not induce hyperglyceridemia in guinea pig (Bar-On and Stein, 1968) which, contrary to rat and man, effectively converts it to glucose at the intestinal wall (Kiyasu and Chaikoff, 1957; Ginsburg and Hers, 1960).

That fructose and glucose have different effects on triglyceride metabolism is not unexpected in view of their widely dissimilar metabolic pathways and consequences. The specific features of fructose handling in the body are too numerous to be dealt with here in any detail (for reviews see Deuel, 1936; Miller *et al.* 1957; Herman and Zakim, 1968), but some most relevant points may be mentioned. Contrary to glucose, fructose coming from the gut is mainly taken up and metabolized by the liver (Bollman and Mann, 1931; Holdsworth and Dawson, 1965). Also, *in vitro* the hepatic uptake of fructose is higher than that of glucose (Renold *et al.*, 1954). Plasma insulin response to oral fructose is much less than to an equal dose of glucose (Samols and Dormandy, 1963; Swan *et al.*, 1966), the difference being partly a result of the lower fructose than glucose blood levels but mainly a result of the weaker stimulating action of fructose on the islet cell (Corvilain and Tagnon, 1961; Grodsky *et al.*, 1963; Coore and Randle, 1964; Boda, 1964). Fructose is metabolized also in adipose tissue (Froesch and Ginsburg, 1962), but since its concentration *in vivo* at the fat cell is smaller than that of glucose the inhibition of FFA and glycerol mobilizations by fructose is less efficient than by glucose. This difference is also partly a result of the different insulin responses. In the liver a considerable part of the fructose molecule enters the glycerol phosphate pool (Muntz and Vanko, 1962), increasing its size (Wieland and Matschinsky, 1962) and although the hepatic glycerol phosphate concentration does not rise during a *chronic* fructose feeding (Zakim *et al.*, 1967a) its rate of production is certainly increased. As indicated several times before, this factor may stimulate both the synthesis and the esterification of fatty acids. An increase of palmitate esterification in liver slices occurs on addition of fructose to the medium (Exton and Edson, 1964).

There is ample evidence that the fructose molecule itself provides more precursor material for the hepatic triglyceride synthesis than glucose. Thus, when liver slices of normally fed rats are incubated in the presence of labeled fructose or glucose at equal substrate concentrations, the incorporation of radioactivity from fructose into tissue lipids is four-to sixfold greater than from glucose (Majchrowitz and Quastel, 1963; Chernick and Scow, 1964; Nikkilä, 1966; Zakim et al., 1967b). A similar though smaller difference is found with human hepatic tissue, where most of the radioactivity is found in phospholipids, however (Kuo et al., 1967). Also, from orally or intravenously administered fructose-C^{14} a much higher proportion is recovered in liver lipids than of glucose-C^{14} given in a like way (Schreier, 1959; Nikkilä, 1966; Bar-On and Stein, 1968). Labeling of plasma triglycerides from exogenous fructose-C^{14} (Nikkilä, 1966; Bar-On and Stein, 1968) or sucrose-C^{14} (Macdonald and Roberts, 1967) is about five times that from glucose-C^{14}, whereas the adipose tissue triglycerides contain more label from glucose than from fructose. Most of the hepatic and plasma triglyceride radioactivity from both hexoses is primarily found in the glycerol moiety, but later it is transferred to fatty acid. The incorporation of C^{14} into the fatty acids of incubated rat liver slices occurs slightly (Chernick and Chaikoff, 1951) or markedly (Zakim et al., 1967b) more from fructose than from glucose. Although it may be argued that the results of the tracer studies are much influenced by the widely different endogenous pool sizes of fructose and glucose, the fact still remains that a higher amount of *exogenous* fructose than of glucose is directly converted into hepatic and plasma esterified lipids. However, since this pathway forms only a very minor fraction (1–3%) of the overall metabolism of both hexoses, it cannot be postulated that the observed differences account for the greater hyperglyceridemic effect of fructose. Other factors must therefore be sought.

On feeding animals with diets high in fructose (or sucrose) a number of enzymatic and metabolic alterations are induced which are more or less different from those observed with corresponding high glucose regimen. One of these is a decreased glucose tolerance, i.e., a decreased ability of glucose utilization. This was first described by Hill et al. in rats (1954) and dogs (Hill and Chaikoff, 1956) and has since been confirmed in animals (Christophe and Mayer, 1959; Cohen and Teitelbaum, 1964) but not in man (Craig et al., 1955; Van Itallie and Shull, 1957). Also, the lipogenesis from glucose-C^{14} in rat liver slices is impaired during fructose feeding (Hill et al., 1954). These changes may result from a low hepatic glucokinase activity produced by the deficient dietary glucose induction, but the fact that they can be seen to develop also with sucrose regimen speaks against this possibility. Of the liver enzymes, which are induced by dietary fructose more than by glucose, may be enumerated glycerophosphate dehydrogenase and malate dehydrogenase (Fitch and Chaikoff, 1960), citrate cleavage enzyme (Kornacker and Lowenstein, 1965b; not verified by Zakim *et al.*, 1967b), pyruvate kinase, and malic enzyme (Bailey *et al.*, 1968). However, none of these differences seems to be of a magnitude great enough to offer an explanation for the dissimilar effects of the two hexoses on fat metabolism.

The hepatic lipogenesis, as estimated from the *in vitro* or *in vivo* incorporation of labeled acetate into fatty acids, is equal in rats fed high glucose and high fructose diets but increased in both as compared to starch (Hill *et al.*, 1954; Zakim *et al.*, 1967a; Cohen and Teitelbaum, 1968; Bar-On and Stein, 1968). Only Christophe and Mayer (1959) have reported a significantly higher *in vivo* incorporation of acetate-C^{14} into hepatic lipids of fructose-fed rats compared to glucose-fed rats but they do not take this as evidence of increased lipogenesis because the dilution of the tracer at the acetyl group pools may be influenced by the diet. In fact, Zakim *et al.* (1967b) have recently shown that the liver acetyl CoA content is greater in fructose-fed rats than in those receiving glucose. This finding gives additional support to the view that more fatty acids are synthesized in the liver from dietary fructose than from glucose. Thus, the hepatic lipogenesis is enhanced on high fructose diet more than on high glucose regimen although this difference is not revealed in acetate incorporation studies.

The hepatic triglyceride synthesis seems also to be similar in fructose-and glucose-fed animals when assessed by tracer methods. Of intravenously injected labeled palmitic or oleic acid the same amount is recovered in liver triglycerides in rats maintained on high fructose as in those given high glucose diet (Nikkilä and Ojala, 1965; Bar-On and Stein, 1968). In these experiments the plasma triglyceride contained more label in the fructose group than in the glucose group, but since the plasma triglyceride pool is higher in the fructose-fed animals this difference reflects an unequal fractional removal rather than stimulation of synthesis of plasma triglyceride by fructose. Also *in vitro* with liver slices of homogenate the incorporation of oleate-H^3, glycerol-C^{14}, and glycerol-C^{14} phosphate into triglyceride is similar in rats fed high fructose and high glucose diet (Bar-On and Stein, 1968; Fallon and Kemp, 1968). In a more detailed kinetic analysis of triglyceride fatty acid fluxes in rat (Nikkilä *et al.*, 1966) it was found that supplementation of basal diet with glucose or fructose increased the rate of hepatic triglyceride secretion and decreased the recycling of plasma triglyceride, but these changes were of similar magnitude in both dietary groups. It must be recognized, however, that because of a fairly large individual variability of triglyceride fluxes small but kinetically significant changes remain virtually undetected by this method.

The half-life of plasma triglyceride increases in a linear correlation to triglyceride concentration, and the regression is similar for glucose- and fructose-fed rats (Nikkilä and Ojala, 1966). The lipoprotein lipase of adipose tissue is not induced by fructose administration as it is with glucose (Bar-On and Stein, 1968), the difference probably resulting from the weaker insulin response elicited by fructose. This finding is important since it may indicate the presence of a *relative* insufficiency of one triglyceride removal mechanism in fructose-loaded animals.

In conclusion it may be stated that the exact cause of the different effects of dietary fructose and glucose on plasma triglyceride level is not known, but the essential factors which might be responsible for the difference are the greater formation of hepatic fatty acids and glycerol phosphate from exogenous fructose than from glucose, the weaker inhibition of fatty acid release from adipose tissue by fructose as compared to glucose, and the less efficient induction of adipose tissue lipoprotein lipase by fructose. Both hexoses increase the influx of plasma triglyceride, fructose probably slightly more than glucose, but the activation of removal system remains deficient with fructose. The crucial point is thus in the disproportionate change of efflux and influx rates on fructose feeding.

7. Conclusions

Diet rich in carbohydrates produces elevation of plasma triglyceride level in man and some animals through (1) increase of the hepatic fatty acid synthesis by supply of more building material (acetyl-CoA) and by stimulation (induction and activation) of enzymes concerned with lipogenesis, (2) increase of glycerol phosphate production, (3) increase of hepatic triglyceride secretion, (4) decrease of hepatic removal and utilization of plasma triglycerides, and probably (5) decreased over-all oxidation of fatty acids. Insulin may be partially responsible for these changes but it is not the key factor. Glucose is more active than starch probably just because a higher plasma insulin levels attained. Fructose (and sucrose) again is a more potent hyperglyceridemic agent than glucose apparently because of its greater hepatic utilization and weaker capacity to activate triglyceride removal from plasma. The differences between the hyperglyceridemic potency of individual carbohydrates in man have not been verified in all studies. Accumulation of triglycerides into the liver is slight, probably because the secretion into plasma (formation of lipoproteins) is held effective by high carbohydrate supply. The effects of dietary carbohydrate on the essential points of triglyceride metabolism are presented schematically in Fig. 4.

VI. The Metabolic Error of Endogenous ("Carbohydrate-Induced") Hyperglyceridemia

Although the scope of the present review does not include any detailed discussion of the investigations made to discover the metabolic error(s) underlying the endogenous hyperlipemia, this disorder is so closely connected to the problems presented above that some comments seem to be warranted. Two excellent review articles on the classification and nature of different hyperlipemias have been recently published by Fredrickson and Lees (1966; Fredrickson *et al.*, 1967). Some kinetic aspects on the production of increased plasma triglyceride levels have been briefly touched upon already (see Section II).

On discussing the pathogenesis of endogenous hyperglyceridemia one important question is to what extent the use of the term "carbohydrate induced" is justified in these cases. Expressed in another way, do the patients with this disorder increase their plasma triglyceride level *relatively more than* the so called normal subjects when put on a high carbohydrate diet, and, furthermore, are their plasma triglycerides normalized when dietary carbohydrate is sharply cut down? It is now well known that some increase of plasma triglyceride level oc-

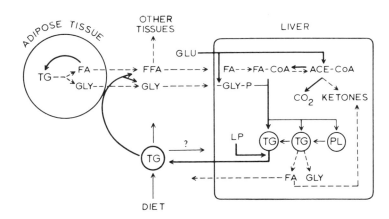

FIG. 4. Alterations in plasma and liver triglyceride kinetics produced by a high carbohydrate diet (chronic insulin and glucose excess. Heavy arrows indicate augmented reaction rates, and dotted arrows stand for inhibited pathways.

118 ESKO A. NIKKILÄ

curs in most (Antonis and Bersohn, 1961; Beveridge et al., 1964; Lees and Fredrickson, 1965; Nestel, 1966a) though not in all (Macdonald, 1965b; Kuo, 1965) normal subjects. It has been recently shown by Bierman and Porte (1968) that the mean *absolute* but not relative increment of plasma triglyceride on substitution of high carbohydrate diet for a "control" diet is significantly related to the initial triglyceride level. This is the result expected if all subjects (normal and abnormal) increase their plasma triglyceride input by a constant *amount* when given a constant supplement of dietary carbohydrate. This observation thus speaks in favor of the view that there is no basic abnormality in the magnitude of plasma triglyceride response to dietary carbohydrate but for confirmation of this concept it is necessary to compare individuals with identical starting plasma triglyceride levels. There are also studies where the correlation between the absolute increment and initial (control or high fat diet) level of plasma triglyceride is poor (Farquhar et al., 1966; Nestel, 1966b).

That the primary error in many cases of endogenous hyperlipemia is something other than an abnormal response to dietary carbohydrate is also shown by the fact that only a minority reaches a normal range even after subtotal calorie restriction. This is shown by our own experience illustrated in Fig. 5 and by the data of Reissell et al. (1966). In agreement with this is the statement of Bierman and Porte (1968) that individuals with endogenous lipemia are characterized by elevated triglyceride levels regardless of diet. Also, in the material of Farquhar et al. (1966) almost all of the patients who developed a significant hyperglyceridemia on high carbohydrate diet had abnormal glyceride levels also during low-carbohydrate high-fat period. It is thus apparent that at least one (or more) subgroup of the family of endogenous hyperlipemias maintains its abnormal triglyceride metabolism independently of dietary carbohydrates but responds to increase of carbohydrate supply by increment of plasma triglyceride level. On the other hand, in many cases of hyperglyceridemia, particularly in those of moderate degree, the only abnormality may be found in the patients' dietary habits and no actual metabolic error is present.

Another problem of central importance in the pathogenesis of endogenous hyperglyceridemia is common to all metabolic abnormalities: Is the primary event an overproduction (increased influx rate) or an under-utilization (decreased efflux rate) of plasma triglyceride? There seems to be so far no agreement on the choice between these alternatives and on the interpretation of tracer kinetic data. Difficulties have arisen mainly from the widely different plasma triglyceride pool sizes of patients and control subjects studied and from the fact that small, undetectable changes in rates may lead to large alterations of masses. It should be advantageous to make kinetic comparisons at a time when the plasma triglyceride levels of hyperglyceridemic patients have been reduced by dietary means to a range which approximates normal as closely as possible.

The concept of an increased hepatic release of triglycerides into plasma (turnover rate) as a primary cause of endogenous hyperglyceridemia has been developed and documented by Farquhar's group (Reaven *et al.*, 1965, 1967) from the measurements of plasma triglyceride turnover by endogenous labeling with glycerol-H^3. Nestel (1966a) has arrived at a similar conclusion using palmitate-H^3 *in vivo*. However, calculating the triglyceride influx rate from conversion of infused palmitate-H^3 into plasma triglyceride, both Ryan and Schwartz (1965) and Sailer *et al.* (1966b) have not been able to demonstrate any relation between plasma triglyceride entry rate and concentration and, accordingly, both groups maintain the view that the primary fault is in the disposal of circulating triglycerides. The reasons for this discrepancy of opinions are not readily apparent, but reference may be made to the remarks presented (Section II) on the validity of palmitate-H^3 infusion method in estimation of triglyceride influx rate.

Fine *et al.* (1962) have studied the incorporation of glucose-C^{14} into plasma triglycerides and found no difference between normal and hyperglyceridemic subjects. If anything, this result favors the interpretation that formation of plasma triglycerides is not increased in hyperlipemia. A different result has been arrived at recently by Brech and Gordon (1967) and Sandhofer *et al.* (1968), who reported an increased incorporation of infused glucose-C^{14} into plasma triglycerides in hyperlipemic subjects. The incorporation rate was in correlation with the plasma triglyceride influx, and the latter authors conclude that the conversion of blood glucose to plasma triglyceride reflects only the rate at which plasma FFA is esterified and secreted into plasma. However, the observed difference may also be accounted for by the decreased fractional removal since the plasma triglyceride pool sizes were far from identical in patients and controls. At any rate, it is obvious that little information can be expected from this type of experiment. When the plasma triglyceride turnover has been measured with glycerol-H^3 technique after reduction of plasma triglyceride level by prolonged periods of fasting it has been revealed that hyperglyceridemic patients have higher turnover rates than normal glyceridemic subjects under the same condition (Nikkilä, 1968, Fig. 5). It

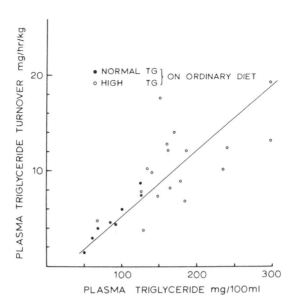

FIG. 5. Plasma triglyceride turnover rate and concentration in hyperglyceridemic and normal glyceridemic patients after subtotal fasting for 4-10 days (Nikkilä and Kekki, unpublished data).

thus seems appropriate to postulate that the production of plasma triglycerides is increased in endogenous hyperglyceridemia also without any stimulus from exogenous carbohydrate.

Attempts made for a closer characterization of the biochemical lesion(s) of endogenous hyperglyceridemia have so far been fairly fragmentary, and no definite picture has emerged from these. Since the plasma FFA forms one major precursor of plasma triglyceride and the triglyceride influx is closely related to plasma FFA turnover, an increased mobilization of FFA could well be one etiological possibility as it is in the hyperlipemia of diabetic ketosis. Hyperglyceridemic patients have slightly or moderately elevated plasma FFA levels, but this may be secondary to the increased degradation of plasma triglyceride (because of expanded pool size). Many obese people without hyperglyceridemia have much higher elevations of plasma FFA. The fall of plasma FFA on acute glucose loading occurs, on an average, more slowly in hyperglyceridemic than in normal subjects, but the final level attained is similar in both groups (Kane et al., 1965). On high carbohydrate diet the mean daily FFA concentrations are similar in normal subjects and patients with endogenous hyperglyceridemia (Fredrickson and Lees, 1966). Some abnormality of FFA mobilization in hyperglyceridemia is possibly indicated by the finding of Nestel (1964b) that there is a correlation between plasma triglyceride level and the change in plasma FFA following administration of norepinephrine and nicotinic acid. When studied *in vitro*, the adipose tissue of hyperglyceridemic patients shows a much higher release of both FFA and glycerol into medium than the tissue of controls (Kuo *et al.*, 1967). This difference is abolished after treatment, however, and its significance in the pathogenesis of the hyperlipemic state thus remains obscure. It seems that all evidence for a primary role of increased lipid mobilization and plasma FFA turnover in the production of hyperglyceridemia is so far inconclusive.

An approach to quantitation of lipogenesis in human liver has been made by Kuo *et al.* (1967), who showed that incorporation *in vitro* of acetate-C^{14}, glucose-C^{14}, and fructose-C^{14} into liver lipids was significantly higher in untreated hyperlipemic patients than in controls. However, most of the tissue radioactivity was present in phospholipid-glycerol and therefore drawing of any conclusions on the activity of lipogenesis or triglyceride synthesis is unwarranted. Since other measurements of hepatic fatty acid synthesis have not been carried out, it is impossible to predict the eventual role of this factor in the production of hyperglyceridemia.

Search for possible defects in the removal process of plasma triglycerides has mainly been limited to assays of lipoprotein lipase in post-heparin plasma or adipose tissue. For plasma, the activities have been found to be either in normal (Ahrens *et al.*, 1961; Fredrickson *et al.*, 1963) or in low normal (Reissell *et al.*, 1966) range in cases with endogenous hyperglyceridemia, but elevated levels have been also reported (Sailer *et al.*, 1965; Sandhofer *et al.*, 1965). Recently, Steiner (1968) has claimed that the postheparin plasma lipase is heterogeneous at least for substrate affinity and that the activity against long-chain triglycerides (as the endogenous triglycerides are) may be low in some types of hyperglyceridemia, while the lipolysis of medium chain triglycerides (as of Ediol, which is much used in the assay) proceeds in a normal way. If confirmed, this report necessitates reevaluation of many previous data. One further abnormality of lipoprotein lipase, which should be considered, is a deficient induction by carbohydrate-rich diet. To be sure, Fredrickson *et al.* (1963) could not record differences in the postheparin plasma lipolytic activity between hyperglyceridemic and normal subjects whether fed a high fat or high carbohydrate diet, but the plasma assay is presumably not fully adequate to exclude partial deficiencies at tissue level. It is therefore significant that Persson *et al.* (1966) have found an inverse correlation between plasma triglyceride level and adipose tissue lipoprotein lipase activity measured from biopsies *in vitro*. More studies of this type are urgently needed.

One metabolic abnormality which is associated with endogenous hyperglyceridemia and cannot be ignored in the discussion of its pathogenesis is chemical or mild clinical diabetes. An impaired glucose tolerance is found in a high percentage of these patients (Reaven *et al.*, 1963; Kane *et al.*, 1965; Albrink and Davidson, 1966; and others), and the blood glucose response to both tolbutamide (Knittle and Ahrens, 1964; Kane *et al.*, 1965; Braunsteiner *et al.*, 1965) and insulin (Davidson and Albrink, 1965; Kane *et al.*, 1965) is diminished. It is thus evident that one or several of the tissues which are mainly responsible for glucose disposal have a decreased ability to take up glucose from blood. The fact that plasma FFA response to glucose is abnormally slow (Kane *et al.*, 1965) indicates that at least glucose utilization of adipose tissue is impaired. Plasma immunoreactive insulin levels after oral glucose are often elevated in hyperglyceridemia (Reaven *et al.*, 1967; Nikkilä *et al.*, 1968; Sailer *et al.*, 1968) even more than predicted from the blood glucose. However, since many of these patients are more or less obese, it is difficult to define the separate contributions of obesity and hyperlipemia for glucose intolerance and hyperinsulinemia. Since both hyperglycemia and hyperinsulinemia are factors which, with all probability, influence the hepatic production of fatty acids and triglycerides, it is of actual interest to establish whether the glucose intolerance and exaggerated insulin response are primary causes or secondary outcomes of elevated plasma triglyceride levels.

A number of facts may be mentioned which speak against the possibility that abnormal glucose and insulin metabolisms are the underlying factor of hyperglyceridemia. First, the majority of obese individuals show an impaired glucose tolerance and hyperinsulinism, but they have normal or mildly elevated plasma triglyceride levels. Second, many subjects with glucose intolerance have normal triglycerides on usual diet (Jakobson *et al.*, 1965; Bierman and Porte, 1968), and the response to high carbohydrate diet is not different from normal (Bierman and Porte, 1968). Third, the magnitude of plasma insulin response to oral glucose is not correlated to plasma triglyceride level (Nikkilä *et al.*, 1965, 1968). Fourth, glucose intolerance and increased plasma insulin are not found in all patients with hyperlipemia. Fifth, elevation of plasma triglyceride by fat infusion decreases glucose tolerance and augments plasma insulin response (Felber and Vannotti, 1964).

None of the above arguments necessarily excludes the possibility that, in some cases, hyperinsulinemia might be involved in the pathogenesis of hyperlipemia. This is particularly noteworthy since Farquhar *et al.* (1966) have been able to demonstrate a good correlation between the level of plasma insulin and the magnitude of triglyceride response to high carbohydrate diet. The fasting plasma triglyceride level was also significantly correlated to the plasma insulin rise observed during oral glucose tolerance test (Reaven *et al.*, 1967). The insulin response to a high carbohydrate diet was not correlated to blood glucose levels or to obesity. On the basis of these results the authors suggest that in most subjects the hyperglyceridemia is secondary to an enhanced postprandial plasma insulin concentration. More recently, Sailer *et al.* (1968) have also found a significant correlation between the postglucose plasma insulin and triglyceride levels in patients with hyperlipemia. Our group has carried out measurements of insulin secretion rates at different blood glucose levels (Nikkilä and Taskinen, 1968) (see Fig. 6). By this method we have found normal, elevated, and decreased insulin secretion rates in patients with hyperglyceridemia. Thus far we believe that the problem of the causal relationship of hyperinsulinemia and hyperglyceridemia is largely unsolved, but the idea on a new disorder which might be called "idiopathic hyperinsulinism" is worthy of thorough investigation.

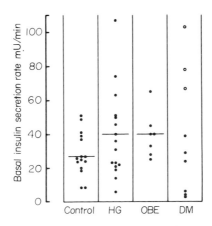

FIG. 6. Insulin secretion rate (out of the splanchnic region) in hyperglyceridemia (HG), obesity (OBE), and diabetes (DM). Determinations made after 12 hours' fasting (Nikkilä and Taskinen, unpublished).

124 ESKO A. NIKKILÄ

ACKNOWLEDGMENTS

During the preparation of this review the writer received grants from Finnish Culture Foundation, Sigrid Jusélius Foundation, and Emil Aaltonen Foundation. The excellent secretarial aid of Miss Pirkko Laine is deeply appreciated.

References

Abraham, S., Matthes, K. J., and Chaikoff, I. L. (1960). *J. Biol. Chem.* **235**, 2551.

Abraham, S., Migliorini, R. H., Bortz, W., and Chaikoff, I. L. (1962). *Biochim. Biophys. Acta* **62**, 27.

Adlersberg, D., and Eisler, L. (1959). *J. Am. Med. Assoc.* **170**, 1261.

Adlersberg, D., and Wang, C. -I. (1955). *Diabetes* **4**, 210.

Ahrens, E. H., Jr., Insull, W., Jr., Blomstrand, R., Hirsch, J., Tsaltos, T. T., and Peterson, M. L. (1957). *Lancet* **i**, 943.

Ahrens, E. H., Jr., Hirsch, J., Oette, A., Farquhar, J. W., and Stein, Y. (1961). *Trans. Assoc. Am. Physicians* **74**, 134.

Albrink, M. J., and Davidson, P. C. (1966). *J. Lab. Clin. Med.* **67**, 573.

Albrink, M. J., and Man, E. B. (1957). *Am. J. Digest. Diseases* **2**, 649.

Albrink, M. J., and Man, E. B. (1958). *Diabetes* **7**, 194.

Albrink, M. J., and Man, E. B. (1959). *A.M.A. Arch. Internal Med.* **103**, 4.

Albrink, M. J., Meigs, W., and Man, E. B. (1961). *Am. J. Med.* **31**, 4.

Albrink, M. J., Lavietes, P. H., and Man, E. B. (1963). *Ann. Internal Med.* **58**, 305.

Alexander, N. M., Scheig, R., and Klatskin, G. (1966). *J. Lipid Res.* **7**, 197.

Allen, F. M. (1918). *Am. J. Med. Sci.* **153**, 313.

Allman, D. W., Hubbard, D. D., and Gibson, D. M. (1965). *J. Lipid Res.* **6**, 63.

Altman, K. I., Miller, L. L., and Bly, C. G. (1951). *Arch. Biochem. Biophys.* **31**, 329.

Anderson, J. T., Grande, F., Matsumoto, Y., and Keys, A. (1963). *J. Nutr.* **79**, 349.

Antonis, A., and Bersohn, I. (1960). *Lancet* **i**, 998.

Antonis, A., and Bersohn, I. (1961). *Lancet* **i**, 3.

Armin, J., Grant, R. T., and Wright, P. H. (1960). *J. Physiol. (London)* **153**, 131, 146.

Armstrong, D. T., Steele, R., Altszuler, N., Dunn, A., Bishop, J. S., and de Bodo, R. C. (1961). *Am. J. Physiol.* **201**, 535.

Bagdade, J. D., Porte, D., Jr., and Bierman, E. L. (1967). *New Engl. J. Med.* **276**, 427.

Bagdade, J. D., Porte, D., Jr., and Bierman, E. L. (1968). *Diabetes* **17**, 127.

Bailey, E., Taylor, C. B., and Bartley, W. (1968). *Nature* **217**, 471.

Baker, N., and Schotz, M. C. (1964). *J. Lipid Res.* **5**, 188.

Baker, N., and Schotz, M. C. (1967). *J. Lipid Res.* **8**, 646.

Baker, N., Chaikoff, I. L., and Schusdek, A. (1952). *J. Biol. Chem.* **194**, 435.

Baker, N., Garfinkel, A. S., and Schotz, M. C. (1968). *J. Lipid Res.* **9**, 1.

Balodimos, M. C., Ball, J. J., and Williams, R. H. (1962). *Metab. Clin. Exptl.* **11**, 365.

Bang, I. (1919). *Biochem. Z.* **94**, 359.

Bar-On, H., and Stein, Y. (1968). *J. Nutr.* **94**, 95.

Bates, M. W., Mayer, J., and Nauss, S. F. (1955). *Am. J. Physiol.* **180**, 304.

Belfrage, P., Edgren, B., and Olivecrona, T. (1964). *Acta Physiol. Scand.* **62**, 344.

Berkowitz, D. (1962). *Diabetes* **11**, 56.

Beveridge, J. M. R., Jagannathan, S. N., and Connell, W. F. (1964). *Can. J. Biochem.* **42**, 999.

Bewsher, P. D., Tarrant, M. E., and Ashmore, J. (1966). *Diabetes* **15**, 346.

Bezman, A., Felts, J. M., and Havel, R. J. (1962). *J. Lipid Res.* **3**, 427.

Bierman, E. L., and Hamlin, J. T., III (1961). *Diabetes* **10**, 432.

Bierman, E. L., and Hamlin, J. T., III (1963). *Metab. Clin. Exptl.* **12**, 666.

Bierman, E. L., and Porte, D., Jr. (1968). *Ann. Internal Med.* **68**, 926.
Bierman, E. L., Dole, V. F., and Roberts, T. N. (1957a). *Diabetes* **6**, 475.
Bierman, E. L., Schwartz, I. C., and Dole, V. P. (1957b). *Am. J. Physiol.* **191**, 359.
Bierman, E. L., Amaral, J. A. P., and Belknap, B. H. (1966). *Diabetes* **15**, 675.
Björntorp, P. (1967). *Acta Med. Scand.* **181**, 389.
Bleisch, V. R., Mayer, J., and Dickie, M. M. (1952). *Am. J. Pathol.* **28**, 369.
Blix, G. (1926). *Acta Med. Scand.* **64**, 142.
Bloch, K., and Kramer, W. (1948). *J. Biol. Chem.* **173**, 811.
Bloor, W. R. (1921). *J. Biol. Chem.* **49**, 201.
Blumenthal, M. D., Abraham, S., and Chaikoff, I. L. (1964). *Arch. Biochem. Biophys.* **104**, 215.
Boda, J. M. (1964). *Am. J. Physiol.* **206**, 419.
Boden, G., and Willms, B. (1966). *Klin. Wochschr.* **44**, 579.
Bøhmer, T. (1967). *Biochim. Biophys. Acta* **144**, 259.
Bøhmer, T., Norum, K. R., and Bremer, J. (1966). *Biochim. Biophys. Acta* **125**, 244.
Bollman, J. L., and Mann, F. C. (1931). *Am. J. Physiol.* **96**, 683.
Bortz, W. M., and Lynen, F. (1963). *Biochem. Z.* **337**, 505.
Bortz, W. M., Abraham, S., and Chaikoff, I. L. (1963). *J. Biol. Chem.* **238**, 1266.
Brady, R. O., and Gurin, S. (1950). *J. Biol. Chem.* **187**, 589.
Brady, R. O., and Gurin, S. (1952). *J. Biol. Chem.* **199**, 421.
Brady, R. O., Lukens, F. D. W., and Gurin, S. (1951). *J. Biol. Chem.* **193**, 459.
Brady, R. O., Scow, R. O., Urgoiti, E., and Bradley, R. M. (1965). *Biochim. Biophys. Acta* **106**, 241.
Bragdon, J. H., and Gordon, R. S., Jr. (1958). *J. Clin. Invest.* **37**, 574.
Bragdon, J. H., Havel, R. J., and Gordon, R. S., Jr. (1957). *Am. J. Physiol.* **189**, 63.
Braunsteiner, H., DiPauli, R., Sailer, S., and Sandhofer, F. (1965). *Klin. Wochschr.* **43**, 715.
Braunsteiner, H., Sailer, S., and Sandhofer, F. (1966). *Klin. Wochschr.* **44**, 116.
Brech, W. J., and Gordon, E. S. (1967). *Congr. Intern. Diabetes Federation, 6th. Excerpta Med. Found. Intern. Congr. Ser.* **140**, 150.
Brown, D. F. (1967). *Diabetes* **16**, 90.
Brown, D. F., and Olivecrona, T. (1966). *Acta Physiol. Scand.* **66**, 9.
Butcher, R. W., Sneyd, J. G. T., Park, C. R., and Sutherland, E. W., Jr. (1966). *J. Biol. Chem.* **241**, 1652.
Butterfield, W. J. H., and Schless, G. (1959). *Diabetes* **8**, 450.
Cagan, R. N., Nichols, R., and Loewe, L. (1956). *Diabetes* **5**, 112.
Cameron, J. S. (1962). *Guy's Hosp. Rept.* **111**, 145.
Carlson, L. A. (1960). *Acta Med. Scand.* **167**, 399.
Carlson, L. A., and Ekelund, L.-G. (1963). *J. Clin. Invest.* **42**, 714.
Carlson, L. A., and Hallberg, D. (1963). *Acta Physiol. Scand.* **59**, 52.
Carlson, L. A., and Nye, E. R. (1966). *Acta Med. Scand.* **179**, 453.
Carlson, L. A., and Östman, J. (1963). *Acta Med. Scand.* **174**, 215.
Carlson, L. A., and Östman, J. (1965). *Acta Med. Scand.* **177**, 631.
Carlson, L. A., and Orö, L. (1962). *Acta Med. Scand.* **172**, 641.
Carlson, L. A., Liljedahl, S. O., and Wirsén, C. (1965). *Acta Med. Scand.* **178**, 81.
Chaikoff, I. L., Smyth, F. S., and Gibbs, G. E. (1936). *J. Clin. Invest.* **15**, 627.
Chang, H. C., Seidman, I., Teebor, G., and Lane, M. D. (1967). *Biochem. Biophys. Res. Commun.* **28**, 682.
Chernick, S. S., and Chaikoff, I. L. (1950). *J. Biol. Chem.* **186**, 535.
Chernick, S. S., and Chaikoff, I. L. (1951). *J. Biol. Chem.* **188**, 389.

Chernick, S. S., and Scow, R. O. (1959). *Am. J. Physiol.* **196**, 125.
Chernick, S. S., and Scow, R. O. (1964). *J. Biol. Chem.* **239**, 2416.
Chernick, S. S., Chaikoff, I. L., Masoro, E. J., and Isaeff, E. (1950). *J. Biol. Chem.* **186**, 527.
Christophe, J., and Mayer, J. (1959). *Am. J. Physiol.* **197**, 55.
Christophe, J., Dagenais, Y., and Mayer, J. (1959). *Nature* **184**, 61.
Christophe, J., Jeanrenaud, B., Mayer, J., and Renold, A. E. (1961). *J. Biol. Chem.* **236**, 642.
Cohen, A. M., and Teitelbaum, A. (1964). *Am. J. Physiol.* **206**, 105.
Cohen, A. M., and Teitelbaum, A. (1968). *Life Sci.* **7**, 23.
Coore, H. G., and Randle, P. J. (1964). *Biochem. J.* **93**, 66.
Corvilain, J., and Tagnon, R. (1961). *J. Physiol. (London)* **155**, 337.
Craig, J. W., Miller, M., and Drucker, W. R. (1955). *J. Clin. Invest.* **34**, 928.
Csorba, T. R., Matsuda, I., and Kalant, N. (1966). *Metab. Clin. Exptl.* **15**, 262.
Dannenburg, W. N., and Burt, R. L. (1965). *Am. J. Obstet. Gynecol.* **92**, 195.
Davidson, P. C., and Albrink, M. J. (1965). *Metab. Clin. Exptl.* **14**, 1059.
Denborough, M. A., and Paterson, B. (1962). *Clin. Sci.* **23**, 485.
Deuel, H. J., Jr. (1936). *Physiol. Rev.* **16**, 173.
DiPietro, D. L., and Weinhouse, S. (1960). *J. Biol. Chem.* **235**, 2542.
Dole, V. P. (1956). *J. Clin. Invest.* **35**, 150.
Dole, V. P., and Hamlin, J. T., III (1962). *Physiol. Rev.* **42**, 674.
Drury, D. R. (1940). *Am. J. Physiol.* **131**, 536.
Dury, A. (1957). *Circulation Res.* **5**, 47.
Eaton, R. P., Steinberg, D., and Berman, M. (1965). *J. Clin. Invest.* **44**, 1042.
Ernest, I., Hallgren, B., and Svanborg, A. (1962). *Metab. Clin. Exptl.* **11**, 912.
Ervin, D. M. (1919). *J. Lab. Clin. Med.* **5**, 146.
Exton, J. H., and Edson, N. L. (1964). *Biochem. J.* **91**, 478.
Exton, J. H., Jefferson, L. S., Butcher, R. W., and Park, C. R. (1966). *Am. J. Med.* **40**, 709.
Fallon, H. J., and Kemp, E. L. (1968). *J. Clin. Invest.* **47**, 712.
Fang, M., and Lowenstein, J. M. (1967). *Biochem. J.* **105**, 803.
Farquhar, J. W., Gross, R. C., Wagner, R. M., and Reaven, G. M. (1965). *J. Lipid Res.* **6**, 119.
Farquhar, J. W., Frank, A., Gross, R. C., and Reaven, G. M. (1966). *J. Clin. Invest.* **45**, 1648.
Felber, J.-P., and Vannotti, A. (1964). *Med. Exptl.* **10**, 153.
Felts, J. M., and Mayes, P. A. (1965). *Nature* **206**, 195.
Felts, J. M., Chaikoff, I. L., and Osborn, M. J. (1951a). *J. Biol. Chem.* **193**, 557.
Felts, J. M., Chaikoff, I. L., and Osborn, M. J. (1951b). *J. Biol. Chem.* **191**, 683.
Fine, M., Michaels, G., Shah, S., Chai, B., Fukayama, G., and Kinsell, L. (1962). *Metab. Clin. Exptl.* **11**, 893.
Fine, M. B., and Williams, R. H. (1960). *Am. J. Physiol.* **199**, 403.
Fitch, W. M., and Chaikoff, I. L. (1960). *J. Biol. Chem.* **235**, 554.
Fitch, W. M., and Chaikoff, I. L. (1962). *Biochim. Biophys. Acta* **57**, 588.
Ford, C. R., Stevens, R., Bolinger, R. E., and Morris, J. H. (1963). *Proc. Soc. Exptl. Biol. Med.* **113**, 177.
Foster, D. W. (1967). *J. Clin. Invest.* **46**, 1283.
Foster, D. W., and Srere, P. A. (1968). *J. Biol. Chem.* **243**, 1926.
Fredrickson, D. S., and Gordon, R. S., Jr. (1958). *Physiol. Rev.* **38**, 585.
Fredrickson, D. S., and Lees, R. S. (1966). *In* "The Metabolic Basis of Inherited Disease" (J. B. Stanbury, J. B. Wyngaarden, and D. S. Fredrickson, eds.), p. 429. McGraw-Hill, New York.

Fredrickson, D. S., Ono, K., and Davis, L. L. (1963). *J. Lipid Res.* **4**, 24.

Fredrickson, D. S., Levy, R. I., and Lees, R. S. (1967). *New Engl. J. Med.* **276**, 32, 94, 148, 215, 273.

French, J. E., and Morris, B. (1957). *J. Physiol. (London)* **138**, 326.

French, J. E., and Morris, B. (1958). *J. Physiol. (London)* **140**, 262.

Friedberg, S. J., Klein, R. F., Trout, D. L., Bogdonoff, M. D., and Estes, E. H. (1961). *J. Clin. Invest.* **40**, 1846.

Fritz, I. (1961). *Physiol. Rev.* **41**, 52.

Fritz, I. B., and Hsu, M. P. (1967). *J. Biol. Chem.* **242**, 865.

Froesch, E. R., and Ginsberg, J. L. (1962). *J. Biol. Chem.* **237**, 3317.

Garfinkel, A. S., Baker, N., and Schotz, M. (1967). *J. Lipid Res.* **8**, 274.

Gebbie, T., and Reid, J. D. (1964). *Lancet* **ii**, 661.

Gellhorn, A., and Benjamin, W. (1964). *Science* **146**, 1166.

Gepts, W., Christophe, J., and Mayer, J. (1960). *Diabetes* **9**, 63.

Ghose, A., Shreeve, W. W., Shigeta, Y., and Schwartz, I. L. (1964). *Nature* **201**, 722.

Gibbs, G. E., and Chaikoff, I. L. (1941). *Endocrinology* **29**, 877.

Gibson, D. M., and Hubbard, D. D. (1960). *Biochem. Biophys. Res. Commun.* **3**, 531.

Gidez, L. I., Roheim, P. S., and Eder, H. A. (1962). *Federation Proc.* **21**, 289.

Gillman, J., Gilbert, C., and Allan, J. C. (1958). *J. Endocrinol.* **17**, 349.

Ginsburg, V., and Hers, H. G. (1960). *Biochim. Biophys. Acta* **38**, 427.

Gofman, J. W., Lindgren, F., Elliott, H., Mantz, W., Hewitt, J., Strisower, B., Herring, V., and Lyon, T. P. (1950). *Science* **111**, 166.

Goldman, J. K., and Cahill, G. F., Jr (1964). *Metab. Clin. Exptl.* **13**, 572.

Gordon, E. E. (1963). *J. Biol. Chem.* **238**, 2135.

Gordon, R. S., and Cherkes, A, (1956) *J. Clin. Invest.* **35**, 206.

Greten, F. A., Potthoff, S., and Jahnke, K. (1967). *Diabetologia* **3**, 311.

Grodsky, G. M., Batts, A. A., Bennett, L. L., Vcella, C., McWilliams, N. B., and Smith, D. F. (1963). *Am. J. Physiol.* **205**, 638.

Gross, R. C., and Carlson, L. A. (1968). *Diabetes* **17**, 353.

Gross, R. C., Eigenbrodt, E. H., and Farquhar, J. W. (1967). *J. Lipid Res.* **8**, 114.

Haahti, E. (1959). *Scand. J. Clin. Lab. Invest.* **11**, 305.

Haft, D. E. (1967). *Am. J. Physiol.* **213**, 219.

Haft, D. E. (1968a). *Diabetes* **17**, 244.

Haft, D. E. (1968b). *Diabetes* **17**, 251.

Haft, D. E., and Miller, L. L. (1958). *Am. J. Physiol.* **192**, 33.

Hagen, J. H. (1961). *Federation Proc.* **20**, 275.

Hagen, J. H. (1963). *J. Lipid Res.* **4**, 46.

Hagen, J. H., Moorhouse, J. A., and Steinberg, J. (1963). *Metab. Clin. Exptl.* **12**, 346.

Hamosh, M., and Wertheimer, E. (1960). Cited in Wertheimer, E., and Shafrir, E. (1960). *Recent Progr. Hormone Res.* **16**, 467.

Harper, A. E., Monson, W. J., Arata, D. A., Benton, D. A., and Elvehjem, C. A. (1953). *J. Nutr.* **51**, 523.

Hatch, F. T., Abell, L. L., and Kendall, F. E. (1955). *Am. J. Med.* **19**, 48.

Haugaard, E. S., and Stadie, W. C. (1952). *J. Biol. Chem.* **199**, 741.

Hausberger, F. X., Milstein, S. W., and Rutman, R. J. (1954). *J. Biol. Chem.* **208**, 431.

Hauss, W. H., and Böhle, E. (1955). *Deut. Arch. Klin. Med.* **202**, 579.

Havel, R. J. (1957). *J. Clin. Invest.* **36**, 855.

Havel, R. J. (1961). *Metab. Clin. Exptl.* **10**, 1031.

Havel, R. J. (1965a). *Ann. N.Y. Acad. Sci.* **131**, 91.

Havel, R. J. (1965b). *In* "Adipose Tissue. Handbook of Physiology" (A. E. Renold and G. F. Cahill, Jr., eds.) p. 499. Am. Physiol. Soc., Baltimore, Maryland.

Havel, R. J., and Carlson, L. A. (1963). *Life Sci.* **3**, 651.
Havel, R. J., Felts, J. M., and Van Duyne, C. M. (1962). *J. Lipid Res.* **3**, 297.
Heald, P. J., McLachlan, P. M., and Rookledge, K. A. (1965). *J. Endocrinol.* **33**, 83.
Heimberg, M., Meng, H. C., and Park, C. R. (1958). *Am. J. Physiol.* **195**, 673.
Heimberg, M., Weinstein, I., Klausner, H., and Watkins, M. L. (1962). *Am. J. Physiol.* **202**, 353.
Heimberg, M., Dunkerley, A., and Brown, T. O. (1966). *Biochim. Biophys. Acta* **125**, 252.
Heimberg, M., van Harken, D. R., and Brown, T. O. (1967). *Biochim. Biophys. Acta* **137**, 435.
Hennes, A. R., and Redding, T. W. (1961). *Diabetes* **10**, 85.
Hennes, A. R., and Shreeve, W. W. (1959). *Proc. Soc. Exptl. Biol. Med.* **100**, 246.
Herman, R. H., and Zakim, D. (1968). *Am. J. Clin. Nutr.* **21**, 245.
Higgins, H. L. (1916). *Am. J. Physiol.* **41**, 258.
Hill, R. J., and Chaikoff, I. L. (1956). *Proc. Soc. Exptl. Biol. Med.* **91**, 265.
Hill, R. J., Baker, N., and Chaikoff, I. L. (1954). *J. Biol. Chem.* **209**, 705.
Hill, R. J., Linazasoro, J. M., Chevallier, F., and Chaikoff, I. L. (1958). *J. Biol. Chem.* **233**, 305.
Hill, R. J., Webster, W. W., Linazasoro, J. M., and Chaikoff, I. L. (1960). *J. Lipid Res.* **1**, 150.
Hirsch, E. F., and Carbonaro, L. (1950). *Arch. Internal Med.* **86**, 519.
Hirsch, E. F., Phibbs, B. P., and Carbonaro, L. (1953). *Arch. Internal Med.* **91**, 106.
Holdsworth, C. D., and Dawson, A. M. (1965). *Proc. Soc. Exptl. Biol. Med.* **118**, 142.
Hollenberg, C. H. (1959). *Am. J. Physiol.* **197**, 667.
Hollenberg, C. H. (1962). *Can. J. Biochem. Physiol.* **40**, 703.
Howard, C. F., Jr., and Lowenstein, J. M. (1965). *J. Biol. Chem.* **240**, 4170.
Jakobson, T., Kahanpää, A., and Nikkilä, E. A. (1965). *Acta Med. Scand.* **178**, 181.
Jansen, G. R., Zanetti, M. E., and Hutchison, C. F. (1967). *Biochem. J.* **102**, 870.
Jones, D. P., and Arky, R. A. (1965). *Metab. Clin. Exptl.* **14**, 1287.
Jones, D. P., Plotkin, G. R., and Arky, R. A. (1966). *Diabetes* **15**, 565.
Joslin, E. P. (1921). *Oxford Med.* **4**, 146.
Jungas, R. L. (1966). *Proc. Natl. Acad. Sci. U. S.* **56**, 757.
Jungas, R. L., and Ball, E. G. (1963). *Biochemistry* **2**, 383.
Kalkhoff, R. K., and Kipnis, D. M. (1966). *Diabetes* **15**, 443.
Kalkhoff, R. K., Hornbrook, K. R., Burch, H. B., and Kipnis, D. M. (1966). *Diabetes* **15**, 451.
Kallio, V. (1967). *Acta Med. Scand. Suppl.* **467**.
Kane, J. P., Longcope, C., Pavlatos, F. C., and Grodsky, G. (1965). *Metab. Clin. Exptl.* **14**, 471.
Kauffman, N. A., Gutman, A., Barzilai, D., Eshchar, J., Blondheim, S. H., and Stein, Y. (1965). *Israel J. Med. Sci.* **1**, 389.
Kauffman, N. A., Poznanski, R., Blondheim, S. H., and Stein, Y. (1966a). *Am. J. Clin. Nutr.* **18**, 261.
Kauffman, N. A., Poznanski, R., Blondheim, S. H., and Stein, Y. (1966b). *Israel J. Med. Sci.* **2**, 715.
Kay, R. E., and Entenman, C. (1961). *J. Biol. Chem.* **236**, 1006.
Kessler, J. I. (1962). *J. Lab. Clin. Med.* **60**, 747.
Kessler, J. I. (1963). *J. Clin. Invest.* **42**, 362.
Kiyasu, J. Y., and Chaikoff, I. L. (1957). *J. Biol. Chem.* **224**, 935.
Knittle, J. L., and Ahrens, E. H., Jr. (1964). *J. Clin. Invest.* **43**, 485.

Korchak, H. M., and Masoro, E. J. (1964). *Biochim. Biophys. Acta* **84**, 750.
Kornacker, M. S., and Lowenstein, J. M. (1964). *Science* **144**, 1027.
Kornacker, M. S., and Lowenstein, J. M. (1965a). *Biochem. J.* **94**, 209.
Kornacker, M. S., and Lowenstein, J. M. (1965b). *Biochem. J.* **95**, 832.
Kreisberg, R. A. (1966). *Am. J. Physiol.* **210**, 379.
Krut, L. H., and Barsky, R. F. (1964). *Lancet* **ii**, 1136.
Kuhfahl, E., Müller, F., and Dettmer, D. (1967). *Acta Biol. Med. Ger.* **18**, 563.
Kuo, P. T. (1965). *Trans. Assoc. Am. Physicians* **78**, 97.
Kuo, P. T., and Bassett, D. R. (1965). *Ann. Internal Med.* **62**, 1199.
Kuo, P. T., Feng, L., Cohen, N. N., Fitts, W. T., Jr., and Miller, L. D. (1967). *Am. J. Clin. Nutr.* **20**, 116.
Kyllästinen, M. J., and Nikkilä, E. A. (1968). To be published.
Landau, B. R., Hastings, A. B., and Zottu, S. (1958). *J. Biol. Chem.* **233**, 1257.
Langdon, R. G. (1957). *J. Biol. Chem.* **226**, 615.
Langdon, R. J. (1960). *In* "Lipid Metabolism" (K. Bloch, ed.), p. 239. Wiley, New York.
Laurell, S. (1956). *Scand. J. Clin. Lab. Invest.* **8**, 81.
Laurell, S. (1959a). *Acta Physiol. Scand.* **46**, 97.
Laurell, S. (1959b). *Acta Physiol. Scand.* **47**, 218.
Lees, R. S. (1965). *Clin. Res.* **13**, 549.
Lees, R. S., and Fredrickson, D. S. (1965). *Clin. Res.* **13**, 327.
Lepkovsky, S., Dimick, M. K., Furuta, F., Snapir, N., Park, R., Narita, N., and Komatsu, K. (1967). *Endocrinology* **81**, 1001.
Lequin, H. C., and Steyn-Parvé, E. P. (1962). *Biochim. Biophys. Acta* **58**, 439.
Levine, R., and Fritz, I. B. (1956). *Diabetes* **5**, 209.
Lowenstein, J. M. (1968) *In* "Metabolic Roles of Citrate" (T. W. Goodwin, ed.), p. 61. Academic Press, New York.
Lyon, I., Masri, M. S., and Chaikoff, I. L. (1952). *J. Biol. Chem.* **196**, 25.
Macdonald, I. (1965a). *Clin. Sci.* **29**, 193.
Macdonald, I. (1965b). *Am. J. Clin. Nutr.* **16**, 458.
Macdonald, I. (1966). *Proc. Nutr. Soc.* **25**, ii.
Macdonald, I., and Braithwaite, D. M. (1964). *Clin. Sci.* **27**, 23.
Macdonald, I., and Roberts, J. B. (1967). *Metab. Clin. Exptl.* **16**, 572.
McElroy, W. T., Jr., Siefert, W. L., and Spitzer, J. J. (1960). *Proc. Soc. Exptl. Biol. Med.* **104**, 20.
McGandy, R. B., Hegsted, D. M., and Stare, F. J. (1967). *New Engl. J. Med.* **277**, 417, 469.
Mahler, R., and Ashmore, J. (1962). *Endocrinology* **71**, 673.
Mahler, R., Tarrant, M. E., Stafford, W. S., and Ashmore, J. (1963). *Diabetes* **12**, 359.
Mahler, R., Stafford, W. S., Tarrant, M. E., and Ashmore, J. (1964). *Diabetes* **13**, 297.
Majchrowitz, E., and Quastel, J. H. (1963). *Can. J. Biochem. Physiol.* **41**, 793.
Man, E. B., and Albrink, M. J. (1956). *Yale J. Biol. Med.* **29**, 316.
Man, E. B., and Peters, J. P. (1934). *J. Clin. Invest.* **13**, 237.
Man, E. B., and Peters, J. P. (1935). *J. Clin. Invest.* **14**, 579.
Markscheid, L., and Shafrir, E. (1965). *J. Lipid Res.* **6**, 247.
Marsh, P. L., and Waller, H. G. (1923). *A.M.A. Arch. Internal Med.* **31**, 63.
Marshall, N. B., and Engel, F. L. (1960). *J. Lipid Res.* **1**, 339.
Marshall, M. W., and Wormack, M. (1954). *J. Nutr.* **52**, 51.
Martin, D. B., and Vagelos, P. R. (1962). *Federation Proc.* **21**, 289.
Maruhama, Y. (1965). *Metab. Clin. Exptl.* **14**, 78.
Masoro, E. J. (1962). *J. Lipid Res.* **3**, 149.

Masoro, E. J., Chaikoff, I. L., Chernick, S. S., and Felts, J. M. (1950). J. Biol. Chem. 185, 845.
Masri, M. S., Lyon, I., and Chaikoff, I. L. (1952). J. Biol. Chem. 197, 621.
Matsuhashi, M., Matsuhashi, S., Numa, S., and Lynen, F. (1962). Federation Proc. 21, 288.
Matthes, K. J., Abraham, S., and Chaikoff, I. L. (1960). Biochim. Biophys. Acta 37, 180.
Mayes, P. A., and Felts, J. M. (1967a). Biochem. J. 105, 18C.
Mayes, P. A., and Felts, J. M. (1967b). Nature 215, 716.
Medes, G., Thomas, A., and Weinhouse, S. (1952). J. Biol. Chem. 197, 181.
Meng, H. C., and Goldfarb, J. L. (1959). Diabetes 8, 211.
Miller, H. I. (1967). Metab. Clin. Exptl. 16, 1096.
Miller, L. L. (1961). Recent Progr. Hormone Res. 11, 539.
Miller, M., Craig, J. W., Drucker, W. R., and Woodward, H., Jr. (1957). Yale J. Biol. Med. 30, 335.
Milstein, S. W., and Hausberger, F. X. (1956). Diabetes 5, 89.
Moloney, P. J., and Coval, M. (1955). Biochem. J. 59, 179.
Morris, B. (1963a). J. Physiol. (London) 168, 564.
Morris, B. (1963b). J. Physiol. (London) 168, 584.
Mueller, P. S., and Evans, W. H. (1963). J. Lab. Clin. Med. 61, 953.
Muntz, J. A., and Vanko, M. (1962). J. Biol. Chem. 237, 3582.
Naidoo, S. S., Lossow, W. J., and Chaikoff, I. L. (1967). Experientia 23, 829.
Nestel, P. J. (1964a). J. Clin. Invest. 43, 77.
Nestel, P. J. (1964b). J. Clin. Invest. 43, 943.
Nestel, P. J. (1966a). Clin. Sci. 31, 31.
Nestel, P. J. (1966b). Metab. Clin. Exptl. 15, 787.
Nestel, P. J. (1967). Metab. Clin. Exptl. 16, 1123.
Nestel, P. J., and Hirsch, E. Z. (1965). Australasian Ann. Med. 14, 265.
Nestel, P. J., and Steinberg, D. (1963). J. Lipid Res. 4, 461.
Nestel, P. J., Havel, R. J., and Bezman, A. (1962). J. Clin. Invest. 41, 1915.
New, M. I., Roberts, T. N., Bierman, E. L., and Reader, G. G. (1963). Diabetes 12, 208.
Nichols, A. V., Dobbin, V., and Gofman, J. W. (1957). Geriatrics 12, 7.
Niemeyer, H., Pérez, N., and Rabajille, E. (1966). J. Biol. Chem. 241, 4055.
Niemeyer, H., Pérez, N., and Codoceo, R. (1967). J. Biol. Chem. 242, 860.
Nikkilä, E. A. (1966). Scand. J. Clin. Lab. Invest. 18, Suppl. 92, 76.
Nikkilä, E. A. (1968). Scand. J. Clin. Lab. Invest. 21, Suppl. 101, 20.
Nikkilä, E. A., and Ojala, K. (1963a). Proc. Soc. Exptl. Biol. Med. 113, 814.
Nikkilä, E. A., and Ojala, K. (1963b). Acta Chem. Scand. 17, 554.
Nikkilä, E. A., and Ojala, K. (1964). Life Sci. 3, 1021.
Nikkilä, E. A., and Ojala, K. (1965). Life Sci. 4, 937.
Nikkilä, E. A., and Ojala, K. (1966). Life Sci. 5, 89.
Nikkilä, E. A., and Pelkonen, R. (1966). Proc. Soc. Exptl. Biol. Med. 123, 91.
Nikkilä, E. A., and Pykälistö, O. (1968a). Biochim. Biophys. Acta 152, 421.
Nikkilä, E. A., and Pykälistö, O. (1968b). Life Sci. 7, 1303.
Nikkilä, E. A., and Pykälistö, O. (1968c). 3rd Intern. Symp. Drugs Affecting Lipid Metabolism, Milan, 1968 (in press).
Nikkilä, E. A., and Taskinen, M.-R. (1968). Ann. Meeting European Assoc. Study Diabetes, 4th, Louvain, 1968. (Abstr.)
Nikkilä, E. A., Miettinen, T. A., Vesenne, M.-R., and Pelkonen, R. (1965). Lancet ii, 508.
Nikkilä, E. A., Kekki, M., and Ojala, K. (1966). Ann. Med. Exptl. Biol. Fenniae (Helsinki) 44, 348.

Nikkilä, E. A., Miettinen, T. A., Pelkonen, R., and Taskinen, M.-R. (1968). *Progr. Biochem. Pharmacol.* **4**, 208.

Nissen, N. I. (1931). *Acta Med. Scand.* **74**, 566.

Numa, S., Bortz, W. M., and Lynen, F. (1965). *Advan. Enzyme Regulation* **3**, 407.

Östman, J. (1965). *Acta Med. Scand.* **177**, 639.

Ogino, K., Doi. H., and Okamoto, H. (1965). *Japan. Circulation J.* **29**, 583.

Olson, R. E., and Vester, J. W. (1960), *Physiol. Rev.* **40**, 677.

Ontko, J. A., and Zilversmit, D. B. (1967). *J. Lipid Res.* **8**, 90.

Osborn, M. J., Chaikoff, I. L., and Felts, J. M. (1951). *J. Biol. Chem.* **193**, 549.

Parmeggiani, A., and Bowman, R. H. (1963). *Biochem. Biophys. Res. Commun.* **12**, 268.

Pelkonen, R., Nikkilä, E. A., and Taskinen, M.-R. (1967). *Scand. J. Clin. Lab. Invest.* **19**, Suppl. 95, 93.

Penhos, J. C., Wu, C. H., Lemberg, A., Daunas, J., Brodoff, B., Sodero, A., and Levine, R. (1968). *Metab. Clin. Exptl.* **17**, 246.

Perry, W. F. (1967). *Clin. Chim. Acta* **16**, 189.

Perry, W. F., and Corbett, B. N. (1964). *Can. J. Physiol. Pharmacol.* **42**, 353.

Persson, B., Björntorp, P., and Hood, B. (1966). *Metab. Clin. Exptl.* **15**, 730.

Pitot, H. C., Peraino, C., Pries, N., and Kennan, A. L. (1964). *Advan. Enzyme Regulation* **2**, 237.

Porte, D., Jr., Bierman, E. L., and Bagdade, J. D. (1966). *Proc. Soc. Exptl. Biol. Med.* **123**, 814.

Porter, J. W., and Long, R. W. (1958). *J. Biol. Chem.* **233**, 20.

Portman, O. W., Lawry, E. Y., and Bruno, D. (1956). *Proc. Soc. Exptl. Biol. Med.* **91**, 321.

Pykälistö, O., and Nikkilä, E. A. (1968). *Scand. J. Clin. Lab. Invest.* **21**, Suppl. 101, 15.

Quarfordt, H. S., and Goodman, D. S. (1966). *Biochim. Biophys. Acta* **116**, 382.

Reaven, G. M., Calciano, A., Cody, R., Lucas, C., and Miller, R. (1963). *J. Clin. Endocrinol. Metab.* **23**, 1013.

Reaven, G. M., Hill, D. B., Gross, R. C., and Farquhar, J. W. (1965) *J. Clin. Invest.* **44**, 1826.

Reaven, G. M., Lerner, R. L., Stern, M. P., and Farquhar, J. W. (1967). *J. Clin. Invest.* **46**, 1756.

Reissell, P. K., Mandella, P. A., Poon-King, T. M. W., and Hatch, F. T. (1966). *Am. J. Clin. Nutr.* **19**, 84.

Renold, A. E., Hastings, A. B., and Nesbett, F. B. (1954). *J. Biol. Chem.* **209**, 687.

Renold, A. E., Hastings, A. B., Nesbett, F. B., and Ashmore, J. (1955). *J. Biol. Chem.* **213**, 135.

Reshef, L., and Shapiro, B. (1965). *Biochim. Biophys. Acta* **98**, 73.

Robinson, J. D., Brady, R. O., and Bradley, R. M. (1963). *J. Lipid Res.* **4**, 144.

Rodbell, M., and Scow, R. O. (1964). *Am. J. Physiol.* **208**, 106.

Rodbell, M., and Scow, R. O. (1965). *In* "Adipose Tissue. Handbook of Physiology" (A. E. Renold and G. F. Cahill, Jr., eds.), p. 491. Am. Physiol. Soc., Baltimore, Maryland.

Rony, H. R., and Ching, T. T. (1930). *Endocrinology* **14**, 355.

Rubenstein, B., and Rubinstein, D. (1966). *Can. J. Biochem.* **44**, 129.

Rudas, B. (1967). *Wien. Klin. Wochschr.* **79**, 377.

Rudas, B., and Reissert, K. (1967). *Med. Pharmacol. Exptl.* **17**, 11.

Ruderman, N. B., Lauris, V., and Herrera, M. G. (1967). *Am. J. Physiol.* **212**, 1169.

Rudman, D., Seidman, F., Brown, S. J., and Hirsch, R. L. (1962). *Endocrinology* **70**, 223.

Ryan, W. G., and Schwartz, T. B. (1965). *Metab. Clin. Exptl.* **14**, 1243.

Sailer, S., Sandhofer, F., and Braunsteiner, H. (1965). *Deut. Med. Wochschr.* **90**, 865.

Sailer, S., Sandhofer, F., and Braunsteiner, H. (1966a). *Metab. Clin. Exptl.* **15**, 135.
Sailer, S., Sandhofer, F., and Braunsteiner, H. (1966b). *Klin. Wochschr.* **44**, 1032.
Sailer, S., Sandhofer, F., and Braunsteiner, H. (1967a). *Klin. Wochschr.* **45**, 86.
Sailer, S., Sandhofer, F., Bolzano, K., and Braunsteiner, H. (1967b). *Klin. Wochschr.* **45**, 918.
Sailer, S., Bolzano, K., Sandhofer, F., Spath, P., and Braunsteiner, H. (1968). *Schweiz. Med. Wochschr.* **98**, 1512.
Salaman, M. R., and Robinson, D. S. (1966). *Biochem. J.* **99**, 640.
Salans, L. B., and Reaven, G. M. (1966). *Proc. Soc. Exptl. Biol. Med.* **122**, 1208.
Salas, M., Viñuela, E., and Solo, A. (1963). *J. Biol. Chem.* **238**, 3535.
Samols, E., and Dormandy, T. L. (1963). *Lancet* **i**, 478.
Sandberg, H., Sok Min, B., Feinberg, L., and Bellet, S. (1960). *A.M.A. Arch. Internal Med.* **105**, 866.
Sandhofer, F., Sailer, S., Herbst, M., and Braunsteiner, H. (1965). *Deut. Med. Wochschr.* **90**, 755.
Sandhofer, F., Bolzano, K., Sailer, S., and Braunsteiner, H. (1968). *Klin. Wochschr.* **46**, 1034.
Scheig, R., Alexander, N. M., and Klatskin, G. (1966). *J. Lipid Res.* **7**, 188.
Schlierf, G., and Kinsell, L. W. (1965). *Proc. Soc. Exptl. Biol. Med.* **120**, 272.
Schnatz, J. D., and Williams, R. H. (1962). *Metab. Clin. Exptl.* **11**, 349.
Schnatz, J. D., and Williams, R. H. (1963). *Diabetes* **12**, 174.
Schotz, M. C., Arnesjö, B., and Olivecrona, T. (1966). *Biochim. Biophys. Acta* **125**, 485.
Schrade, W., Boehle, E., and Biegler, R. (1960). *Lancet* **ii**, 1409.
Schrade, W., Boehle, E., Biegler, R., and Harmuth, E. (1963). *Lancet* **i**, 285.
Schreier, K. (1959). *Mod. Probl. Paediat.* **4**, 93.
Schultz, G., Senft, G., and Munske, K. (1966). *Naturwissenschaften* **53**, 529.
Scow, R. O., and Chernick, S. S. (1960). *Recent Progr. Hormone Res.* **16**, 497.
Seidman, I., Horland, A. A., and Teebor, G. W. (1967). *Biochim. Biophys. Acta* **146**, 600.
Shafrir, E., Sussman, K. E., and Steinberg, D. (1959). *J. Lipid Res.* **1**, 109.
Shafrir, E., Sussman, K. E., and Steinberg, D. (1960). *J. Lipid Res.* **1**, 459.
Shamoian, C. A., Masoro, E. J., Derrow, A., and Canzanelli, A. (1964). *Endocrinology* **74**, 21.
Sharma, C., Manjeshwar, R., and Weinhouse, S. (1963). *J. Biol. Chem.* **238**, 3840.
Shigeta, Y., and Shreeve, W. W. (1964). *Am. J. Physiol.* **206**, 1085.
Shigeta, Y., Nakamura, K., Hoshi, M., Kim, M., and Abe, H. (1967). *Diabetes* **16**, 238.
Shoemaker, W. C., Ashmore, J., Carruthers, P. J., and Schulman, M. (1960). *Proc. Soc. Exptl. Biol. Med.* **103**, 585.
Shrago, E., Lardy, H. A., Nordlie, R. C., and Foster, D. O. (1963). *J. Biol. Chem.* **238**, 3188.
Shreeve, W. W. (1965). *Ann. N.Y. Acad. Sci.* **131**, 464.
Siperstein, M. D. (1958). *Diabetes*, **7**, 181.
Siperstein, M. D., and Fagan, V. M. (1958). *J. Clin. Invest.* **37**, 1196.
Söling, H. D., Kneer, P., Drägert, W., and Creutzfeldt, W. (1966). *Diabetologia* **2**, 32.
Spencer, A. F., and Lowenstein, J. M. (1967). *Biochem. J.* **103**, 342.
Spencer, A. F., Corman, L., and Lowenstein, J. M. (1964). *Biochem. J.* **93**, 378.
Spitzer, J. J., and McElroy, W. R., Jr. (1960). *Am. J. Physiol.* **199**, 876.
Spitzer, J. J., and McElroy, W. R., Jr. (1962). *Diabetes* **11**, 222.
Stauffacher, W., Lambert, A. E., Vecchio, D., and Renold, A. E. (1967). *Diabetologia* **3**, 230.
Steiner, G. (1968). *New Engl. J. Med.* **279**, 70.

Sterky, G., Larsson, Y., and Persson, B. (1963). *Acta Paediat.* **52**, 11.
Stetten, D., Jr., and Boxer, G. E. (1944). *J. Biol. Chem.* **156**, 271.
Stetten, D., Jr., and Klein, B. V. (1945). *J. Biol. Chem.* **159**, 593.
Stetten, D., Jr., and Klein, B. V. (1946). *J. Biol. Chem.* **162**, 377.
Stone, D. B., and Connor, W. E. (1963). *Diabetes* **12**, 127.
Stormont, J. M., and Waterhouse, C. (1963). *J. Lab. Clin. Med.* **61**, 826.
Swan, D. C., Davidson, P., and Albrink, M. (1966). *Lancet* **i**, 60.
Sweeney, M. J., and Ashmore, J. (1965). *Metab. Clin. Exptl.* **14**, 516.
Swynghedauw, B. (1965). *Pathol. Biol. Semaine Hop.* **13**, 74.
Swynghedauw, B., Claude, J. R., and Beaumont, J. L. (1965). *Rev. Franc. Etudes Clin. Biol.* **10**, 427.
Takeda, J., Inoue, H., Honjo, K., Tanioka, H., and Daikuhara, Y. (1967). *Biochim. Biophys. Acta* **136**, 214.
Taketa, K., and Pogell, B. M. (1966). *J. Biol. Chem.* **241**, 720.
Tarrant, M. E., and Ashmore, J. (1965). *Diabetes* **14**, 179.
Tarrant, M. E., Thompson, R. H. S., and Wright, P. H. (1962). *Biochem. J.* **84**, 6.
Tarrant, M. E., Mahler, R., and Ashmore, J. (1964). *J. Biol. Chem.* **239**, 1714.
Tepperman, H. J., and Tepperman, J. (1958). *Diabetes* **7**, 478.
Tepperman, H. M., and Tepperman, J. (1968). *Am. J. Physiol.* **214**, 67.
Traisman, H. S., Newcomb, A. L., Sever, J. L., and Hammes, R. (1960). *Diabetes* **9**, 481.
Tubbs, P. K., and Garland, P. B. (1964). *Biochem. J.* **93**, 550.
Tzur, R., Tal, E., and Shapiro, B. (1964). *Biochim. Biophys. Acta* **84**, 18.
Vagelos, P. R. (1964). *Ann. Rev. Biochem.* **33**, 139.
Vagelos, P. R., Majerus, P. W., Alberts, A. W., Larrabee, A. R., and Ailhaud, G. P. (1966). *Federation Proc.* **25**, 1485.
van Eck, W. S. (1959). *Am. J. Med.* **27**, 196.
van Harken, D. R., Brown, T. O., and Heimberg, M. (1967). *Lipids* **2**, 231.
Van Itallie, T. B., and Shull, K. H. (1957). *J. Lab. Clin. Med.* **50**, 391.
Viñuela, E., Salas, M., and Sols, A. (1963). *J. Biol. Chem.* **238**, 1175.
Waddell, W. R., and Geyer, R. B. (1957). *Proc. Soc. Exptl. Biol. Med.* **96**, 251.
Waite, M., and Wakil, S. J. (1962). *J. Biol. Chem.* **237**, 2750.
Walker, W. J., Lawry, E. Y., Love, D. E., Mann, G. V., Levine, S. A., and Stare, F. J. (1953). *Am. J. Med.* **14**, 654.
Waterhouse, C., Kemperman, J. H., and Stormont, J. M. (1964). *J. Lab. Clin. Med.* **63**, 605.
Watkin, D. M., Froeb, H. F., Hatch, F. T., and Gutman, A. B. (1950). *Am. J. Med.* **9**, 441.
Weber, G., and Hird Convery, H. J. (1966). *Life Sci.* **5**, 1139.
Weber, G., and Singhal, R. L. (1965). *Life Sci.* **4**, 1993.
Weber, G., Singhal, R. L., and Srivastava, S. K. (1965a). *Proc. Natl. Acad. Sci. U.S.* **53**, 96.
Weber, G., Stamm, N. B., and Fisher, E. A. (1965b). *Science* **149**, 65.
Weber, G., Lea, M. A., Fisher, E. A., and Stamm, N. B. (1966). *Enzymol. Biol. Clin.* **7**, 11.
Wenkeová, J., and Páv, J. (1959). *Nature* **184**, 1147.
West, C. E., and Passey, R. F. (1967). *Biochem. J.* **102**, 58.
Westman, S. (1968). *Diabetologia* **4**, 141.
Westman, S., and Hellman, B. (1963). *Med. Exptl.* **8**, 193.
Whitney, J. E., and Roberts, S. (1955). *Am. J. Physiol.* **181**, 446.
Wieland, O., and Eger-Neufeldt, I. (1963). *Biochem. Z.* **337**, 349.
Wieland, O., and Matschinsky, F. (1962). *Life Sci.* **1**, 49.

Wieland, O., and Weiss, L. (1963). *Biochem. Biophys. Res. Commun.* **13**, 26.
Wieland, O., Neufeld, I., Numa, S., and Lynen, F. (1963a). *Biochem. Z.* **336**, 455.
Wieland, O., Weiss, L., Eger-Neufeldt, I., and Müller, U. (1963b). *Life Sci.* **2**, 441.
Wieland, O., Weiss, L., Eger-Neufeldt, I., Teinzer, A., and Westermann, B. (1965). *Klin. Wochschr.* **43**, 645.
Wilcox, H. G., Dishmon, G., and Heimberg, M. (1968). *J. Biol. Chem.* **243**, 665.
Williams, W. R., Hill, R., and Chaikoff, I. L. (1960). *J. Lipid Res.* **1**, 236.
Williamson, J. R., Garcia, A., Renold, A. E., and Cahill, G. F., Jr. (1966). *Diabetes* **15**, 183, 188.
Winand, J., Furnelle, J., and Christophe, J. (1968). *Biochim. Biophys. Acta* **152**, 280.
Windmueller, H. G., and Spaeth, A. E. (1967). *Arch. Biochem. Biophys.* **122**, 362.
Yudkin, J. (1964). *Lancet* **ii**, 4.
Zakim, D., Pardini, R., Herman, R., and Sauberlich, H. (1967a). *Biochim. Biophys. Acta* **137**, 179.
Zakim, D., Pardini, R. S., Herman, R. H., and Sauberlich, H. E. (1967b). *Biochim. Biophys. Acta* **144**, 242.
Zomzely, C., and Mayer, J. (1959). *Am. J. Physiol.* **196**, 956.

Lipid Metabolism in Tissue Culture Cells[1]

GEORGE H. ROTHBLAT

The Wistar Institute of Anatomy and Biology, Philadelphia, Pennsylvania

I.	Introduction	135
II.	Fatty Acids, Triglycerides, and Phospholipids	137
	A. Source and Cellular Content of Fatty Acids	137
	B. Polyunsaturated Fatty Acids	138
	C. Utilization of Fatty Acids	140
	D. Cellular Phospholipid Content and Synthesis	144
III.	Cholesterol	145
	A. Free Cholesterol Content and Incorporation	145
	B. Cellular Sterol Excretion	150
	C. Cholesterol Synthesis	151
	D. Utilization of Esterified Cholesterol	153
IV.	General Considerations of Lipid Metabolism in Tissue Culture Cells	155
	References	161

I. Introduction

The development of methods for routine cultivation of cells *in vitro* has provided the biochemist with a useful system for the study of cellular lipid metabolism, making it possible to obtain large quantities of a homogeneous population of cells. Furthermore, the degree of biological variation generally encountered in a tissue culture system is less than that obtained from studies employing whole animals. In addition, experimental conditions can be easily varied at will in cell culture systems.

The differences between tissue culture systems and other experimental systems must also be kept in mind when evaluating metabolic data obtained from *in vitro* cell studies. Most of the cells maintained in tissue culture are dedifferentiated in the sense that they do not carry out many of the specialized functions found in differentiated

[1]This investigation was supported in part by Public Health Service Research Grant 5-RO1-HE 09103 from the National Heart Institute and Public Health Service Research Fellowship 5-F3-AM-34, 974 from the National Institute of Arthritis and Metabolic Diseases.

cells. In addition, these cells are not organized into specialized tissues as are cells *in vivo*, thus limiting some aspects of cellular interactions. Cells in culture are generally rapidly proliferating, and most lipid studies have been conducted with mixoploid cells derived from malignant tissue. The cellular growth environment of cells cultivated *in vitro* differs considerably from that of cells *in vivo*. For example, although serum is usually present in tissue culture medium, its concentration is low, ranging from 2.5 to 25%. Also, tissue culture cells, growing in the closed system of a test tube, in which substrates are depleted and end products accumulate, may exhibit a dynamic state different from those of the same cells *in vivo*. Keeping these considerations in mind, investigation of the lipid metabolism of tissue culture cells has nevertheless supplied important concepts which will aid in elucidating mechanisms of intermediary metabolism of cellular lipids.

The present report deals with data obtained from studies on lipid metabolism in some tissue culture cell lines. It does not present data on lipid metabolism of macrophages, a subject which has been reviewed by Day (1967), nor does it discuss data on steroid synthesis, which has been reported to occur in some endocrine cells maintained in culture. Furthermore, no attempt has been made to correlate information obtained from tissue culture cell lines with data from other experimental systems such as liver and aorta slices or everted aorta, or from clinical observations, although many such correlations are possible.

There is a pronounced heterogeneity and variability in the types of lipids present in any cell system. Therefore, a simple categorization of the various data in terms of each lipid class leads to considerable confusion, particularly since large gaps still remain in our knowledge of intermediary lipid metabolism. In the light of current knowledge, a more rewarding approach to a discussion of cellular lipid metabolism is the consideration of various lipid classes (i.e., glycerides, free fatty acids, phospholipids, and sterols) in terms of their functional metabolism. This approach, in addition to elucidating metabolic functions of the lipids, can help to demonstrate the interrelationships among different types of cellular lipids.

Of the major lipid classes present in tissue culture cells, the free fatty acids and the triglycerides supply energy through the oxidation of fatty acids, or supply carbon either directly as the entire fatty acid molecule or indirectly by reutilization of fatty acid carbon atoms. At the other functional extreme are the sterols, which serve as structural units in cellular membranes and which seem to undergo little or no oxidative change in tissue culture cells. Between these two extremes are the steryl esters and the phospholipids. Esterified sterol, upon hydrolysis, can supply free fatty acids and free sterol, whereas the phospholipids, which play a major structural role in cellular membranes, can probably also act as a carbon and energy source under certain circumstances.

II. Fatty Acids, Triglycerides, and Phospholipids

A. Source and Cellular Content of Fatty Acids

The free fatty acids of both serum and cells seem to be the key to the metabolism of those cellular lipids utilized by tissue culture cells for the production of carbon and energy. Studies on rabbit liver cells (Mackenzie *et al.*, 1967a) and the human fibroblast cell strain WI38 (Howard, 1968), using labeled exogenous fatty acids, have shown that under standard cultural conditions exogenous fatty acids carried in serum contribute from 80 to 95% of the fatty acid carbon incorporated into cellular glycerides and phospholipid. Further confirmation of the importance of exogenous fatty acids has been obtained from studies conducted to determine the amount of cellular lipid synthesized *de novo*. Mackenzie *et al.* (1967a) have shown that no more than 10% of the fatty acid carbon of cellular lipids in Chang human liver, rabbit liver, rat liver, and L cells[2] was derived from glucose when the cells were grown in rabbit or horse serum. A similar low value for lipid synthesis was obtained by these investigators utilizing the same cell lines growing in tritiated water. In a different series of experiments using WI38 cells, it was determined that glucose contributed 7.7% of the total cell lipid carbon, whereas exogenous acetate supplied only 0.7% (Howard, 1968).

The actual cellular level of free fatty acids is generally low and varies among different cell lines, with values ranging from 0.010 μM/mg dry weight (L cells and L5178Y cells) to 0.073 μM/mg dry weight (muscle fibroblasts) (Howard, 1968). In terms of free fatty acids as a percent of total cellular lipid, these values ranged from 1.0% (L cells) (Weinstein, 1968; Howard, 1968) to 4.7% (HeLa cells) (Howard, 1968).

---

[2]The following abbreviations are used: L cells, mouse fibroblast cell line; MBIII, mouse lymphosarcoma cell line; HeLa, human epithelioid carcinoma cell line; and KB, human epidermoid carcinoma cell lines.

The level of free fatty acids within a given cell line, however, seems to be quite stable and is not readily influenced by varying conditions of growth (monolayer versus suspension culture) or by the type of serum incorporated into the culture medium (Howard, 1968).

B. POLYUNSATURATED FATTY ACIDS

A number of studies have reported the total fatty acid composition of various cells grown in tissue culture medium containing serum (Boyle and Ludwig, 1962; Smith *et al.*, 1965; Gerschenson *et al.*, 1967a,b; Geyer *et al.*, 1962; Johnson and Mora, 1967; Kagawa, 1967). These studies have demonstrated that, in general, the fatty acid patterns of cells are similar to that of serum; the major fatty acids are palmitic (16:0), stearic (18:0), and oleic (18:1), comprising from 50 to 75% of the total cellular fatty acids. The level of linoleic acid (18:2) in cells cultivated in medium with serum ranges from 7 to 17%; the level of arachidonic acid (20:4) ranges between 4 and 15%.

When cells were removed from medium containing serum and cultivated in a lipid-free system, there was a decrease in the relative levels of $C_{18:2}$ and $C_{20:4}$ fatty acids. This decrease in polyunsaturated fatty acid was generally accompanied by an increase in the relative percent of $C_{18:1}$ (Gerschenson *et al.*, 1967b; Geyer, 1967; Harary *et al.*, 1967; Kagawa, 1967). When cells were cultured in medium supplemented with only one fatty acid, it was found that if the fatty acid was a nonessential fatty acid such as oleic, there was a simple dilution of the cellular fatty acids (Geyer, 1967). On the other hand, addition of either linoleic or arachadonic acids to the medium produced an increase in the cellular level of these fatty acids without producing a consistent change in the level of other cellular fatty acids (Gerschenson *et al.*, 1967b; Geyer, 1967; Harary *et al.*, 1967).

Several investigations (Bailey and Menter, 1967; Bailey, 1967; Geyer *et al.*, 1962; Geyer, 1967; Kagawa, 1967) have reported data on the cellular level of polyunsaturated fatty acids in L cells grown in serum-free medium for prolonged periods of time. These studies indicate that L cells are incapable of synthesizing polyunsaturated fatty acids; it is possible that this is also the case with all mammalian cells which have been established in culture. It has also been reported that L cells, upon continued cultivation in lipid-free medium, contain no detectable amounts of polyunsaturated fatty acids (Geyer *et al.*, 1962; Geyer, 1967; Kagawa, 1967). On the other hand, a subline of L cells (L 2071) was found to contain appreciable levels of linoleic acid (6%) after continued cultivation in lipid-free medium. Since it has been shown that this fatty acid is not a product of cellular synthesis, it was suggested (Bailey and Menter, 1967) that linoleic acid could be efficiently conserved by these cells and accumulated from trace amounts of fatty acid present in the growth medium below the level of detection. Such conservation of linoleic acid would be accentuated by the prolonged generation time (1 week) of these cells (Bailey and Menter, 1967) and by the metabolic stability of fatty acids once they are incorporated into other cellular lipids (Geyer, 1967).

Studies by Haggerty *et al.* (1965), using isotopically labeled linoleic acid, indicated that a negligible amount of label appeared as arachidonic acid. Although these studies, which examined the total cellular fatty acids, suggested that HeLa cells could not synthesize arachidonic acid, they did show that the cells had the ability to elongate $C_{18:2}$ to $C_{20:2}$ but lacked the ability to desaturate this intermediate to $C_{20:4}$. Similar studies (Haggerty *et al.*, 1965; Harary *et al.*, 1967) with primary rat heart cells showed active metabolism of linoleic acid leading to the formation of arachidonic acid. However, it was observed that the ability of heart cells to produce arachidonic acid decreased as the cells were maintained in culture over a period of 3 weeks, and the data indicated that the desaturation mechanism is lost as a result of continued cultivation of the heart cells. In a different series of experiments Stoffel and Scheid (1967), also using HeLa cells, demonstrated some conversion of labeled linoleic acid to arachidonic acid. This study examined only the fatty acids of the cellular phospholipids and, for this reason, it is possible that low levels of synthesized arachidonic acid were detected.

A number of different parameters have been used to study the role played by fatty acids in the growth and function of tissue culture cells. These studies, utilizing cells cultivated in lipid-free medium, have determined the effect of added fatty acids on cell growth, mitochondrial function and respiration, and the beating of primary heart cells. In a series of investigations on the effect of fatty acids on HeLa cells and on primary rat heart cells, it was shown that neither albumin-bound linoleic acid nor palmitic acid was capable of promoting growth of heart cells maintained in a serum-free medium; however, both linoleic acid and arachidonic acid stimulated the growth of HeLa cells (Gerschenson *et al.*, 1967a,b; Harary *et al.*, 1967). It has also been shown that linoleic acid can serve as a replacement for serum or albumin for clonal growth of Chinese hamster cells (Ham, 1963).

In investigations of the effect of fatty acids on mitochondrial function in HeLa and rat heart cells, it was found that linoleate or arachidonate were effective in both cell systems in maintaining normal

ADP:O[3] ratios and respiratory control; palmitic acid, however, was not capable of sustaining mitochondrial function in cells maintained in serum-free medium (Gerschenson *et al.*, 1967a,b; Harary *et al.*, 1967). Investigations of the ability of fatty acids to sustain the beating of primary heart cells (Gerschenson *et al.*, 1967a; Harary *et al.*, 1967) have shown that although linoleic acid was necessary for normal mitochondrial function, its presence in a lipid-deficient medium would not support the beating of rat heart cells. On the other hand, palmitic acid, which had no effect on mitochondrial function or cell growth, did support the beating of heart cells placed in a lipid-deficient medium.

C. Utilization of Fatty Acids

Although the cellular free fatty acid pool represents a relatively small percent of the total cellular lipid, it is probably turning over rapidly as free fatty acids are oxidized and/or incorporated into glycerides and phospholipids. The amount of fatty acids oxidized or incorporated into cellular lipid is probably extremely variable and is directly influenced by the type of cells as well as the conditions under which the cells are cultivated.

As one example of the influence of culture medium on fatty acid utilization, Geyer (1967) has shown that a portion of the exogenous long-chain saturated fatty acids taken up by HeLa cells are oxidized to CO_2. When these cells were incubated in the absence of glucose in the culture medium, the amount of CO_2 derived from fatty acid oxidation increased; at the same time, less of the fatty acid was incorporated into cellular triglycerides and phospholipids.

Although some fatty acid is oxidized by tissue culture cells, most of the exogenous fatty acids incorporated from the growth medium are incorporated into triglycerides and phospholipids. The proportion of fatty acid incorporated into either class of cellular lipid seems to be directly related to the conditions under which the cells are cultivated. In a culture in which more exogenous fatty acids are present than are required for phospholipid synthesis or are necessary for a carbon and energy source, the excess fatty acids are incorporated into cellular triglycerides.

The accumulation of neutral lipids (i.e., triglyceride) was noted in many of the early experiments on tissue culture cells, when it was observed that many cells contained cellular lipid particles or droplets.

---

[3]Here ADP:O indicates the increase in O_2 uptake caused by addition of adenosine diphosphate.

Lipid droplet formation has since been thoroughly studied, and it has been demonstrated to be directly related to the cellular incorporation of exogenous fatty acids (Geyer, 1967; Moskowitz, 1967; Mackenzie *et al.*, 1967a). The cultivation of cells in medium containing added fatty acids results in the appearance of cellular lipid droplets (Geyer, 1967; Moskowitz, 1967) composed almost entirely of triglyceride (Geyer, 1967; Moskowitz, 1967; Mackenzie *et al.*, 1967a). Although triglycerides accumulate in these cells, there is no corresponding change in the cellular level of phospholipids or sterols (Moskowitz, 1967). The level of exogenous fatty acid necessary to provoke cellular triglyceride accumulation can be quite low; L cells will produce a detectable response to 10^{-4} μM/ml of oleic acid when added to serum-free medium bound to albumin; maximal lipid accumulation was obtained in this system with 10^{-1} μM/ml of oleic acid (Moskowitz, 1967).

Tissue culture cells produce triglycerides not only when grown in medium containing added free fatty acid but also show this response to other environmental changes. Thus, Mackenzie *et al.* (1967a,b) were able to show cellular triglyceride droplet formation in cells cultivated at low pH (6.9) in the presence of glycerol (5%) or phenol (2 mM), and in medium containing rabbit serum (Mackenzie *et al.*, 1964a, 1966, 1967a). This ability to respond to changes in the environmental conditions by increased triglyceride synthesis is variable among different cell lines: L cells will exhibit a 74% increase in cellular lipid (primarily triglyceride) when rabbit serum is substituted for horse serum; under the same conditions HeLa cells showed less than a 10% increase in lipid, and a line of rabbit liver cells exhibited an 85% increase in lipid. Chang human liver cells and a line of rat liver cells showed a 13 and 18% increase in lipid, respectively (Mackenzie *et al.*, 1967a). The increased triglyceride content of these cells when grown in rabbit serum has been directly associated with the albumin fraction of this serum (Mackenzie *et al.*, 1967a), which may supply fatty acids more readily to the cells than does albumin from sera of other species. This difference may be related to the fatty acid content of rabbit serum albumin or to its fatty acid binding constants (Mackenzie *et al.*, 1967a).

The appearance and chemical composition of the lipid droplets formed in tissue culture cells in response to added exogenous fatty acids (Geyer, 1967; Moskowitz, 1967), low pH (Mackenzie *et al.*, 1967a,b), and rabbit serum (Mackenzie *et al.*, 1967a) have been thoroughly studied. The droplets, which are located in the cytoplasm of the cell, vary in diameter from approximately 0.5 to 1.0 μ (Mackenzie *et al.*, 1967a; Moskowitz, 1967). Under conditions favorable to high cellular lipid accumulation these particles may occupy almost the entire non-nuclear space; however, even when present in large numbers they remain as discrete units and show no tendency to coalesce into larger vacuoles (Geyer, 1967; Moskowitz, 1967; Mackenzie *et al.*, 1967a). The lack of coalescence can be attributed to the presence of a limiting membrane surrounding each droplet (Mackenzie *et al.*, 1966, 1967a; Moskowitz, 1967).

The staining properties of these droplets vary, depending on the type of fatty acid used to induce triglyceride accumulation. Thus, it has been demonstrated (Moskowitz, 1967) that the cytoplasm of L cells incubated in medium containing unsaturated fatty acids readily stained with Nile blue; however, no such reaction was obtained from cells exposed to saturated fatty acids, even though these cells also contained lipid droplets. It has been proposed (Moskowitz, 1967) that this difference in staining may be attributed to the fact that triglycerides composed of saturated fatty acids would be solidified at the temperature at which these experiments were conducted and, therefore, as such, would not stain with Nile blue. This histological observation, together with results from direct chemical analysis (Geyer, 1967), demonstrate that fatty acids added to the growth medium are incorporated into cellular triglycerides without extensive change in the fatty acid molecule.

Studies (Mackenzie *et al.*, 1966, 1967a) on the chemical composition of a purified lipid droplet cell fraction obtained from L cells and rabbit liver cells grown in rabbit serum demonstrated that these droplets were composed of 2–4% protein and 90–91% lipid. Triglycerides accounted for 90–92% of the total particle lipid, whereas phospholipid content ranged from 1 to 2% of the total lipid, and sterol content was less than 0.2%. The most prominent fatty acids recovered in this fraction were palmitic acid (27% of total fatty acids) and linoleic acid (25%).

The reversible nature of cellular lipid accumulation has been demonstrated by several investigators (Mackenzie *et al.*, 1964a; Geyer, 1967; Moskowitz, 1967). The disappearance of cellular lipid droplets and the decrease in accumulated triglycerides can usually be linked to changes in environmental conditions which favor reduced exogenous fatty acid incorporation. Thus, when this triglyceride accumulation was induced by cultivation of tissue culture cells in medium containing rabbit serum, replacement of the rabbit serum with horse serum resulted in a marked reduction in cellular triglyceride levels (Mackenzie *et al.*, 1964a); with the triglyceride fatty acid probably being used for continued cellular phospholipid synthesis (Geyer,

1967). In other experiments in which L cells had accumulated triglycerides because of the addition of free fatty acids to the culture medium, removal of these cells to a control medium containing albumin resulted in a disappearance of cellular lipid particles (Moskowitz, 1967).

Utilization and disappearance of accumulated triglycerides may not only result from changes in environmental conditions, but may also result from an adaptive response of the cell, provoked by continued cultivation under conditions which result in triglyceride accumulation. Moskowitz (1967) has demonstrated that L cells grown in medium to which oleic acid has been added accumulated triglycerides in lipid droplets within the cells during the first 2 days of incubation. Following this initial accumulation period, there was a marked decrease in cellular triglyceride droplets. Histochemical examination showed that a marked increase in cellular lipase could be correlated with the disappearance of triglycerides. This cellular response (i.e., increase in lipase and utilization of triglycerides) was demonstrated in cells exposed to unsaturated fatty acids. There was no pronounced appearance of lipase in cells grown in medium containing either palmitic or stearic acids, and the triglycerides synthesized in response to the saturated fatty acids persisted within the cells.

Although considerable quantities of exogenous fatty acids may be initially incorporated into cellular triglycerides, studies by Geyer (1967) indicated that the cellular triglyceride fatty acids may, in turn, be utilized by the cells for phospholipid synthesis. He showed that, upon continued incubation of L cells prelabeled with acetate-C^{14}, there was a shift in C^{14} from triglyceride to phospholipids. These observations, together with others indicating that accumulated triglycerides are reutilized by cells, suggest that exogenous fatty acids are a prime requirement for phospholipid synthesis. The accumulation of triglycerides probably occurs in response to conditions which supply fatty acid in excess of that needed for phospholipid synthesis. Thus, several investigators (Geyer, 1967; Moskowitz, 1967; Mackenzie *et al.*, 1967a) have recently concluded that the accumulation of lipid droplets within tissue culture cells is not a degenerative process, as some earlier investigators had suggested, but rather one which permits these cells to store excess fatty acid. Data obtained from studies utilizing L cells also indicate that after labeled exogenous fatty acid is incorporated into cellular triglycerides or phospholipids, these fatty acids are not readily utilized as an energy source (Geyer, 1967). In this system a large percentage of the $C^{14}O_2$ resulting from the oxidation of C^{14}-fatty acid was produced during the initial labeling period, suggesting that fatty acids are most available for oxidation when they are first incorporated into tissue culture cells and are present in the cellular free fatty acid pool.

D. CELLULAR PHOSPHOLIPID CONTENT AND SYNTHESIS

Although phospholipids represent the largest single class of lipids present in tissue culture cells, they have, in the past, received the least attention. One of the prime functions of the fatty acids incorporated by cells from the culture medium is to supply fatty acid for cellular phospholipid synthesis. Thus, following a 24-hour growth period under conditions which do not favor excessive triglyceride synthesis, most of the labeled exogenous free fatty acid incorporated by HeLa cells could be recovered as phospholipids (Geyer, 1967).

Studies of a number of different cell lines (Bole and Castor, 1964; Carruthers, 1966; Kritchevsky and Howard, 1966; Weinstein, 1968; Gaush and Youngner, 1963) have demonstrated that the phospholipid spectra of tissue culture cells is similar to that obtained from most animal tissue, with lecithin the major phospholipid present, followed by phosphatidylethanolamine. Phosphatidylserine and sphingomyelin are present in appreciable amounts with lower levels of lysolecithin, phosphatidic acid and phosphatidylinositol. Various fractionation studies of tissue culture cells (Tsao and Cornatzer, 1967a; Weinstein, 1968) have demonstrated the presence of these phospholipids in all subcellular fractions studied, with the mitochondrial fraction yielding the highest lipid phosphorus–protein ratio (Tsao and Cornatzer, 1967a). Studies utilizing purified L cell plasma membrane preparations have shown that phospholipids comprise a smaller percentage of the total lipids of isolated plasma membrane (59.5%) than that of whole L cells (80.5%) (Weinstein, 1968). These membranes have a higher percentage of sphingomyelin and a lower lecithin and phosphatidylethanolamine content than the whole L cell (Weinstein, 1968).

A number of cell lines have been successfully cultured in serum-free medium (Higuchi, 1963; Evans et al., 1964; Healy and Parker, 1966), thus demonstrating that these cells are capable of synthesizing sufficient phospholipids for continued growth. Data obtained from a study (Bailey, 1964a) on L cells grown in a lipid-free chemically defined medium showed that these cells had a phospholipid content of 6.8% of the cellular dry weight, whereas the same cells grown in medium containing 25% human serum had a phospholipid content equivalent to 11.2% of the cellular dry weight. This study (Bailey,

1964a) also showed that labeled acetate incorporation into cellular phospholipids was inhibited by 86% when cells were grown in the presence of serum.

Very few studies have been made of the synthesis of the individual cellular phospholipids. In experiments measuring the percent distribution of P^{32} incorporated into the phospholipids obtained from four different cell lines (HeLa, bovine lymphosarcoma, monkey heart, chick embryo endothelium), the label appeared first in phosphatidylinositol, after which the percent activity of this fraction decreased (McCarl and Triebold, 1963). The incorporation of P^{32} into lecithin increased gradually for approximately 20 hours; at this time its percent activity was greater than the other phospholipids examined.

A similar study (Tsao and Cornatzer, 1967b) which examined the specific activity of P^{32} in cellular phospholipids of HeLa, KB, human heart, and human liver cells during a 3–4-hour incubation period showed the greatest incorporation of P^{32} in the phosphatidylinositol fraction. This was followed in order by polyglycerol phosphate, phosphatidylethanolamine, lecithin, sphingomyelin, and phosphatidylserine. This study also demonstrated that, although there were some differences in the incorporation of P^{32}, the general labeling pattern was similar in all of the cells investigated.

Studies on fatty acid incorporation into the phospholipids of HeLa cells showed an asymmetric incorporation into the 1 and 2 position of the glycerol moiety of cellular lecithin and phosphatidylethanolamine (Stoffel and Scheid, 1967). Sixteen carbon fatty acids were preferentially incorporated into lecithin; C_{18} acids were approximately equally distributed between lecithin and phosphatidylethanolamine; and C_{20} polyenoic acids were recovered mainly in the 2 position of the glycerol of phosphatidylethanolamine. Other polyunsaturated fatty acids also demonstrated a preferential incorporation at the 2 position of the glycerol moiety (Stoffel and Scheid, 1967).

III. Cholesterol

A. Free Cholesterol Content and Incorporation

Of all of the lipid classes present in tissue culture cells, the sterols, particularly unesterified cholesterol, have been the most thoroughly studied. The data suggest that free cholesterol primarily plays a structural role in the cell. This conclusion is based on the observations that no tissue culture cell line has been examined which actively metabolizes cholesterol, converting it ultimately to products other than cholesteryl esters. It has been shown that there is no extensive catabolism of cholesterol in MBIII cells (Bailey, 1967) or in L5178Y cells (Rothblat *et al.*, 1966, 1967). In both cases all of the incorporated sterol can be recovered from the cells. However, L cells and L5178Y cells are capable of esterifying a portion of the free sterol taken up from the growth medium (Rothblat and Kritchevsky, 1967a). In contrast to these findings, Bensch *et al.* (1961) reported that up to 50% of the labeled cholesterol incorporated by L cells could not be recovered as digitonin-precipitable material following saponification. This observation could not be confirmed in recent experiments in which it was found that all of the cellular label present in L cells grown in medium containing cholesterol-4-C^{14} could be recovered as digitonin-precipitable material following saponification (Rothblat, 1968, unpublished). It is obvious, however, that the assumption that all tissue culture cells do not actively metabolize cholesterol can be fully justified only after additional studies, particularly of primary cells, since it is possible that the enzymic pathways necessary for the conversion of sterol to other products are lost upon continued cultivation.

Many of the studies on sterol metabolism in tissue culture cells have dealt with the factors which influence the cellular uptake and content of sterol. These studies can be divided into two general types: (1) those in which the incorporation of sterol is measured directly (usually through the use of labeled sterol), and (2) those which measure the change in cellular cholesterol levels in cells grown under various conditions. Although results obtained from the two techniques often complement each other, factors producing changes in cholesterol incorporation may not always lead to changes in cellular cholesterol content.

The free and esterified sterol content of various cell strains and lines has been studied by various investigators. Values for free cholesterol content have ranged from approximately 6 μg free cholesterol per milligram dry weight to 25 μg/mg dry weight (Rothblat and Kritchevsky, 1968). With only two exceptions the esterified sterol content of tissue culture cells has been lower than the free sterol content. These values have ranged from 0.3 μg cholesteryl ester per milligram dry weight to 6.4 μg/mg dry weight, with the cholesteryl ester-free cholesterol ratio ranging from 0.01 to 0.41 (Rothblat and Kritchevsky, 1968). The L5178Y line of mouse lymphoblasts (Rothblat *et al.*, 1967) and a cell line derived from a human mesothelium carcinoma (Carruthers, 1966) have been shown to contain a cholesteryl ester–free cholesterol ratio greater than 1.0. However, the esterified cholesterol content of the L5178Y cell line is variable, depending on the type of serum in which these cells are grown. Thus, growth in fetal calf serum yields cells with a cholesteryl ester–free cholesterol ratio of less than 1.0, whereas growth in other types of sera increases the esterified sterol content without producing a proportionate increase in free sterol content (Rothblat *et al.*, 1967).

The influence of the serum in the growth medium on cellular sterol content has been extensively studied. Comparative studies using five different cell lines (L, HeLa, Chang liver, rat liver, and rabbit liver) grown in medium containing horse and rabbit serum (20%) demonstrated no marked difference in cell sterol content (Mackenzie *et al.*, 1964a). Similar studies using L5178Y mouse lymphoblasts grown in medium containing calf, fetal calf, or horse serum (2.5%) showed that changing the type of serum in the medium did produce changes in the level of esterified sterol; however, no effect was observed on cellular free sterol content (Rothblat *et al.*, 1967). In other investigations, Bailey (1961) showed that MBIII cells cultivated in medium with rabbit serum (25%) had a higher cellular cholesterol content than did similar cells grown in the same medium with human serum (25%), although the rabbit serum itself had a lower cholesterol content than did the human serum.

It is obvious that the question of the effect of various types of sera on cellular sterol content remains to be resolved by additional experiments utilizing a wide variety of cell lines and strains. Aside from the obvious differences which might be encountered in experiments using different types of cells, other variables such as age and metabolic condition of the cells may also influence cellular sterol content. Also, the concentration at which various sera are incorporated into the growth medium could result in differences in cellular sterol levels. A limited amount of experimental data, however, indicates that varying the cholesterol content of the medium does not always influence cellular cholesterol levels; these levels, for example, remained constant even when MBIII cells were grown in medium in which serum was added at varying concentrations to give cholesterol values ranging from 16 to 80 mg-% (Bailey, 1961, 1967). Although increasing the cholesterol concentration of the medium by increasing the serum level of the medium did not produce changes in cellular cholesterol, Bailey found that the addition of free cholesterol to the growth medium as a Tween emulsion resulted in a preferential uptake of the added sterol and a marked increase in the cellular sterol levels. A similar cellular response to the addition of free cholesterol to the growth medium was obtained by Morrison *et al.* (1963) in studies employing chick aorta and HeLa cells and by Rutstein *et al.* (1958) using human aortic cell cultures.

The changes in sterol content of tissue culture cells grown in different types of sera and the lack of cellular response to changes in the serum concentration in the medium, together with the observation that added free sterol is taken up preferentially by cells, led Bailey (1961, 1967) to conclude that cellular cholesterol levels are determined by the ratio of cholesterol to other components in the serum. This observation has received support from free cholesterol uptake studies conducted on L5178Y mouse lymphoblasts in an experimental system utilizing delipidized rabbit serum protein as a carrier of the sterol (Rothblat and Kritchevsky, 1967b; Rothblat *et al.*, 1968b). It was observed that the addition of phospholipid markedly reduced free sterol adsorption during a 5-hour incubation period and that individual phospholipids differed in their ability to reduce this cholesterol uptake. The efficiency of inhibition among the various phospholipids studied was in the order of sphingomyelin > lecithin > phosphatidyl-ethanolamine > phosphatidylserine.

The amount of labeled cholesterol incorporated into L5178Y cells during a 5-hour incubation period was shown to be related to the free cholesterol-phospholipid ratio in the incubation medium. Although the cholesterol to phospholipid ratio was of prime importance, the amount of protein present also influenced uptake. In addition to the observation that varying the ratio of individual lipoprotein components influenced free cholesterol adsorption, it was also found that proportionally increasing the concentration of all of the components resulted in increased adsorption.

The addition of glycerides or various free fatty acids to the cholesterol-protein complex had no marked effect on free cholesterol incorporation. The lack of a pronounced effect of free fatty acids on cholesterol adsorption during short-term experiments supports the observation that the addition of either saturated or unsaturated fatty acid had no effect on the cellular cholesterol content of MBIII cells growing in medium containing added free cholesterol (Bailey, 1961, 1967). These observations of MBIII cells do not agree with those which have been obtained by Rutstein *et al.* (1958), using human aortic cells, who demonstrated histologically that the intracellular deposition of lipid caused by adding cholesterol to the culture medium is completely inhibited by the simultaneous addition of linolenic acid. Deposition of lipid within the cell was increased by the simultaneous addition of stearic acid. In a different series of experiments with cultured aorta cells under similar experimental conditions, Curtis and Galvin (1963) demonstrated that a wide variety of compounds, including vitamins, steroids, phospholipids, and fatty acids, could reduce or eliminate lipid deposition in the cells as shown by histological examination. However, conclusions based only on histological examination may be misleading, since this experimental method cannot distinguish between true uptake and differential mobilization of lipids within the cell. It is also possible that the difference obtained in similar studies on mouse lymphoblasts and human aorta cells may reflect fundamental differences in the metabolism of various cells in culture.

In studies on arterial cells maintained in culture, Robertson (1961, 1963, 1967) demonstrated that the surface charge of the cell also plays a role in sterol incorporation. He found that the presence of cationic compounds such as protamine sulfate or methylated bovine serum albumin increased the cellular incorporation of isotopically labeled free cholesterol, whereas anionic compounds such as sodium stearate, n-acetylated bovine serum albumin and heparin reduced free cholesterol uptake. In addition, Robertson (1967) found that the presence of ATP in the culture medium stimulated the cellular uptake of labeled free cholesterol and that reduction in oxygen concentration in the medium also stimulated cholesterol uptake. In contrast to these data on cultured arterial cells, which suggest enzymic uptake of free cholesterol, it was observed (Rothblat et al., 1966, 1967) that heating L5178Y cells (60°C for 30 minutes) reduced incorporation of free cholesterol by $30 \pm 5\%$ over a 1-hour incubation period. It was also found that exposure of the cells to both KCN and NaF did not reduce the uptake of labeled sterol in short-term experiments (Rothblat et al., 1967).

The intracellular location of cholesterol is a topic of considerable interest but one which has not received thorough investigation. One of the major questions which must be resolved is the extent to which both free and esterified sterol are maintained within the cell, either associated with cellular membranes or in lipid vacuoles. Mackenzie et al. (1964b), in a study on five mammalian cell lines growing in culture under normal conditions, concluded that cholesterol is confined almost entirely to unit membrane structures. These investigators (Mackenzie et al., 1966, 1967a,b) observed that the lipid-rich particles found in many cells growing in high levels of rabbit serum contained mainly triglycerides with very low levels of sterol. Although cells cultured under normal conditions may not exhibit accumulation of sterol in vacuoles or lipid particles, cells can be forced to accumulate excess sterol which probably is not membrane-associated. Microscopic examination of L cells grown in medium containing added free cholesterol (Bailey, 1961, 1967) showed that these cells contained cholesterol microcrystals. The addition of excess free cholesterol to the culture was also shown to result in the formation of Liebermann-Burchard positive granules in cultured human aorta cells (Rutstein *et al.*, 1958), and in lipid deposition and necrosis in both human and canine aorta cells (Curtis and Galvin, 1963). By the combined use of autoradiography and electron microscopy, Robertson (1967) demonstrated the incorporation of exogenous labeled free cholesterol into lipid vacuoles in cultured human arterial cells. Robertson (1963, 1967) also showed the progressive movement of labeled free cholesterol from cell membrane "ghosts" into the "microsomal-cell sap."

The presence of sterol in the cellular plasma membrane was clearly demonstrated by comparative lipid studies on intact L cells and their isolated plasma membranes (Weinstein, 1968). The neutral lipid fraction of purified plasma membranes represented 40.5% of the total lipids, whereas neutral lipids comprised only 19.4% of the total lipids of whole L cells. In the membrane preparations there was a relative enrichment of cholesterol and glyceride, with 93% of the sterol in the plasma membrane being recovered as free cholesterol.

The intracellular distribution of esterified sterol among subcellular organelles has received even less study than has that of free cholesterol, probably because of the low cellular level of esterified sterol in most cells maintained in culture. Robertson (1968) studied human arterial cells and found 65–86% of the total cholesterol isolated from cell vacuoles to be esterified, while studies on L5178Y mouse lymphoblasts have revealed that following cell disruption 82% of the total cell cholesterol ester could be recovered in a "debris" fraction consisting of membrane and nuclear fragments and other material which pelleted under low centrifugal force (Rothblat *et al.*, 1967). A difference in the intracellular distribution of free and esterified sterol in these cells was demonstrated by the observation that only 51% of the free cholesterol was recovered in this "debris" fraction.

B. CELLULAR STEROL EXCRETION

The observation by Bailey (1961) that the growth of cells in culture resulted in a depletion of cholesteryl esters but not of free sterol from the medium, together with the finding that free sterol is incorporated from the culture medium by cells, suggested that free cholesterol is excreted by tissue culture cells. This suggestion was later confirmed in a series of studies conducted on L cells and MBIII cells (Bailey,

1964b, 1965, 1967). Using cultures prelabeled with radioactive cholesterol, it was demonstrated that there was a continuous excretion of cholesterol into the culture medium. At the end of the growth cycle approximately 60% of the labeled free sterol in the cells at the start of the experiment could be recovered from the culture medium. The cellular excretion of sterol was dependent on some component in serum since no sterol was released into serum-free medium. Release of sterol into medium was related to serum concentrations and to the species of serum used, with rabbit serum being the least efficient in promoting excretion. In additional studies, cholesterol synthesized by L cells from mevalonate-C^{14} and acetate-C^{14} was also excreted into the culture medium. Fractionation of serum on ion-exchange cellulose columns showed that most of the excretion catalyzing ability of serum was recovered in the α-globulin fraction. The association of cellular sterol excretion activity with the α-globulin fraction of serum may be explained by studies utilizing delipidized rabbit serum as the acceptor of excreted free cholesterol from prelabeled L5178Y cells (Burns and Rothblat, 1969). These studies have shown that the amount of free sterol released into the culture medium from prelabeled cells is significantly increased when phospholipids are added to the culture medium together with either delipidized serum protein or bovine serum albumin. Thus, following a 6-hour incubation period in medium containing delipidized rabbit serum protein, 11% of the cellular radioactive free cholesterol was released into the medium. When albumin was substituted for delipidized protein the excretion value was 4%. When albumin or delipidized serum protein was present, together with a mixture of serum phospholipids, the cholesterol released rose to 21 and 17%, respectively. These values compare favorably with that of 24% obtained when whole rabbit serum was present at equivalent concentrations. It was found that the amount of excretion obtained in this system was related to phospholipid-protein ratios of the delipidized protein and to the total concentration of the phospholipid-protein complex in the medium.

C. CHOLESTEROL SYNTHESIS

Although it is generally assumed that cells in culture are capable of synthesizing cholesterol, there have been few reported studies of cellular sterol synthesis. If, however, the assumption is made that all cells in culture require cholesterol for growth, then the number of cell lines capable of sterol synthesis is quite large. Since many cell lines have been cultivated in defined media containing no added cholesterol

(Higuchi, 1963; Evans *et al.*, 1964; Healy and Parker, 1966), it follows that these cells have the potential to synthesize the required sterol. Berliner *et al.* (1958) demonstrated cholesterol synthesis from acetate in U12-72 human fibroblasts grown in serum-containing medium; however, the amount of sterol synthesized was not estimated. Similar results were obtained from studies on L5178Y cells (Rothblat *et al.*, 1967) and with L cells (Bensch *et al.*, 1961) grown in serum-containing medium. Robertson (1967), using aorta cells, demonstrated the incorporation of labeled acetate into cholesterol and showed that cultivating these cells under low oxygen concentrations reduced acetate utilization for cholesterol synthesis. In experiments conducted with WI38 diploid human cells and WI38 VA13, a transformed mixoploid cell line, it was observed that both cell types had the ability to synthesize cholesterol from acetate (Cristofalo *et al.*, 1969). The transformed cell line synthesized cholesterol at a rate significantly greater than that of the normal cells. It was calculated, however, that the amount of sterol synthesized in both cell lines was not sufficient for most cellular sterol requirements, suggesting that much of this cellular potential for sterol biosynthesis was inhibited by the presence of serum cholesterol in the growth medium. The ability of serum to suppress *de novo* cholesterol synthesis is clearly illustrated in studies conducted by Bailey (1964a, 1966, 1967) on MBIII and L cells. By growing these cells on a chemically defined medium, he demonstrated that the cells were capable of synthesizing all of the sterol necessary for continued growth. L cells grown in this serum-free medium had a cellular sterol level similar to cells grown in medium containing 25% human serum, and the incorporation of acetate into cellular cholesterol was reduced by 96%. The addition of free cholesterol to the growth medium in the absence of serum also suppressed sterol synthesis to a similar extent. Glucose was shown to be an efficient precursor for cell cholesterol. When serum was added to the growth medium, however, the depression of glucose incorporation was much less than that observed with acetate, which suggests a block in the conversion of acetate to acetyl-CoA. In the same cell systems, Bailey (1966, 1967) observed that the effect of serum on mevalonic acid incorporation into cellular cholesterol was somewhat different in the two cell lines. In L cells grown in serum-free medium containing mevalonic-2-C^{14} acid, cholesterol accounted for over 75% of the total radioactivity incorporated into cellular lipids but for only about 45% in the presence of serum. In MBIII cells grown in serum-free medium, cholesterol comprised a much smaller fraction of the labeled lipids (44%); addition of serum to the medium had no effect on this level. These observations led Bailey

(1966, 1967) to conclude that the major block in cellular sterol synthesis produced by exogenous cholesterol is at the level of acetate incorporation at the two-carbon level. He also suggested that minor blocks may occur in the conversion of glucose to acetyl-CoA and between isopentenyl pyrophosphate and cholesterol.

D. Utilization of Esterified Cholesterol

Because of a lack of satisfactory experimental conditions for the *in vitro* addition of labeled esterified sterol into serum in any truly physiological manner, there is less information available concerning the factors which influence cholesteryl ester incorporation and utilization by tissue culture cells as compared to that available for the incorporation of free sterol. The information available suggests that esterified cholesterol is, for the most part, not utilized by tissue culture cells as a completely separate lipid class but rather that the ester is hydrolyzed to its sterol and fatty acid components, which are then utilized by the cells.

Although most tissue culture cells which have been examined contain much smaller amounts of esterified than free sterol, they have been shown to incorporate exogenous cholesteryl ester from the growth medium. Studies on L5178Y cells exposed to rabbit serum labeled *in vivo* by cholesterol C¹¹ feeding (Rothblat *et al.*, 1966, 1967) show that serum cholesteryl ester is taken up by cells in culture. It was observed that esterified sterol was incorporated by cells at a rate considerably lower than that found with free cholesterol; however, no specific data were obtained on the nature of the uptake process.

Additional data demonstrating the cellular incorporation of esterified sterol using MBIII cells have been presented by Bailey (1961). Although almost all of the sterol in these cells was present as free cholesterol, during the growth of the cells most of the decrease in sterol in the medium occurred in the ester fraction. Depletion of the cholesteryl esters from the medium occurred during cellular growth, but isotopic studies indicated that free cholesterol was being incorporated by the cells, even though this uptake was not paralleled by a depletion of free sterol from the culture medium. These data suggested that the cholesteryl esters were hydrolyzed by cellular enzymes to free cholesterol and fatty acids, after which the free cholesterol was excreted into the culture medium. Data confirming hydrolysis of cholesteryl esters by tissue culture cells were obtained from comparative studies on L cells and L5178Y cells (Rothblat *et al.*, 1967, 1968a). Growing cultures of cells were exposed to cholesteryl-4-C^{14} esters which had been added to the culture medium in trace amounts. Following an incubation period of 18–24 hours, the amount of free sterol present in the cell which was a product of cellular ester hydrolysis was determined. The data obtained showed that from 9 to 54 % of the total label in the cells could be recovered as free cholesterol. It was evident that tissue culture cells could hydrolyze esterified sterol and that the amount of cholesteryl ester hydrolyzed differed in various cells.

Although considerable excretion of free sterol from cells can be demonstrated, studies with L5178Y and L cells have shown that very little esterified sterol is returned to the growth medium (Rothblat and Kritchevsky, 1967a), even though the L5178Y cell line contains considerable quantities of esterified sterol. Whereas very little esterified sterol was excreted from these cells, it was demonstrated that the free cholesterol liberated from cholesteryl esters by cell hydrolysis was recovered in the medium. This observation confirms the speculation of Bailey (1961) that free cholesterol levels of this medium could be maintained during the growth of cells in culture through the cellular hydrolysis of esterified sterol followed by the excretion of the free cholesterol obtained upon hydrolysis.

Additional experiments using cholesteryl 1-palmitate-C^{14} have been conducted to determine the metabolic fate of the fatty acid liberated upon cellular cholesteryl ester hydrolysis (Rothblat *et al.*, 1967, 1968a). It was found that in both L cells and L5178Y cells a major portion of the fatty acid which was released from the cholesteryl ester could be recovered in the cellular phospholipid fraction. All other lipids were also labeled, and small but detectable amounts of C^{14} were recovered as C^{14}O$_2$ and in the defatted cellular residue.

Although tissue culture cells can incorporate exogenous cholesteryl ester from the growth medium, they may also synthesize some esterified sterol even when the cells are grown in the presence of exogenous cholesteryl ester. Thus, acetate incorporation into cellular cholesteryl esters has been demonstrated in primary chicken cells and in HeLa and Chang liver cells (Halevy and Geyer, 1961). This study did not, however, determine if the labeled acetate was incorporated into both the cholesteryl and fatty acid moieties of the ester. The cholesteryl ester synthesis from acetate in cells grown in serum-containing medium probably represents only a small percentage of the actual cellular capability for ester synthesis. As in the case of other lipid classes, acetate incorporation into cholesteryl esters of L cells is reduced by 60 % when serum is added to the growth medium (Bailey, 1964a). Other studies on L5178Y cells grown in serum-containing medium showed that only 7.5% of the total cellular sterol synthesized from labeled acetate was recovered as ester (Rothblat *et al.*, 1967). Exogenous free cholesterol can also be incorporated into cellular cholesteryl esters; it has been shown that both L cells and L5178Y cells are capable of incorporating exogenous labeled free cholesterol into cellular esters, although the amount esterified was relatively small (Rothblat and Kritchevsky, 1967a) with values ranging from less than 1 to 15% of the exogenous free cholesterol taken up being recovered as cholesteryl esters.

IV. General Considerations of Lipid Metabolism in Tissue Culture Cells

The information available on lipid metabolism in tissue culture cells is insufficient to allow the formulation of precise metabolic principles governing lipid metabolism. There are sufficient data, however, to develop working hypotheses which, to a large extent, can be tested and which, in turn, suggest other questions to be developed in the future.

The first generalization, based on data derived from only one thoroughly studied cell line (L cell) (Bailey, 1964a, 1966, 1967), is that cells in culture can derive almost all of their required lipid from the serum lipids in the medium. If this is the case, then the mechanism by which these lipids gain entrance into the cells is of prime importance. Two general theoretical mechanisms for lipid uptake, the "particulate" and the "molecular" theories (Bailey, 1967), have been proposed. In both cases the lipids in the medium would be associated with serum proteins. Basically, according to the "particulate" theory, the whole serum lipoprotein molecule gains entrance into the cell and, once inside, the individual lipid components are then utilized. The mechanism by which whole lipoprotein molecules are incorporated would probably be the process of pinocytosis. An objection to the pinocytotic uptake of serum lipid by tissue culture cells is based on the assumption that if whole lipoprotein molecules were taken up the individual components of the lipoprotein molecule would probably be depleted from the culture medium at rates equivalent to the relative amounts of each component in the lipoprotein. As shown by Bailey (1967; Bailey *et al.*, 1959), this is not the case. In a tissue culture system utilizing MBIII cells, he showed that the most rapidly depleted lipid class was triglycerides, followed by phospholipids, and then cholesterol. It has been estimated that triglycerides are incorporated at rates similar to those of glycerol or lactic acid (Bailey, 1967).

In addition, it has been demonstrated (Rothblat *et al.*, 1966, 1967) that cholesteryl esters are taken up by cells at a rate lower than that of free cholesterol, even though esters are present in serum in higher concentrations. In other quantitative studies by Robertson (1965, 1967) it has been shown that there is a difference in the cellular incorporation rates of cholesterol and protein in a system in which aorta cells are exposed to double-labeled lipoprotein containing protein-I^{131} and cholesterol-H^3. Although this differential utilization of exogenous lipids suggests that the "particulate" theory of lipid uptake is not applicable, extensions of this theory could be developed which would be consistent with the available data.

One such extension would be a system in which the lipoprotein molecule is incorporated *in toto*, after which some of the individual lipids are utilized, and the remaining "depleted" molecule is then returned to the growth medium. Such a "protein return" mechanism may explain the relatively high level of free cholesterol excretion observed in a number of cell lines (Bailey, 1964b, 1965; Rothblat and Kritchevsky, 1967a); thus, lipid which had previously been incorporated could be returned to the growth medium on the "depleted" serum lipoprotein carrier.

According to the "molecular" theory of cell lipid uptake the lipoprotein molecule does not enter the cell but remains at the cell surface. At this site the individual lipids of serum lipoproteins are transferred to plasma membrane lipoproteins. Exogenous lipid is then transferred from the plasma membrane to various other internal cellular membranes. In this case, separate uptake mechanisms may be operating for each of the individual lipid classes.

It is obvious that both the "molecular" and "particulate" mechanisms are not mutually exclusive and that both systems could be operating simultaneously to supply lipid to the cells. Future detailed studies using isotopically labeled serum proteins should be able to resolve many questions related to the possible incorporation and utilization of serum proteins by tissue culture cells.

No detailed investigations have been conducted on free fatty acid uptake employing tissue culture cells. However, the ability to regulate free fatty acid incorporation and subsequent cellular triglyceride accumulation by controlling both fatty acid and albumin concentrations in the medium suggests a system similar to that which has been reported for ascites tumor cells. In this case, nonenzymic uptake of fatty acid is governed by the molar ratio of fatty acid to albumin ($\bar{v}$) in the medium, independent of total concentrations of fatty acid–albumin complex (Spector *et al.*, 1965; Spector and Steinberg, 1965).

Data on triglyceride and phospholipid incorporation are insufficient to permit the formulation of any specific mechanism by which these lipids are incorporated into tissue culture cells. Calculations based on data obtained from MBIII cells indicate, however, that pinocytosis cannot account for the observed rate of utilization of either triglycerides or phospholipids (Bailey, 1967). Although many assumptions are made in such calculations, the data suggest that exogenous glycerides are incorporated by tissue culture cells, in large part, through a "molecular" mechanism of uptake. This may be accomplished either by the transfer of the entire lipid molecule into the cell or through hydrolysis by serum or cellular enzymes, followed by the subsequent uptake of the liberated fatty acids.

Of all lipid classes, the incorporation of free cholesterol has been studied most extensively; however, it is still impossible to formulate a definite conclusion concerning the mechanism of uptake. Although the "molecular" type of uptake would seem to offer the best explanation of the available data, the question remains whether enzymes participate in the transfer of free cholesterol from serum to cell. The observation (Rothblat *et al.*, 1967) that heated (60°C for 30 minutes) cells retained much of their ability to incorporate free sterol suggests a nonenzymic process; however, the demonstration of increased uptake of sterol with the addition of ATP to the culture medium (Robertson, 1965, 1967) implicates the participation of enzymes. One possible explanation of these seemingly contradictory data is that the initial adsorption of lipoprotein to the cells and the transfer of free to sterol to plasma membrane lipoprotein may be a physical process, whereas the movement of the sterol within the cell and its incorporation into cellular membrane systems may be enzymic and stimulated by ATP.

Although serum cholesteryl esters are taken up by tissue culture cells, the mechanism by which this occurs has also not been elucidated. Both the "particulate" and "molecular" theories of sterol uptake may explain the reduced cellular incorporation of esters when compared to incorporation of free sterol. Differences have been observed in the binding of cholesteryl esters in serum lipoproteins compared to the binding of free cholesterol (Roheim *et al.*, 1963; Sodhi and Gould, 1967). A stronger binding of esters in serum lipoproteins might result in a reduced rate of transfer of esters from serum lipoprotein to plasma membrane lipoprotein or might make it necessary for the cell to incorporate the whole lipoprotein to obtain exogenous esters.

Although the exact nature of the various lipid uptake processes operating in tissue culture cells is not yet fully elucidated, it is possible to construct a hypothetical scheme for the cellular metabolism of lipids. Such a system is based on the assumption that even though cells in culture are capable of synthesizing a part or all of the lipids needed for growth the synthesis of fatty acids and sterol would be spared by the presence of serum lipids in the culture medium. Thus, fatty acids and sterols needed by the cells would be derived from exogenous sources.

In this hypothetical scheme (Fig. 1) the cells derive fatty acids from exogenous free fatty acids; the rate of uptake is governed by the molar ratio of albumin to free fatty acid. This exogenous supply of fatty acid may be supplemented by glyceride fatty acid made available through the hydrolysis of serum glycerides by serum or cell lipases. In cultures with a high cell density or low serum concentration, exogenous phospholipids may also be hydrolyzed as glyceride fatty acid becomes depleted. As free fatty acids are incorporated they are rapidly utilized, primarily for phospholipid synthesis. Almost all of this cellular phospholipid is incorporated into various cellular membranes. At this time, a considerable portion of the fatty acid is also utilized as an energy source, resulting in its ultimate oxidation to CO_2. Under conditions in

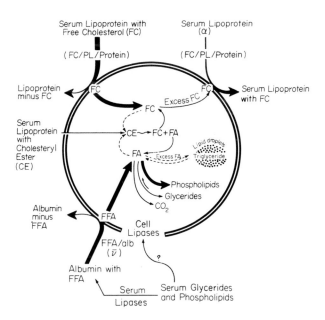

FIG. 1. A hypothetical scheme for lipid metabolism in tissue culture cells: FC, free cholesterol; CE, cholesteryl ester; FFA, free fatty acids; (FC/PL/protein), concentration and composition of lipoprotein; and $\bar{v}$, molar ratio of fatty acid to albumin.

which cells are grown in medium containing a high fatty acid–albumin ratio, increased fatty acid uptake occurs. However, no pronounced accumulation of cellular free fatty acid occurs; rather, the fatty acid in excess of that needed for phospholipid synthesis and as an energy source is synthesized into triglyceride. This lipid is stored within the cell as discrete lipid droplets. Triglyceride is then utilized, when needed, as a carbon and energy source. Because of its role as a reservoir for excess fatty acid, triglyceride is the major component of cellular lipid droplets or vacuoles. Thus, cellular levels of triglyceride are readily influenced by variations in conditions under which cells are grown.

In this hypothetical scheme, the cellular utilization of free sterol is closely linked to the serum lipoproteins present in the culture medium. Uptake of free sterol occurs through a physical process and is not mediated by cellular enzymes. In such a process, the exchange of cholesterol between serum lipoprotein and cell surface lipoprotein may be regulated, in large part, by the cholesterol, phospholipid, and protein composition of the individual lipoproteins. Changes in concentration or composition of serum lipoproteins could then result in changes in the rate and perhaps the amount of free sterol incorporated. Cellular sterol content is probably also a function of the cellular lipoprotein content and composition, since almost all of the cellular free sterol seems to be membrane-associated.

In this system, the exogenous free sterol entering cells is not oxidized but is incorporated as a structural unit in cellular membranes. Since the rate of free sterol uptake is, in large part, a function of the composition of the serum lipoprotein, the amount of free sterol incorporated into the cell may often exceed that which is needed for new membrane synthesis. In this case, however, no free sterol will accumulate, since the cells excrete excess free cholesterol in the presence of a serum lipoprotein "acceptor." This excretion process also depends in part on the concentration and composition of the serum lipoprotein; the data available indicate that the α-lipoproteins play a major role in excretion. Such a two-step exchange process, i.e., uptake and excretion, may explain the variation in cellular cholesterol levels sometimes obtained when cells are cultivated in different types of sera, since this cellular variation may result from differences in both the composition and concentration of the lipoproteins present in different sera. The observation that cellular cholesterol levels do not vary with changes in serum concentration in the medium could be explained by the fact that increasing the serum concentration does not change either the composition or ratio of the lipoproteins present;

thus, although more sterol may be adsorbed, more could be excreted. A concept similar to the one proposed by Gurd (1960) for the exchange of lipids between lipoproteins could be applied to both the uptake and release of free cholesterol in tissue culture cells. According to this hypothesis diffusion of free cholesterol would take place when serum lipoproteins come in contact with cell membrane lipoproteins forming a collision complex. The composition of the particular lipoproteins involved in this reaction would determine the partition coefficient of free cholesterol within the collision complex which, in turn, would govern the rate and direction of diffusion of cholesterol.

The cellular utilization of cholesteryl ester in this system is primarily that of ester hydrolysis, with the subsequent liberation of free cholesterol and fatty acids. The fatty acids liberated upon ester hydrolysis are utilized for a carbon and energy source. It is also possible that the liberated cholesteryl ester fatty acid is selectively utilized by the cells. Such a selective utilization may conserve the cholesteryl ester fatty acids which generally contain high percentages of polyunsaturated fatty acid. In this proposed system the synthesis of cholesteryl esters would occur only to a limited extent.

The free cholesterol is produced upon the cellular hydrolysis of incorporated exogenous cholesteryl ester pools with other cellular free sterol and is then used for membrane synthesis or returned to the culture medium. If the serum in the medium contains an active lecithin-cholesterol acyltransferase (Glomset, 1968), it is possible for the excreted cholesterol to serve as a substrate for the formation of newly esterified cholesterol, thus replacing that which has been depleted through cellular cholesteryl ester hydrolysis. However, it is probable that in a closed tissue culture system, which generally does not utilize fresh serum, enzymic activity would be low or nonexistent, and little or no esterified sterol would be regenerated.

This hypothetical metabolic system for cellular lipid metabolism is undoubtedly oversimplified. For example, no consideration has been given to such factors as the role of polyunsaturated fatty acids as essential metabolites in cellular nutrition, of cellular membrane turnover in the reutilization or excretion of cellular lipids, or of the negative feedback inhibition of various hydrolytic and synthetic mechanisms. Furthermore, the protein moiety of the serum lipoproteins has been treated as a simple carrier of lipid; its possible role in specifically associating with plasma membrane has not been discussed.

Finally, it must be noted that many of the principles proposed in this review may eventually be proved incorrect. However, this working hypothesis has the advantage of explaining much of the data available in the literature, and it may act as a framework for designing experiments for the study of lipid metabolism that will extend our understanding of these problems in the future, both in the whole animal and at the cellular level.

References

Bailey, J. M. (1961). *Proc. Soc. Exptl. Biol. Med.* **107**, 30.
Bailey, J. M. (1964a). *Proc. Soc. Exptl. Biol. Med.* **115**, 747.
Bailey, J. M. (1964b). *Am. J. Physiol.* **207**, 1221.
Bailey, J. M. (1965). *Exptl. Cell Res.* **37**, 175.
Bailey, J. M. (1966). *Biochim. Biophys. Acta* **125**, 226.
Bailey, J. M. (1967). *In* "Lipid Metabolism in Tissue Culture Cells" (G. H. Rothblat and D. Kritchevsky, eds.), Wistar Symp. Monograph No. 6, p. 85. Wistar Inst. Press, Philadelphia, Pennsylvania.
Bailey, J. M., and Menter, J. (1967). *Proc. Soc. Exptl. Biol. Med.* **125**, 101.
Bailey, J. M., Gey, G. O., and Gey, M. K. (1959). *Proc. Soc. Exptl. Biol. Med.* **100**, 686.
Bensch, K. G., King, D. W., and Socolow, E. L. (1961). *J. Biophys. Biochem. Cytol.* **9**, 135.
Berliner, D. L., Swim, H. E., and Dougherty, T. F. (1958). *Proc. Soc. Exptl. Biol. Med.* **99**, 51.
Bole, G. G., Jr., and Castor, C. W. (1964). *Proc. Soc. Exptl. Biol. Med.* **115**, 174.
Boyle, J. J., and Ludwig, E. H. (1962). *Nature* **196**, 893.
Burns, C. H., and Rothblat, G. H. (1969). *Biochim. Biophys. Acta.* **176**, 616.
Carruthers, C. (1966). *Oncologia* **20**, 167.
Cristofalo, V. J., Howard, B. V., and Kritchevsky, D. (1969). *In* "Research Progress in Organic-Biological and Medicinal Chemistry" (U. Gallo and L. Santamaria, eds.). North-Holland Publ., Amsterdam. In press.
Curtis, R. G., and Galvin, M. P. (1963). *Australian J. Exptl. Biol.* **41**, 687.
Day, A. J. (1967). *Advan. Lipid Res.* **5**, 185.
Evans, V. J., Bryant, J. C., Kerr, H. A., and Schilling, E. L. (1964). *Exptl. Cell Res.* **36**, 439.
Gaush, C. R., and Youngner, J. S. (1963). *Proc. Soc. Exptl. Biol. Med.* **112**, 1082.
Gerschenson, L. E., Harary, I., and Mead, J. F. (1967a). *Biochim. Biophys. Acta* **131**, 50.
Gerschenson, L. E., Mead, J. F., Harary, I., and Haggerty, D. F. (1967b). *Biochim. Biophys. Acta* **131**, 42.
Geyer, R. P. (1967). *In* "Lipid Metabolism in Tissue Culture Cells" (G. H. Rothblat and D. Kritchevsky, eds.), Wistar Symp. Monograph No. 6, p. 33. Wistar Inst. Press, Philadelphia, Pennsylvania.
Geyer, R. P., Bennett, A., and Rohr, A. (1962). *J. Lipid Res.* **3**, 80.
Glomset, J. A. (1968). *J. Lipid Res.* **9**, 155.
Gurd, F. R. N. (1960). *In* "Lipide Chemistry" (D. J. Hanahan, ed.), p. 282. Wiley, New York.
Haggerty, D. F., Gerschenson, L. E., Harary, I., and Mead, J. F. (1965). *Biochem. Biophys. Res. Commun.* **21**, 568.
Halevy, S., and Geyer, R. P. (1961). *Proc. Soc. Exptl. Biol. Med.* **108**, 6.
Ham, R. G. (1963). *Science* **140**, 802.

Harary, I., Gerschenson, L. E., Haggerty, D. F., Desmond, W., and Mead, J. F. (1967). *In* "Lipid Metabolism in Tissue Culture Cells" (G. H. Rothblat and D. Kritchevsky, eds.), Wistar Symp. Monograph No. 6, p. 17. Wistar Inst. Press, Philadelphia, Pennsylvania.

Healy, G. M., and Parker, R. C. (1966). *J. Cell Biol.* **30**, 531.

Higuchi, K. (1963). *J. Infect. Diseases* **112**, 213.

Howard, B. (1968). Ph.D. Thesis, Univ. of Pennsylvania, Philadelphia, Pennsylvania.

Johnson, M., and Mora, P. F. (1967). *Virology* **31**, 230.

Kagawa, Y. (1967). *Program 9th Japan. Conf. Biochem. Lipids, Tokyo,* p. 91.

Kritchevsky, D., and Howard, B. V. (1966). *Ann. Med. Exptl. Biol. Fenniae (Helsinki)* **44**, 343.

McCarl, R. L., and Triebold, H. O. (1963). *Exptl. Cell Res.* **29**, 475.

Mackenzie, C. G., Mackenzie, J. B., and Reiss, O. K. (1964a). *Exptl. Cell Res.* **36**, 533.

Mackenzie, C. G., Mackenzie, J. B, Reiss, O. K., and Philpott, D. E. (1964b). *Federation Proc.* **23**, 375.

Mackenzie, C. G., Mackenzie, J. B., Reiss, O. K., and Philpott, D. E. (1966). *Biochemistry* **5**, 1454.

Mackenzie, C. G., Mackenzie, J. B., and Reiss, O. K. (1967a). *In* "Lipid Metabolism in Tissue Culture Cells" (G. H. Rothblat and D. Kritchevsky, eds.), Wistar Symp. Monograph No. 6, p. 63. Wistar Inst. Press, Philadelphia, Pennsylvania.

Mackenzie, C. G., Mackenzie, J. B., and Reiss, O. K. (1967b). *J. Lipid Res.* **8**, 642.

Morrison, L. M., Schjeide, O. A., Quilligan, J. J., Jr., Freeman, L., and Holeman, R. (1963). *Proc. Soc. Exptl. Biol. Med.* **113**, 362.

Moskowitz, M. S. (1967). *In* "Lipid Metabolism in Tissue Culture Cells" (G. H. Rothblat and D. Kritchevsky, eds.), Wistar Symp. Monograph No. 6, p. 49. Wistar Inst. Press, Philadelphia, Pennsylvania.

Robertson, A. L., Jr. (1961). *Angiology* **12**, 525.

Robertson, A. L., Jr. (1963). *Proc. 1st Intern. Pharmacol. Meeting, Stockholm, 1961* **2**, 193.

Robertson, A. L., Jr. (1965). *In* "Biophysical Mechanisms in Vascular Homeostasis and Intravascular Thrombosis" (P. N. Sawyer, ed.), p. 267. Appleton-Century-Crofts, New York.

Robertson, A. L., Jr. (1967). *In* "Lipid Metabolism in Tissue Culture Cells" (G. H. Rothblat and D. Kritchevsky, eds.), Wistar Symp. Monograph No. 6, p. 115. Wistar Inst. Press, Philadelphia, Pennsylvania.

Robertson, A. L., Jr. (1968). Personal communication.

Roheim, P. S., Haft, D. E., Gidez, L. I., White, A., and Eder, H. A. (1963). *J. Clin. Invest.* **42**, 1277.

Rothblat, G. H., and Kritchevsky, D. (1967a). *Biochim. Biophys. Acta* **144**, 423.

Rothblat, G. H., and Kritchevsky, D. (1967b). *Circulation* **36**, 35. (Abstr.)

Rothblat, G. H., and Kritchevsky, D. (1968). *Exptl. Mol. Pathol.* **8**, 314.

Rothblat, G. H., Hartzell, R. W., Jr., Miahle, H., and Kritchevsky, D. (1966). *Biochim. Biophys. Acta* **116**, 133.

Rothblat, G., Hartzell, R., Miahle, H., and Kritchevsky, D. (1967). *In* "Lipid Metabolism in Tissue Culture Cells" (G. H. Rothblat and D. Kritchevsky, eds.), Wistar Symp. Monograph No. 6, p. 129. Wistar Inst. Press, Philadelphia, Pennsylvania.

Rothblat, G. H., Hartzell, R., Miahle, H., and Kritchevsky, D. (1968a). *Progr. Biochem. Pharmacol.* **4**, 317.

Rothblat, G. H., Buchko, M., and Kritchevsky, D. (1968b). *Biochim. Biophys. Acta* **164**, 327.

Rutstein, D. D., Ingenito, E. F., Craig, J. M., and Martinelli, M. (1958). *Lancet* i, 545.
Smith, S. C., Strout, R. G., Dunlop, W. R., and Smith, E. C. (1965). *J. Atherosclerosis Res.* **5**, 379.
Sodhi, H. S., and Gould, R. G. (1967). *J. Biol. Chem.* **242**, 1205.
Spector, A. A., and Steinberg, D. (1965). *J. Biol. Chem.* **240**, 3747.
Spector, A. A., Steinberg, D., and Tanaka, A. (1965). *J. Biol. Chem.* **240**, 1032.
Stoffel, W., and Scheid, A. (1967). *Z. Physiol. Chem.* **348**, 205.
Tsao, S. S., and Cornatzer, W. E. (1967a). *Lipids* **2**, 41.
Tsao, S. S., and Cornatzer, W. E. (1967b). *Lipids* **2**, 424.
Weinstein, D. B. (1968). *In* "Biological Properties of Mammalian Surface Membrane" (L. H. Manson, ed.), Wistar Symp. Monograph No. 8, p. 17. Wistar Inst. Press, Philadelphia, Pennsylvania.

Carcinogenic Effects of Steroids

FRITZ BISCHOFF

Santa Barbara Cottage Hospital Research Institute, Santa Barbara, California

I. Introduction 165
   A. The Ultimate Goal 165
   B. Terms 166
   C. Carcinogenic Mechanisms 167
II. Cholesterol and Derivatives 168
   A. Cholesterol Solid State Carcinogenesis 168
   B. Cholesterol Oxidation Products 176
III. Neoplasms Induced by Steroid Hormones 190
   A. Estrone-Dependent Rat Adrenal Cortex Carcinoma .. 190
   B. Anterior-Lobe Chromophobe Adenomas 190
   C. Endometrial Neoplasms in Rodents 191
   D. Interstitial Cell Tumors of the Testes 193
   E. Local Sarcomas 193
   F. Tumors of Lymphocyte, Monocyte, and Myeloid Cell
      Origin 195
   G. Mammary Carcinoma 197
   H. Uterine-Vaginal Neoplasms 206
   I. Granulosa-Cell Ovarian Tumors and Progestins 207
   J. The Golden Hamster 208
IV. Theoretical Considerations 209
   A. Steroid Hormone Transport 209
   B. Cell Permeability 211
   C. The Blocking Theories 212
   D. Carcinogenic Hydrocarbons from Steroids 216
   E. Tissue Culture 218
V. The Human Scene 222
   A. Etiology and Treatment of Endocrine-Linked
      Neoplasms 222
   B. Cholesterol Solid State Carcinogenesis 229
VI. Discussion 231
VII. Summary 235
   References 237

I. Introduction

A. THE ULTIMATE GOAL

Involvement of viruses in rodent and fowl cancer etiology is indisputable. To date such a relationship in humans remains unproved

(National Advisory Cancer Council, 1967). It is timely to reappraise the role of smaller molecules in human cancer and consider the production of carcinogens endogenously from normal body constituents. The structural similarities between the classic carcinogenic hydrocarbons and the steroids are obvious. Steroids may under certain conditions, at least in rodents, produce carcinogenic effects as dramatic as those of the hydrocarbons. The concept of a normal body constituent functioning as a carcinogen might appear paradoxical. It is precisely under such a circumstance that areas of contemporary thought regarding the carcinogen and carcinogenesis are challenged.

This review will not be concerned with the carcinogenic effects of radiation. Viruses will be considered only when steroids are also involved in the carcinogenic mechanism. However, the nonspecific surface phenomenon of solid state carcinogenesis must be evaluated, as well as the effects of caloric restriction and specific nutrients upon tumor growth. If the cancer cell is indeed a super cell, cancer cells derived from hormone-producing cells would in many cases continue hormone production. An extensive review of the steroid hormones produced by such cells will not be given.

Bischoff and Maxwell (1930) introduced the expression "hormones and cancer" and said: "The conception that the origin or extension of neoplastic tissue is due to the lack or imbalance in growth-regulating hormones (is) veiled in a varied phraseology . . . through the cancer literature." In an editorial of the *Journal of the American Medical Association* (*J. Am. Med. Assoc.*, 1930) referring to this work, the rationale for studying the influence of various organ extracts on cancer growth was challenged since cancer grows freely in organs with high hormone activity. At that time, general lack of knowledge concerning target site phenomena fostered the view that hormone activity was unrelated to normal and neoplastic extension. However, standardized growth hormone fractions of the pituitary anterior lobe were shown to accelerate the tumor growth of transplanted and spontaneous rodent neoplasms (Bischoff *et al.*, 1932) and to abolish the growth-retarding effect of pituitary destruction (Bischoff *et al.*, 1931). At the same time, Lacassagne (1932) induced mammary tumors in male mice by purified estrogens. Since then, an extensive literature concerned with the relation of hormones to cancer has evolved and within this category the steroid hormones play a major role.

B. Terms

The literal meaning of carcinogenic, "cancer producing," is legitimately applied. Although the word "carcinogen," cancer-producing substance, is often used in this broad sense, ambiguity may result. The distinction between a high-grade and low-grade carcinogen and a cocarcinogen is often confused. It is questionable whether the term "carcinogen" is correctly applied whenever the end result of a stimulus is cancer producing or whether its application should be restricted to an agent acting at the molecular level. A metabolic derivative of a substance may be carcinogenic at the cellular level: The derivative is a carcinogen; the substance, strictly speaking, is not. Since the mechanism at the cellular level is in doubt in most cases, the validity of considering a substance as a carcinogen will remain doubtful in many cases. Since all inert, relatively smooth solid substances of sufficient area when implanted subcutaneously produce sarcomas in rodents (solid state carcinogenesis), these substances should not be spoken of as carcinogens, although they are definitely carcinogenic under these circumstances. The mechanism of solid state carcinogenesis is conjectural: There may be no carcinogen involved—only cellular totipotency; a metabolite produced under stressful conditions may act as a carcinogen or an immune reaction may fail because of continued loss of proximity. A chemical carcinogen will have a minimal effective dose and will enhance cancer production with increasing dosage. A weak carcinogen requires many times the effective dose of a strong carcinogen and may not show increasing tumorigenesis with increasing dosage. A cocarcinogen does not produce cancer by itself but in conjunction with another substance, which is carcinogenic in its own right. The concept of cocarcinogens is useful for the two step theory of carcinogenesis. A cocarcinogen is, strictly speaking, not a substance which reacts endogenously with another substance to produce a carcinogen.

Definitions of terms used in animal tissue culture are given in *Cancer Research* (1967) and have been followed in this review.

C. Carcinogenic Mechanisms

1. *Unitary Theory*

With the local action of the chemical carcinogens there ensues death of cells, impairment of physiological function, and survival of cell variants better adapted to the changed environment. With the hormones injected at a site removed from the target organ, stimulation exceeding normal physiological levels for protracted periods of time induces excessive proliferation of the target cells. The carcinogenic hydrocarbons may also stimulate cells removed from the injection site. According to Poel's (1964) unitary concept of cancer causation, it is the progressive proliferation of normal cells caused either by a lessening of the homeostatic controls which govern normal cell reproduction or excessive stimulation to reproduction, which initiates the process of malignancy. The first process is illustrated by the local action of the carcinogenic hydrocarbons, the second by the steroid hormone acting upon the endocrine-sensitive target organ.

2. *Autoimmune Theory*

Because the carcinogenic hydrocarbons engender an autoimmune reaction, readily demonstrated by their ability to reduce the capacity to reject homographs, the unitary concept appears oversimplified. Since the activity of the carcinogenic hydrocarbons is correlated with their immunological properties, they may be breaking down a defense mechanism to a phenomenon which is taking place in the normal organ at all times — the initiation of unrestricted growth (Rubin, 1964). In the course of everyday life, cancers are continually begun and abruptly terminated.

3. *Two-Step versus Summation Theories*

Nakahara (1961) challenged the two-step theory of carcinogenesis, which postulated an initiative and a promotional phase (Berenblum, 1954), by showing that the initiation and promoting agents may be reversed with the same ultimate effect. This led to the summation theory: It makes no difference whether a subthreshold dose of a chemical carcinogen produces the first precancerous phase followed by sufficient amounts of a weak carcinogen which produces another precancerous phase, or whether the weak carcinogen is applied first. Cancer development depends upon the sum total of multiple discontinuous effects — intramolecular irreversible alterations of duplicants. The term "duplicant" was first introduced by Nothdurft (1949).

II. Cholesterol and Derivatives

A. CHOLESTEROL SOLID STATE CARCINOGENESIS

1. *Historical Background*

Schabad (1937) induced sarcomas in mice by injecting benzene extracts of human tissues including livers of patients with cancer. Similar results were reported by Des Ligneris (1940), Hieger (1940), Kleinenberg *et al.* (1940), Steiner (1941), and Sannié *et al.* (1940-1941). Steiner (1943) and Steiner *et al.* (1947) found no difference in the effect of extracts of the livers of patients with carcinoma and those without. Hieger's (1949) work on cholesterol, the major constituent of such liver extracts, led to the contention that cholesterol was a low-grade chemical carcinogen. Of 1434 mice which had received subcutaneous injections of cholesterol in oily vehicles, 70 developed local sarcomas (Hieger, 1958); 1122 controls which received oily vehicles alone developed 5 sarcomas. These results are a summation of a series of experiments which were not performed at one time. Because of the low incidence of tumor yield, results of individual experiments did not in themselves indicate significance. Thus 5 sarcomas in 172 mice dosed with cholesterol in olive oil compared with 1 in 134 mice dosed with olive oil alone were not significant. Since it is legitimate to combine data of a series of concurrent comparisons, Hieger's overall results conclusively proved a carcinogenic effect.

For laboratories other than Hieger's, Hartwell (1951) cites 39 references in which cholesterol administered by various routes had produced negative tumorigenic results. On comparing the different experimental techniques used in all these laboratories, and on the basis of their own experiences, Bischoff and Bryson (1960, 1961, 1963) concluded that the critical difference between the results of Hieger and other workers arose from the physical state of the cholesterol at the injection site. Beginning with a 10% solution of cholesterol in the oily vehicle, which was effected at 99°C and hence supersaturated at 38°C, Hieger's injection technique produced cholesterol crystals at the dose site. Biologically, it is immaterial whether these crystals began forming in the syringe, at the injection site, or whether the cooled solution was administered as a sludge. In the experiments of Bischoff and Rupp (1946) and Bischoff (1957) which produced negative tumorigenic results, the concentration of cholesterol in the oily vehicle (sesame oil) was under 4% and hence undersaturated.

Differing with Hieger, who held that cholesterol acted as a low-grade carcinogen under his experimental conditions, Nothdurft (1949) suggested a nonspecific reaction to local irritation. Falk *et al.* (1949), Fieser (1954), and Kennaway (1957) postulated that a carcinogenic conversion product of cholesterol was the offender. Bischoff and Bryson (1960, 1961) contended that Hieger's results were an example of smooth surface carcinogenesis resulting from the presence of cholesterol crystal surfaces. Highly unreactive substances such as gold, platinum, tin, and solid saturated hydrocarbons induce local sarcomas when implanted subcutaneously in rodents. Tumor yield depends critically on the extent and texture of the surface. Since liquids such as the oily vehicles used in carcinogen testing and semisolids under certain conditions also present smooth surfaces but do not per se lead to a local carcinogenic response, Bischoff and Bryson (1963) defined the tumorigenic phenomenon more accurately as solid state carcinogenesis. Shubik *et al.* (1962) have demonstrated the relationship between liquid, semiliquid, and solid smooth surfaces in their study of five petroleum waxes with different melting points and different physical states at the body temperature. The higher cancer incidence was correlated with the high melting point wax.

2. *Solid State Carcinogenesis*

Although the basis for explaining Hieger's results with cholesterol as a manifestation of solid state carcinogenesis was originally circumstantial, Bischoff and Bryson subsequently supported their contention with experimental evidence:

(1) The solubility of cholesterol in the natural oils (Bischoff, 1963) used in the testing experiments and the relations of the needle, plate and pseudomorph crystal forms (Stauffer and Bischoff, 1964, 1966) of cholesterol to solubility in these and related solvents were determined. The original cholesterol introduced into the oily vehicle was of the needle type; however, it would from a supersaturated solution on equilibration with the oil and body fluid revert to hydrated plates at the injection site. The plates have a lower solubility than the needles in the original oily vehicle.

(2) Hieger's and Bischoff's original techniques under comparative biological conditions were duplicated (Bischoff and Bryson, 1964). Cholesterol plates did form at the subcutaneous site only under Hieger's conditions; their arrangement produced baffle effects. A fibrous hyaline capsule, characteristic of solid state carcinogenesis, developed.

(3) In Marsh mice, Hieger's technique produced the 5% incidence of local sarcomas, Bischoff's technique produced negative results.

(4) Cholesterol hydrate plates, 1–2 mm in diameter, were compared with powdered plates, 2–4 times the diameter of a red cell, at the subcutaneous implant site in Marsh mice. The plates produced more of a hyaline, collagenous reaction, the powder more of a granulomatous reaction (Bischoff and Bryson, 1964). These were the effects Vasiliev *et al.* (1962) found characteristic for the malignant versus the nonmalignant course that these tissue reactions would follow.

(5) In female Evans rats, cholesterol administered subcutaneously as powdered crystals in saline or as unsaturated and supersaturated solutions in sesame oil produced no local cancers. At a level of 40 mg/rat cholesterol so administered was absorbed, and the failure to produce local cancers indicated the absence of chemical carcinogenicity (Bischoff and Bryson, 1964).

(6) Local sarcomas were produced in male or female Evans rats when disks of cholesterol hydrate plates or needles, 18 by 3 mm in diameter, were implanted subcutaneously. Concurrent surgical controls developed no local tumors. For females surviving 18 months or developing local tumors the sarcoma yield was 4/17 in disk implanted rats versus 0/26 in control rats (Bischoff *et al.*, 1966; Dryson and Bischoff, 1967a,b). For males these figures were 5/26 versus 0/30 and 6/27 versus 0/30 (Bryson and Bischoff, 1967a,b). There was a sex-linked difference in rejection of disks in Evans rats, 16/30 versus 4/30 for females versus males. No tumors arose at the implant site once the cholesterol disks were rejected.

Because cholesteryl palmitate and glyceryl palmitate are widely distributed in the mammalian organism, experiments were designed to ascertain whether these compounds would also induce local cancers by solid state carcinogenesis. Disks of cholesteryl palmitate (mp 78°C) and glyceryl palmitate (mp 65.5°C), 19 by 2 mm, were subcutaneously implanted into Evans male rats at 2 months of age. An equal number of littermates served as surgical controls and developed no local cancers. At 16 months after implantation, 27 control rats, 16 rats with cholesteryl palmitate implants, and 18 rats with glyceryl palmitate implants were living without local tumors. At this time one and two living rats in each implant group had lost their implants. Eight and 6 local sarcomas had developed for the cholesteryl and glyceryl palmitate groups, respectively. Three of 36 cholesteryl palmitate disks and 1 of 36 glyceryl palmitate disks sloughed before 3 months after implantation. The disks which did not slough remained intact at the implantation site to the end of the experiment. The hyaline capsules which enveloped the disks after implantation remained intact to the end of the experiment or were invaded by the locally developing sarcomas. These hyaline capsules were similar to those which develop around subcutaneously implanted inert substances of similar size. The sarcomas arose 8–16 months after implantation for the cholesteryl palmitate and 12–15 months for the glyceryl palmitate. For 8/25 versus 0/27, $p < 0.01$; for 6/26 versus 0/27, $p = 0.01$ (Bischoff and Bryson, 1968b) (see Fig. 1). Two additional local fibrosarcomas were found in the glyceryl palmitate group 17 months after implantation.

Hieger tested the postulate of Falk and others that a decomposition product of cholesterol acted as the carcinogen by heating a 10% solution of cholesterol in olive oil for 75 hours at 99°C. As tested in 50 mice, this produce was not carcinogenic in contrast to the original mixture. On duplicating these experiments, Bischoff and Bryson (1963) found that the cholesterol esterfies by alcoholysis during the

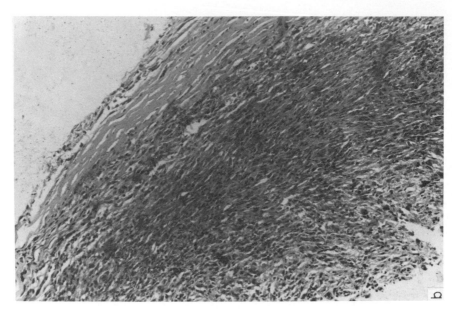

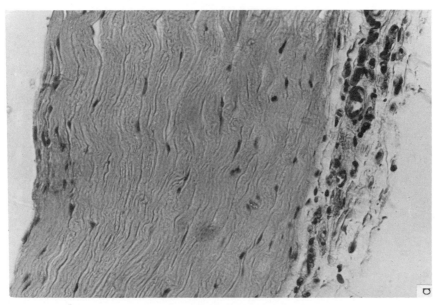

FIG. 1. Illustration of phases of solid state carcinogenesis induced by the subcutaneous implantation of cholesteryl palmitate or glyceryl palmitate disks in the rat. (a) The hyalinized fibrous capsule, rich in collagen and poor in cells which surrounded an implant

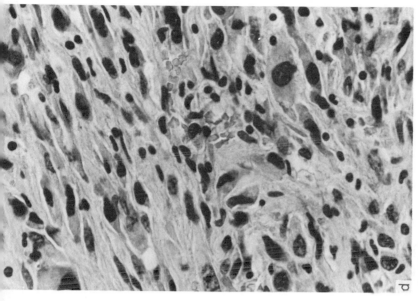

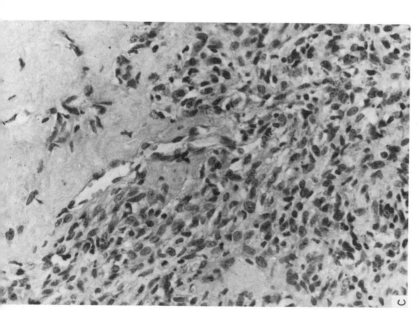

FIG. 1. (*Continued*). (c) A local fibrosarcoma invading the fibrous capsule which had surrounded a glyceryl palmitate disk: 15 months after implantation (×310). (d) A pleomorphic sarcoma which developed at the implant site of a glyceryl palmitate disk 15 months after implantation (×500).

heating procedure, viz., the digitonin precipitate of cholesterol is markedly reduced as compared with a control and the end product is clear with no cholesterol crystals forming at 37°C from the original supersaturated solution. Nothdurft (1955) called attention to the importance of the formation of the local depot with the cholesterol solution but not with the control vehicle as described by Hieger and Orr (1954).

Taken as a whole the results of the experiments in both rats and mice from different laboratories are formidable evidence against the concept that cholesterol functions as a low-grade chemical carcinogen and support the concept of solid state carcinogenesis.

3. *The Bantu Liver Extracts*

The interest in the work of Des Ligneris, who reported that nonsaponifiable extracts of the livers of the Bantus were carcinogenic when tested in rodents, has been revived by Higginson *et al.* (1964) and Dunn (1965). Upon subcutaneous injection of the nonsaponifiable extract of livers of Swiss mice as a 10% solution-suspension in olive oil, 8 sarcomas arose in 29 dosed mice as compared with 1 sarcoma in 50 controls which received olive oil alone. The present reviewer was able to correlate carcinogenesis with the physical state of cholesterol in these experiments because the authors presented a detailed analysis of all injection solutions. Thus the liver extract contained 78% cholesterol in the above experiment so that the solubility of cholesterol in the olive oil was exceeded by about 45 mg at equilibrium with the body fluids at the injection site. The physical state of the cholesterol in this experiment approaches that of Hieger (1962) and Bischoff and Bryson (1964), which produced sarcomas by solid state carcinogenesis.

In the experiments in which nonsaponifiable extracts of human livers were administered subcutaneously in Hauschka mice, the series in which the cholesterol content was undersaturated in the injection oil (control and white subjects) produced no local sarcomas. The series in which the cholesterol content exceeded the solubility (noncancerous Bantu livers and hepatoma Bantu livers) produced 5 sarcomas. The survival rates in these experiments were low: Less than 40% of the original 30-60 mice survived to 18 months of age. No significance can therefore be attached between tumor incidences in the various experimental groups. The experiments failed to confirm Des Ligneris' (1940) contention that livers from Bantus with or without primary liver cancers contained a carcinogen as contrasted with livers from white subjects.

Since the experimental conditions which produced sarcomas all contained cholesterol in a state which exceeded saturation, the conditions of solid state carcinogenesis which produced sarcomas in Hieger's and Bischoff and Bryson's experiments with cholesterol were met.

4. Biological Use of Cast Cholesterol Pellets

The widespread use (Wieder and Shimkin, 1964) of cholesterol pellets, cast above the melting point, as vehicles for implant studies of hormones and carcinogens may be challenged for a number of reasons. Fieser (1953) has shown that the melting point of purified cholesterol determined in air may be several degrees lower than that determined *in vacuo* because of decomposition. Pellets of Eastman cholesterol mp 149°-150°C when cast from a melt under nitrogen showed evidence of dehydration as demonstrated by ultraviolet spectroscopy with an induced maximum at 235-238 mμ corresponding to a product calculated as 0.23% 3,5-cholestadiene (Bischoff *et al.*, 1966). When cast in air the diene equivalent was 0.36%. In evacuated tubes heated for 20 hours at 100°, 120°, 130°, and 150°C cholesterol produced 0.02, 0.11, 0.12, and 0.19% diene equivalents, respectively, for 20 minutes at 150°C, 0.18%. Thirty female Evans rats, implanted with 200 mg cholesterol cast in pellets under nitrogen and powdered in order to circumvent solid state carcinogenesis, developed 1 local fibrosarcoma versus no local neoplasms in 30 concurrent controls subjected to the same surgical technique. In previous experiments comprising 120 dosed rats, purified cholesterol administered as an aqueous suspension or in an oily vehicle had not produced any cancer (Bischoff and Bryson, 1964). The 1 sarcoma produced in 30 rats by cholesterol heated above the melting point does not prove the carcinogenicity of the heated product. It is of interest because 3,5-cholestadiene, 235 mμ, has been reported as carcinogenic by two laboratories (Schubert and Fischer, 1963). The importance of these combined observations is that whether heated *in vacuo*, under nitrogen, or in air cholesterol decomposes at the melting point. Products other than the diene are formed as indicated by discoloration and lowering of the melting point. Their identity was not established.

5. Cholesterol Pellets in the Bladder

In order to study the carcinogenic properties of chemical carcinogens and their metabolites at the bladder epithelium, pellets containing the compound have been surgically implanted in the lumen of the bladder (Jull, 1951). No suitable vehicle has to date been found

(Clayson, 1966). Paraffins have caused inflammation and metaplasia and produced local carcinomas—0-4.5%—in experimental groups ranging from 34 to 89 test mice. Stearic acid was dispersed too early and produced 4.8% cancer in 62 mice. Cholesterol was unsuitable because it produced from 6.5 to 9% bladder carcinomas in experimental groups ranging from 55 to 87 mice as tested in three laboratories (Bonser et al., 1963; Clayson et al., 1958; Bryan et al., 1963). Since the three vehicles all produced cancers and are not related structurally, a chemical carcinogenic effect is not indicated. Physical factors related to solubility, adsorption, size and physical adhesion, or formation of concretions are to be considered. The solid state again produces cancers with the saturated hydrocarbons and cholesterol. Although in this case the fibrous capsule is not involved, the bladder epithelium may be serving an analogous function. The results with cholesterol indicate that this substance should not be used as a vehicle in the routine testing for carcinogens (Clayson, 1966).

B. Cholesterol Oxidation Products

1. Historical Background

A crude progesterone preparation was compared with crystalline progesterone by subcutaneous administration in sesame oil to ovariectomized mice (Bischoff and Rupp, 1946). At 18 months of age, the local cancer incidence was 32% (37 mice) for the crude versus 0% (34 mice) for the pure. The total amount of progesterone per mouse was 10 mg in each series. In addition, there were 20 mg/mouse of unidentified cholesterol oxidation products in the crude preparation which had been made by permanganate oxidation of cholesterol dibromide with subsequent debromination. The results of these experiments prompted an extended investigation of the relation of cholesterol oxidation products to carcinogenesis (Bischoff, 1957). Eight known products, 7-oxocholesterol, 7α-hydroxycholesterol, 7β-hydroxycholesterol, cholestane-3β,5α,6β-triol, 3,5-cholestadien-7-one, 6-cholestene-3β,5α-diol, 4-cholesten-3-one, and dihydrocholesterol had been isolated from an aqueous colloidal solution of cholesterol exposed to air (Bergström and Wintersteiner, 1941; Mosbach et al., 1952). This mild oxidative environment could conceivably occur under biological conditions. Other oxidation products of cholesterol were possible intermediates in the endogenous production of steroids. This review will cover in detail the compounds which have produced positive carcinogenic results in rodents.

2. The Oily Vehicle

The relation of the oily vehicle to positive tumorigenic results as a cocarcinogenic factor emerged in the preceding studies (Bischoff, 1957). Banning of the natural oily vehicle in all carcinogenic testing was recommended (Bischoff, 1963), and at the International Symposium on Carcinogenesis and Carcinogen Testing, Bryson and Bischoff (1969) listed seven objections to the use of the oily vehicle as one of the factors in the limitations of safety testing:

(1) A particular batch of oil can never be exactly duplicated since it has been shown that minor constituents such as sesamol in sesame oil may vary seasonally by 1000%.

(2) The control vehicle is not a true control since it may react metabolically and with the carcinogen. Oxidation of phenols and unsaturated fats are obvious targets.

(3) Vehicle constituents may react with the test compound, so a reaction product not formed when an aqueous vehicle is used is the actual agent tested.

(4) Solubility factors may lead to crystal formation and the phenomenon of solid state carcinogenesis.

(5) The test colony may be in a pathological condition since the injection of fats and oils may lead to amyloidosis.

(6) An inhibited inflammatory reaction known to influence carcinogen response may be induced.

(7) Naturally occurring carcinogens in subthreshold doses may be contained in the oils.

3. 5-Cholesten-3-one

5-Cholesten-3-one has a methylene group at the four position which is activated by a carbonyl group at one side and a double bond at the other. This C-4 group has the same high degree of vulnerability to substitution as the methylene group of methylcholanthrene and the mesonuclear position of 3,4-benzpyrene. On the basis of this property, Fieser (1954) felt that 5-cholesten-3-one was a nonhormone steroid likely to produce cancer. He had ruled out cholesterol as a chemical carcinogen because it was a widely distributed natural body constituent and postulated that a derivative of cholesterol was the carcinogenic agent in Hieger's experiments with cholesterol (see Section II,A,1). 5-Cholesten-3-one was tested in 32 intact female Marsh mice as an aqueous suspension administered 20 mg/mouse subcutaneously (Bischoff, 1957). At 18 months there were three nontumor deaths. However, the 58% incidence of spontaneous mammary tumors reduced the chance of local sarcoma formation. One local fibrosarcoma developed. Hieger (1959) also reported one local fibrosarcoma in stock and C57 mice, using olive oil as the vehicle. The survival for the stock mice was 8 and that for the C57 mice 29 at 18 months. In 30 female Evans rats (Bischoff and Bryson, 1968a) which received 40 mg/rat as an aqueous suspension in saline containing 1% rat serum, 25 survived 19 months. No local sarcomas appeared, but 7 rats developed calcified fibrous capsules around the dose areas. Of 30 controls 8 died before the age of 19 months. The essentially negative results in two species and in two laboratories for two strains of mice (the survival rate for the stock mice was too low) do not substantiate Fieser's selection of 5-cholesten-3-one as a likely carcinogen. However, considering the numbers of animals used experimentally a low-grade carcinogenic potential has not yet been ruled out. The one sarcoma produced in each of Bischoff's and Hieger's mouse experiments is not statistically significant when compared with the control incidence for the respective colonies. Only experiments conducted on large series of test animals would conclusively settle the question of a low-grade carcinogenic effect for this or any other compound in the same category.

4. 4-Cholestene-3,6-dione

Experiments with 4-cholestene-3,6-dione have produced conflicting results. Bischoff (1957) noted a 34% incidence of local sarcomas in 34 male Marsh mice which had received 20 mg in sesame oil subcutaneously per mouse. In 33 castrated female mice of this strain only one local sarcoma developed. The melting point for 4-cholestene-3,6-dione, 117°–119°C was 6° below the melting point reported for the pure compound (Bischoff and Turner, 1958). The purity of the compounds tested in other laboratories has not been indicated though in two instances the samples were also prepared in Fieser's laboratory. With 4-cholestene-3,6-dione in olive oil, Hieger (1959) reported no sarcomas for 16 stock mice which survived 16 months. Dannenberg (1963a) also reported negative results for 20 Swiss mice. However, Neukomm *et al.* (1960) observed a positive result by his newt test.

The study of Kühl and Schubert (1960) with 4-cholestene-3, 6-dione did not specify the numbers of animals in control and experimental groups with and without cortisone. Bruns *et al.* (1963) have reevaluated these results and consider the local carcinomas as possible spontaneous mammary carcinomas. They report experiments in AB female and male mice which had received 20 mg of 4-cholestene-3, 6-dione subcutaneously in sesame oil with or without cortisone per mouse. There were only 5 mice in each control group, with 10–15 in the dosed series. A lengthy discussion of significance by statistical analysis is provided. Groups of females pooled with males do not form a statistical population nor does the combination of groups with and without cortisone. In one experiment, 10 females which received the dione developed 5 local carcinomas, 5 controls did not; with cortisone superimposed, 3 out of 15 dione-dosed mice developed local carcinomas; 5 controls did not. The incidence of spontaneous mammary carcinomas for the strain was 21.4%. Evaluation of the significance of these results is not possible. The number of controls was inadequate. Whether the local carcinomas were induced by the dione or were spontaneous mammary tumors remains speculative. In an experiment in C57BL male mice, 1 local sarcoma developed; there were no controls. These experiments only serve to confuse the issue.

It is apparent that 4-cholestene-3, 6-dione is not a high-grade chemical carcinogen in the mouse. The sex difference noted by Bischoff, the negative results for small numbers of test animals as reported by Hieger and Dannenberg, and the doubtfully significant results reported by Kuhl and Schubert, are all complicated by use of a natural oil vehicle and doubtful purity of the compound. Only large experimental series in nonoily vehicles will show whether this compound is a low-grade carcinogen. The positive newt test indicates that such studies might produce positive results.

5. 6β-Hydroxy-4-cholesten-3-one

This compound was tested in male and castrated female Marsh mice (Bischoff, 1957) as an equal molecular complex with epicholesterol prepared in the laboratory of Fieser. In groups of 32 and 33 mice which received 20 mg/mouse, the incidence of local sarcomas when administered subcutaneously in sesame oil was 19 and 15%, respectively. Similar results were obtained by Dannenberg (private communication) in Swiss mice which received a comparable dose of the 6β-hydroxy compound in sesame oil. In 20 mice, 4 local spindle cell sarcomas, 1 myelosarcoma, 2 myelogenous leukemias, and 1 lung adenoma developed. The results carried to 600 days were significant, since no tumors developed in an equal number of controls. Dannenberg cautioned that since encapsulated dose sites were observed, the carcinogenic effect may have been nonspecific (Oberflächen-carcinogeneses). With a survival rate of 13 and 21 mice at 18 months of age, Hieger (1959) reported 1 local sarcoma each for groups of stock mice which subcutaneously received the compound in olive oil or sesame oil. Administered in an oily vehicle, this compound has produced an incidence of local sarcomas varying from 5 to 20% in three laboratories and with three strains of mice. The agreement between the three strains tested is quite remarkable being within once the standard deviation of the mean. Considering that the cocarcinogenic factor of the oily vehicle, the possibility of solid state carcinogenesis and species difference have not been ruled out, a test in rats was made (Bischoff and Bryson, 1967). Thirty female Evans rats received 40 mg of 6β-hydroxy-4-cholesten-3-one per rat subcutaneously as an aqueous suspension in 1% rat serum-saline. Thirty littermates receiving only the vehicle served as controls. The survival rate of 87% to 19 months was excellent. No local cancer developed either in control or dosed rats. Three local areas of fibrosis were observed at the end of the experiment. The status of this compound as a low-grade carcinogen in its own right cannot be settled until large series of mice receive aqueous suspensions of the compound.

6. 5α-Hydroperoxy-6-cholesten-3β-ol

Dannenberg (1958) obtained negative carcinogenic results with this compound upon subcutaneous injection of 15 mg/mouse in sesame oil into 24 mice of a mixed strain. He was aware that with the numbers used, a weak carcinogenic potential was not eliminated. In irradiated rats, the compound again produced negative results (Koch and Schenck, 1961).

A comparative test of 5α-hydroperoxy-6-cholesten-3β-ol, 7α-hydroperoxy-5-cholesten-3β-ol and cholesterol was made on intraperitoneal injection of 5 mg in olive oil in female mice of an inbred strain over a 2 year period (Koch et al., 1964). The cholesterol was administered as a 2.5% solution, the peroxy compounds as 2.5% solid suspensions. Cholesterol and the 7α-hydroperoxy produced tumorigenic results which were not significantly different from vehicle-dosed or undosed controls: 8, 10, 4, and 6%, respectively. The tumor incidence for the 5-hydroxy compound, 30.3% was highly significant ($p = 0.01$–0.001), as well as the malignant tumor incidence. The adequate numbers of surviving mice used for the statistics, 50, 66, 60, 92, and 94, completely justify the conclusion that the 5-hydroperoxy compound produced carcinogenesis. This carefully planned and executed experiment using sufficient test animals, pure compounds, and adequate controls is weak in one respect: the use of olive oil as the vehicles. Koch et al. felt that the 5-hydroperoxy compound acted as a cocarcinogen augmenting the endogenous carcinogens in the strain. This remains a matter of conjecture. Reaction of the hydroperoxy compound with the triolein in the vehicle is another possibility.

It should be noted that cholesterol was administered as an undersaturated solution (the experiment was repeated with five times the dose and did not produce cancer). This confirms Bischoff and Bryson's (1964) contention that in the absence of the solid state, carcinogenesis would not ensue.

Koch and Schenck (1967) repeated their experiments with 5α-hydroperoxy-6-cholesten-3β-ol using male mice of the same strain previously tested on females. However, the injection route was changed from the intraperitoneal to the subcutaneous and the dose doubled to 10 mg/mouse. Cholesterol was used as a reference control. On the basis of total tumor yield Koch and Schenck conclude that there is a sex difference in response, the male mice being resistant to the effect of the 5α-hydroperoxide. However, the use of a different injection site challenges any direct comparison between the experiments.

7. 6β-Hydroperoxy-4-cholesten-3-one

The results for 6β-hydroperoxy-4-cholesten-3-one are given in Table I. Castrated male Marsh mice developed significant incidences of local sarcomas ranging from 9 to 59% when the vehicle was sesame oil or triolein and with doses per mouse ranging from 5 to 20 mg (Bischoff, 1957; Bryson and Bischoff, 1964) In BALB/c male mice with sesame oil as a vehicle but not with triolein hemorrhagic cysts were observed. These cysts characteristically develop instead of fibrosarcomas when BALB/c mice are subjected locally to carcinogenic hydrocarbons. With sesame oil as the vehicle Hieger (1962) obtained a 13% incidence of local sarcomas in C57 mice. Although he began with 36 Marsh mice, only 4 survived 12 months after initial dosage, so his incidence of local sarcomas, 1 out of 4 (25%), is in line with the results reported by Bischoff (1957) for this strain. Dunn (1965) and Dannenberg (1963a) both used Swiss mice. Since survivors in Dunn's experiments are 10 or less and not available from Dannenberg's data, the negative data for Dunn and 1 tumor for Dannenberg may not be inconsistent with those for Marsh and C57 mice. In Evans female rats, 23 of which survived 19 months after dosing or evolving tumors, 5 developed local sarcomas with a 40 mg/rat subcutaneous dose of the hydroperoxy compound in sesame oil. These positive tumorigenic results cross the species barrier (Bischoff, 1963). Administered subcutaneously in cottonseed oil, 6β-hydroperoxy-4-stigmastadien-3-one produced 2 local fibrosarcomas in 33 Marsh mice each receiving 10 mg (Bischoff, 1963).

Administered subcutaneously in aqueous suspension, 6β-hydroper-

Table I
CARCINOGENIC EFFECTS OF 6β-HYDROPEROXY-4-CHOLESTEN-3-ONE ADMINISTERED SUBCUTANEOUSLY IN MICE

Experimental details		Strain of mice[a]	Initial No. of animals	Effective No. of animals	Effective test period (months)	Local sarcomas (%)	Lung tumors (%)
Vehicle	Milligrams/animal						
Sesame oil	–	♂ C Marsh	33	26	12	0	
Sesame oil	15	♂ C Marsh	32	29	12	59	
Saline	15	♂ C Marsh	32	25	12	4	
Triolein	–	♂ C Marsh	33	29	15.5	0	
Triolein	20	♂ C Marsh	33	31	15.5	19	
Sesame oil	–	♂ C Marsh	33	30	16	0	10
Sesame oil	5	♂ C Marsh	33	30	16	9	17
Triolein	5	♂ C Marsh	33	30	16	18	17
2% Serum	10	♂ BALB	28	25	15.5	0	44
Sesame oil	–	♂ BALB	28	25	15.5	0	20
Sesame oil	10	♂ BALB	28	23	15.5	9[b]	35
Triolein	–	♂ BALB	28	24	15.5	0	16
Triolein	10	♂ BALB	28	21	15.5	0	19

Sesame oil[c]	20	C57	50	38	15 ?	13
Tricaprylin	—	♂ Swiss	10	?	16	0
Tricaprylin	25	♂ Swiss	10	9	16	0
Tricaprylin	—	♀ Swiss	10	?	16	0
Tricaprylin	25	♀ Swiss	10	10	16	0
Sesame oil	—	♀ Hauschka	20	?	16	0
Sesame oil	25	♀ Hauschka	20	10	16	0
Sesame oil	—	Swiss	24	?	20	4?
Sesame oil	21	Swiss	21	?	20	5?
Sesame oil[c]	20	Buffalo	36	4	12	25

[a] C indicates castrated.
[b] Hemorrhagic cysts.
[c] Colony control, apparently no concurrent series: 0.5% local fibrosarcomas.

oxy-4-cholesten-3-one developed 1 local sarcoma in 25 Marsh mice with an effective test period for 12 months. The space isomer, 6α-hydroperoxy-4-cholesten-3-one (mp 149°-150°C), also subcutaneously tested as an aqueous suspension in Marsh mice, developed 3/25 local sarcomas within 16 months. In female Evans rats, saline suspensions of 40 mg 6β-hydroperoxy-4-cholesten-3-one per rat administered subcutaneously or 90 mg administered intraperitoneally produced no local cancers. One local subcutaneous nonmalignant granuloma developed; the effective number of animals 20 months after dosing was 21; at 16 months it was 27. The incidence of lymphoid tumors (reticulum cell and lymphosarcomas) of the lung and peritoneal area is about 10% in Evans and most other strains of rats. Seventeen months after dosing the 6β-hydroperoxy compound intraperitoneally, no local tumors other than lymphoid tumors had developed in 33 rats which survived or developed these tumors. Their incidence was not significantly different from that of 23 comparable controls, viz., 6%. Small intraperitoneal encapsulated areas of dosed material were found in a few rats at the end of the experiment (Bischoff and Bryson, 1968a).

Hence, the 6β-hydroperoxy compound was carcinogenic or characteristically tumorigenic when injected in triolein or a naturally occurring oily vehicle containing triolein in adequate series of Evans rats and three strains of mice: Marsh, C57, and BALB/c. In order to determine whether the 6-hydroperoxy-4-cholesten-3-one compounds are low-grade carcinogens in their own right, experiments on a much larger scale with isotonic saline as the vehicle would be required. The local results with the α compound at the subcutaneous site in Marsh mice, and the increase of lung adenomas in BALB/c mice indicate such studies would be desirable. Tumor production at the site of exogenous triolein may reflect the formation of a reaction product with triolein. This reaction would occur to a lesser extent with the much lower concentrations of endogenous triolein: In the Evans rat, the β-hydroperoxy compound administered in saline was not tumorigenic at two sites.

The carcinogenicity of 6β-hydroperoxy-4-cholesten-3-one has been cited as of interest in relation to the hydroperoxy derivatives of squalene and the phytodienes, which form in air. The hydrocarbons are present in cigarette smoke (Advisory Committee, 1962). This report fails to note that proof is lacking that the 6β-hydroperoxy compound is carcinogenic per se and that a reaction product may be the carcinogen.

8. Cholesterol α-Oxide

At the subcutaneous and intratesticular routes as an aqueous suspension, cholesterol α-oxide has produced local sarcomas in Marsh mice. In Evans rats a positive tumorigenic response at the subcutaneous but not intratesticular route was obtained (Bischoff, 1963). The thymus and intraperitoneal routes yielded negative results in Marsh mice. In Swiss mice, Dannenberg observed 2 tumors in 20 Swiss mice which had received the α-oxide subcutaneously. In order to conclusively prove the carcinogenicity of α-oxide, it was necessary to test on the basis of an extended series of experiments. Problems of purity, dosage, latent period, and target site had to be solved before meaningful interpretation of results could be ascertained. A summary of the data is given in Table II to illustrate the extent of the work. The experiments recorded in Table II comprise 866 mice and 180 rats. In all experiments, control littermates, which approximately equaled the α-oxide-dosed rodents in numbers, developed no local tumors. This is the ideal situation, since with an incidence of experimental tumors under 20%, tumors in the controls – even 1 in 30 – jeopardize the significance of results.

When the α-oxide is dosed subcutaneously as an aqueous suspension, it is mostly retained at the injection site and accumulates metabolites to produce a viscous liquid suspension. The change in content of this local deposit was studied over a period ranging from 5 to 485 days after dosing. The α-oxide was dosed subcutaneously, 10 mg/mouse as a suspension in 2% serum in saline in groups of 5 males and 5 females. Five days after dosing, the α-oxide content was 30–50% with no cholesterol. At 14 days, the α-oxide content had fallen to 13–15%. Lower percentages ranging from 4 to 7% were found 200, 320, and 485 days after dosing. At this time, the ethanol soluble fraction ranged from 10 to 14%, the protein (calculated as albumin) from 2.5 to 6.5%. The cholesterol content gradually increased with time, reaching 2%, 485 days after dosing. Calcium contents ranged from 0.7 to 8.8%, and calcified areas were often noted upon histological examination.

During 1942–1951, the mp of cholesterol α-oxide was reported as ranging between 141° and 144°C by six authors as recorded in the chemical literature. In *Steroids* (Fieser and Fieser, 1959) the mp is given as 142.5°C. This was an error as Fieser and Rajagopalan (1949) had already reported a mp of 147°–148°C. On the assumption that the correct mp was 142.5°C, the material available and used in the early work had a mp in the range 141–142. When the correct mp was discovered the work had to be repeated and a sample having a mp of 146°–147°C was obtained. Analyses of the older lower melting point samples by the method of Bischoff and Turner (1958) showed that all samples analyzed within 99% of the new reference standard. Because the α- and β-oxides cannot be distinguished by this procedure, the

Table II

Carcinogenic Effects of Cholesterol α-Oxide in Marsh Mice and Evans Rats[a]

| Vehicle[b] | α-Oxide administration | | | Test animals | | | Effective No. | Effective time (months) | Local sarcomas (%) |
	Dose site[b]	Milligram/animal	Mp α-oxide	Sex[b]	Species	No. at start			
C.S. oil	Subcu 2	–		♀ C	Mouse	33	27	12	0
C.S. oil	Subcu 2	20	144	♀ C	Mouse	33	31	12	19
3% Albumin	Subcu	10	144	♂ C	Mouse	33	32	15	25
3% Albumin[c]	Subcu	10	144	♂ C	Mouse	33	29	15	3
Saline	Intrap 2	–		♂ C	Mouse	33	31	14	0
Saline	Intrap 2	20	140	♂ C	Mouse	40	33	14	0
Saline	i. thymus	–		♀	Mouse	33	31	15	0
Saline	i. thymus	5	140	♀	Mouse	30	24	15	0
Saline[d]	Subcu	–		♂ C	Mouse	33	26	15	0
Saline[d]	Subcu	10	140	♂ C	Mouse	33	31	15	19
2% Serum	Subcu	–		♂	Mouse	29	22	15	0
2% Serum	Subcu	10	140	♂	Mouse	29	27	15	22
2% Serum	Subcu	–		♀	Mouse	28	20	15	0
2% Serum	Subcu	10	140	♀	Mouse	28	22	15	18

2% Serum	Subcu	—		♀	Mouse	32	28	16	0
2% Serum	Subcu	20	147	♂	Mouse	30	22	16	5
2% Serum	Subcu	—		♀	Mouse	38	32	18	0
2% Serum	Subcu	20	147	♂	Mouse	38	24	18	29
2% Serum	Subcu	—		♀	Mouse	55	42	18	0
2% Serum	Subcu	20	147	♂	Mouse	55	41	18	20
Saline	i. testes	—		♂	Mouse	81	58	13-14	0
Saline	i. testes	10	140	♂	Mouse	89	72	13-14	10
Sesame oil	Subcu	—		♀	Rat	30	23	19	0
Sesame oil	Subcu	40	140	♀	Rat	30	25	19	0
Saline	Subcu	—		♀	Rat	30	26	19	0
Saline	Subcu	40	140	♂	Rat	30	26	19	19
Saline	i. testes	—		♂	Rat	30	21	15	0
Saline	i. testes	20 each	140	♂	Rat	30	21	15	0

[a] From Bischoff and Bryson.
[b] Abbreviations: C.S. indicates cottonseed; i., intra; C, castrated; subcu, subcutaneous, and intrap, intraperitoneal.
[c] 16 mg of sesame oil antioxidant fraction per mouse.
[d] Adjacent to polyethylene implant 0.12 by 0.002 by 1 in.

lower melting point samples contained some β-oxide which is always formed during the preparation. Since the starting material is cholesterol and the oxidizing agent perphthalic acid made with perboric acid, the samples were tested for boric acid and phthalic acid by microcolor techniques. The sensitivity for these tests was 0.05% for the samples used, so that the negative results obtained indicated that less than 10 μg/dose of these contaminants in 20 mg of α-oxide were present if at all in any of the samples tested, including that with a mp of 140°C. Any impurity would have to be a potent carcinogen to be effective at this level.

In conclusion, cholesterol α-oxide administered in an aqueous vehicle has been carcinogenic in both rats and mice. Sensitive target sites are subcutaneous for both species and intratesticular for mice. It is the only oxidation product of cholesterol which has been shown to produce cancer in the absence of the oily vehicle.

9. 3,5-Cholestadiene

3,5-Cholestadiene is of particular interest as the primary dehydration derivative of cholesterol. Twenty Wistar rats of both sexes were followed 13-16 months after the subcutaneous implantation of 14-15 mg 3,5-cholestadiene pellets. Also, 29 male C3H mice were followed 13-15 months after the subcutaneous implantation of 11-15 mg 3,5-cholestadiene pellets. No local tumors were observed for either species (Larsen and Barrett, 1944). The size of the pellet would be too small to evoke any degree of solid state carcinogenesis; resorption would be reduced to a minimum since exposed surface area would be much less than that for a powder.

Schubert and Fischer (1963) describe the carcinogenic effect of 3,5-cholestadiene in 50 mice of the AB strain and 50 mice of the C57 black strain; both sexes were used. The data were later subjected to statistical analysis by Fritsch (1965) who concluded that no carcinogenic effect was indicated. A discrepancy of some possible significance between the two reports is the difference of local fibrosarcomas and local adenocarcinomas. Thus, Schubert and Fischer report 3 local fibrosarcomas and 1 local adenocarcinoma for the AB mice, and 1 local fibrosarcoma and 1 local carcinoma for the C57BL mice. Fritsch reports only 1 local fibrosarcoma and 2 local adenocarcinomas for the AB females, none for the males and no local fibrosarcoma for the C57BL mice. Fritsch shows that the males of the AB strain died approximately 5 months before the females, indicating that the experimental period for the males was not long enough. He does not consider the difference of mammary adenocarcinomas for the AB mice, 8/23 versus 123/550 for the control colony ($p = 0.05$), significant.

The experiments of Larsen and Barnett were not carried out sufficiently long. Discrepancies in observation along with high spontaneous tumor yields resulting in reduced numbers complicated the experiments of Schubert and Fischer. The local sarcomas reported by the latter authors indicate that the compound warrants further study, administered as an aqueous suspension in strains with low spontaneous tumor incidence. The one local subcutaneous sarcoma in Evans rats (Bischoff *et al.*, 1966) for a cholesterol powder which contained a diene as indicated by adsorption spectroscopy has been noted in Section II, A, 4. See Section VI for Grasso and Golberg's view on the significance of 1 sarcoma under conditions for which there are no sarcomas for concurrent controls nor for the strain.

10. *The Newt Test*

A screening test for carcinogenic compounds, devised by Neukomm (1944) and extended by Arffmann and Christensen (1961), is based on the local action of carcinogenic hydrocarbons on sensitive areas of both female and male newts. Since the end point of the test is not frank carcinogenesis, conclusions made from these data are at best circumstantial. As tested by Neukomm *et al.* (1960) deoxycorticosterone, 4-cholestene-3,6-dione, 5-hydroxycholestane-3,6-dione, and 3,6-dimethylsteranthrene produced positive results; cholesterol, cholesterol α-oxide, and 6β-hydroperoxy-4-cholesten-3-one produced negative results. Products of estrone, testosterone, and progesterone formed by air oxidation also produced positive results. Arffmann and Glavind (1967) found that the hydroperoxides of the ethyl and glyceryl esters of oleic, linoleic, and linolenic acids and their reduction products produced positive results. Cholesterol and a hydroperoxy compound formed by ultraviolet radiation of cholesterol in air were also tested. The solubility of the latter compounds was so low in the test vehicle, arachidis oil, that comparative tests with the fatty acid ester hydroperoxides could not be made. Thus 9 peroxide units of the cholesterol derivative (the maximum amount tested) produced a positive test of 1/19, while 600 units of the trilinolein hydroperoxide produced a test of 0/19 and 1800 units a result of 6/6. Since the reduced hydroperoxy unsaturated fatty acid compounds also produced positive results, Arffmann and Glavind feel a hydroxy group adjacent to a double bond is a critical linkage as well as conjugated double bonds. The hydroperoxy oleic acid ester would not form conjugated double bonds on reduction, nor would the hydroperoxide of squalene which also yielded a positive newt test. Consequently, linkage of carcinogenic properties to structure as indicated by this test remains obscure.

III.   Neoplasms Induced by Steroid Hormones

A. ESTRONE-DEPENDENT RAT ADRENAL CORTEX CARCINOMA

In a strain of hooded rats, in which 5% of the females may show spontaneous adrenal tumors, implants of estrone pellets in females produce a 20% incidence of unilateral adrenal carcinomas, apparently from the zona fasciculata (Noble, 1967). Results with 16 transplant lines of such carcinomas indicated that there are no takes in males, few in untreated females, and many in estronized females. Hormone dependency of tumors persists on retransplantation. Removal of the estrone pellet is followed by cessation of tumor growth or by regression. Tumors metastasize to the lung and liver. Most transplanted tumor lines do not produce measurable corticoid secretion but are associated with extramedullary hematopoiesis.

B. ANTERIOR-LOBE CHROMOPHOBE ADENOMAS

Pituitary adenomas have been produced in rodents by prolonged estrogen administration or by induced hypothyroidism. These tumors grow to a large size and are lethal because of pressure trauma. They are strain-linked in mice; this relationship appears to be more limited in rats (Gardner and Strong, 1940; Saxton and Graham, 1944; Segaloff and Dunning, 1945; Dunning et al., 1947). Pituitary adenomas have been produced in hamsters (Vazquez-Lopez, 1944; Koneff et al., 1946). The C57BL and CE mouse strains are susceptible; the C3H, CBA, C121, JK, and N are not. With the latter, the most pronounced estrogenic response is a threefold pituitary hypertrophy. In the mouse, weekly doses of estradiol in the range 2–20 μg have produced the adenomas — in the rat 14 μg to mg. Fifty to 100 μg of either diethylstilbestrol or estradiol daily are equally effective in rats producing a 100% tumor yield if dosage is carried on over a year (Nelson, 1942). While lethal, attaining a weight of 150 mg, these tumors were regarded as nonmalignant; transplantation failed.

In all the species and strains studied, estrogen or hypothyroidism stimulates the increase in chromophobes of the pituitary and leads to hypertrophy. Depending on species and strain, the effect is self-limiting or uncontrolled to the extent that marked hypertrophy or adenoma production results. In no case, however, does the adenoma on further stimulation undergo malignant degeneration. In the initial phases of stimulation the pituitary and mammary glands respond in a similar manner. The question relating to the fundamental concept of malignant degeneration is why the pituitary has a defense mechanism which the mammary gland does not. The rat which continuously receives estrogen develops a malignant tumor of the breast and a benign tumor of the pituitary. The explanation of this phenomenon would be a major contribution to the understanding of the nature of cancer.

Both augmentative and inhibiting effects of progesterone have been reported when used in conjunction with estrogen (Albert and Selye, 1942; Selye, 1940). The androgens do not produce pituitary tumors but inhibit both the hypertrophy induced by estrogens and the production of adenomas: 5-androstene-3β,17α-diol, 5-androsten-3β-ol-17-one, methyltestosterone, and testosterone are in this category. 4-Androstene-3,17-dione and *cis*-testosterone are effective (Selye, 1940; Albert and Selye, 1942). The latter compound is practically without biological hormonal effects indicating a blocking mechanism.

Intermediate-lobe pituitary adenomas have also been produced both in rats and hamsters after prolonged estrogen administration (McEuen *et al.*, 1939; Koneff *et al.*, 1946; Vazquez-Lopez, 1944).

C. Endometrial Neoplasms in Rodents

1. Estrogen Linked Carcinoma

Carcinoma of the endometrium has been reviewed by Baba and von Haam (1967) who concluded that in rats and mice it occurs spontaneously only rarely and in some strains of rabbits more frequently. By local, oral, or parenteral administration, estrogens have produced a low or no yield of endometrial carcinoma in mice and rats. Gardner and Ferrigno (1956) describe 8 adenomas or adenocarcinomas of the endometrium in their series of estrogen-exposed mice. Considering their large experimental series, the incidence, which was not given, must be low. Fifty virgin female mice of the BALB/cf C3HCb/Se substrain given 1.2 mg of estradiol benzoate subcutaneously over 24 weeks developed 6 carcinomas and 1 adenoma of the uterus (Barbieri *et al.*, 1958).

Intramuscular injections of 75 mg of diethylstilbestrol dipalmitate in peanut oil over 45 weeks produced 6 endometrial carcinomas in 18 rabbits, 11 of which also received alloxan intravenously to produce alloxan diabetes. Ten controls and 20 alloxan-dosed rabbits developed no endometrial neoplasms. The observed precancerous abnormalities like metaplasia, hyperplasia, polyps, adenomyosis, and endometriosis, which are found spontaneously in women, were estrogen-linked (Meissner *et al.*, 1957). Baba and von Haam, using higher doses of stilbestrol, observed only 2 adenocarcinomas in 78 treated rabbits. This incidence was actually lower than that for their controls, 15/117. The experiments of Meissner *et al.* were complicated by the introduction of alloxan.

Evidence other than that of Meissner *et al.* (1957) links ovarian hormone activity with endometrial hyperplasia and subsequent carcinoma development in the rabbit. A strain of rabbits developing carcinoma of the endometrium was described by Greene (1939) and Griffiths *et al.* (1963). An estrogen-dependent carcinoma of the endometrium was induced by methylcholanthrene (Murphy, 1961).

On the basis of their experiments with rabbits, rats, and mice, using 3-methylcholanthrene and diethylstilbestrol, Baba and von Haam (1967) concluded that estrogen was promotional rather than initiating and consequently could not be considered as a complete carcinogen. In female rats, stilbestrol alone produced 1/36 squamous-cell uterine carcinomas. It did not augment the effect of methylcholanthrene, 12/35 carcinomas without and 13/40 with the estrogen. However, castration reduced the tumor incidence with methylcholanthrene alone, 12/35 to 0/10. In mice, castration also reduced the effect of locally inserted methylcholanthrene-impregnated strings from 22/53 to 0/12. Diethylstilbestrol with methylcholanthrene increased the incidence of squamous-cell carcinoma from 22/53 to 24/36 ($p = 0.02$). The estrogen had no effect by itself, 0/37. The reviewer cannot agree with Baba and von Haam that diethylstilbestrol significantly augmented the effects of methylcholanthrene in rabbits. In this species where adenocarcinoma of the endometrium is characteristically produced, an increase of 7/24 over 3/20 is not significant, $p > 0.2$.

In monkeys, carcinoma of the endometrium has not resulted with estrogen administration. Further work is required because too few animals were used and periods of dosage in most cases were too brief (Hertz, 1965); moreover, in the monkey, continued dosage develops resistance to response manifested by atrophy rather than adenomatous hyperplasia (Hisaw, 1950).

2. *Endometrial Sarcomas*

One to 4 sarcomas per 15–44 animals arose in the endometrial stroma of BALB/c mice which had absorbed 18–900 μg of progesterone per day over an 18-month period. Norethindrone produced similar results in one experiment. Results of this magnitude are significant only if the tumor incidence in concurrent controls of equal numbers is zero. Control data in this series are not mentioned (Lipschutz *et al.*,

1967). Mirand *et al.* (1954) noted the development of a number of fibrosarcomas of the uterine horn or cervix in Marsh mice which had subcutaneously received deoxycorticosterone in sesame oil. Since many local subcutaneous sarcomas developed in these experiments the uterine tumors may have been of metastatic origin.

Women who received 19-norprogestational hormones have developed nonmalignant uterine tumors similar to those produced in mice (Charles, 1964). The former might be mistaken for sarcoma of the endometrium. In mice, the hormone stimulus was continuous over most of the animals' life span, whereas in women it was of much shorter duration.

D. INTERSTITIAL CELL TUMORS OF THE TESTES

Prolonged estrogen administration by subcutaneous injection in oil or pellet implantation leads to interstitial cell tumors of the testes in certain strains of mice including the Strong A (Hooker *et al.*, 1940; Bonser and Robson, 1940), C albino (Shimkin *et al.*, 1941), JK, CBA, IFS, and C3H. Natural and synthetic estrogens, viz., estradiol, stilbestrol, triphenylethylene, and tri-*p*-anisyl-chloroethylene, have produced this tumor in periods covering 4 months to a year of administration. Weekly doses of 0.25 mg of stilbestrol, 3 mg of triphenylethylene, or 50 μg of estradiol indicate the dose range required.

The initial response is hypertrophy of the interstitial cells which are of mesenchymal origin (Bonser, 1944). The first generation tumor cells are large foamy cells developing in nodules. The second generation of tumor cells resemble normal Leydig cells (Hooker and Pfeiffer, 1942); within areas of these cells small, hyperchromatic cells of a more primitive nature arise as the third generation. Malignancy is manifested by metastatic extension of the first stage through the lymphatics and direct invasion by cells of the second and third stages.

E. LOCAL SARCOMAS

A number of workers have reported that local sarcomas arise in mice after the subcutaneous injection of estrogens and other steroid hormones. Loeb *et al.* (1937) felt there was a nonspecific etiology resulting from irritation and that the connective tissue was not specifically stimulated as the glandular tissue was in the case of estrogen-related carcinoma. Lacassagne (1937) believed that the estrogenic hormones can direct cellular multiplication of various tissues not part of the genital system, provided the stimulus is of sufficient duration. While considering the irritative and possibly carcinogenic or cocarcinogenic properties of the oily vehicle, Gardner *et al.* (1959) failed to note that the most significant results were for estrogens introduced in aqueous, not oily solutions. Thus, 10 local sarcomas arose in 247 mice injected subcutaneously with various hormone preparations (Burns *et al.*, 1938). Six of the sarcomas arose in mice which received 50 rat units of estrogen in isotonic saline six or two times weekly. In 128 noninjected control mice no sarcomas developed. Five male mice of the C3H strain all developed local sarcomas on prolonged injection of an aqueous solution of estrogen (theelin), followed by injections in oil of keto-estrin benzoate (Gardner *et al.*, 1936). Six C3H mice which received the same estrogen in oil injections without the aqueous injections developed no local sarcomas. In the A strain no local sarcomas developed under conditions which produced sarcomas in the C3H strain. A yield of 90% local fibro- or myosarcomas was observed by Mirand *et al.* (1953) following the injection of deoxycorticosterone acetate in sesame oil (daily injections of 0.2 mg/0.1 ml for 3 months) in 20 Marsh mice. Twenty-four noninjected controls developed no tumors. The effect of extended multiple injections of the control vehicle was unknown. Weekly subcutaneous injections (Gardner and Rygaard, 1954) of 0.05 ml of sesame oil or sesame oil plus 1.25 mg of testosterone propionate in groups of 100 irradiated BC mice with equal numbers of males and females, produced 9 and 19 local fibrosarcomas, respectively. The difference is significant on the basis of original numbers used but cannot be adequately appraised because the survival rate is not given. Sesame oil controls for nonirradiated mice were not available, although C3H mice had developed local fibrosarcomas with weekly sesame oil injections. Olivi *et al.* (1965) demonstrated the genetic and sex factors in the production of local subcutaneous sarcomas following multiple injections of estradiol benzoate in olive oil. Virgin mice of both sexes of the C57BL/Cb and CBA/Cb strains were compared. The tumor incidences for the two strains and sexes were, respectively: 20/25 and 4/15 for females and males of the C57BL/Cb strain and 0/25 and 0/15 for the CBA/Cb strain. Controls injected with olive oil developed no tumors. The results indicate significant differences. The natural oily vehicle and multiple dosage are undesirable; a single injection of an aqueous suspension would have demonstrated unequivocally whether estradiol is directly carcinogenic to cells of mesenchymal origin. In the experiments of Cutts (1966), epidermoid carcinomas arose in 4 rats at the site of or adjacent to subcutaneous implants of 8–11 mg estrone pellets. The size of such pellets would be subthreshold for solid state carcinogenesis; a direct local carcinogenic effect of estrone is therefore indicated.

F. TUMORS OF LYMPHOCYTE, MONOCYTE, AND MYELOID CELL
   ORIGIN

1. *Estrogen Induced in the Mouse*

Estrogen administration enhances the development of lymphoid tumors in some strains of mice. Dependent upon estrogen dosage, 15–25% mice of the C3H, CBA, and PM strains died with lymphomas. Mice of the A, C57, JK, and C121 strains showed a low or completely refractory response. These deductions are based on experimental series comprising 64–747 estrogenized mice with 37–481 controls (Gardner *et al.*, 1944). In 461 male mice of the Andervont subline of the C3H strain, estrogens did not significantly increase the incidence of lymphomas in doses which produced a 32% incidence of adenocarcinoma of the breast (Shimkin and Wyman, 1946). With a total subcutaneous dose per mouse of 1.0 mg of estradiol in 7 months, treated castrated females and treated intact females of the Marsh strain showed no significant increase in lymphoid tumors over those in intact controls in experiments comprising groups of 40 mice (Bischoff *et al.*, 1945).

However, when castrated male Marsh mice received the same level of estradiol, the 32% accumulative incidence of lymphoid tumors was greater than the 9 or 10% incidence observed for intact and castrated controls. On the basis of terminal survivors at 17 months plus those developing lymphoid tumors, p for 11/28 versus 3/23 and 3/22 is 0.05. When the total dose of estradiol was raised to 3.5 mg/mouse over a 12-month period, a toxic effect was revealed since 56% of 36 intact male Marsh mice died by the fourteenth month. At this time 34% of 36 dosed castrated male mice had developed lymphoid tumors in contrast to 5% in 43 untreated controls. On the basis of survivors plus those developing lymphoid tumors, p for 12/27 versus 2/36 is < 0.01 (Bischoff *et al.*, 1942). Similar results were reported at the cutaneous site in H mice (Dmochowski and Horning, 1947). By painting with 0.01% estrone in chloroform over a 4–6-month period, castrated male mice developed a 39% incidence of lymphoid hyperplasia of both local and generalized lymph nodes and thymus, while the incidence for dosed intact and control mice was 11 and 0%, respectively. With 84 controls and over 97 mice in each dosed series, p is < 0.01.

The factor of time elapsing between castration, performed at 3–4 weeks, and estrogen dosage (0.03 mg of α-estradiol benzoate once a week for 5 months) was tested in C3H mice (Silberberg and Silberberg, 1949). The lymphoma incidences for mice which received the estrogen at the age of 1 month versus those which received it at the age of 4 months was 6/19 versus 2/34 ($p < 0.02, > 0.01$). This was interpreted as indicating an extra testicular aging factor possibly developing in the aging hemopoietic tissues and dependent on strain.

The simultaneous administration of testosterone and estrone or estradiol reduced the incidence of lymphoid tumors, 6/182, in C3H mice to the control value (Gardner *et al.*, 1944). The incidence of leukemia of the lymphoid type was 5/19 in virgin female mice of the A/Jax X AKR₁F₁ strain, given 20 μg of estradiol benzoate per week for 20 weeks; for 30 controls the incidence was 2/30. Whole body radiation, 150 r per week in 4 weeks, produced 18/24 similar leukemias (Nakakuki, 1962).

In summation, exogenous estrogen increased both the lymphoid tumor and mammary carcinoma incidence markedly in C3H and CBA strains of mice. For the PM, JK, and Marsh strains estrogens increased lymphoid tumor incidence under conditions which produced low or negative mammary tumorigenic responses. For the A and Andervont subline of the C3H strain, lymphoid tumor response was nil under conditions which induced mammary tumors. The influence of sex and administration of sex hormones upon lymphoid tumors produced by whole body irradiation of mice follows in general the quantitative effects produced in nonirradiated mice (Furth and Furth, 1936; Kirschbaum and Mixer, 1947).

2. *Estrogen-Inhibiting Mouse Virus Leukemia*

The incidence of a myeloid leukemia induced in RF mice by a leukemogenic ultrafiltrate was lowered 40% by estradiol; the latent period was reduced 20 days by this hormone. Testosterone was without effect (Jenkins *et al.*, 1966). Weekly intramuscular injections of 0.33 mg of estradiol benzoate or 1 mg of testosterone propionate were made beginning at the time of virus inoculation and continuing for 90 days. Since estradiol is a very powerful hormone on a milligram per kilo basis and testosterone a very weak one as measured by visceral effects (uterine versus prostate hypertrophy), the dose relationship in these experiments may have been pharmacological versus physiological. A possible explanation for the results was that estradiol reduced the number of target cell granulocytes in the bone marrow susceptible to the virus. As previously described, estrogen enhances the development of spontaneous lymphomas and lymphomas induced by radiation. This has been explained as a toxic effect on the thymus. An alternate explanation for the myeloid phenomenon might be that estradiol and the virus are both competing at the same target; the space configurations which make them carcinogenic also make them mutually inhibiting. A virus-estradiol effect for the lymphoma, if a virus is indeed involved, would have to be quite different.

3. *Other Species*

The production of lymphoid tumors in certain strains of mice by exogenous estrogen administration is thus well documented. However, in the dog where high estrogen dosage produces defective bone marrow development, no lymphoid tumors have been reported with estrogen administration (Gardner *et al.*, 1959).

In the rat, lymphoid tumors are one of the most common spontaneous tumors. Both the round cell and reticulum cell types prevail. Pulmonary and mesenteric tumor sites are common (Bischoff, 1963; Bryson and Bischoff, 1969; Bullock and Curtis, 1930). Evidence that estrogens produce lymphoid tumors in rats has not been forthcoming, with the exception of a study by McEuen (1938) in which 30 or 120 μg of estrone daily produced 4 lymphosarcomas in 34 rats while only 1 lymphoma occurred in 106 controls.

4. *Cortisol and Plasma Cell Tumors*

The high incidence (over 80%) of plasma cell neoplasms which may be produced in male and female BALB/c mice by intraperitoneal injection (Potter and Boyce, 1962) of 0.5 ml of mineral oil per mouse is markedly reduced by the daily subcutaneous injection of cortisol, 0.1 mg/mouse over the experimental period; the onset of the smaller number of tumors is delayed (Takakura *et al.*, 1966). The mice which receive mineral oil alone develop peritoneal lipogranulomas, hypercellular inflammatory ascites, and sustained hyperglobinemia; these inflammatory manifestations were suppressed by cortisol. The authors suggest a possible causal relationship between plasma cell tumor induction and the inflammatory process. See Section VI for discussion.

G. MAMMARY CARCINOMA

1. *In Mice*

The field of steroid hormone research related to the induction of cancer has been most extensively investigated for mammary cancer of the mouse via the estrogens. Early work has been reviewed by Shimkin (1945) and Gardner *et al.* (1959). No attempt is made in this review to repeat all the references, especially when experimental results were in agreement, but rather to single out the exceptions. It was the exceptions that called attention to the cofactors which were of crucial importance, viz., genetic, metabolic, and viral. The genetics of mammary tumors in mice is a broad field of its own and has been reviewed by Heston (1945). The results of reciprocal hybridization of low and high mouse mammary cancer strains indicated an extrachromosomal factor leading to the discovery of the milk factor (Bittner, 1936), subsequently identified as a virus and referred to as MTV (mammary tumor virus) in this review.

The spontaneous occurrence of mammary carcinoma varies with mouse strain and ranges from 90 to 0% in females. With the exception of the H strain of mice, the testes of which show spontaneous lesions produced in other strains by estrogens, males do not develop spontaneous mammary carcinoma (Athias, 1945). Breeding females in high breast cancer strains generally show a higher incidence of breast cancers than do virgins. In the A strain, the incidence of 83% cancer among breeding females versus 5% among virgins is more pronounced than in other strains.

Ovariectomy at an early age, but not after the age of 7 months, prevents the development of spontaneous breast cancer, unless, as in certain strains, the adrenals take over ovarian function by elaborating estrogens when the ovaries have been removed (Fekete et al., 1941). Males of most strains in which the females have a high spontaneous incidence of breast cancer develop these cancers after receiving ovarian transplants or exogenous estrogen. The tumor incidence of non-breeding females is generally increased by estrogen administration. The tumorigenic effect of an estrogen is correlated with its comparative physiological activity; viz., estradiol which is more potent than estrone in producing uterine hypertrophy would manifest a more enhanced cancer effect on an equal dose level. In the C57 strain, which is a low breast cancer strain, estrogen administration is without tumorigenic effect (Shimkin and Andervont, 1942). In some low cancer strains, estrogenized males develop more tumors than breeding females. Prolonged and high dosage of estrogen has not produced mammary cancer in males of some low tumor strains. In the high cancer Marsh strain, there is no difference in mammary cancer incidence between virgins and breeding females: Estrogens are without effect either in intact males or females, also gonadotropins. Estrogenized castrated males developed only 3 breast cancers in 71 mice. In a comparison of estrogenized littermate male and female Marsh mice, castrated at 30 days of age, 23% of the females (40 mice) developed mammary cancer in contrast to 3% of the males (35 mice). Even at this early age of castration, factors came into play in the females, predisposing them to a precancerous state, which factors were almost negligible in males (Bischoff et al., 1945). A similar situation prevails regarding the vulnerability of the liver of rats to heptacarcinogens, conditioned by neonatal administration of estrogens or androgens.

Changed endocrine characteristics of both sexes so prenatally treated are also manifested (Weisburger *et al.*, 1968).

As summarized by Moore (1965) on the basis of an informal working conference at Inverness, California in 1964, there are two viruses which are responsible for inducing mammary cancers in mice. The mammary tumor virus associated with the so-called B particles is the agent transmitted through the mother's milk and is the causative agent of most spontaneous mammary cancers in mice. The nodule-inducing virus (NIV) produces mammary cancers in mice, which have escaped the MTV virus by foster nursing. Nodule-inducing virus is transmitted by either parent at fertilization and manifests its cancer-promoting effect in the host late in life. Nodule-inducing virus, a mouse leukemia virus, LDH, the lactate dehydrogenase-elevating virus (Riley, 1966), and substances of unknown constitution acting possibly through an immunological mechanism can inhibit the action of MTV.

While conceding that the action of MTV, NIV, and the leukemia virus in promoting cancer is regulated by hormonal and genetic factors, it is held that hormones cannot produce the cancers without the virus and assumed that so-called virus-free strains were actually virus-containing. On the basis of inhibitors and the synergism of hormones and genetic factors, any experimental observation can thus be rationalized — anything and everything is possible consequently if applied to chemical carcinogenesis in general; little of anything would have real significance.

Any concrete evidence that chemical carcinogens or hormones can exert their cancer-promoting effect without viruses is therefore of paramount importance.

Mühlbock's (1963) studies in castrated male mice on the relation of the mammary tumor agent to estrone clearly indicate the dominant role of hereditary influences. In these experiments 2 mg of estrone per liter were administered in the drinking water. A high incidence of mammary tumors (over 70%) was produced in the C3H strain with estrone either in the presence or absence of the mammary tumor agent. In the WLL strain, tumors were only produced in the presence of the mammary tumor agent, whereas in the C57BL strain no tumors were produced either in the presence or absence of the agent. Again using castrated male mice, Mühlbock found that tumor yield was correlated with estrone dosage, that continuous dosage produced higher yields than intermittent doses, and that tumor yield was also correlated with length of dosed periods. For estrone to produce mammary cancer, mammary gland development followed by hyperplasia of the nodules is required. The nodules are regarded as precancerous, representing the hormone-dependent stage. The carcinoma itself is not hormone dependent. The tumorigenic effects of estrogen according to Lipschutz (1950) were dependent upon a continuous action which did not occur normally because of cyclic variations in level. For mouse mammary cancer of the breast, this thesis is well documented (Burns and Schenken, 1940; Shimkin, 1945; Mühlbock, 1960; Okey and Gass, 1968) in experiments comparing the influence of daily continuous versus intermittent doses of estrogen. The enhanced effect of continuous liberation of estrogen is not only demonstrated with tumorigenesis but also with normal hypertrophy. Estradiol in aqueous solution or suspension produces the same degree of uterine hypertrophy in young rats with less than one-fourth the total daily dose if it is administered three times daily instead of once (Bischoff and Pilhorn, 1947).

Evidence presented by Gardner (1941) and by Haagensen and Randall (1942) indicated that estrogens administered to virus-free strains of mice did not induce mammary carcinomas. Using estradiol benzoate, no tumors appeared in 53 mice when the mother was of an agent-free C57BL strain; the incidence of mammary tumors was 60% in 52 mice when the mother was of the agent-bearing CBA strain. Using estrone benzoate to the limit of tolerance, the agent-free C57BL strain developed no tumors; the RIII agent-containing strain did. Boot and Mühlbock (1956) and Mühlbock (1956), however, produced mammary tumors in C3H, DBA, O_{20}, and C57BL virus-free mice. Heston and Deringer (1953) also produced mammary tumors in C3Hf male mice by diethylstilbestrol pellet implantation and in virgin C57BL/He mice by hypophyseal grafts (Heston, 1964). In explaining these discrepancies, Hall and Moore (1966) refer to three categories: (1) so-called agent-free mice, when no extractable and assayable tumor agent is forthcoming and the spontaneous tumor incidence is low; (2) agent-bearing mice, when the agent is assayable and the incidence of cancers is high; and (3) mice showing no cancers, no assayable agent, and no tumorigenic response to estrogen.

The conditions of the third category were met in studying castrated agent-bearing males of the (C3H X A)F_1 X C3H/Bi/Miroff strain and castrated agent-free males of the (C3Hf X Ax)F_1 X C3Hf/Bi/Miroff strains. Of 22 mice of the former given diethylstilbestrol (0.37–0.75 mg/week) 18 of 20 survivors developed mammary carcinomas. Of two groups of 30 mice of the latter strains receiving either diethylstilbestrol or half as much estradiol valerate none developed tumors. Hall and Moore concluded that the agent is therefore required before hormone stimulation can be effective.

Nandi's (1966) dual virus concept is based on data for three strains of mice: the C3Hf, C3H, and A. While containing the MTV virus, strain A does not contain the NIV virus. It does not respond to hormone stimulation. Strain C3Hf, which does not carry the MTV virus, carries the NIV virus and responds to hormone stimulation. Strain C3H contains both viruses and is hormone-stimulated. It is, therefore, concluded that NIV is required for hormonal activity. Nandi is careful to note that the evidence is based on few strains. The question, therefore, hinges on whether mammary tumor NIV viruses will ultimately be detected in all so-called agent-free strains.

In C3H mice, progesterone in weekly subcutaneous doses of 12.5 mg acts as a potent cocarcinogen with either mammary tumor virus or 20-methylcholanthrene (Poel, 1967). In virgin mice progesterone was tumorigenic only when the strain carried the virus. In a strain presumably free from the virus, 28/28 receiving progesterone plus 5 mg/week of 20-methylcholanthrene developed tumors by the twenty-eighth week, but only 10/28 with the hydrocarbon alone. By the thirty-second week the hydrocarbon alone produced 22/26 tumors. Progesterone alone, controls for sesame oil (the vehicle used for progesterone), Tween 60 (the vehicle used for the oral administration of hydrocarbon), sesame oil and Tween 60, and untreated mice developed no tumors. Adenocarcinomas occurred with the tumor virus alone, whereas sarcomas and anaplastic carcinomas occur with the hydrocarbon. The virus is apparently more target specific than the hydrocarbon which has a more diffuse distribution.

An autonomous adenocarcinoma of the breast (AST 115) derived from a breeder mouse of the DD/Sio strain initially took well on transplantation in both sexes. On serial transplantation in male mice of the same strain, the rapidity of tumor growth increased. At the nineteenth passage, the tumor no longer took in females and was named "Shionogi carcinoma 115" to distinguish the androgen-dependent clone from the original tumor (Minesita and Yamaguchi, 1965). Evidence of androgen dependency follows:

(1) The tumor took only in intact males and not in females or castrated males of the DD/Sio strain.

(2) Injection of androgens in females or castrated males produced tumor takes equal to that of intact males. Testosterone, norandrostenolone, and 2-hydroxymethylene-17α-methyldihydrotestosterone in castrated males with doses of 0.5 mg in 20 days for the two former and 1.0 mg in 20 days for the latter compound were effective. Androstenediol, which has both androgenic and estrogenic properties, was without effect in a dose range of 0.5–8.0 mg in 20 days.

(3) When male hosts were castrated after the implant had been established, the implant regressed or atrophied after a few days; growth was restored on administration of testosterone.

(4) Implanted into newborn mice, the tumor developed only in males 40 days later at sexual maturity.

(5) Tumor growth in males was completely inhibited by estrogen administration of estradiol-17β hexestrol, or chloro-tris(p-methoxyphenyl)ethylene in subcutaneous doses of 0.1 mg in 15 days. Hydrocortisone retarded tumor growth on the high dose of 10 mg in 15 days.

2. In Rats with Estrogen

With the rat, no mammary tumor virus has to date been implicated in mammary adenocarcinoma etiology. The incidence of spontaneous mammary adenocarcinomas is low; however, adenofibromas are quite common. The spontaneous adenocarcinoma incidence in rats has been reported as 2/489 (Bullock and Curtis, 1930), 2/15,625 (Dunning and Curtis, 1946), 2/125 Sprague-Dawley rats (Thompson et al., 1961), 15/150 female random-bred Sprague-Dawley rats (Davis et al., 1956), 50/1000 (Dao, 1964), 5/316 Evans females (Bischoff and Bryson, 1968a).

In a number of laboratories, prolonged release of exogenous estrogen either by repeated injection over extended periods or from implanted pellets has produced mammary adenocarcinomas in rats (Geschickter, 1939; Noble et al., 1940; Eisen, 1942; Mark and Biskind, 1941; Nelson, 1944; Dunning and Curtis, 1952; Cutts and Noble, 1964). Strain differences in tumor yield are marked; on release of from 6 to 7 μg estrone per day, the incidences of tumor production for the Fisher, Wistar, Lewis, Sprague-Dawley, and hooded strains varied from 16 to 86% (Cutts, 1966). Estrogens without either viruses or carcinogenic hydrocarbons on prolonged dosage produce mammary carcinomas. Whether the estrogens act directly, as carcinogens in their own right, upon the acinar cells or whether the stimulus is mediated through release of pituitary hormones acting solely or synergistically with estrogens is still controversial. Carcinogenic hydrocarbons also produce mammary carcinomas but only in conjunction with estrogen.

Estrogen-induced mammary carcinomas are hormone dependent and regress upon removal of the estrogen pellet. The process is, however, reversible on reimplantation of pellets (Noble and Collip, 1941; Noble and Cutts, 1958; Cutts, 1966). In hypophysectomized rats estrone does not induce mammary tumors and permanent regression results when hypophysectomy is performed after estrone-induced tumors have developed (Cutts, 1964). Testosterone, 7- or 10-mg pellet, growth hormone (0.5 mg three times weekly), or progesterone (0.3 mg three times weekly) extend the latent period of tumor development slightly, 12–21% (Cutts, 1964). A temporary reduction in tumor size occurs after adrenalectomy or ovariectomy.

Since hypophysectomy abolishes the induction or growth of these tumors, it would appear that the effect of estrogen is mediated primarily via the pituitary by the release of the mammotropic hormone. A combination of direct and indirect effects remains a possibility. In studying a hormone-dependent rat mammary adenocarcinoma, Kim *et al.* (1963) found that after hypophysectomy in rats previously implanted with this tumor, estradiol retarded the tumor regression; implants of a tumor which secreted mammotropic hormones restored tumor growth. Although these experiments answer pertinent questions regarding the maintenance of tumor growth, they do not settle the origin of the primary stimulus. The question of direct estrogen carcinogenic effects is covered in other sections of this review.

Neither prolactin nor growth hormone produces mammary carcinoma in rats. Since estrogen has not produced these tumors in hypophysectomized rats, it must be assumed that hypophysectomy per se is too debilitating or that the pituitary hormones act as synergists. Hypophysectomy involves the loss of the specific action of the pituitary growth hormone and the influence of caloric restriction. Bischoff and Long (1938) by maintaining essential nutrients constant and optimal and by varying intake of carbohydrate or fat demonstrated that caloric restriction per se inhibits tumor growth. In the case of hypophysectomy, there is a greater weight loss than in controls on the same caloric consumption. Whereas the controls spare nitrogen at the expense of body fat, the hypophysectomized rats show a loss of body nitrogen (Lee and Ayres, 1936). This would indicate that the growth hormone effect is mediated through changes in both nitrogen catabolism and caloric intake. Hypophysectomy may influence tumor induction not only with estrogen but also with carcinogenic hydrocarbons (Gardner *et al.*, 1959). With the rat mammary carcinoma, hormones other than the growth hormone appear to be involved.

Since pretreatment of female rats with large doses of 7,12-dimethylbenz (α) anthracene (DMBA) or methylcholanthrene (MC) more than doubled the hepatic production of estrogen metabolites devoid of estrogenic activity, Jellinck (1966) suggested that DMBA acts indirectly by producing hormonal imbalance in rats which develop mammary carcinomas. Earlier experiments had shown that tumors in males (Bock and Dao, 1961; Dao *et al.*, 1959) were produced only rarely by MC although the concentration of the hormone at the breast site was the same in the males as it was in the females where the effect was highly carcinogenic. By grafting ovaries in males receiving MC, mammary tumors were produced (Dao and Greiner, 1961). Ovariectomy (Dao, 1962) during the 7-day period following administration of the carcinogen produced negative or greatly reduced tumorigenic results; ovariectomy after this date did not alter the response to the hydrocarbon. Thus the ovaries and the hydrocarbon are intimately involved in this particular carcinogenic process at the mammary gland site.

Mammary gland transplantation from random bred Sprague-Dawley rats was accomplished with both autografts and homografts. When females were fed 20 mg of DMBA 4 hours before their mammary glands were used as grafts, 13 out of 15 successful takes developed cancers, mostly adenocarcinomas. With male donors, 3 out of 11 cancers were so produced in female recipients. These tumors were hormone dependent because they regressed following ovariectomy (Dao et al., 1964). Subsequent studies showed that in older nonlittermate rats the incidence of cancer in the transplant was much lower, comparing to that with the male donors (Dao et al., 1964). Undefined was the role of hyperplasia as a prelude to carcinogenesis, in this case whether resulting from the carcinogenic hydrocarbon, transplant site, or use of young recipients. Ovarian stimulation is required for the formation but not maintenance of preneoplastic hyperplastic alveolar nodules induced by DMBA in Lewis rats (Beuving, 1968). Alveolar development was suppressed in 60-day-old rats ovariectomized 10 days prior to DMBA administration; another series ovariectomized 80 days after administration of the carcinogen manifested the hyperplasia.

3. In Rats with Progesterone

In the induction of mammary carcinomas, progesterone has a synergistic effect with carcinogenic hydrocarbons both in the mouse and the rat. The inclusion of 0.03% 2-acetaminofluorene in the diet of Sherman and Wistar female rats, yielded an incidence of 30% mammary tumors. Simultaneous intramuscular administration of 1.5 mg of progesterone per week increased the tumor yield to 85%. The effect was highly significant 17/57 versus 22/26. Estradiol or the pregnant mare serum hormone was without quantitative effect in intact rats; since no tumors developed in a group of 11 castrated females which received both the carcinogen and progesterone, it was concluded that small amounts of estrogen were necessary but progesterone was the limiting factor (Cantarow et al., 1948). Sydnor and Cockrell (1963) concur showing that in ovariectomized Sprague-Dawley rats optimal response to 3-methylcholanthrene administered by mouth (210–420 mg in 7 weeks) required small doses of estradiol-17β (0.01–0.2μg) with progesterone (2–4 mg). Ovariectomy did not abolish the tumorigenic effect completely, but a combination of ovariectomy and adrenalectomy did, indicating that the adrenals had taken over the hormonal role of the ovaries.

Given a single oral dose of 20 mg of 7,12-dimethylbenz (α) anthracene the yield of adenocarcinoma of the breast in virgin Sprague-Dawley rats was about 80% (Jull, 1966). Three hormone preparations, progesterone, 4 pregnen-21-hydroxy-3,20-dione and 2-methyl-1,2-di-3-pyridyl-1-propane, administered subcutaneously for a 5 day period just before and after hydrocarbon dosage reduced the tumor yield markedly, viz., from 82% (32/39) to 42% (8/19), 25% (5/20) and 20% (4/20), respectively. The total doses per rat, 180 mg for the first two compounds and 320 mg for the latter compound were extremely high. No completely satisfactory explanation for the reversal of the progesterone effect was given. A blocking effect for progesterone, viz., a competition with the hydrocarbon at the target site, does not appear satisfactory since many tumors appeared and then regressed. The authors felt that the DMBA action in the progesterone experiment may have been less complete than it was in the experiments with DMBA alone. This would appear to indicate that the experiments were not adequately controlled.

4. *In Monkeys*

Both Pfeiffer and Allen (1948) and Geschickter and Hartman (1959) studied the effects of large doses of estrogens, carcinogenic hydrocarbons (methylcholanthrene, benzpyrene, and dibenzanthrene) and their combination in rhesus monkeys. A total of 71 monkeys were observed; no animal developed a local or endocrine-linked cancer. The weakness of this research is the combined effect of both estrogen and carcinogenic hydrocarbon in so many of the experiments, the use of multiple dose sites in the same animal, variable dose level and compound, variable period of treatment, and variable observation periods. Pfeiffer and Allen report on 10 monkeys which received only estrogens and 18 which received only hydrocarbons. In a few cases treatment was carried over a 7–11-year period. The experiments are important in showing that in a primate large doses of carcinogenic hydrocarbons, estrogens, or their combination are noncarcinogenic. Mammary ducts and cervical epithelium are stimulated by both the carcinogenic hydrocarbons and estrogens, but the proliferative stimulus never triggers the target tissue into a true cancerous state. Engle *et al.* (1943) studied the effect of approximately 700 mg of α-estradiol implanted subcutaneously at intervals of 5 or 6 weeks during a 24–28-month period in 5 old rhesus female monkeys. Survival after the last implant was 6 months or less. No cancers developed, but a cystic change was produced in the mammary gland.

The normal life span of rhesus monkeys in the wild state is not known. In the rhesus monkey experiments cited, the period of observation for estrogens may not have been long enough as based on experiments with rodents. For the carcinogenic hydrocarbons, which have a much shorter tumorigenic latent period, the time of observation would appear to have been adequate. The production of inflammatory or noninflammatory fibrotic masses, areas of granulation tissue or encapsulated cysts for oil injections of the carcinogenic hydrocarbons and encapsulation of pellets with dense fibrous connective tissue, are of interest because in rodents these reactions precede the production of cancer (Vasiliev *et al.*, 1962). Solid state carcinogenesis in rodents at the subcutaneous site also is preceded by formation of the hyaline fibrous capsule. It is interesting that examples of solid state carcinogenesis for humans at the subcutaneous site are nil (Bischoff and Bryson, 1964) although here the fibrous capsule also forms. Primates appear to be protected from malignant development at this site.

H. Uterine-Vaginal Neoplasms

Uterine-vaginal neoplasms but not endometrial carcinomas occur in mice after prolonged estrogen treatment. In a number of studies there were no concurrent controls, and the significance of the observations is doubtful. Although no spontaneous malignant epithelial uterine, uterine-cervical, or vaginal tumors have been observed in A, C3H, CBA, JK, C121, or C57 inbred strains, 5 carcinomas, 7 malignancies of undifferentiated cells, and 1 spindle cell sarcoma occurred spontaneously in the uterus or vagina of 56 PM stock untreated mice (Gardner and Pan, 1948). In 35 mice of the BC strain which had received estradiol or stilbestrol alone or in combination with testosterone, 13 developed uterine-cervical carcinomas or infiltrative lesions. None of the 82 controls developed comparable epithelial tumors (Pan and Gardner, 1948). Prolonged administration of estradiol benzoate, 17 μg or more per week, produced lesions and carcinoma of the uterine cervix in 15 of 24 and 10 of 20 C57 and CBA hybrids after 400 days. Equal numbers of controls developed no lesions or tumors. Genetic factors which influence mammary adenocarcinoma development did not influence uterine-cervix carcinoma (Allen and Gardner, 1941). Other estrogens like stilbestrol, triphenylethylene, and estrone have had a similar uterine carcinogenic effect.

Eight of 40 mice of the BC strain implanted with stilbestrol-cholesterol pellets in the upper vagina developed uterine-cervical or vaginal carcinomas (Gardner, 1959). Several hundred mice of the strain, serving as controls in other experiments, did not develop this type of tumor. One of 43 concurrent littermates used as controls developed an anaplastic epidermoid carcinoma on the dorsal vaginal wall. Thirty control mice bearing cholesterol intravaginal implants developed no tumors of the type produced with stilbestrol. However, one epidermoid carcinoma of the vulva occurred. Mice of the BC strain also developed vaginal carcinomas upon intravaginal instillation of a powder containing carboxymethyl-cellulose. This substance has produced a 43% local sarcoma incidence in rats when injected subcutaneously (Lusky and Nelson, 1957). The estrogen, the carcinogenic hydrocarbons, and the polymer have in common an apparently local carcinogenic effect producing the same local vaginal lesion. Here the direct carcinogenic activity of estrogen is indicated.

Pellets (1.2 mg) of testosterone propionate implanted twice weekly into 42 hybrid (C57BL X DBA) female mice from the age of 6-13 weeks, produced 26 uterine tumors mainly in the cervix (Van Nie *et al.*, 1961). Ten metastasized to the lung. The tumors were probably of decidua cell origin.

Macacus rhesus monkeys subjected to prolonged subcutaneous estrone administration along with cervical trauma developed lesions resembling early epidermoid carcinoma. Estrone produced metaplasia (Overholser and Allen, 1933).

I. GRANULOSA-CELL OVARIAN TUMORS AND PROGESTINS

BALB/c mice implanted with progesterone pellets at 2 months of age developed granulosa-cell tumors of the ovary in 25-50% of the animals (19-28) when the daily liberation of progesterone was 59-665 μg/day over an 18-month period. Thirty-three controls developed 1 spontaneous tumor. Nine hundred micrograms per day did not produce a significant increase of tumor incidence over controls (Lipschutz *et al.*, 1967). 19-Norprogesterone had a more powerful effect than progesterone since 8 of 33 animals developed granulosa-cell tumors with a resorption of 15 μg/day over a minimum 13-month period (Lipschutz *et al.*, 1962, 1963). These workers also studied two contraceptives, 17α-ethinyl-19-nortestosterone (norethindrone) and 17α-ethinyl $\Delta^{5,10}$-19-nortestosterone (norethynodrel). Norethindrone

produced a 52% ovarian tumor incidence (25 mice) on a daily liberation of 7.7μg. The results with norethynodrel were nontumorigenic.
In a series of 47 controls apparently used for studies with 19-norpro-
gesterone, no ovarian tumors were observed (Lipschutz *et al.*, 1963).

Ovaries grafted into the spleens of hosts of the same strain also develop granulosa-cell tumors in rats (Biskind and Biskind, 1944), mice
(Li and Gardner, 1947; Furth and Sobel, 1947), guinea pigs
(Lipschutz, 1957), and rabbits (Peckham *et al.*, 1948; Peckham and
Greene, 1952). In spleen-transplanted ovaries the granulosa-cell tumors develop from a luteoma arising from the stroma; the steroid-in-
duced tumors begin from granulosa cells of possible follicle or ger-
minal epithelial origin.

J. THE GOLDEN HAMSTER

1. *Estrogen-Dependent Renal Carcinoma*

Of the varied species of mammals that have received large amounts
of estrogens continuously over long periods, only the golden hamster
develops malignant estrogen-dependent renal tumors (Kirkman and
Bacon, 1952a,b; Horning, 1956). Subcutaneous injections or implantation of diethylstilbestrol or α-estradiol designed to release about 0.1
mg hormone per day over 250-450 days, produce nearly 100% carcinomas of the kidney in intact or gonadectomized males and in gonadectomized females. To establish whether ethinyl estradiol and 7-
methyl-bis-dehydrodoisynolic acid are ineffective or have a greatly
reduced effect would require a larger series of animals than have been
studied. Involution of primary tumors and transplants, which take in
estrogenized hosts, follows on withdrawal of estrogen. Testosterone
blocks the induction of primary tumors but is without effect on transplant growth (Kirkman, 1957). Anti-estrogens like deoxycorticosterone
and progesterone inhibit induction and growth of transplants. The
tumor has become autonomous after 14 serial transfers and survives in
untreated male hosts.

2. *Three Golden Hamster Androgen–Estrogen-Induced Tumors*

Three other steroid-linked tumors may be produced in the golden
hamster with a high incidence. They differ from the renal tumor in
that both estrogen and testosterone (each about 0.1 mg/day) are required for induction and transplantation. The two of uterine-endometrial (Bacon, 1951) or ductus-deferens-epididymal tail (Bacon, 1952)
origin are histologically identical and regress rapidly after cessation

of estrogen-androgen treatment (Kirkman, 1957). Although characterized as benign (Kirkman, 1957), the ductus deferens tumor was later
designated as a leiomyosarcoma (Kirkman and Algard, 1965). These
tumors have not become autonomous on serial transplantation. The
third tumor, which may occur spontaneously, is a potentially malignant basal-cell epithelioma associated with the flank organ and requires an induction period of 110-500 days. Its induction is not inhibited by the administration of progesterone and it remains viable after
cessation of androgen-estrogen hormone administration; however,
growth is dependent upon an androgen-estrogen maintenance level.
In tissue cell cultures it survives without hormones (Algard, 1960).
Twenty-one serial passages have not produced an autonomous transplantable tumor (Kirkman and Algard, 1964). The sequence of events
leading to the production of the basal-cell epithelioma, beginning
with the normal organ, may be traced through late hyperplasia and
beginning neoplasia. The original lamellated corpuscles develop
normally in males through endogenous androgens. It is the combined
androgen-estrogen stimulus which pushes increasing hyperplasia
over to malignancy (Kirkman and Algard, 1964).

IV. Theoretical Considerations

A. STEROID HORMONE TRANSPORT

Interest in the physiochemical state of the circulating steroids as
related to tumorigenic phenomena was repeatedly manifested at the
Steroid Hormone Conference at Hershey, Pennsylvania (Bischoff,
1945). Roberts and Szego (1946), in allocating endogenous estrogens
in serum protein fractions, reported that practically all the estrogen
occurred in the Cohn lipoprotein fraction III-O, indicating that the
lipoproteins transported the estrogens. Results based on solubility
and distribution coefficients (Bischoff and Pilhorn, 1948; Bischoff and
Katherman, 1948, 1952) indicated that testosterone, progesterone, estradiol, and estrone were primarily transported by plasma albumin
and estrogen also by hemoglobin in the red cells (Bischoff and Katherman, 1948; Bischoff and Bryson, 1960). The attraction between steroid
and protein was not covalent. The transport role of albumin was confirmed in 12 publications from 1954-1962. Among these are Eik-Nes
et al. (1954), Westphal (1955), and Sandberg *et al.* (1957). The reported concentration of estrogen in the lipoprotein fraction (Roberts
and Szego, 1946) was not confirmed by Bischoff *et al.* (1954) nor by
MacArthur (as quoted by Sandberg *et al.*, 1957). The latter authors

also showed that on administration of radioactive estrone and estradiol to humans, the greatest concentration was in fraction V (albumin) and its supernatant. Antoniades *et al.* (1957) found that after administration of estrone and estrone sulfate to humans, the albumin fraction carried most of the activity. It has been suggested that postmenopausal gonadotropin may have accounted for the activity of fraction III-O erroneously interpreted by Szego and Roberts as estrogen. A specific protein which binds testosterone is elaborated during conditions in which the estrogen level is elevated (Guériguian and Pearlman, 1968).

Thus, the androgens and estrogens are transported primarily by plasma albumin, some corticosteroids by a specific protein, and cholesterol by a lipoprotein. A red cell enzyme converts estrone to estradiol in rodent and human blood (Bischoff *et al.*, 1951a; Bischoff and Bryson, 1960; Repke and Markwardt, 1954; Wall and Migeon, 1959; Nyman *et al.*, 1959; Migeon *et al.*, 1962). Moreover, the uterus, lung, and testes convert estrone to estradiol in four tested species, viz., mouse, rat, rabbit, and man (Bischoff *et al.*, 1953a). The enzymic conversion of testosterone to 4-androstene-3,17-dione by red cells (Bischoff *et al.*, 1953b) was confirmed by Migeon *et al.* (1962). These enzymic conversions are reversible (Portius and Repke, 1960). The significance of the red cell enzyme systems involving the 17-steroid oxygen linkage therefore depends upon whether the net result is an increase or decrease in biological activity under physiological conditions. Since bioassays are currently out of fashion, there is much reporting in the literature of conversions of isotope-tagged steroids in artificial enzyme systems. The results are not meaningful to the understanding of physiological and carcinogenic mechanisms unless biological activity of reaction products has been ascertained. The increases in biological activity with estrone sulfate and estrone palmitate as the substrates with rabbit serum-red cells were not significant, viz., $p = 0.1$ (Bischoff *et al.*, 1951a). For estrone under comparable conditions the increase was over 100% ($p < 0.0001$). For human red cells, 17β-estradiol 3-sulfate was shown by chemical means to react more rapidly than 17β-estradiol under optimal but not physiological conditions (Jacobsohn and Hochberg, 1968). The difference between the biological activity of estradiol and estrone is twentyfold. Estrone sulfates administered parenterally have one-fourth the activity of estrone. Although plasma albumin is not involved in the enzyme reaction itself, it regulates to a large extent the course of the reaction by its selective affinity for the reaction products. This can be measured by the distribution coefficients of the steroids between plasma and red cells. Since estradiol is more firmly bound to albumin than estrone, biological activation would ensue with conversion of estrone to estradiol. The sulfates are more firmly bound to albumin than the free sterols. Whereas estradiol and not estrone is removed by the target site, estradiol would be replenished by the enzyme system. Species differences exist: 17α instead of 17β-estradiol is formed by cow, sheep, and goat red cells (Portius and Repke, 1960).

Szego (1953) claimed that the liver was able to conjugate an estroprotein, which was theorized as being the one present in the circulating estrogen-protein (III-O) complex previously described by her. Results of others did not support this claim. Riegel and Mueller (1954) showed that a metabolite of radioactive estradiol, without perceptible biological activity, was formed on liver incubation; and Bischoff and Bryson (1962) found that less than 0.2% of the biological activity of an estrone- or estradiol-17β containing incubated liver brei was associated with liver or plasma protein after hydrolysis. The direct action of estrogen in tissue culture (Section IV,E,1,2,4) further invalidates the contention of Szego and Roberts (1953) that estrogens do not become biologically effective unless activated by the liver. Jensen (1966) failed to detect any appreciable protein-bound estradiol or estriol in the uterus 2 or 6 hours after injection of these hormones. The precise state and form of the circulating steroids is of great importance when designing tissue culture experiments, for the added steroids should be in the state in which they would reach the target organ. Problems related to solubility have been one of the limiting factors in tissue culture studies with steroid hormones.

B. CELL PERMEABILITY

1. *At the Target Site*

In certain species and strains the relation of estrogens to both benign and malignant neoplastic extension is well documented for tissues like the mammary gland, anterior pituitary, cervix, kidney, lymph tissue, testes, and uterus. Jensen (1966) felt that the study of basic mechanisms by which steroid hormones stimulate normal growth would contribute information concerning abnormal growth. Jensen administered radioactive estrogens to intact and ovariectomized rats in doses of 0.01-0.1 μg and found that estradiol and estriol, but not estrone, are taken up and retained by the uterus against a marked concentration gradient as measured by blood levels. The interaction at the target site is not covalent and initiates growth processes without the estrogen itself being destroyed or conjugated. Receptor sites can be blocked by certain estrogen antagonists.

2. Semipermeability of Fat-Cell Membrane

Many synthetic and natural substances like trans-diethylstilbestrol, which produce effects like the estrogenic hormones in target organs, are not steroids. Strictly speaking, these nonsteroid estrogens should not be covered in this review. Since, however, they have in many instances demonstrated the same carcinogenic effects as the steroid estrogens, while in other instances steroid estrogens were not even explored, the nonsteroid estrogens are included. From the standpoint of exogenous steroid carcinogenesis, it is unfortunate that the steroid hormones were not used at least as a reference in all cases. Since the action of the estrogens has been explained on the basis of fat solubility, a marked difference in the permeability of the fat-cell membrane between the steroid and some nonsteroid estrogens should be noted. The relative impermeability of the fat-cell wall upon intravenous injection of estradiol into rabbits was noted by Bischoff et al. (1951b); muscle cells took up 2.5 times as much estradiol as fat cells. In rats tri-p-anisyl chloroethylene (Tace) was stored in the fat, whereas meso-3,4-bis(p-hydroxyphenyl)-n-hexane (hexestrol) was not present to any extent as measured by bioassay. In humans, Tace was also stored in the fat but estrone, estradiol, or estrone sulfate were not detected (Greenblatt and Brown, 1952). A more sensitive method using tagged estradiol, (Twombly et al., 1961) showed that 15-19 hours after intramuscular injection of estradiol-17β-16-C^{14} about 0.1% was found per pound fat. In an obese woman, 100 pounds of fat would thus account for 10% of the injected estradiol. Tagged progesterone showed an even higher accumulation in the body fat depots, as high as 46%, 19 hours after administration (Davis and Plotz, 1958).

C. The Blocking Theories

The bacteriostatic and toxic effects of the sulfa drugs are explained on the basis of the blocking of the vitamin, p-aminobenzoic acid, which has structural similarities. Death of cells with survival of resistant variants is quite analogous to the local cellular action of the carcinogenic hydrocarbons. The effects of carcinogenic hydrocarbons have been blocked by noncarcinogenic hydrocarbons. Pretreating a skin area with the noncarcinogenic octahydro derivative of 1,2,5,6-dibenzanthracene virtually abolished the powerful carcinogenic effect of 1,2,5,6-dibenzanthracene (Fürst, 1966). A number of blocking theories have been proposed to explain carcinogenic mechanisms. Jull (1956) suggested that the carcinogen replaces a structurally related hormone in normal cellular metabolism; the peculiar structure of the carcinogen produces loss of controlled cellular development because it has replaced a hormone at a strategic metabolic site. Yang *et al.* (1961) have refined this theory by postulating that in addition to similarity in structural groups (electronic factors) there must be similarity in steric configuration. A carcinogenic hydrocarbon must resemble the steroid which it replaces, in steric configuration. Their studies indicate that the closer the resemblance the higher the carcinogenicity of the hydrocarbon. Dannenberg (1963b) explored the anchoring site as the helix in DNA.

Since the purines are weak acceptors, the higher electron density of the hydrocarbon is required as a sufficiently high electron donor to accomplish strong binding in the transfer complex. The aromatic hydrocarbons possess the space configuration required to achieve the close proximity of the donor and acceptor. A group larger than the methyl prevents the close proximity which is required for strong binding to DNA. The binding of the hydrocarbon prevents a suitable separation of the DNA strands in cell division and a damaged system results. The slipping mechanism widens the DNA strands which are tightly packed normally. Steroids like cholesterol would not achieve the close proximity because of the side chain size, so that blocking effects of cholesterol would have to be achieved by other mechanisms.

Bischoff and Bryson (1960) called attention to the relation between cholesterol and its α-oxide, which differed structurally only by an oxygen which has broken a cholesterol double bond. They postulated a blocking effect analogous to that of *p*-aminobenzoic acid by the sulfa drugs. Under conditions in which cholesterol was not carcinogenic the α-oxide was. This concept gained support from (*a*) inhibition by cortisone of skin cancers induced in Swiss mice by methylcholanthrene (Baserga and Shubik, 1954); (*b*) the similarity of breast changes induced by carcinogenic hydrocarbons and progesterone (Jull, 1956); and (*c*) the blocking of estradiol by testosterone in blood transport via albumin (Bischoff and Katherman, 1948). The histological events which ultimately lead to carcinogenesis via the α-oxide of cholesterol at the subcutaneous rodent test site are illustrated (Fig. 2). The initial effect is death of cells.

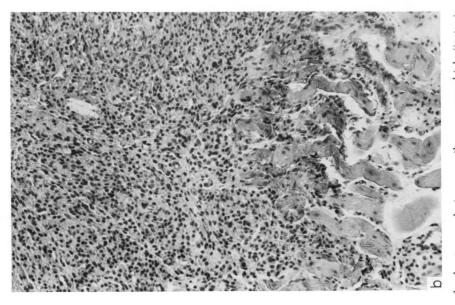

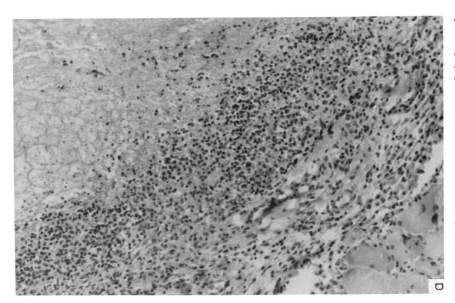

FIG. 2. Local tissue reaction to 10 mg of cholesterol α-oxide administered subcutaneously in a nonoily aqueous vehicle (isotonic saline) to Marsh mice (×140). (a) After 5 days—death of cells characteristic of a chemical carcinogen. (b) After 14 days—development of vascularized granulation tissue.

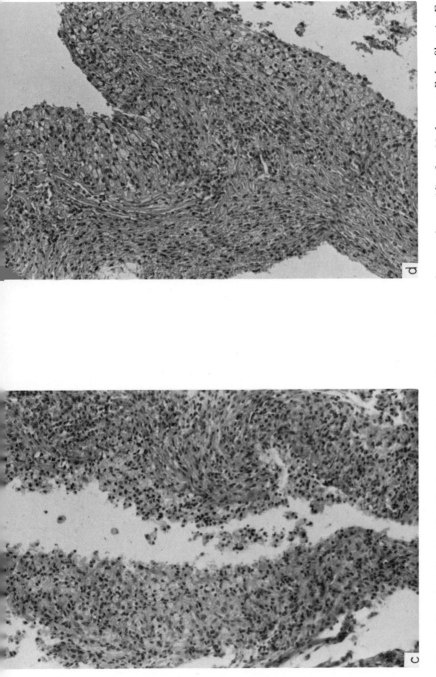

FIG. 2. (*Continued*). (c) After 30 days—fibroplasia, with lymphocytes and macrophages. (d) After 90 days—cellular fibrosis. For photomicrographs of sarcomas induced by cholesterol α-oxide administered in oily or aqueous vehicles see Bischoff (1957, 1963).

D. Carcinogenic Hydrocarbons from Steroids

In the laboratory, deoxycholic acid may be converted to 12-keto-cholanic acid, which by pyrolysis at 330°C is converted to dehydronor-cholene (Wieland and Wiedersheim, 1930). By dehydration with sele-nium the latter compound forms 20-methylcholanthrene (Wieland and Dane, 1933). Cholic acid may also be used as the starting material, whence the intermediates are dehydrocholic acid and 3,7-dihydroxy-12-ketocholanic acid (Fieser and Newman, 1935). These are drastic chemical procedures, the counterpart of which through enzyme reac-tions in physiological systems has not been observed. The pyrolysis could, presumably, take place in cooking.

Bergmann (1939) noted that the eight carbon side chain of choles-terol lends itself to a two ring cyclization with a methyl group on each ring. The six ring parent hydrocarbon has not been found in nature. Its dimethyl derivative, steranthrene, corresponding to the cholesterol side chain sequence is highly carcinogenic when tested by injection or skin painting (Dannenberg, 1958). The results indicated that it was as potent as 3-methylcholanthrene and 3,4-benzpyrene.

Three aromatic carcinogenic derivatives have been prepared with cholesterol as the starting material by Dannenberg (1964). By dehy-drogenation of cholesterol with chloranil, D ring unsaturated cyclo-pentadienophenanthrenes characterized as $\Delta^{2'}$-3′ methyl and $\Delta^{1'}$-1′ methyl formed and were moderately carcinogenic by skin painting in mice (Dannenberg, 1960).

Stigmasterol which has a double bond at the C-22 to C-23 carbons and two more carbons than cholesterol, as an ethyl group at C-24 is converted by pyrolysis at 750°C to benzo(a)pyrene and pyrene (Van Duuren, 1962).

Dehydration of the steroid hormones leads to derivatives of 1,2-cy-clopentenophenanthrene. Incorporation of the C-18 angular carbon into the five-membered ring of the steroids leads to derivatives of chrysene. A number of methyl homologs of these two parent hydrocar-bons have been shown to be carcinogenic (Fürst, 1966). While theo-retically possible, there is no indication that such changes occur en-dogenously.

To make the B ring of the steroids aromatic it is necessary to elimi-nate the angular methyl group which serves as a protective agent. This has been accomplished under drastic conditions by pyrolysis of 1,4-androstadien-17β-ol-3-one at 325°C (Inhoffen, 1940). A yield of 5% estradiol was obtained.

Where there is a 6 hydroxy group the angular methyl group is eliminated by oxidation via the intermediary formation of an epoxide (Fürst, 1966).

For methylcholanthrene, the introduction of a hydroxyl group at the 15 position decreases the carcinogenic potency. Substitution of a keto group for the OH group at the 15 position (Shear and Leiter, 1941) further reduces carcinogenic potency. It is important that for 11 methyl-15,16-dihydro-17-oxocyclopenta(a)phenanthrene, the keto group at the 17 position produces a powerful carcinogenic effect in contrast to the deoxo derivative [11-methyl-16,17-dihydro-15H-cyclopenta(a) phenanthrene] which is weakly carcinogenic. The latter compound was studied by Dannenberg (1960), the former by Coombs and Croft (1966). The importance of the methyl group at position 11 is critical, even in the presence of the 17 ketone oxygen, because substitution of a hydrogen for methyl at 11, shifting of the methyl group to position 12, or introduction of a methoxy group at position 3, with positions 11,12 devoid of methyls produces biological inactivity (Coombs and Croft, 1966). The substitution of a methoxy group at position 11 instead of a methyl group also favors carcinogenicity (Coombs and Croft, 1967).

About half of 20 hydrocarbon and ketone derivatives of cyclopenta(a)phenanthrene which were structurally related to the natural steroids produced skin tumors in mice. The high carcinogenicity of 11-methoxy ketones is an exception to previously held concepts that oxygenation of polycyclic hydrocarbons leads to reduced carcinogenicity. Coombs and Croft (1969) felt that recent advances in steroid biosynthesis and metabolism indicated possible routes for the production of cyclopenta(a)phenanthrenes in the living organism and that a reappraisal of steroids as precursors of endogenous carcinogens was in order. Oxygen at the 17 position occurs with testosterone, estradiol, and their many related derivatives, and oxygen at the 11 position occurs in cortisone, cortisol, etc.

In the 1940's a situation arose regarding deoxycholic acid similar to that regarding the alleged chemical carcinogenicity of cholesterol. Application of deoxycholic acid to the skin of mice in alcohol or benzene produced negative tumorigenic results, and in many laboratories (Hartwell, 1951, cites 13 references) subcutaneous injections into mice or rats also produced negative results. However, using sesame oil as a vehicle, 11 local subcutaneous sarcomas were produced in stock or C3H mice (Badger *et al.*, 1940). When these experiments were repeated under essentially similar experimental conditions but using a different batch of sesame oil, no local tumors were produced (Kennaway, as cited by Klein, 1963). Kennaway felt that the original tumorigenic results resulted from a cocarcinogen in the particular batch of sesame oil used. Ghiron (1939) had also reported that in rats and mice a high percentage of local fibrosarcomas developed upon injection of deoxycholic acid. The details of these experiments are not available. By oral administration in 7–8-day-old $B6AF_1/J$ male mice, deoxycholic acid tested in a total dose of 0.75 mg produced negative tumorigenic results. Under similar conditions 0.1 or 0.75 mg of 1,2-benzanthracene and 0.75 mg of 3-methylcholanthrene produced significant increase in hepatomas and pulmonary adenomas (Klein, 1963). A summation of results indicates that in rodents deoxycholic acid does not act as a chemical carcinogen. The conflicting results introduced by the use of sesame oil as a vehicle are another example of the undesirability of natural oils as vehicles in testing for carcinogens (Bischoff, 1957, 1963; Bryson and Bischoff, 1969). Lacassagne *et al.* (1967) found that in rats lithocholic and cholic acid administered by mouth did not accelerate the carcinogenic activity of butter yellow. The dietary mixture contained 0.6 gm/kg of p-dimethylaminobenzene and 0.5 gm/kg of either of the bile acids.

In this section a critical appraisal of significance of results in biological tests has not been made because in many instances the information was not available. The impression was gained that in some instances the testing was inadequate because of too few test animals and poor survival rates; more extensive experimentation may be necessary. This is particularly true if evaluation of degrees of carcinogenic potency is attempted. In general, 20 test animals are not sufficient especially when the mortality of controls is 50% by the twelfth month.

E. TISSUE CULTURE

A sequence of events transpires between the oral, cutaneous, or subcutaneous administration of a steroid hormone or a carcinogen to an experimental animal and the direct or indirect effect upon the target tissue. Because of many uncontrollable or unknown variables, deductions based upon the production of cancer are at best circumstantial. Metabolites of the hormone or carcinogen, release of target-active products at other body sites through stimulation, time factors involving variable concentration gradients at other body sites, elimination rates, etc., are encountered difficulties. Tissue culture of the target with the target stimulus is theoretically an answer to the problem. Generally, the time necessary to produce cancer *in vivo* exceeds the time target tissues have been at present successfully maintained in culture. A compromise can be effected by treating the target organ with the stimulus in tissue culture for several days and then transplanting the organ into a receptive host (Jull, 1966).

The spontaneous transformation of normal rodent, human, and plant cells to malignant cells in tissue culture has been repeatedly demonstrated (for review, see Sanford, 1967). The etiology of this phenomenon is obscure since foreign protein, radiation, chemical carcinogens, and mitotic stimulation have been without effect. Viruses have not been shown to be a factor. Noting that the physical conditions in the cell tissue–culture environment resembled those which produced cancer with implants at the rodent subcutaneous site, Bischoff and Bryson (1964) postulated a relationship between the two phenomena. To date, steroid hormones have not led to cancer production in tissue cultures, though carcinogenic hydrocarbons have unequivocally for hamster cells and mouse ventral prostates. Normal hamster embryo fibroblastic and epithelial type of cells were transformed into malignant cells (Berwald and Sachs, 1965). Earlier experiments performed by others with carcinogenic hydrocarbons for other rodent cells were unsuccessful because of the complications of spontaneous tumor transformation as mentioned above. The malignant transformation in ventral prostates from C3H mice grown in organ culture was induced by methylcholanthrene and DMBA (Iype and Heidelberger, 1967). The *in vitro* malignant transformation of mouse prostate cells by carcinogenic hydrocarbons has also been accomplished in cell cultures (Chen and Heidelberger, 1968). Steroid hormones do, however, influence the growth and fate of tissue cultures.

1. *Prostate*

In tissue cultures (Lasnitzki, 1954) of mouse ventral prostate glands from 6-week-old and 6-month-old mice, 2 μg of estrone produced hyper- and squamous metaplasia in the former and considerable stimulation of the stroma in the latter. Testosterone maintained the mouse prostate histological architecture in organ culture (Lasnitzki, 1955). Bengmark *et al.* (1959) and Wagenseil (1956) were unable to influence the growth of rat prostate tissue cultures by adding testosterone, androsterone, and estradiol. Gaillard (1942) had reported results similar to those of Lasnitzki (1955). Källén and Röhl (1960) reported results at variance with those of Gaillard and of Lasnitzki, viz., an inhibitory effect of antiandrogens. Wojewski and Przeworska-Kaniewicz (1965) using 5–25 mcg/ml of testosterone or 20–200 mcg/ml of stilbestrol found no effect upon explants of prostate tissues of young rats. These steroids lowered the percentage of takes of prostatic adenomas taken from humans. Stilbestrol inhibited the growth of the epithelial type. A low percentage of human prostatic cancers demonstrated epithelial growth. Wojewski and Przeworska-Kaniewicz concluded it was not possible to determine hormone dependence of prostatic cancer *in vivo* by their tissue culture procedure. Their studies were initiated because the degree of hormonal dependence cannot be determined before therapy for human prostatic cancer; dose relations are empirical and tumor remission, which is transitional, is followed by an increased growth rate and resistance to hormonal effects. This pessimistic therapeutic prognosis is characteristic of many experiences with other human cancers of endocrine-linked tissues (see Section V,A,7).

2. Mammary Gland

The hormone requirements of normal (prelactating lobules), precancerous (hyperplastic alveolar nodules), and neoplastic (adenocarcinoma) mouse mammary gland tissues in organ culture indicated that hormone dependency was correlated in descending order. Cortisone and mammotropin maintained the normal and precancerous tissue and stimulated secretory activity. Estrone, progesterone, and somatropin singly or in combination were without influence in these organ tissue culture studies. The carcinoma was maintained with reorganization of peripheral cells in synthetic culture medium without hormone addition (Elias and Rivera, 1959). Cultures were only maintained for 5 or 10 days; long-term hormone effects remain unknown. Estrone, estradiol-17β, progesterone, cortisol, corticosterone, aldosterone, and deoxycorticosterone in high concentrations (200 μg/ml) were all toxic to organ cultures of C3H mouse adenocarcinoma. Progesterone was the most toxic, but its toxicity was reduced by the addition of serum (Rivera et al., 1963). This illustrates, as previously mentioned, the importance of transport mechanisms in tissue culture work. Under proper conditions, estradiol and progesterone maintained the structure of mouse mammary gland organ cultures (Rivera, 1964). In organ cultures of human mammary carcinoma, estradiol or progesterone stimulated growth, hydrocortisone secretory activity, and estradiol lactic dehydrogenase activity (Mioduszewaka, 1966).

3. Testicular Tumors

In monolayer cell cultures of a mouse interstitial cell testicular tumor, the luteinizing, follicle-stimulating, human chorionic gonadotropic and mammotropic hormones were nonsteroidogenic as well as nontoxic. The cells themselves produced progesterone and its reduced derivatives. 3',5'-Cyclic adenosine monophosphate, TPNH, and DPNH stimulated steroid synthesis, whereas cycloheximide completely inhibited their effects. The loss of response to tropic hormones may be involved in the original process of tumorigenesis; thus, the action of protein hormones is blocked while steroid hormones remain functional (Shin, 1967).

4. Transplantable Leukemia

Tumor transplants are, in a sense, *in vivo* tissue cultures. Dunning *et al.* (1967) studied the effects of subcutaneously injected estrogens, androgens, progestens, and corticoids upon 3 acute, 1 subacute, and 2 chronic isologously transplantable leukemias in Fisher rats. Two of the strains were refractory to all the steroid hormones tested. Estrogen was markedly effective as measured by survival and growth-retarding effects for one strain. One strain responded to estrogen, progesten, and androgen but not to corticoids; two responded to corticoids; and another to estrogens and corticoids. This extensive study illustrates the individual variation of tumors of the same cell-type origin to steroid hormones.

5. Miscellaneous Sites

Hydrocortisone at a concentration of 2.5–10 μg/ml greatly extended the duration of healthy growth of human epidermoid carcinoma and osteogenic sarcoma in cell cultures (Arpels *et al.*, 1964). 17-Hydroxy-11-deoxycorticosterone and the parent compound produced increased size of cells in chick and mouse fibroblasts at rather high concentrations of 35–70 μg/ml (Gillette and Buchsbaum, 1955). Estradiol did not produce this effect. Growth of intestinal epithelial cells was not inhibited by hydrocortisone (Grossfeld and Ragan, 1954), whereas a reversible inhibition was observed with chick heart fibroblasts. Geiger *et al.* (1956) observed a similar effect for cortisone on adult but not on embryonic fibroblasts. In the case of a mouse mammary tumor, which developed mostly sarcoma cells in tissue culture, epithelial cells predominated when cortisone was added. Prednisolone (Δ^1-hydrocortisone) inhibits the growth of human liver cells in monolayer cultures. The response is logarithmic to concentration; glucose utilization and lactate production are increased (Pihl and Eker, 1966). In cultures of normal human bone marrow, granulopoiesis was increased by estrone and erythropoiesis by testosterone. The latter and prednisolone inhibited fibroblast formation (Reisner, 1966). For a summary of steroid hormone effects on the cultures of other cell types see Gillette *et al.* (1967).

V. The Human Scene

A. ETIOLOGY AND TREATMENT OF ENDOCRINE-LINKED NEOPLASMS

Positive tumorigenic results in animal experiments suggest a relationship between prolonged therapeutic administration of steroid hormones and cancer production in humans. Estrogens have been extensively used after ovariectomy, during and after the menopause, for the anginal syndrome and in the treatment of carcinoma of the prostate. Estrogen administered to males with carcinoma of the prostate produces hypertrophy of the breasts, but the survival rate is usually too short with carcinoma of the prostate to expect neoplastic changes in the breast.

1. *Fibrocystic Disease of the Breast*

An exhaustive statistical survey correlating fibrocystic disease with carcinoma of the breast was made by Davis *et al.* (1964). Women with cystic disease have 2.6 times more cancer of the breast than do women in general. Breast tissue removed for cystic disease showed an 18% incidence of malignant degeneration. This survey included the large series of Warren (1940) and Foote and Stewart (1945). Womack (1958) suggests that prolonged estrogen activity is the etiological factor for cystic disease, as well as for carcinogenesis when it ensues. A lack of progesterone which is antagonistic to estrogen contributes to a prolonged rather than intermittent estrogen action. See Section III,G,1 for experiments in mice which support this theory. Cystic disease is associated with varying degrees of fibrosis, which would entrap epithelial cells and subject them to an unnatural environment. A similar relationship to cancer has been well documented in the case of burn scars, asbestosis, and silicosis, all of which entail pathological fibrosis and are associated with a higher than normal incidence of local cancer (Bryson and Bischoff, 1967b). For fibrocystic disease, the steroid hormones might be directly carcinogenic or lead to the production of a carcinogenic environment.

2. *Estrogens and Breast Carcinoma*

Reports of cancer of the breast in males who had received estrogen therapy for cancer of the prostate have been challenged on the basis that these lesions were metastases. In some cases they undoubtedly were (Fauvet and Juret, 1964). Abramson and Warshawsky (1948) reported bilateral carcinomas of the male breast in an individual who had received approximately 1 gm of diethylstilbestrol over a 500-day period. In a similar case (Gripe and Von Hedenberg, 1967), the two breast cancers were histologically verified as primary and distinct from lung, liver, and other metastases originating from the prostatic cancer. Fauvet and Juret (1964) cite the rare occurrence of human mammary cancers in females developing rapidly after estrogen therapy. The phenomenon is quite spectacular and justifies caution regarding the widespread use of estrogens. Metastasizing primary carcinoma of the breast developed in two males who underwent castration, mammoplasty, and prolonged estrogen administration in order to change sex from male to female (Symmers, 1968). These may be examples of solid state or estrogen-engendered carcinogenesis, or a combination of both. An example of male carcinoma of the breast in an individual who had been subjected to estrogen therapy over a 4-5-year period for cardiovascular disease has come to the attention of the reviewer as have two cases in which mumps produced testicular atrophy prior to cancer development. The etiology of gynecomastia resulting from the failure of the liver to inactivate estrogen is correlated with liver disease and testicular atrophy. In a study of 40 men with carcinoma of the breast, Liechty *et al.* (1967) reported an incidence of 17.5% gynecomastia and one case in which the breast cancer developed after gynecomastia was induced by bilateral castration and daily administration of 5 mg of Tace (an estrogen). Gilbert (1933) had previously reported that 19% of 47 cases of male breast cancer were coincident with gynecomastia, and Sirtori and Veronesi (1957) correlate 51 cases of cancer of the male breast with 218 cases of gynecomastia. Evidence is thus accumulating that estrogen stimulation of the male breast, without the inhibitory effect of testosterone, may lead to cancer. Since estrogens in feminizing doses were formerly used for treatment of the anginal syndrome and hypercholesterolemia, a statistical population for this category of males exists. It is difficult to obtain such data because drugs previously taken are apt to escape inclusion in hospital chart records. Hopefully complete data for therapeutic agents will some day be computerized for every individual in the culture.

Both artificial menopause induced by bilateral ovariectomy with hysterectomy before the age of 40 and irradiation of the pelvis at the age of 40-44 significantly reduced the incidence of breast cancer in women as compared with controls. After the age of 40, gynecological surgery with or without castration failed to reduce breast cancer rates. It was concluded that by curtailing cyclic ovarian function before the age of 40 the risk of developing breast cancer was reduced 75%. Pelvic irradiation may have produced a similar situation (Feinleib, 1968).

The effect of ovariectomy is quite similar to experiments reported for mice (see Section III,G,1); however, the effect of irradiation is not. Four-hundred roentgens irradiation of the ovaries of Marsh mice reduced the incidence of cornified epithelial cells in the vaginal smear significantly over a 13.5-month period but did not influence the incidence of adenocarcinomas of the breast and increased the incidence of lymphoid tumors (Bischoff et al., 1944). Functional impairment and carcinogenic effects of radiation on two types of cells are coexistent in this mouse experiment and demonstrate the carcinogenic potential at a low level of cell impairment as measured by physiological activity.

3. Hormone Treatment of Carcinoma of the Breast

Clinical trials with estrogens, androgens, their combination, progesterone and derivatives, and the latter with estrogens, have been made in advanced cases of human female mammary carcinoma. The results are not impressive; a progesterone derivative produced a favorable response over estrogen alone, varying from 9 to 104 weeks (Crowley and Macdonald, 1965). Comparing patients who responded to steroid hormone therapy with those who were resistant, the median survival for the responsive group over the nonresponsive group was 3 months for androgen, 6 months for estrogen, and 1 month for combined therapy (Kennedy and Brown, 1965). These studies lack control groups with no steroid hormone treatment at all.

4. Endometrial Carcinoma

Continued estrogen liberation without periodic progesterone inhibition has been tentatively linked to another human carcinogenic process, carcinoma of the endometrium. In a statistical study, De Waard (1964) noted that of 344 women over 50 who had estrogen-producing neoplasms, 85 also had carcinoma of the endometrium. Seven of 221 women under 50 with estrogen-producing tumors developed carcinoma of the endometrium. These 7 had a long-standing history of nonovulation, indicating absence of progesterone. Numerous references supporting the general relationship between endometrial carcinoma and the estrogens are in the older literature. Seventy-three cases of endometrial carcinoma associated with estrogen-secreting granulosa-cell tumors were reported by Diddle (1952). On the basis of 291 histories of granulosa and thecal cell tumors present after the menopause, Larson (1954) found about 10% had developed endometrial carcinoma. Prolonged estrogenic stimulation may lead to cystic glandular hyperplasia of the endometrium. Hertig and Sommers (1949) correlated this condition with carcinoma of the endometrium but suggested an additive factor of anterior pituitary stimulation.

The correlation of endometrial carcinoma with estrogen-secreting tumors and also with obesity led Twombly *et al.* (1961) to attempt to relate these two observations. Since body fat was shown to take up considerable amounts of progesterone and to a lesser degree estrogen, they theorized that in fat individuals there was a prolonging of the estrogen effect making the release more continuous, as it is with estrogen-producing tumors (see Section IV, B, 2 for details).

The injection of liquid silicone into the female human breast in a total dose of 400 ml/breast to produce mammary amplification raises the question of an ultimate carcinogenic potential either directly or by steroid hormone extraction. Solid state carcinogenesis would not be involved. Animal experiments have not completely precluded the possibility that liquid silicone might act as a chemical carcinogen and little is known concerning the macromolecular syndrome in carcinogenesis (Bryson and Bischoff, 1967b). It is of interest in relation to the observation of this reviewer that solubility determinations of estradiol, estrone, testosterone, and progesterone in a medical grade liquid silicone show marked differences so that large amounts of liquid silicones could presumably by extraction mechanisms cause a local or systemic steroid hormone imbalance. The solubilities at 38°C in a medical grade liquid silicone were 0.25 mg/ml for testosterone, 1.1 mg/ml for progesterone and for cholesterol, and less than 0.02 mg/ml for estradiol and for estrone (Stauffer and Bischoff, 1968). These are values obtained from supersaturation. This silicone injected subcutaneously into Marsh mice contained 0.4 mg/ml cholesterol 19 months after injection, at which time it was surrounded by a hyaline fibrous capsule.

The silicone used in the above steroid solubility determinations was tested for carcinogenic activity (Bryson, 1969). Dow Corning 360 dimethylpolysiloxane medical fluid, 350 cstks viscosity, was injected intraperitoneally into female Evans rats at 2 months of age, subcutaneously into male Marsh mice, and intraperitoneally into female Marsh mice at 3 months of age. Each rat received 1.0 ml; each mouse 0.4 ml total liquid in a single injection. Littermate controls received equal volumes of isotonic saline. Seventeen months after dosage, 8/34 of the silicone-dosed rats had developed reticulum cell sarcomas in the lung or peritoneal cavity and 1 local adenocarcinoma. One such reticulum cell sarcoma arose in 27 controls; also 1 with lymphosarcomatous characteristics. Twenty months after subcutaneous dosing, 22 silicone-dosed mice and 27 controls were living. Local reactions to silicone demonstrated 1 heterotopic bone formation with an ulcerating fibrous capsule, 1 fibrosarcoma, 1 neurofibroma, 1 diffuse lymphoma, and 1 ulcerating benign hyperplasia of the skin.

There was no subcutaneous pathology for the controls. Eighteen months after intraperitoneal dosing, 22 silicone-dosed mice and 23 controls were living. Local malignancies from the silicone-dosed group demonstrated 1 malignant histiocytic proliferation of the liver and 1 fibrosarcoma; also observed were 2 instances of extramedullary hematopoiesis of the liver, 1 fatty liver, 1 lipogranuloma, 1 fatty infiltration of lymph nodes, 1 local necrosis with focal calcification, and 1 clear-walled silicone cyst. These pathological manifestations were absent in the controls. Relative immobility of silicone at the subcutaneous site contrasted with intraperitoneal mobility. Since the silicone-oxygen bond is ionic as well as covalent, tissue reactions including tumorigenic responses analogous to those of the silicates might be expected.

The characteristic pattern of endometrial hyperplasia observed with granulosa tumors, prolonged exogenous estrogen stimulation with or without endometrial adenocarcinoma and with recurrent functional bleeding, led Gusberg (1947) to suggest that exogenous or endogenous estrogens are involved in the production of endometrial carcinoma. Novak and Novak (1958) warn that such reasoning is syllogistic but they concur that while many observations of diverse nature are merely suggestive, taken together they are quite impressive.

Carcinoma of the endometrium has also been correlated with uterine myoma, a common nonmalignant tumor of smooth muscle cell origin (Noble, as quoted by Novak and Novak, 1958). Many could find no rational explanation for such an etiological relationship. Although the myoma is not of fibroblastic origin it is of mesenchymal origin and shares many of the characteristics of pathological fibrosis. The reviewer therefore suggests that the myoma could well share an etiological role, as pathological fibrosis does in the pneumoconioses, tuberculosis, cutaneous cysts, gallbladder cancer, etc. (Bryson and Bischoff, 1967b). The role of estrogen in myoma production is controversial.

Prolonged treatment with progesterone or derivatives resulted in regressions from 9 to 54 months for advanced carcinoma of the human endometrium in 6 of 21 patients (Kelley and Baker, 1961). Continuing with their treatment and surveying the literature, Kelley and Baker (1965) found objective remissions of 1 month to 9 years in 32% of 165 cases. Radiation therapy of the pelvis prior to the development of recurring endometrial carcinoma appeared to interfere with the palliative efficacy of progestin administration in humans (Kennedy, 1968).

5. Carcinoma of the Cervix

Endocrine disturbances have not been linked with carcinoma of the cervix, but the histological type of tumor ultimately developing has.

Postmenopausal women with cervical carcinoma are known to produce exfoliated vaginal cells. This has been linked to estrogen activity. Squamous-cell carcinomas account for 75% of the cervical carcinomas of nonpregnant women but only 25% of those occurring during pregnancy (Cherry and Glucksmann, 1961). These observations are important in understanding the role of a steroid as directing rather than promoting carcinogenesis. Adenomatous and cribriform hyperplasia of cells of the uterine cervix, resembling carcinomatous processes, have been ascribed to progesterone (Candy and Abell, 1968).

6. *Renal Carcinoma*

The influence of the estrogen antagonist, 1-{2-[*p*-(3,4-dihydro-6-methoxy-2-phenyl-1-naphthyl) phenoxy] ethyl} pyrrolidine hydrochloride, administered subcutaneously 1 mg/day markedly inhibited the growth of a transplanted stilbestrol-induced renal tumor in hamsters. Matched tumors were set up in four experimental groups comprising 10–11 hamsters each: an oily vehicle control, estradiol alone, the naphthylene derivative alone, and this derivative with estradiol. The control tumor series was in a terminal condition 5 weeks after inoculation. The naphthylene derivative prolonged the life of 7 hamsters 13–15 weeks; estradiol inhibited this effect. The possible endocrine relation of adenocarcinoma of the kidney in man had prompted the use of a progestational steroid and testosterone in treatment of metastisizing human renal carcinomas. Signs of regression appeared in 21%. The naphthylene derivative effective in hamsters indicated it should be tried with humans (Bloom *et al.*, 1967).

7. *Carcinoma of the Prostate*

In a 7-year study comprising 2300 patients with carcinoma of the prostate, half of which were given 5 mg of diethylstilbestrol daily, the other half placebos, the group with beginning or less extensive carcinoma did very much better on the placebo. Only 9% as the group with symptoms of the more advanced stages of the disease did better on estrogen. Estrogen caused earlier death by heart disease (Bailar, 1967). This is, of course, the kind of study that should be pursued in evaluating therapeutic procedure. Such studies are much needed in endocrine therapy as, for example, carcinoma of the breast as well as for evaluation of the alleged effectiveness of radiation treatments which are often based on studies devoid of control series. The results of the human prostate cancer situation correlate well with the tissue culture studies: Many carcinomas of the prostate are not steroid-hormone sensitive. The rationale for the treatment of human prostatic cancer was based on the observation that spontaneous neoplasms (mostly benign) of the prostate in old dogs were associated with interstitial cell tumors of the testes and that shrinkage of these prostatic tumors was caused by castration or estrogen administration (Huggins and Clark, 1940).

Statistical surveys of human populations are in agreement that the genetic factor is of primary importance for human prostatic carcinoma: a lower frequency among Orientals and Indians as compared with whites (King *et al.*, 1963). Sociocultural variables are also indicated: a higher frequency among the ever married as compared with bachelors, particularly high for the divorced, widowed, and those with many children. After the age of 30 the bachelor has a higher sexual outlet than the divorcee or widower (see Kinsey *et al.*, 1948). For the father with many children, abstinence during his wife's pregnancy is indicated on the basis of Judeo-Christian taboos. Periods of prolonged sexual inactivity may account for the higher incidence of prostatic carcinoma in these groups. A local unpublished survey of hospital records by the present reviewer (Bischoff and Stauffer, 1968) confirms previously published data. It is presented because some published data are not exclusively for the prostate but include other genital organs and hence reduce the differences between the ever married and the bachelors. At the Cottage Hospital there were 403 clinical carcinomas of the prostate during the period April 1955 to October 1968. Of the 403 cases, 3.5% were bachelors; the others were ever married, viz., widowers, divorcees, and currently married. The incidence of bachelors in the population of the United States as a whole (Bureau of Census, 1960) weighted for the respective age groups is 7.1%. In addition to the 403 clinical carcinomas of the prostate, there were 9 occult carcinomas found at autopsy. These were restricted to the ever married. Since the integrity of the prostate is steroid-hormone dependent, it would be desirable to ascertain how sociocultural variables influence the hormone balance.

Studies of urinary and plasma steroid hormone levels indicate that shifts from the normal are associated with cancers of the breast and prostate in Europeans and cancer of the nasopharynx in Kenyan males (Wang *et al.*, 1968). This appears to be a fruitful field of investigation in the etiology of these neoplasms.

8. *Estrogen Stimulation with Pathological Fibrosis*

Among pathological fibrosis associated with a malignant potential, two additional diseases with a possible estrogen etiology should be mentioned. In Albright's syndrome (Albright *et al.*, 1937) with a cancer incidence of 4%, excess female steroid hormone activity associated with fibrous dysplasia has been indicated. The steroid hormone action would appear to be indirectly connected with tumorigenesis, possibly contributing only through pathological fibrosis. In cirrhosis of the liver, for which there is an incidence of 8.5% primary carcinoma, inactivation of estrogens by the liver is reduced. Pathological fibrosis along with stimulation of cells, not normally estrogen targets, are a consideration in the etiology of malignant degeneration.

9. Adrenal Steroid Hormones in Treatment of the Lymphomas

The atrophy of lymphoid tissue during the alarm reaction, which is mediated via adrenal steroid hormones, prompted clinical trials with these hormones for the lymphomas and related diseases. In Hodgkin's disease the metabolic disturbances resulting from hormone administration in most cases outweighed any temporary remissions noted. In acute lymphatic leukemia and in chronic lymphocytic leukemia, the adrenal steroids induce a temporary abatement of the proliferative processes. Prednisone is useful because it produced less undesirable side effects. The early optimism accorded the adrenal steroids in the treatment of these types of cancer has gone the way of all hormone treatments for neoplastic extension (see Pack and Ariel, 1964).

B. CHOLESTEROL SOLID STATE CARCINOGENESIS

There is some correlation of cholesterol crystal deposition under human pathological conditions with local neoplastic activity:

(1) This has been observed for 100 cutaneous cysts of which the five malignant cysts contained cholesterol crystals (Sirtori and Veronesi, 1953).

(2) Gallstones, with their high cholesterol content and intramural etiology (Grasso, 1931), have a high degree of correlation with cancer of the gallbladder (Bischoff and Bryson, 1964). Approximately 90% of human cancer of the gallbladder is associated with gallstones. The incidence of cancer associated with gallstones is in the order of 5%.

(3) In silicosis (Cole and Cole, 1940) and tuberculosis (Spencer, 1962) cholesterol crystals are often associated with the fibrotic lesions. Carcinomas adjacent to old pleuropulmonary scars in which there were cholesterol crystal deposits were described by Rössle (1943). Both silicosis and tuberculosis are correlated with local neoplastic extension (Bryson and Bischoff, 1969). In these examples, fibrosis, akin to the subcutaneous rodent fibrous capsule, is probably of primary etiological importance, but cholesterol crystals would presumably enhance the effect.

1. *The Cholesterol Laden Atheroma*

Primary cancers of the arteries, including the atherosclerotic, are rare, so that cholesterol and/or its esters which are often deposited in atheromas in crystal form do not in this instance induce cancer. The significance of Hieger's work on cholesterol carcinogenesis in mice was at one time challenged on the basis of the above observation (Hueper, 1961). Hieger's experiments with mice have now been confirmed, the species barrier has been crossed for rats and apparently for humans, and the mechanism is clearly that of solid state carcinogenesis (see Section II,A,2).

Bischoff and Bryson (1964) explained the reversal of the cholesterol crystal effect at certain sites other than the atheroma on the basis of the difference in inflammatory responses at different sites in humans. The conditions held prerequisite for solid state carcinogenesis are local nonvascularity, a latent period with low inflammatory activity and a low rate of metabolic exchange. The atheroma is part of the vascular system. At this site, the formation of cholesterol crystals from extracellular breakdown of lipoprotein is accompanied by an inflammatory reaction (Robertson *et al.*, 1963) similar to that following the initial implantation into the rodent subcutaneous site. The normal intima and inner media are avascular and function as filter-beds for the transfer of nutrients. With thickening of the intima and atherosclerotic changes, neovascularization occurs. Intimal capillaries along with vascularization of the atheroma from the wall beneath would not contribute to a metabolic barrier. When ischemia occurs at a later phase of development, degeneration of the sclerotic cap, ulceration, and release of debris may occur. Unlike the atheroma, the premalignant rodent capsule of solid state carcinogenesis manifests no calcification. The processes of vascularization are held in abeyance in the rodent capsule and are well defined in the initial phase of atheroma development. The response to ischemia is unremarkable through a long latent period in the rodent capsule, whereas it presumably accelerates cell destruction in the atheroma.

Kritchevsky (1964) has emphasized the differences between species in the atherosclerotic processes. These species differences are pronounced and varied as are those for the tissue responses to inert solid surfaces. In humans neither the subcutaneous nor arterial sites respond to the carcinogenic potential of solid state surfaces to any measurable extent. The differences between the atheroma and the rodent solid state capsule noted above may or may not be as significant as genetic factors and target site sensitivity to malignant degeneration. A statistically significant association between bronchial carcinoma and severe generalized arteriosclerosis has been found for humans (Abdelhamid *et al.*, 1967). Since the lungs under conditions of generalized arteriosclerosis are frequently immune from arterial changes, the etiological relationship remains obscure unless it can be shown that local arteriosclerotic changes preceded malignant degeneration.

VI. Discussion

The experimental material covered in this review demonstrates that the most important factor in carcinogenesis is the genetic. Extreme variation in tumorigenesis between species, strains within a species, target site, and dose level are effectively illustrated. Whether for the carcinogenic hydrocarbons, the steroids, or the solid state surface, the genetic factor is always dominant. It is unfortunate that failure to recognize the importance of genetic factors created subjective barriers between some researchers working within these variables.

The cancer incidence for any particular type in humans is always lower than the significant incidence induced by steroids in groups of experimental animals conventionally used. This applies even to breast carcinoma of the adult human female which is 5% and higher than most other human cancer incidences. Significant results for carcinogens in experimental animal groups thus represent a situation greatly exaggerated from the human biological norm. The World Health Organization (1961) and the Food Protection Committee (1960) give tables for evaluating experimental tumor significance. These show a marked disagreement between the two methods cited. That of Boyland indicates that when there are no tumors in an equal number of controls at least four tumors must be present in the experimental groups for p to be 0.025. The method of Vos indicates that under the same conditions five or six tumors must appear in the experimental group for p to be 0.05. An extreme view is taken by Grasso and Golberg (1966) regarding subcutaneous sarcomas: Since the spontaneous incidence of these tumors in rats or mice is under 1% in most strains, any increase in tumor incidence in experimental series of these strains should not be regarded as random. The present reviewer takes the position that when less than four cancers appear in the experimental series, experiments should be repeated with sufficiently large series of animals to establish significance. Numerous examples are illustrated in the present review. Mantel (1969) in "Some Statistical Viewpoints in the Study of Carcinogenesis" makes a plea for more detailed reporting of data in a compact form. It is important that the reader of an article should be able to make his own statistical appraisal rather than categorically accepting some statistical approach of the author. In order to have some uniform base line for appraisal of significance, the reviewer has used the chi square fourfold table with 1 degree of freedom. This is essentially that used by Boyland, noted above. The actual numbers are also given.

This review indicates that for a low-grade carcinogen the doubtfully significant results obtained with the use of conventional numbers of test animals did not usually lead to further research to unequivocally settle the status of the compound. Although the low-grade carcinogenic effect is the rule rather than the exception for humans, researchers in general were not interested in compounds which did not elicit a near 100% carcinogenic response. Compounds were supposed to be carcinogenic or not carcinogenic. The marginal area between the decisive and the obscure was avoided. Two examples, cholesterol α-oxide and 6β-hydroperoxy-4-cholesten-3-one, requiring the use of large numbers of animals and repeated experiments illustrate the necessity of further pursuing an initial doubtfully significant status of a compound even at the rather prohibitive cost entailed.

Campbell (1939) and Salyamon (1961) theorized that carcinogenesis depended upon an inhibited inflammatory local tissue reaction. With solid state carcinogenesis there is evidence to support this theory because the initial inflammatory reaction to the foreign body gives way to a period of inhibited cellular proliferation and decreased metabolic activity (Bischoff and Bryson, 1964). Some evidence may not support the universal application of this premise. Induced by intraperitoneal injections of mineral oil, plasma cell tumor formation in BALB mice was delayed and tumor incidences were decreased by continued cortisol administration. An inflammatory reaction to the oil characteristically preceding tumor formation did not occur with cortisol present (Takakura et al., 1966). Both spontaneous and radiation-induced leukemia in mice is suppressed by hydrocortisone or cortisone, an exception being a myeloid leukemia induced by radiation. Although inflammation may be causative in plasma cell tumor formation, the leukemogenic process in general is not associated with an inflammatory process and the inhibitory effects of the glucocorticoids have been ascribed to the pronounced lysis of lymphoid cells produced by these hormones (Dougherty and White, 1945). In tissue culture leukemic lymphoid tissue of mice has a much greater cortisone or cortisol metabolism than does normal tissue (Berliner et al., 1956). With mineral oil at the intraperitoneal site in BALB mice, the inflammatory reaction may not be inhibited by cortisol but completely abolished. Whereas both cortisone and irradiation are destructive to lymphoid tissue, leukemogenesis is subsequent only with the latter. Radiation is known to be mutagenic, a property which would not be expected to be shown by a steroid hormone. Whether anti-inflammatory or lympholytic hormonal effects are decisive agents in suppressing tumor growth would appear to follow a pattern related to the severity of transmittable damage to the target cell. Conditions in which tumors occur under changes apparently not directly related to DNA, such as the inert agents of solid state carcinogenesis, would more likely favor a dependence upon the local histological reactions including the inhibition of inflammation, cellular proximity, etc. These conditions are often indicated by characteristic lengthy latent periods and benign hyperplasia as a prelude to carcinogenesis. With a strong mutagenic agent like radiation or effects anatomically remote from the carcinogenic hydrocarbon dose site, the outcome is critical on the basis of what happens to a few cells. Sedallian (1966) has explained such differences as a cancer cell which may be a new cell with different proteins and antigens or a damaged cell with loss of proteins and antigens. In either case the cell becomes free from the control of the host and can then proliferate freely.

Demonstration of a direct carcinogenic effect of steroid hormones in tissue culture has been long overdue. There have been a number of direct local carcinogenic effects for estrogens at the subcutaneous site with aqueous suspension or pellet implants and at the vaginal surface. Until tissue culture techniques can cope with the problems of steroid hormone transport—a continuous hormone stimulus at a noncytotoxic level and culture maintenance for periods corresponding to *in vivo* carcinogenesis—success in achieving a direct carcinogenic response appears remote. Two observations have been cited which support the view that estrogens are involved in the carcinogenic process via an extrachromosomal event. The type of cervical carcinoma, whether squamous cell or columnar type, which is dependent upon the degree of estrogen stimulation is within this category (see Section V,A,5). Nakahara (1961) has called attention to three concepts regarding malignant degeneration of the cell: (1) an abrupt change, (2) a gradual change toward one goal, and (3) the combined effect of a series of irreversible changes. According to the third concept, estrogen would actuate the final irreversible change to a squamous-cell rather than a columnar type of cervical cancer. It could not, however, initiate the original irreversible change. Another example is the renal carcinoma produced in the golden hamster through exogenous estrogen. In tissue culture of this renal cancer, the typical "cell culture" is not dependent upon estrogen for survival, in contrast to the "organotype" which fails to survive beyond the second week (Algard, 1963) without estrogen. The dependence of this tumor upon estrogen appears to be destroyed when the architectural pattern is broken as in cell culture. The hormone dependence of the organ culture architecture and the original tumor may be involved with the supporting mesenchymal tissue. The cell itself, therefore, has no hormone requirement.

The demonstrable effects of steroid hormones in producing cancer at certain target-sensitive tissues raised hopes for a potent therapeutic tool based on application of the theoretically correct physiological antagonist to the given steroid involved in the production of the hormone-induced tumor. Unfortunately, the promise of hormone therapy has been vastly disappointing, especially in the treatment of carcinoma of the prostate, mammary adenocarcinoma, and the lymphoma related diseases. Although many cases show a temporary remission of tumor mass, the long-range prognosis remains pessimistic if not virtually hopeless concerning advanced inoperable cases. The failure of the hormonal therapeutic course beyond the merely palliative in the treatment of human cancers has been best evidenced by the unimpressive gains, if any, in the median survival rates of treated patients compared with those untreated. The existence of hormone-dependent mammary carcinomas in humans has not been documented. A cancer cell can synthesize the essential metabolites that a normal cell cannot produce for its development, provided the genetic code is properly programmed (Wood, 1967); this probably accounts for the manifest hormone independence many experimental tumors undergo and no doubt explains the failure of steroid hormones in long-term human therapy. If, indeed, the hormone-dependent tumor becomes inevitably hormone autonomous, the therapeutic outlook considering autoimmunity would appear more rewarding than the temporary remissions brought about by steroid hormone therapy. It has been proposed that cortisone acts similarly to X-radiation by interfering with normal immune mechanisms (Shklar, 1966). To the extent that X-radiation lowers the organism's resistance to neoplastic extension by inhibiting the autoimmune reaction (Toolan, 1951), the rationale for its current widespread use in therapy appears contentious. Even as a postsurgical adjunct to therapy, the cellular damage from X-radiation is an undesirable side effect upon the healing tissue matrix already surgically disturbed. An example of adjacent cellular cancer-inhibiting properties come from solid state carcinogenesis (Bryson and Bischoff, 1969):

The original neoplasm rarely metastasizes, but on transplantation or following surgical trauma, lung and lymph node metastases are common. Even though surgery at times may aggravate neoplastic extension, it remains the preferable therapeutic procedure. After decades of clinical trial, there is little promise that steroid hormones will be used as decisively in cancer therapy.

The emphasis in the studies of steroids and cancer should be on causative rather than curative aspects. The widespread use of stilbestrol in livestock feed and as a functional caponizing agent make it almost inescapable in the human diet. The pronounced carcinogenic effects of continuous estronization in lower animals and humans as illustrated in this review suggest that stilbestrol in livestock and poultry feeds may lead to harmful effects in humans.

Although fashion in cancer research is currently centered on the rodent, it is evident that meaningful data must eventually await exhaustive studies on primates.

VII. Summary

At the subcutaneous site in mice, deposits of cholesterol hydrate plate crystals produce a low incidence of local sarcomas. In rats, such cluster deposits are absorbed without a carcinogenic response; however, when implanted in disk form of sufficient size, cholesterol needles, hydrate plates, cholesteryl palmitate, and also glyceryl palmitate produce sarcomas arising adjacent to the disk surface. Chemical carcinogenesis is not indicated since cholesterol in powder form involving a much larger surface area exposure is nontumorigenic. Pathological fibrosis with cholesterol crystal deposits is correlated with cancer at a number of human sites: cutaneous cysts, intramural gallstones, silicosis, tuberculosis, and peripheral pulmonary scars in general. A mechanism of cholesterol carcinogenesis through solid state surfaces is indicated for rodents and humans.

Cholesterol α-oxide injected in an aqueous vehicle is carcinogenic at the subcutaneous site in rats and mice and also at the intratesticular site in mice.

Administered in olive oil, sesame oil, or triolein, 5α-hydroperoxy-6-cholesten-3β-ol and 6β-hydroperoxy-4-cholesten-3-one are locally carcinogenic at a number of sites in some strains of mice and rats. 6β-Hydroxy-4-cholesten-3-one, which conceivably could form from the hydroperoxy compound in the oily vehicle, was locally carcinogenic in three strains of mice when injected in an oily vehicle at the subcutaneous site. Another possible local carcinogenic mechanism is the formation of the hydroperoxide of triolein in the oily vehicle. This compound behaves like a chemical carcinogen in the "newt test."

The status of certain cholesterol oxidation products as low-grade carcinogens is jeopardized by experimental use of oily vehicles with reactive components, by failure to test with aqueous suspensions in large series of animals, and by use of injection techniques which produce local crystal deposits leading to solid state carcinogenesis.

Through exogenous estrogen stimulation, a number of rodent target sites respond with the production of cancer in susceptible strains. Response may vary from 0 to 100%. Cancers or adenomas produced by estrogens include an adrenal cortex tumor in a strain of rats; anterior lobe chromophobe tumors in rats, mice, and hamsters; intermediate lobe pituitary tumors in rats and hamsters; interstitial cell tumors of the testes in mice; local subcutaneous tumors in mice and rats; lymphoid tumors in mice; mammary carcinoma in rats and mice; uterine-vaginal tumors in mice; and renal carcinoma in hamsters.

Exogenous testosterone has induced cervical-uterine tumors in mice. Both exogenous testosterone and estrogen are required to induce the uterine-endometrial, ductus deferens, and flank organ neoplasms of the golden hamster.

Progesterone induces granulosa-cell ovarian tumors in mice and is cocarcinogenic in producing mammary gland carcinoma in rats and mice.

Whereas most steroid hormones influence some type of growth in tissue culture, a direct carcinogenic effect as produced by the carcinogenic hydrocarbons has not been demonstrated.

The concept that oxygenation of polycyclic carcinogenic hydrocarbons abolishes carcinogenesis has to be abandoned, since 17-keto-derivatives of 11-substituted cyclopenta(α)phenanthrene series have a more powerful effect than their parent hydrocarbons.

Human fibrocystic disease of the breast is linked with prolonged estrogen stimulation uninterrupted by progesterone inhibition and shows a higher incidence of breast cancer than is found in the normal population. A similar endocrine dyscrasia occurs preceding and during the development of human endometrial carcinoma. Steroid hormones do not promote carcinoma of the cervix but determine the histological type.

Steroid hormone therapy for human carcinoma of the prostate, mammary adenocarcinoma, the lymphoma-related diseases, and other human endocrine-linked cancers has to a large extent been merely palliative or completely ineffective, indicating that hormone independence and hormone autonomy characterize these cancer cells. Any

effect as from X-irradiation or cortisone administration which interferes with the normal autoimmune reaction is a compromise. Human
male carcinoma of the breast may be linked with estrogen stimulation.

ACKNOWLEDGMENTS

The author wishes to express his appreciation to Drs. D. R. Dickson, R. M. Failing,
and W. E. Carroll for their histological advice; to Mr. G. Bryson for advice in organization of the material; to Mr. T. Holgin for experimental work; and to Miss H. Bischoff
and Mrs. M. Stauffer for assistance in preparing the manuscript.

References

Abdelhamid, S., Hempel, K.-J., and Lange, H.-J. (1967). *Deut. Med. Wochschr.* **92**, 442.
Abramson, W., and Warshawsky, H. (1948). *J. Urol.* **59**, 76.
Advisory Committee (1962). "Smoking and Health," *U.S. Public Health Serv. Publ.*
    1103, 51-52.
Albert, S., and Selye, H. (1942). *J. Pharmacol. Exptl. Therap.* **75**, 308.
Albright, F., Butler, A. M., Hampton, A. O., and Smith, P. (1937). *New Engl. J. Med.* **216**,
    727.
Algard, F. T. (1960). *J. Natl. Cancer Inst.* **25**, 557.
Algard, F. T. (1963). *Natl. Cancer Inst. Monograph* **11**, 215.
Allen, E., and Gardner, W. U. (1941). *Cancer Res.* **1**, 359.
Antoniades, H. N., McArthur, J. W., Pennell, R. B., Ingersoll, F. M., Ulfelder, H., and
    Oncley, J. L. (1957). *Am. J. Physiol.* **189**, 455.
Arffmann, E., and Christensen, B. C. (1961). *Acta Pathol. Microbiol. Scand.* **52**, 330.
Arffmann, E., and Glavind, J. (1967). *Acta Pathol. Microbiol. Scand.* **70**, 185.
Arpels, C., Babcock, V. I., and Southam, C. M. (1964). *Proc. Soc. Exptl. Biol. Med.* **115**,
    102.
Athias, M. (1945). *Arquiv. Patol. (Lisbon)* **17**, 397.
Baba, N., and von Haam, E. (1967). *Progr. Exptl. Tumor Res.* **9**, 192.
Bacon, R. L. (1951). *Anat. Record* **109**, 265. (Abstr.)
Bacon, R. L. (1952). *Anat. Record* **112**, 305. (Abstr.)
Badger, G. M., Cook, J. W., Hewett, C. L., Kennaway, E. L., Kennaway, N. M., Martin,
    R. H., and Robinson, A. M. (1940). *Proc. Roy. Soc. (London)* **B129**, 439.
Bailar, J. C. (1967). *Med. World News* **8**, 27.
Barbieri, G., Olivi, M., and Sacco, O. (1958). *Lavori Ist. Anat. Univ. Perugia* **18**, 165.
Baserga, R., and Shubik, P. (1954). *Cancer Res.* **14**, 12.
Bengmark, S., Ingemanson, B., and Källén, B. (1959). *Acta Endocrinol.* **30**, 459.
Berenblum, I. (1954). *Advan. Cancer Res.* **2**, 129.
Bergmann, W. (1939). *Z. Krebsforsch.* **48**, 546.
Bergström, S., and Wintersteiner, O. (1941). *J. Biol. Chem.* **141**, 597.
Berliner, M. L., Berliner, D. L., and Dougherty, T. F. (1956). *Proc. Am. Assoc. Cancer
    Res.* **2**, 94.
Berwald, Y., and Sachs, L. (1965). *J. Natl. Cancer Inst.* **35**, 641.
Beuving, L. (1968). *Proc. Am. Assoc. Cancer Res.* **9**, 5.
Bischoff, F. (1945). Steroid Hormone Conference at Hershey, Pennsylvania.
Bischoff, F. (1957). *J. Natl. Cancer Inst.* **19**, 977.
Bischoff, F. (1963). *Progr. Exptl. Tumor Res.* **3**, 412.

Bischoff, F., and Bryson, G. (1960). *Abstr. Am. Chem. Soc.* Sept., C62.
Bischoff, F., and Bryson, G. (1961). *Federation Proc.* **20**, 282.
Bischoff, F., and Bryson, G. (1962). *Federation Proc.* **21**, 209.
Bischoff, F., and Bryson, G. (1963). *Federation Proc.* **22**, 315.
Bischoff, F., and Bryson, G. (1964). *Progr. Exptl. Tumor Res.* **5**, 85.
Bischoff, F., and Bryson, G. (1967). Unpublished data.
Bischoff, F., and Bryson, G. (1968a). Unpublished data.
Bischoff, F., and Bryson, G. (1968b). *Abstr. Am. Chem. Soc.* Sept., 193.
Bischoff, F., and Katherman, R. E. (1948). *Am. J. Physiol.* **152**, 189.
Bischoff, F., and Katherman, R. E. (1952). *Federation Proc.* **11**, 188.
Bischoff, F., and Long, M. L. (1938). *Am. J. Cancer* **32**, 418.
Bischoff, F., and Maxwell, L. C. (1930). *J. Pharmacol. Exptl. Therap.* **40**, 97.
Bischoff, F., and Pilhorn, H. R. (1947). *Am. J. Physiol.* **150**, 444.
Bischoff, F., and Pilhorn, H. R. (1948). *J. Biol. Chem.* **174**, 663.
Bischoff, F., and Rupp, J. J. (1946). *Cancer Res.* **6**, 403.
Bischoff, F., and Stauffer, M. (1968). Unpublished data.
Bischoff, F., and Turner, J. G., Jr. (1958). *Clin. Chem.* **4**, 300.
Bischoff, F., Maxwell, L. C., and Ullmann, H. J. (1931). *Science* **74**, 16.
Bischoff, F., Maxwell, L. C., and Ullmann, H. J. (1932). *J. Biol. Chem.* **97**, cii.
Bischoff, F., Long, M. L., Rupp, J. J., and Clarke, G. J. (1942). *Cancer Res.* **2**, 198.
Bischoff, F., Ullman, H. J., and Ingraham, L. P. (1944). *Radiology* **43**, 55.
Bischoff, F., Ingraham, L. P., and Clarke, G. J. (1945). *Cancer Res.* **5**, 579.
Bischoff, F., Katherman, R. E., and Yee, Y. S. (1951a). *Am. J. Physiol.* **164**, 774.
Bischoff, F., Katherman, R. E., and Favati, V. (1951b). *Am. J. Physiol.* **165**, 667.
Bischoff, F., Gray, C. L., and Katherman, R. E. (1953a). *Endocrinology* **53**, 321.
Bischoff, F., Katherman, R. E., and Gray, C. L. (1953b). *Am. J. Physiol.* **172**, 281.
Bischoff, F., Stauffer, R. D., and Gray, C. L. (1954). *Am. J. Physiol.* **177**, 65.
Bischoff, F., Stauffer, R. D., and Bryson, G. (1966). *Abstr. Am. Chem. Soc.* Sept., C311.
Biskind, M. S., and Biskind, G. R. (1944). *Proc. Soc. Exptl. Biol. Med.* **55**, 176.
Bittner, J. J. (1936). *Science* **84**, 162.
Bloom, H. J. G., Roe, F. J. C., and Mitchley, B. C. V. (1967). *Cancer* **20**, 2118.
Bock, F. G., and Dao, T. L. (1961). *Cancer Res.* **21**, 1024.
Bonser, G. M. (1944). *J. Pathol. Bacteriol.* **56**, 15.
Bonser, G. M., and Robson, J. M. (1940). *J. Pathol. Bacteriol.* **51**, 9.
Bonser, G. M., Boyland, E., Busby, E. R., Clayson, D. B., Grover, P. L., and Jull, J. W. (1963). *Brit. J. Cancer* **17**, 127.
Boot, L. M., and Mühlbock, O. (1956). *Acta Unio Intern. Contra Cancrum* **12**, 569.
Bruns, G., Schubert, K., Zschiesche, W., and Rose, G. (1963). *Arch. Geschwulstforsch.* **22**, 52.
Bryan, G. T., Brown, R. R., and Price, J. M. (1963). *Ann. N.Y. Acad. Sci.* **108**, 924.
Bryson, G. (1969). Unpublished data.
Bryson, G., and Bischoff, F. (1964). *Federation Proc.* **23**, 106.
Bryson, G., and Bischoff, F. (1967a). *Proc. Am. Assoc. Cancer Res.* **8**, 7.
Bryson, G., and Bischoff, F. (1967b). *Progr. Exptl. Tumor Res.* **9**, 77.
Bryson, G., and Bischoff, F. (1969). *Progr. Exptl. Tumor Res.* **11**, 100.
Bullock, F. D., and Curtis, M. R. (1930). *J. Cancer Res.* **14**, 1.
Bureau of Census (1960). *In* "World Almanac," p. 264. (March, 1958 census.) New York World Telegram and The Sun, New York.
Burns, E. L., and Schenken, J. R. (1940). *Proc. Soc. Exptl. Biol. Med.* **43**, 608.
Burns, E. L., Suntzeff, V., and Loeb, L. (1938). *Am. J. Cancer* **32**, 534.

Campbell, J. A. (1939). *Brit. J. Exptl. Pathol.* **20**, 122.
Cancer Res. (1967). **27**, 828.
Candy, J., and Abell, M. R. (1968). *J. Am. Med. Assoc.* **203**, 323.
Cantarow, A., Stasney, J., and Paschkis, K. E. (1948). *Cancer Res.* **8**, 412.
Charles, D. (1964). *J. Clin. Pathol.* **17**, 205.
Chen, T. T., and Heidelberger, C. (1968). *Proc. Am. Assoc. Cancer Res.* **9**, 13.
Cherry, C. P., and Glucksmann, A. (1961). *Surg. Gynecol. Obstet.* **113**, 763.
Clayson, D. B. (1966). *Proc. Can. Cancer Res. Conf.* **6**, 186.
Clayson, D. B., Jull, J. W., and Bonser, G. M. (1958). *Brit. J. Cancer* **12**, 222.
Cole, L. G., and Cole, W. G. (1940). *In* "Pneumoconiosis" p. 37. John B. Pierce Found., New York.
Coombs, M. M., and Croft, C. J. (1966). *Nature* **210**, 1281.
Coombs, M. M., and Croft, C. J. (1969). *Progr. Exptl. Tumor Res.* **11**, 69.
Crowley, L. G., and Macdonald, I. (1965). *Cancer* **18**, 436.
Cutts, J. H. (1964). *Cancer Res.* **24**, 1124.
Cutts, J. H. (1966). *Proc. Can. Cancer Res. Conf.* **6**, 50.
Cutts, J. H., and Noble, R. L. (1964). *Cancer Res.* **24**, 1116.
Dannenberg, H. (1958). *Deut. Med. Wochschr.* **83**, 1726.
Dannenberg, H. (1960). *Z. Krebsforsch.* **63**, 523.
Dannenberg, H. (1963a). *Progr. Exptl. Tumor Res.* **3**, 412 (personal communication).
Dannenberg, H. (1963b). *Deut. Med. Wochschr.* **88**, 605.
Dannenberg, H. (1964). *Ann. Chem.* **675**, 109.
Dao, T. L. (1962). *Cancer Res.* **22**, 973.
Dao, T. L. (1964). *Progr. Exptl. Tumor Res.* **5**, 157.
Dao, T. L., and Greiner, M. J. (1961). *J. Natl. Cancer Inst.* **27**, 333.
Dao, T. L., Bock, F. G., and Crouch, S. (1959). *Proc. Soc. Exptl. Biol. Med.* **102**, 635.
Dao, T. L., Tanaka, Y., and Gawlak, D. (1964). *J. Natl. Cancer Inst.* **33**, 963.
Davis, H. H., Simons, M., and Davis, J. B. (1964). *Cancer* **17**, 957.
Davis, M. E., and Plotz, E. J. (1958). *Am. J. Obstet Gynecol.* **76**, 939.
Davis, R. K., Stevenson, G. T., and Busch, K. A. (1956). *Cancer Res.* **16**, 194.
Des Ligneris, M. J. A. (1940). *Am. J. Cancer* **39**, 487.
De Waard, F. (1964). *Ned. Tijdschr. Geneesk.* **108**, 592.
Diddle, A. W. (1952). *Cancer* **5**, 215.
Dmochowski, L., and Horning, E. S. (1947). *J. Pathol. Bacteriol.* **59**, 307.
Dougherty, T. F., and White, A. (1945). *Am. J. Anat.* **76**, 81.
Dunn, J. A. (1965). *Brit. J. Cancer* **19**, 496.
Dunning, W. F., and Curtis, M. R. (1946). *Cancer Res.* **6**, 61.
Dunning, W. F., and Curtis, M. R. (1952). *Cancer Res.* **12**, 702.
Dunning, W. F., Curtis, M. R., and Segaloff, A. (1947). *Cancer Res.* **7**, 511.
Dunning, W. F., Curtis, M. R., Stevens, M. L., and Dumenigo, F. (1967). *Cancer Res.* **27** (2), 696.
Eik-Nes, K., Schellman, J. A., Lumry, R., and Samuels, L. T. (1954). *J. Biol. Chem.* **206**, 411.
Eisen, M. J. (1942). *Cancer Res.* **2**, 632.
Elias, J. J., and Rivera, E. (1959). *Cancer Res.* **19**, 505.
Engle, E. T., Krakower, C., and Haagensen, C. D. (1943). *Cancer Res.* **3**, 858.
Falk, H. L., Goldfein, S., and Steiner, P. E. (1949). *Cancer Res.* **9**, 438.
Fauvet, J., and Juret, P. (1964). *Rev. Praticien* **14**(17), 2209.
Feinleib, M. (1968). *J. Natl. Cancer Inst.* **41**, 315.
Fekete, E., Woolley, G., and Little, C. C. (1941). *J. Exptl. Med.* **74**, 1.

Fieser, L. F. (1953). *J. Am. Chem. Soc.* **75**, 4395.

Fieser, L. F. (1954). *Science* **119**, 710.

Fieser, L. F., and Fieser, M. (eds.). (1959). "Steroids," p. 24. Reinhold, New York.

Fieser, L. F., and Newman, M. S. (1935). *J. Am. Chem. Soc.* **57**, 961.

Fieser, L. F., and Rajagopalan, S. (1949). *J. Am. Chem. Soc.* **71**, 3938.

Food Protection Committee (1960). "Problems in the Evaluation of Carcinogenic Hazard from Use of Food Additives." *Natl. Acad. Sci.—Natl. Res. Council, Publ.* **749**, pp. 25, 26.

Foote, F. W., and Stewart, F. W. (1945). *Ann. Surg.* **121**, 197.

Fritsch, S. (1965). *Arch. Geschwulstforsch.* **25**, 265.

Fürst, W. (1966). *Pharm. Zentralhalle* **105**, 515.

Furth, J., and Furth, O. B. (1936). *Am. J. Cancer* **28**, 54.

Furth, J., and Sobel, H. (1947). *J. Natl. Cancer Inst.* **8**, 7.

Gaillard, P. (1942). *In* "Hormones Regulating Growth and Differentiation in Embryonic Explants." Hermann, Paris.

Gardner, W. U. (1941). *Cancer Res.* **1**, 345.

Gardner, W. U. (1959). *Cancer Res.* **19**, 170.

Gardner, W. U., and Ferrigno, M. (1956). *J. Natl. Cancer Inst.* **17**, 601.

Gardner, W. U., and Pan, S. C. (1948). *Cancer Res.* **8**, 241.

Gardner, W. U., and Rygaard, J. (1954). *Cancer Res.* **14**, 205.

Gardner, W. U., and Strong, L. C. (1940). *Yale J. Biol. Med.* **12**, 543.

Gardner, W. U., Smith, G. M., Strong, L. C., and Allen, E. (1936). *A.M.A. Arch. Pathol.* **21**, 504.

Gardner, W. U., Dougherty, T. F., and Williams, W. L. (1944). *Cancer Res.* **4**, 73.

Gardner, W. U., Pfeiffer, C. A., and Trentin, J. J. (1959). *In* "The Physiopathology of Cancer" (F. Homburger, ed.), 2nd Ed., pp. 152-237. Harper & Row (Hoeber), New York.

Geiger, R. S., Dingwall, J. A., and Andrus, W. DeW. (1956). *Am. J. Med. Sci.* **231**, 427.

Geschickter, C. F. (1939). *Science* **89**, 35.

Geschickter, C. F., and Hartman, C. G. (1959). *Cancer* **12**, 767.

Ghiron, V. (1939). *Proc. 3rd Intern. Cancer Congr. Atlantic City*, p. 116.

Gilbert, J. B. (1933). *Surg. Gynecol. Obstet.* **42**, 451.

Gillette, R., and Buchsbaum, R. (1955). *Proc. Soc. Exptl. Biol. Med.* **89**, 146.

Gillette, R. W., Goulian, D., Jr., and Conway, H. (1967). *J. Natl. Cancer Inst.* **39**, 947.

Grasso, P., and Golberg, L. (1966). *Food Cosmet. Toxicol.* **4**, 297.

Grasso, R. (1931). *Policlinico (Rome), Sez. Chir.* **38**, 335.

Greenblatt, R. B., and Brown, N. H. (1952). *Am. J. Obstet. Gynecol.* **63**, 1361.

Greene, H. S. N. (1939). *J. Exptl. Med.* **70**, 147.

Griffiths, C. T., Tomic, M., Craig, J. M., and Kistner, R. W. (1963). *Surg. Forum* **14**, 399.

Gripe, K., and Von Hedenberg, C. (1967). *Opuscula Med.* **12**, 37.

Grossfeld, H., and Ragan, C. (1954). *Proc. Soc. Exptl. Biol. Med.* **86**, 63.

Guériguian, J. L., and Pearlman, W. H. (1968). *J. Biol. Chem.* **243**, 5226.

Gusberg, S. B. (1947). *Am. J. Obstet. Gynecol.* **54**, 905.

Haagensen, C. D., and Randall, H. T. (1942). *A.M.A. Arch. Pathol.* **33**, 411.

Hall, W. T., and Moore, D. H. (1966). *J. Natl. Cancer Inst.* **36**, 181.

Hartwell, J. L. (1951). "Survey of Compounds which have been Tested for Carcinogenic Activity," 2nd Ed. *U.S. Public Health Serv. Publ.* **149**, pp. 384-386.

Hertig, A. T., and Sommers, S. C. (1949). *Cancer* **2**, 946.

Hertz, R. (1965). *Cancer Res.* **25**, 1188.

Heston, W. E. (1945). *Publ. Am. Assoc. Advan. Sci.* **22**, 55.

Heston, W. E. (1964). *J. Natl. Cancer Inst.* **32**, 947.

Heston, W. E., and Deringer, M. K. (1953). *Proc. Soc. Exptl. Biol. Med.* **82**, 731.
Hieger, I. (1940). *Am. J. Cancer* **39**, 496.
Hieger, I. (1949). *Brit. J. Cancer* **3**, 123.
Hieger, I. (1958). *Brit. Med. Bull.* **14**, 159.
Hieger, I. (1959). *Brit. J. Cancer* **13**, 439.
Hieger, I. (1962). *Brit. J. Cancer* **16**, 716.
Hieger, I., and Orr, J. W. (1954). *Brit. J. Cancer* **8**, 274.
Higginson, J., Dunn, J. A., and Sutton, D. A. (1964). *Exptl. Mol. Pathol.* **3**, 297.
Hisaw, F. L. (1950). *In* "Factors Influencing Endometrial Growth in Monkeys. A Symposium on Steroid Hormones" (E. S. Gordon, ed.), p. 259. Univ. of Wisconsin Press, Madison, Wisconsin.
Hooker, C. W., and Pfeiffer, C. A. (1942). *Cancer Res.* **2**, 759.
Hooker, C. W., Gardner, W. U., and Pfeiffer, C. A. (1940). *J. Am. Med. Assoc.* **115**, 443.
Horning, E. S. (1956). *Brit. J. Cancer* **10**, 678.
Hueper, W. C. (1961). *Arch. Pathol.* **71**, 237.
Huggins, C., and Clark, P. J. (1940). *J. Exptl. Med.* **72**, 747.
Inhoffen, H. H. (1940). *Angew. Chem.* **53**, 471.
Iype, P. T., and Heidelberger, C. (1967). *Proc. Am. Assoc. Cancer Res.* **8**, 33.
Jacobsohn, G. M., and Hochberg, R. B. (1968). *J. Biol. Chem.* **243**, 2985.
J. Am. Med. Assoc. (1930). **95**, 1350.
Jellinck, P. H. (1966). *Proc. Can. Cancer Res. Conf.* **6**, 124.
Jenkins, V. K., Odell, T. T., Jr., and Upton, A. C. (1966). *Cancer Res.* **26**, 454
Jenson, E. V. (1966). *Proc. Can. Cancer Res. Conf.* **6**, 143.
Jull, J. W. (1951). *Brit. J. Cancer* **5**, 328.
Jull, J. W. (1956). *Acta Univ. Intern. Contra Cancrum* **12**, 653.
Jull, J. W. (1966). *Cancer Res.* **26**, 2368.
Källén, B., and Röhl, L. (1960). *Acta Pathol. Microbiol. Scand.* **50**, 283.
Kelley, R. M., and Baker, W. H. (1961). *New Engl. J. Med.* **264**, 216.
Kelley, R. M., and Baker, W. H. (1965). *Cancer Res.* **25**, 1190.
Kennaway, E. L. (1957). *In* "Cancer" (R. W. Ravin, ed.), Pt. I, p. 24. Butterworth, London and Washington, D. C.
Kennedy, B. J. (1968). *Proc. Am. Soc. Clin. Oncol.* **4**, 21.
Kennedy, B. J., and Brown, J. H. (1965). *Cancer* **18**, 431.
Kim, U., Furth, J., and Yannopoulos, K. (1963). *J. Natl. Cancer Inst.* **31**, 233.
King, H., Diamond, E., and Lilienfeld, A. M. (1963). *J. Chronic Diseases* **16**, 117.
Kinsey, A. C., Pomeroy, W. B., and Martin, C. E. (1948). "Sexual Behavior in the Human Male," p. 266. Saunders, Philadelphia, Pennsylvania.
Kirkman, H. (1957). *Cancer* **10**, 757.
Kirkman, H., and Algard, F. T. (1964). *Cancer Res.* **24**, 1569.
Kirkman, H., and Algard, F. T. (1965). *Cancer Res.* **25**, 141.
Kirkman, H., and Bacon, R. L. (1952a). *J. Natl. Cancer Inst.* **13**, 757.
Kirkman, H., and Bacon, R. L. (1952b). *Cancer Res.* **10**, 122.
Kirschbaum, A., and Mixer, H. W. (1947). *J. Lab. Clin. Med.* **32**, 720.
Klein, M. (1963). *Cancer Res.* **23**, 1701.
Kleinenberg, H. E., Neufach, S. A., and Schabad, L. M. (1940). *Am. J. Cancer* **39**, 463.
Koch, R., and Schenck, G. O. (1961). *Strahlentherapie* **116**, 364.
Koch, R., and Schenck, G. O. (1967). *Naturwissenschaften* **54**(7), 172.
Koch, R., Schenck, G. O., and Neumüller, O.-A. (1964). *Strahlentherapie* **124**, 626.
Koneff, A. A., Simpson, M. E., and Evans, H. M. (1946). *Anat. Record* **94**, 169.
Kritchevsky, D. (1964). *In* "Lipid Pharmacology" (R. Paoletti, ed.), p. 63. Academic Press, New York.

242   FRITZ BISCHOFF

Kühl, I., and Schubert, K. (1960). *Experientia* **16**, 549.
Lacassagne, A. (1932). *Compt. Rend.* **195**, 630.
Lacassagne, A. (1937). *Compt. Rend.* **126**, 190.
Lacassagne, A., Buu-Hoi, N. P., and Hurst, L. (1967). *Tumori* **53**, 43.
Larsen, C. D., and Barrett, M. K. (1944). *J. Natl. Cancer Inst.* **4**, 587.
Larson, J. A. (1954). *Obstet. Gynecol.* **3**, 551.
Lasnitzki, I. (1954). *Cancer Res.* **14**, 632.
Lasnitzki, I. (1955). *J. Endocrinol.* **12**, 236.
Lee, M., and Ayres, G. B. (1936). *Endocrinology* **20**, 489.
Li, M. H., and Gardner, W. U. (1947). *Science* **105**, 13.
Liechty, R. D., Davis, J., and Gleysteen, J. (1967). *Cancer* **20**, 1617.
Lipschutz, A. (ed.). (1950). *In* "Steroid Hormones and Tumors," p. 174. Williams & Wilkins, Baltimore, Maryland.
Lipschutz, A. (ed.). (1957). *In* "Steroid Homeostasis,Hypophysis and Tumorigenesis," Heffer, Cambridge, England.
Lipschutz, A., Iglesias, R., and Salinas, S. (1962). *Nature* **196**, 946.
Lipschutz, A., Iglesias, R., and Salinas, S. (1963). *J. Reprod. Fertility* **6**, 99.
Lipschutz, A., Iglesias, R., Panasevich, V. I., and Salinas, S. (1967). *Brit. J. Cancer* **21**, 144.
Loeb, L., Burns, E. L., Suntzeff, V., and Moskop, M. (1937). *Am. J. Cancer* **30**, 47.
Lusky, L. M., and Nelson, A. A. (1957). *Federation Proc.* **16**, 318.
McEuen, C. S. (1938). *Am. J. Cancer* **34**, 184.
McEuen, C. S., Selye, H., and Collip, J. B. (1939). *Proc. Soc. Exptl. Biol. Med.* **40**, 241.
Mantel, N. (1969). *Progr. Exptl. Tumor Res.* **11**, 441.
Mark, J., and Biskind, G. R. (1941). *Endocrinology* **28**, 465.
Meissner, W. A., Sommers, S. C., and Sherman, G. (1957). *Cancer* **10**, 500.
Migeon, C. J., Lescure, O. L., Zinkham, W. H., and Sidbury, J. B., Jr. (1962). *J. Clin. Invest.* **41**, 2025.
Minesita, T., and Yamaguchi, K. (1965). *Cancer Res.* **25**, 1168.
Mioduszewaka, O. (1966). *Intern. Cancer Congr. 9th, Tokyo* Sect. I-03, p. 53. (Abstr.)
Mirand, E. A., Reinhard, M. C., and Goltz, H. L. (1953). *Proc. Soc. Exptl. Biol. Med.* **83**, 14.
Mirand, E. A., Reinhard, M. C., and Goltz, H. L. (1954). *Proc. Am. Assoc. Cancer Res.* **1**, 32.
Moore, D. H. (1965). *Science* **147**(3662), 1158.
Mosbach, E. H., Neirenberg, M., and Kendall, F. E. (1952). *Abstr. Am. Chem. Soc.* Sept., C10.
Mühlbock, O. (1956). *Advan. Cancer Res.* **4**, 371.
Mühlbock, O. (1960). *In* "Biological Activities of Steroids in Relation to Cancer" (G. Pincus and E. P. Vollmer, eds.), p. 333. Academic Press, New York.
Mühlbock, O. (1963). *Neoplasma* **10**(4), 337.
Murphy, E. D. (1961). *J. Natl. Cancer Inst.* **27**, 611.
Nakahara, W. (1961). *Progr. Exptl. Tumor Res.* **2**, 158.
Nakakuki, K. (1962). *Nippon Katsueki Gakkai Zasshi* **25**, 786.
Nandi, S. (1966). *Proc. Can. Cancer Res. Conf.* **6**, 69.
National Advisory Cancer Council (1967). "Progress Against Cancer." U.S. *Public Health Serv. Publ.* **1720**, p. 24.
Nelson, W. O. (1942). *Cancer Res.* **2**, 728.
Nelson, W. O. (1944). *Yale J. Biol. Med.* **17**, 217.
Neukomm, S. (1944). *Mem. Soc. Vaudoise Sci. Nat.* **53**, 8.
Neukomm, S., Bonnet, J., Baer, T., and de Trey, M. (1960). *Oncologia* **13**, 279.

Noble, R. L. (1967). *Proc. Am. Assoc. Cancer Res.* **8**, 51.
Noble, R. L., and Collip, J. B. (1941). *Can. Med. Assoc. J.* **44**, 1.
Noble, R. L., and Cutts, J. H. (1958). *Proc. 17th Intern. Cancer Congr., London,* pp.192, 193.
Noble, R. L., McEuen, C. S., and Collip, J. B. (1940). *Can. Med. Assoc. J.* **42**, 413.
Nothdurft, H. (1949). *Z. Krebsforsch.* **56**, 234.
Nothdurft, H. (1955). *Naturwissenschaften* **42**, 106.
Novak, E., and Novak, E. R. (1958). *In* "Gynecologic and Obstetric Pathology," p. 247. Saunders, Philadelphia, Pennsylvania.
Nyman, M. A., Geiger, J., and Goldzieher, J. W. (1959). *J. Biol. Chem.* **234**, 16.
Okey, A. B., and Gass, G. H. (1968). *J. Natl. Cancer Inst.* **40**, 225.
Olivi, M., Barbieri, G., and Paoletti, I. (1965). *Lavori Ist. Anat. Univ. Perugia* **25**, 97.
Overholser, M. D., and Allen, E. (1933). *Proc. Soc. Exptl. Biol. Med.* **30**, 1322.
Pack, G. T., and Ariel, I. M. (1964). *In* "Treatment of Cancer and Allied Diseases. Vol. IX: Lymphomas and Related Diseases, pp. 137-164, 167, 200-202.
Pan, S. C., and Gardner, W. U. (1948). *Cancer Res.* **8**, 337.
Peckham, B. M., and Greene, R. R. (1952). *Cancer Res.* **12**, 654.
Peckham, B. M., Greene, R. R., and Jeffries, M. F. (1948). *Science* **107**, 319.
Pfeiffer, C. A., and Allen, E. (1948). *Cancer Res.* **8**, 97.
Pihl, A., and Eker, P. (1966). *Intern. Cancer Congr. 9th, Tokyo* Sect. I-03, p. 56. (Abstr.)
Poel, W. E. (1964). *Progr. Exptl. Tumor Res.* **5**, 53.
Poel, W. E. (1967). *Proc. Am. Assoc. Cancer Res.* **8**, 54.
Portius, H. J., and Repke, K. (1960). *Arch. Exptl. Pathol. Pharmakol.* **239**, 144, 184.
Potter, M., and Boyce, C. R. (1962). *Nature* **193**, 1068.
Reisner, E. H., Jr. (1966). *Blood* **27**, 460.
Repke, K., and Markwardt, F. (1954). *Naturwissenschaften* **41**, 258.
Riou, L. L., and Mueller, G. C. (1954). *J. Biol. Chem.* **210**, 249.
Riley, V. (1966). *Science* **153**(3744), 1657.
Rivera, E. M. (1964). *J. Endocrinol.* **30**, 33.
Rivera, E. M., Elias, J. J., Bern, H. A., Napalkov, N. P., and Pitelka, D. R. (1963). *J. Natl. Cancer Inst.* **31**, 671.
Roberts, S., and Szego, C. M. (1946). *Endocrinology* **39**, 183.
Robertson, W. B., Geer, J. C., Strong, J. P., and McGill, H. C. (1963). *Exptl. Mol. Pathol.* **2**, Suppl. 1, 28.
Rössle, R. (1943). *Schweiz. Med. Wochschr.* **73**, 1200.
Rubin, B. A. (1964). *Progr. Exptl. Tumor Res.* **5**, 217.
Salyamon, L. S. (1961). *Probl. Oncol. (USSR) (English Transl.)* **7**, No. 5, 44.
Sandberg, A. A., Slaunwhite, W. R., Jr., and Antoniades, H. N. (1957). *Recent Progr. Hormone Res.* **13**, 209.
Sanford, K. K. (1967). *Natl. Cancer Inst. Monograph* **26**, 387.
Sannié, C., Truhaut, R., Guérin, M., and Guérin, P. (1940-1941). *Bull. Assoc. Franc. Etude Cancer* **29**, 106.
Saxton, J. A., Jr., and Graham, J. B. (1944). *Cancer Res.* **4**, 168.
Schabad, L. (1937). *Compt. Rend. Soc. Biol.* **124**, 213.
Schubert, K., and Fischer, W. (1963). *Arch. Geschwulstforsch.* **20**, 177.
Sedallian, J. (1966). *Lyon Med.* **215**, 1647.
Segaloff, A., and Dunning, W. F. (1945). *Endocrinology* **36**, 238.
Selye, H. (1940). *Can. Med. Assoc. J.* **42**, 113.
Shear, M. J., and Leiter, J. (1941). *J. Natl. Cancer Inst.* **2**, 99.
Shimkin, M. B. (1945). *Publ. Am. Assoc. Advance. Sci.* **22**, 85.
Shimkin, M. B., and Andervont, H. B. (1942). *J. Natl. Cancer Inst.* **2**, 611.

Shimkin, M. B., and Wyman, R. S. (1946). *J. Natl. Cancer Inst.* **7**, 71.
Shimkin, M. B., Grady, H. G., and Andervont, H. B. (1941). *J. Natl. Cancer Inst.* **2**, 65.
Shin, S.-I. (1967). *Endocrinology* **81**, 440.
Shklar, G. (1966). *Cancer Res.* **26**, 2461.
Shubik, P., Saffioti, U., Lyinsky, W., Pietra, G., Rappaport, H., Toth, B., Raha, C. R., Tomatis, L., Feldman, R., and Ramalie, H. (1962). *Toxicol. Appl. Pharmacol.* **4**, Suppl., 1.
Silberberg, M., and Silberberg, R. (1949). *A.M.A. Arch. Pathol.* **47**, 340.
Sirtori, C., and Veronesi, U. (1953). *Tumori* **39**, 365.
Sirtori, C., and Veronesi, U. (1957). *Cancer* **10**, 645.
Spencer, H. (ed.). (1962). *In* "Pathology of the Lung," pp.286, 288, 289, 341, 344, 725, 730, 731, 756. Macmillan, New York.
Stauffer, R. D., and Bischoff, F. (1964). *Abstr. Am. Chem. Soc.* Aug.-Sept., C29.
Stauffer, R. D., and Bischoff, F. (1966). *Clin. Chem.* **12**, 206.
Stauffer, R. D., and Bischoff, F. (1968). Unpublished data.
Steiner, P. E. (1941). *Cancer Res.* **1**, 750.
Steiner, P. E. (1943). *Cancer Res.* **3**, 385.
Steiner, P. E., Stanger, D. W., and Bolyard, M. N. (1947). *Cancer Res.* **7**, 273.
Sydnor, K. L., and Cockrell, B. (1963). *Endocrinology* **73**, 427.
Symmers, W. St. C. (1968). *Brit. Med. J.* **ii**, 83.
Szego, C. M. (1953). *Endocrinology* **52**, 669.
Szego, C. M., and Roberts, S. (1953). *Recent Progr. Hormone Res.* **8**, 419.
Takakura, K., Mason, W. B., and Hollander, V. P. (1966). *Cancer Res.* **26**, 596.
Thompson, S. W., Huseby, R. A., Fox, M. A., Davis, C. L., and Hunt, R. D. (1961). *J. Natl. Cancer Inst.* **27**, 1037.
Toolan, H. W. (1951). *Proc. Soc. Exptl. Biol. Med.* **77**, 572.
Twombly, G. H., Scheiner, S., and Levitz, M. (1961). *Am. J. Obstet. Gynecol.* **82**, 424.
Van Duuren, B. L. (1962). *In* "Tobacco and Health" (G. James and T. Rosenthal, eds.), p. 33. Thomas, Springfield, Illinois.
Van Nie, R., Benedetti, E. L., and Mühlbock, O. (1961). *Nature* **192**, 1303.
Vasiliev, J. M., Olshevskaja, L. V., Raikhlin, N. T., and Ivanova, O. J. (1962). *J. Natl. Cancer Inst.* **28**, 515.
Vazquez-Lopez, E. (1944). *J. Pathol. Bacteriol.* **56**, 1.
Wagenseil, F. (1956). *Z. Mikroskop.-Anat. Forsch.* **62**, 451.
Wall, P. E., and Migeon, C. J. (1959). *J. Clin. Invest.* **38**, 611.
Wang, D. Y., Bulbrook, R. D., and Clifford, R. (1968). *Lancet* **i**, 1003.
Warren, S. (1940). *Surg. Gynecol. Obstet.* **71**, 257.
Weisburger, E. K., Yamamoto, R. S., Glass, R. M., Grantham, P. H., and Weisburger, J. H. (1968). *Endocrinology* **82**, 685.
Westphal, U. (1955). *Endocrinology* **57**, 456.
Wieder, R., and Shimkin, M. B. (1964). *J. Natl. Cancer Inst.* **32**, 957.
Wieland, H., and Dane, E. (1933). *Z. Physiol. Chem. Hoppe-Seylers* **219**, 240.
Wieland, H., and Wiedersheim, V. (1930). *Z. Physiol. Chem. Hoppe-Seylers* **186**, 229.
Wojewski, A., and Przeworska-Kaniewicz, D. (1965). *J. Urol.* **93**, 721.
Womack, N. A. (1958). *Am. Surgeon* **24**, 618.
Wood, H. N. (1967). *Progr. Exptl. Tumor Res.* **9**, 286.
World Health Organization (1961). "Fifth Report of the Joint FAO/WHO Expert Committee on Food Additives." *World Health Organ. Tech. Rept. Ser.* **220**.
Yang, N. C., Castro, A. J., Lewis, M., and Wong, T.-W. (1961). *Science* **134**, 386.

The Chemical and Biological Properties of Heated and Oxidized Fats

NEIL R. ARTMAN

The Procter & Gamble Company, Miami Valley Laboratories, Cincinnati, Ohio

I.	Introduction	245
	A. Purpose and Scope	245
	B. Previous Reviews	246
II.	Auto-oxidation	247
	A. Chemistry of Peroxides	247
	B. Biological Properties of Peroxides	253
	C. Secondary Oxidation Products	254
	D. Biological Properties of Oxidized Fats	259
III.	Thermal Reactions in the Absence of Air	261
	A. Chemical Changes	261
	B. Biological Properties of Fats Heated in the Absence of Air	267
IV.	Oxidation at High Temperatures	269
	A. Chemical Reactions	269
	B. Products of Thermal Oxidation	272
	C. Biological Properties of Thermally Oxidized Fats	276
V.	Commercial Processing Conditions	289
VI.	Frying	290
	A. Chemical and Physical Changes during Frying	290
	B. Biological Properties of Used Frying Fats	300
VII.	Carcinogenicity Studies	303
VIII.	Metabolic Effects of Heated and Oxidized Fats.	306
IX.	Interactions of Oxidized Fats with Other Dietary Components	309
X.	Analytical Methods	310
XI.	Summary	314
	References	315

I. Introduction

A. PURPOSE AND SCOPE

The central question to which this review is directed is this: "Are fats that have been heated in cooking harmful to people who eat them?" The weight of available evidence answers this question with a strong "No." But since direct experimentation relative to this question

245

is impossible, investigators have used many different indirect approaches, and have come up with quite disparate results, conclusions, and implications. In this review these different results will be examined and attempts will be made to trace among them a unifying path of explanation, noting along the way the inexplicable divergences and contradictions.

Because the biological properties of heated fats are closely related to their chemical properties, these two aspects of the subject will be discussed side by side. The chemical changes that occur when fats are subjected to abusive conditions will first be examined, and then the biological properties of the abused fats.

Fats used in cooking are almost always heated in air. Therefore, oxidative changes usually accompany and probably precede the purely thermal changes. Even when fats are heated with exclusion of air under laboratory conditions, it is possible that the observed thermal changes depend upon either the presence of traces of oxygen in the environment or upon the presence of fat components which have already suffered oxidation before the heating. For these reasons, heating and oxidation must be considered together. This review will look first at fats which have been oxidized at low temperatures, and then move progressively along to the more extreme conditions of heating, and of both heating and oxidation together. Finally, it will attempt to relate the observations which have been made on artificially heated and oxidized fats to actual frying practice.

B. Previous Reviews

Numerous reviews on fat oxidation have appeared in the past. The standard reference work on auto-oxidative processes in all kinds of materials is the two-volume compendium edited by Lundberg (1961–1962). This work is sufficiently comprehensive and up to date so that it is unnecessary to do more than touch upon the chemistry and mechanisms of auto-oxidation in the present review. Only enough detail will be offered so that the reader who is not already familiar with the subject can follow the rest of the review.

Another volume which covers many aspects of fat oxidation is the one edited by Schultz *et al.* (1962). This report presents the viewpoints of many experts on areas with which they are most familiar. It contains both information not readily available elsewhere and interpretive discussions. The papers deal with the biological and organoleptic aspects of fat oxidation, as well as the strictly chemical processes.

Two important reviews on the chemical aspects of auto-oxidation have been published more recently by Skellon and Wharry (1963) and by Uri (1967). These reports convey an idea of the present thrust of research on auto-oxidation mechanisms. In addition, Marcuse (1967) has recently furnished an informal review describing his impressions of work now going on in the United States on all aspects of fat oxidation.

The interested reader may also wish to look into the older reviews of Gillam (1949), Frank (1950), and Loury (1957, 1961).

The biological problems associated with heated or oxidized fats have been reviewed by Melnick (1957a,b), Rao (1960), Kaunitz (1960, 1967), Perkins (1960, 1967), Timms (1963), Hanson (1964), Lea (1965), and Kohn and Nahar-Rahman (1966). None of these reviews is altogether comprehensive, but each provides a useful interpretation of a literature which is otherwise characterized to a large extent by contradictory reports and implications based on inadequate data.

II. Auto-oxidation

A. CHEMISTRY OF PEROXIDES

1 *Formation*

In most pathways of fat deterioration, the first step is an attack by oxygen on an unsaturated fatty acyl group to form a peroxide. A wealth of experimental detail has been accumulated to support the mechanism proposed by Farmer *et al.* (1942). According to our present understanding of the mechanism, when a fat is exposed to air there first ensues an induction period during which antioxidants are consumed and free radicals or their precursors begin to accumulate. The source of the original free radicals is not known for all situations, but it is clear that the initiation of oxidation can be greatly accelerated by copper, iron, manganese, or other transition metals. It is generally supposed that these metals, in undergoing redox reactions involving one-electron valence changes, generate odd-electron species such as hydroxyl radicals. Light and other radiation can also initiate auto-oxidation.

However formed, the radicals eventually reach such a concentration that the induction period ends and is followed by a period of rapid oxygen absorption. This is an autocatalytic radical chain reaction, which involves the usual steps of chain propagation and chain termination. Chain propagation is visualized as the abstraction, by a radical, of a hydrogen atom from the allylic position of an unsaturated fatty chain. The newly formed fatty radical may combine immediately with oxygen to form a peroxy radical, or the double bonds may rearrange before the radical combines with oxygen. The peroxy radical, in turn, abstracts hydrogen from another fatty chain to form a new radical, and is itself thereby converted to a hydroperoxide. These steps are shown schematically in Fig. 1. Since the hydroperoxide is readily susceptible to homolytic cleavage, which forms two new radicals from it, manifold possibilities exist for increasing the numbers of radical chains.

The kinetics and mechanism of the reaction have been widely explored under a variety of experimental conditions. (Kern and Dulog, 1959a; Tobolsky et al., 1950). The length of the induction period is shortened by, and the rate of oxidation after the induction period is increased by, the following factors: increases in temperature (Gunstone and Hilditch, 1945; Popov et al., 1967), irradiation (Swift et al., 1946; Ross et al., 1949; Slover and Dugan, 1957; Kern and Dulog, 1959b; Popov et al., 1967), use of a nonpolar solvent (Howard and Ingold, 1967), increasing surface-volume ratio (Becker and Niederstebruch, 1966; Pokorny, 1966), increasing number of double bonds in the fatty acid chain (Gunstone and Hilditch, 1945; Paquot and Mercier, 1962), and the presence of catalysts or initiators such as preformed hydroperoxides (Kern et al., 1959; Kern and Schnecko, 1959),

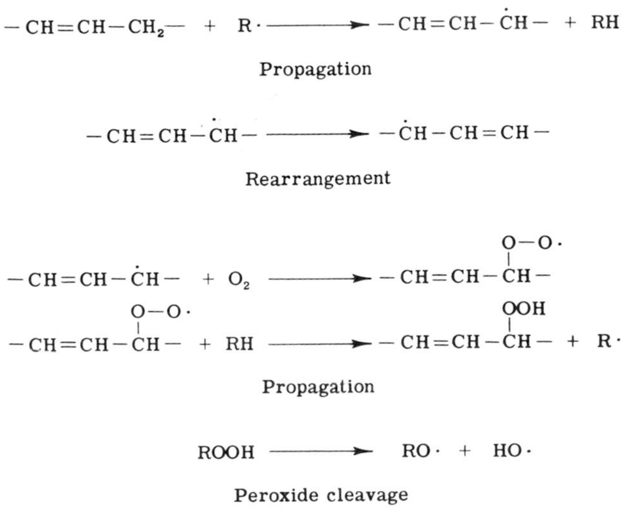

$$-CH=CH-CH_2- \ + \ R \cdot \longrightarrow -CH=CH-\overset{\cdot}{C}H- \ + \ RH$$

Propagation

$$-CH=CH-\overset{\cdot}{C}H- \longrightarrow -\overset{\cdot}{C}H-CH=CH-$$

Rearrangement

$$-CH=CH-\overset{\cdot}{C}H- \ + \ O_2 \longrightarrow -CH=CH-\overset{\overset{\textstyle O-O\cdot}{|}}{C}H-$$

$$-CH=CH-\overset{\overset{\textstyle O-O\cdot}{|}}{C}H- \ + \ RH \longrightarrow -CH=CH-\overset{\overset{\textstyle OOH}{|}}{C}H- \ + \ R\cdot$$

Propagation

$$ROOH \longrightarrow RO\cdot \ + \ HO\cdot$$

Peroxide cleavage

FIG. 1.   The reaction steps of auto-oxidation.

chlorophyll (Cobern *et al.*, 1966; Hall and Roberts, 1966; Hall and Mackintosh, 1964), or transition metals (Fox and Mickelsen, 1959; Vioque *et al.*, 1964, 1965a,b; Jacini *et al.*, 1966; Pokorny and Kondratenko, 1967; Pokorny *et al.*, 1967b). There is disagreement in the literature concerning the role of oxygen pressure on oxidation rate (Dulog and Kern, 1960; Marcuse *et al.*, 1964), which is not surprising since diffusional effects are probably often rate limiting.

The hydroperoxy radical, HOO·, appears to be the principal chain propagating species in at least some auto-oxidations (Howard and Ingold, 1967).

Reaction rates are usually measured by measuring the disappearance of oxygen from a closed manometric system (Kern and Dulog, 1959a), but other methods are usable since oxidation generally parallels changes in such other measurements as iodine value and percent conjugation of double bonds (Notevarp and Sellaeg, 1961).

2. *Structures of Hydroperoxides*

Although kinetic studies have been helpful, much of the present understanding of auto-oxidation mechanisms has come from knowledge of the structures of the hydroperoxides formed during auto-oxidation.

For structural investigations, quite high concentrations of peroxides have been attained by carrying out the reaction at low temperature with a catalyst or under the influence of light. The peroxides can be further concentrated by countercurrent extraction (Sephton and Sutton, 1953; Kern and Schnecko, 1959; Banks *et al.*, 1961, Frankel *et al.*, 1961a; Fukuzumi *et al.*, 1965) or by chromatography (Kokatnur *et al.*, 1965; Hall and Roberts, 1966), or, preferably, by combinations of both techniques (Begemann *et al.*, 1968). Earlier workers relied on crystallization (Ross *et al.*, 1949) or molecular distillation (Swift *et al.*, 1946). Various combinations of reactions have been used to establish the structures of the isolated peroxides. Typical of well-conceived schemes are those of Frankel *et al.* (1961a), who reduced, dehydrated, and oxidatively cleaved their products, or of Cobern *et al.* (1966), who hydrogenated their peroxides to saturated hydroxy esters, oxidized these to ketones, and cleaved the ketones by the Beckmann rearrangement. A particularly elegant method of determining the hydroperoxide structures was that of Schoellner and Herzschuh (1966a). They oxidized methyl oleate in acidic methanol solution; in that medium the peroxides decomposed as rapidly as they formed, yielding aldehydes which were isolated as acetals.

There have been a few claims in the literature (Khan, 1954, 1964,

1965a,b; Francois and Loury, 1964) that the primary point of attack by oxygen is at the double bond, but the weight of evidence is in support of the theory of Farmer *et al.* (1942), namely, that the primary point of attack is at a methylene group adjacent to a double bond (Swift *et al.*, 1946; Ross *et al.*, 1949; Mukherjee, 1951; Slover and Dugan, 1957; Privett and Nickell, 1959; Hall and Roberts, 1966; Schoellner and Herzschuh, 1966a).

When oleate undergoes auto-oxidation, abstraction of a hydrogen atom from either the 8 or 11 position yields a radical which reacts with oxygen to form either the 8- or 11-hydroperoxide; rearrangement of the radical can lead to the formation of either 9-hydroperoxy-10-octadecenoate or 10-hydroperoxy-8-octadecenoate (Perlstein *et al.*, 1966). All four of these isomers have been found in oxidizing fats.

The situation is more complicated for linoleate since here the hydroperoxy group can become attached at any position from 8 through 14, depending on which hydrogen was originally abstracted and on the direction in which the double bonds shift. Shifting of the double bonds is accompanied by cis-trans isomerization, with the trans configuration being favored (Knight *et al.*, 1951). Cobern *et al.* (1966) and Hall and Roberts (1966) examined oxidized linoleate by mass spectroscopic and nuclear magnetic resonance techniques, respectively. Both groups concluded that auto-oxidation is invariably accompanied by double bond rearrangement, and that for air oxidation (not catalyzed by chlorophyll) the rearrangement is always in the direction of conjugation. Their findings confirm earlier work based on infrared and ultraviolet spectroscopy (Farmer *et al.*, 1943; Cannon *et al.*, 1952; Williamson, 1953; Tsukamoto, 1960). Hoffmann and Keppler (1960) concluded from their examination of the aldehydes formed by decomposition of linoleate hydroperoxide that the primary product of linoleate oxidation is the 9-hydroperoxy-10,12-octadecadienoate. However when Schoellner and Herzschuh (1966b) carried out the oxidation in acidic methanol in order to destroy the peroxides immediately after they formed, they found oxidation products which must have come from 11-hydroperoxylinoleate, the unrearranged product.

For linolenate, the situation is still more complicated. Nevertheless, Frankel *et al.* (1961a) isolated four isomeric linolenate hydroperoxides, all with at least two of the double bonds conjugated.

The structures that have been established for the peroxides of linoleate and linolenate indicate that a methylene group between two double bonds is much more vulnerable to radical attack than a methylene group adjacent to only one double bond. This finding is in accord with the long-recognized fact (Gunstone and Hilditch, 1945) that linoleate is more sensitive to oxidation than oleate by an order of magnitude, while linolenate is only about twice again as sensitive.

3. *Other Peroxides*

Peroxides other than the familiar allylic hydroperoxides are also present in oxidizing fats. Dulog and Burg (1963) found two classes of peroxides in auto-oxidized methyl linoleate. These were hydroperoxides, which can easily be reduced with triphenylphosphine, and dialkyl peroxides, which can be reduced with triphenylphosphine only by prolonged refluxing. Dulog and Burg measured each class separately by means of the triphenylphosphine reduction, supporting their assignment of the two reductive classes to mono- and dialkyl peroxides by molecular weight determinations. They found that with prolonged oxidation the initially formed hydroperoxides disappear, while the dialkyl peroxides form more slowly but persist.

Pokorny (1962) had already pointed out that auto-oxidation is more effectively catalyzed by hydroperoxides than by other peroxide types. Francois and Loury (1964) postulated the existence in heated fats of, not only Farmer's allylic hydroperoxides, but also epiperoxides (1) and polyperoxides (2). Recently, however, Loury (1967) has stated that there is no evidence to support these structures. Fukuzumi *et al.* (1963, 1965) postulated that the dihydroperoxides of methyl docosa-

(1)   (2)   (3)

hexenoate were in part transformed to cyclic structures containing an unsaturated 1,2-dioxane group (3). They warned that this structure might have arisen during the isolation of the material by partition chromatography.

Kartha (1964) reviewed earlier polarographic evidence for the existence of more than one kind of peroxide but questioned its validity because of the possibility that the peroxides were being altered by the acidic alcohol medium required for polarography. Therefore he sought other evidence and was able to distinguish two types of peroxides on the basis of differences in the rates of their destruction by antioxidants. He offered no suggestions as to the structural differences which might be responsible for their different behaviors. Oette (1965) separated polar and nonpolar peroxides by thin-layer chromatography and supposed that the less polar ones were monohydroperoxides, while the more polar ones were more highly peroxidized or polymeric.

Only recently has firm information been realized concerning the structures of some of the other peroxides in auto-oxidizing fats, with the announcement by Begemann *et al.* (1968) that they had isolated from mildly oxidized methyl linolenate two compounds having structures (4) and (5).

(4)   (5)

These compounds were isolated by a combination of countercurrent distribution, partition chromatography, and thin-layer chromatography. The structures were proved by two routes. The first involved hydrogenation to trihydroxystearates, followed by periodate oxidation to recognizable fragments. For the second route, the hydroperoxy groups were reduced with dimethyl sulfide; opening of the ring then gave dihydroxyketostearates, which were identified by mass spectrometry. The mechanism proposed for the formation of the com-

(6)   (7)

pounds involves cyclization of an unsaturated peroxy radical (6) to form a cyclic radical (7). The radical (7) can react with oxygen to form the hydroperoxide (5). This mechanism requires that there be a hydroperoxy group on a carbon atom which is in a β position, relative to the double bond entering into the cyclization. The peroxy radicals formed from oleate and linoleate always have the peroxy group alpha to the double bond. Therefore compounds of this sort should form only from trienoic or more highly unsaturated fatty acids.

B. Biological Properties of Peroxides

In the whole subject of fat deterioration, peroxides are of interest chiefly as intermediates, rather than as end products, for they are inherently unstable. Although substantial levels of peroxides can build up during oxidation of unsaturated fats at low temperature, their formation is accompanied by simultaneous decomposition, and they are rapidly destroyed by heating or by contact with the phenolic antioxidants (Privett and Quackenbush, 1954; Kern and Schnecko, 1959; Crossley and Thomas, 1964; Watanabe and Toyama, 1958; Franks and Roberts, 1963; Kadar, 1961; Gaddis *et al.*, 1965; Lea and Hobson-Frohock, 1965; Swoboda and Lea, 1965; Lea and Jackson, 1964; Ellis *et al.*, 1966; Fuller, 1967). The products formed when peroxides decompose accelerate the decomposition of peroxides; thus, the decomposition process is autocatalytic (Popov and Yanishlieva, 1967).

Although hydroperoxides exist only at low levels in fats which have been heated or used for frying, their toxicological properties have been studied. It is important to recognize that much of the published work that purports to bear on the toxicological properties of peroxides was actually carried out with oxidized fatty materials which almost certainly contained substantial levels of peroxide decomposition products or secondary oxidation products.

Concentrated lipid peroxides are toxic to rats when administered orally in doses as large as 16 meq of oxygen per kilogram of body weight (Olcott and Dolev, 1963; Andrews *et al.*, 1960). They appear to be destroyed at the intestinal mucosa (Glavind and Tryding, 1960), and it is there that their harmful effects are manifested. For injury to occur, it is apparently necessary to achieve fairly high concentrations of peroxide in the intestine, since Czok (1965) observed no impairment of liver function or other injury after prolonged feeding of rats with a peroxidized fish oil which contained almost no secondary oxidation products. Holman and Greenberg (1954, 1958) reported that rats tolerated daily doses of 75 mg of concentrated peroxides for six weeks. The published information is inadequate to permit direct comparison of their findings with those mentioned above.

Kaneda *et al.* (1955) reported an LD_{50} of 17 meq/kg in mice, based on feeding concentrates obtained by urea adduction of highly auto-oxidized linseed oil or fish oil esters. The toxic effects disappeared when the preparations were reduced with iodide before feeding. The apparent disagreement between this work and that mentioned above can be most easily explained by supposing that since Kaneda *et al.* fed crude fractions of oxidized fats rather than pure peroxides the toxic effects which they observed may have been caused by simultaneous feeding of peroxides and secondary oxidation products.

The absorbability of lipid peroxides was studied by Bunyan *et al.* (1968), who fed graded levels of oxidized corn oil or cod liver oil to vitamin E–deficient rats. The peroxide values of the oils ranged from 2 to 230 meq/kg. When rats received these fats as 10% of the diet for 4 weeks, they accumulated peroxides in their adipose tissues. But there was no accumulation of peroxides after only 5 days of feeding, or even after 4 weeks on a diet containing only 4% of the oxidized lipid. Peroxides deposited in the adipose tissues of animals had a half-life of about 6 days.

Fatty peroxides are toxic when administered parenterally, with reported LD_{50} values ranging from 0.26 meq/kg for auto-oxidized linoleic acid (Horgan *et al.*, 1957), through 1.5 meq/kg for methyl linoleate peroxide (Olcott and Dolev, 1963), to greater than 3 meq/kg for peroxidized trilinolein (Glavind *et al.*, 1961). These reported differences might reflect differences in the extent to which the peroxide preparations had been freed of secondary oxidation products.

Kokatnur *et al.* (1966a) showed methyl linoleate hydroperoxide to be toxic to rabbits when low levels of it were administered intravenously each day for 10–14 days, or when it was administered continuously for 26–30 hours. The rabbits used had previously been depleted of vitamin E, and the toxic effects of the hydroperoxide could be largely suppressed by simultaneous administration of vitamin E.

C. Secondary Oxidation Products

1. Volatile Products

The substances which accompany peroxides in oxidized fats, and which result, at least in part, from peroxide breakdown, have been of interest chiefly because of their potent and undesirable flavor properties.

In fats that have suffered flavor deterioration, the components that have received the most attention are the volatile aldehydes and ketones. This is true partly because the carbonyl compounds are more readily detected and isolated (by dinitrophenylhydrazine or Girard's reagents) than are the other classes of compounds present. Another reason is that some of the carbonyl compounds, especially the unsaturated ones, are extremely potent flavoring agents (Patton *et al.*, 1959; Taeufel and Zimmermann, 1960; Guadagni *et al.*, 1963; Swoboda and

Lea, 1965; Rothe *et al.*, 1967). Therefore, even though they are present at only low concentrations in off-flavored fats, their contribution to the flavor has been recognized and they have received attention. Because the strong and unpleasant flavors of these compounds make fats containing even extremely low levels of them unpalatable, the physiological effects of ingesting them have received little attention.

The complete list of volatile compounds isolated from mildly oxidized fats has now grown quite long. Detailed analyses of volatiles from olive oil (Cruz and Gonzales-Quijano, 1965), sunflower oil (Swoboda and Lea, 1965), butterfat (Forss *et al.*, 1967), and soybean oil (Smouse and Chang, 1967) have now been published. Their lists of compounds have been compiled below and supplemented by the addition of compounds which have been found in oxidized fats by many other workers (Corbin *et al.*, 1960; Chang *et al.*, 1966, 1967; Cobb and Day, 1965a,b; Ellis *et al.*, 1961, 1966; Evans *et al.*, 1967; Fioriti *et al.*, 1967; Gaddis *et al.*, 1960, 1961, 1964, 1965, 1966; Hammond and Hill, 1964; Hill and Hammond, 1965a,b; Hoffmann, 1961a,b, 1962; Hoffmann and Keppler, 1960; Horikx, 1965; Horvat *et al.*, 1964, 1965, 1966; Iwata *et al.*, 1965, 1967; Johnson *et al.*, 1953; Lea and Hobson-Frohock, 1965; Lea and Jackson, 1964; Kadar, 1961; Klocpffer *et al.*, 1965; Loury *et al.*, 1965; Parks *et al.*, 1963; Powick, 1923; Smouse *et al.*, 1965; Stapf and Daubert, 1950; Suzuki and Takeuchi, 1964; Taeufel and Heder, 1963; vander Poel, 1961; Wilkinson and Stark, 1967). Some of the compounds on the list have been reported by many authors. Others have been reported in only one paper. Some workers have restricted their searches to single classes of compounds, while some have attempted comprehensive analyses. Not all of the substances listed would be expected in all kinds of fat. Some of the compounds, for instance, probably arose from linolenate; of all the fats which have been examined for flavor deterioration only soybean oil contains more than traces of this fatty acid.

The compounds that have been reported can be divided into several broad categories.

Aldehydes: Saturated aldehydes from C_2 to C_{11}, 2-enals from C_4 to C_{11}, 3-hexenal, 2,4-dienals from C_6 to C_{11} (both *trans,cis*- and *cis,trans*-dienals have been reported), 2,6-nonadienal, trienals of unspecified structure, 3-methylbutanal, 4-methylpentanal, 2,3-dimethoxybutanal, epihydrin aldehyde, glyoxal, pyruvaldehyde, 2-ketoalkanals from C_6 to C_9, malonaldehyde, and but-2-en-1,4-dial.

Ketones: 2-Alkanones having 3, 5, 7, 8, and 9 carbon atoms, 3-octanone, 1-pentene-3-one, 1-octene-3-one, 4-octene-3-one, 2-methyl-5-

octene-4-one, 3,6-nonadien-5-one, 7-methyl-2-octene-4-one, 2,3-bu-tanedione.

Alcohols: 1-Alkanols from C_2 to C_6, 2-pentanol, 1-pentene-3-ol, 1-octene-3-ol.

Acids: Alkanoic acids from C_1 to C_9, 2-alkenoic acids from C_3 to C_8, 2-methylpropanoic acid, 3-hydroxyheptanoic acid, 4-ketohexanoic acid, 7-ketooctanoic acid.

Esters: Lower *n*-alkyl esters of formic, acetic and propionic acids, methyl esters of alkanoic acids from C_6 to C_8 (isolated from oxidized methyl linoleate), and pentyl hexanoate.

Hydrocarbons: Normal alkanes from C_1 to C_{12}, 1-octene, 1-decene, and 1-decyne.

Lactones: Saturated γ- and δ-lactones from C_4 to C_{11}, and the lactone of 4-hydroxy-2-hexenoic acid.

Miscellaneous: A series of 2,4,6-trialkyl-1,3,5-trioxanes evidently formed by trimerization of some of the alkanals, a series of 2-alkyl-4-pentyldioxolanes, 1,1-dimethoxyhexane (the acetal of hexanal), and *n*-pentylfuran.

Aromatic Compounds: Benzene, benzaldehyde, benzoic acid, acetophenone.

When the auto-oxidation of methyl linoleate is carried out in dilute aqueous dispersion, it is possible to isolate some additional substances, probably because under these conditions they are extracted into the aqueous phase as rapidly as they form, and are thus protected against further attack by fatty radicals (Schauenstein, 1967; Esterbauer, 1968; Schauenstein and Esterbauer, 1968). Although many compounds have been detected in this system, the ones which have been identified are *trans*-2-octenal, 1-pentylhydroperoxide, methyl 8-hydroperoxyoctanoate, methyl 8-hydroxyoctanoate, 4-hydroperoxy-2-nonenal, 1-hydroxy-2-heptanone, and 4-hydroxy-2-octenal. The incompletely identified compounds contained various combinations of hydroxyl, carboxyl, and carbonyl functions.

Some of the compounds in the above lists are noted by the authors to have been only tentatively identified. For most of them, reasonable mechanisms based on peroxide decompositions have been offered, although not all authors agree on the details of these mechanisms.

It is known that the level of carbonyl compounds which can be detected in an oxidized fat depends on the method of separation and detection used. There is general agreement that a substantial fraction of the carbonyl compounds which can be measured by analyses are not present as such, but rather are liberated from their precursors or from a bound form by the analytical treatments used.

2. Nonvolatile Products

Aldehydoglycerides, unsaturated aldehydoglycerides, and ketoglycerides have been detected in oxidized fats (Crossley and Thomas, 1964; Horikx, 1965). Such products would be expected from fatty peroxides. If the fatty acid chain breaks on one side of the hydroperoxy group, then short-chain volatile aldehydes and ketones form. If the chain breaks on the other side of the hydroperoxy group, then the same aldehyde and ketone functional groups are formed but remain attached to the glyceride end of the chain. Probably glycerides containing many of the other groups mentioned above as characterizing the volatile oxidation products are also present, but have not been detected. Other, more complex substances may also be present, but they have not been reported as components of mildly oxidized fats. Therefore consideration of them will be deferred until the discussion of products formed by high-temperature oxidations for under those conditions the concentrations of such products become great enough for them to be detected and isolated.

Other products are formed by processes that do not involve chain scission. These include hydroxyl-containing and carbonyl-containing substances (O'Neill, 1954; Evans *et al.*, 1960), and conjugated diene ketones (Franks and Roberts, 1963). Ellis (1950) oxidized oleic acid in thin films at temperatures of 50°-100°C and detected epoxides, acyloxy hydroxy compounds formed by acidolysis of the epoxides, ketooleate, and the dimeride of ketooleate. Paquot *et al.* (1967) reported that hydroperoxyoleate could be transformed to epoxyhydroxystearate by vanadium acetylacetonate, and also found a mixture of isomeric epoxyhydroxystearates among the products formed by oxidizing methyl oleate at 50°C with a vanadium catalyst.

Dimers and polymers in oxidized fats have received considerable attention. Peroxide formation at low temperatures is accompanied by decreases in iodine value, which are attributed to the formation of either cyclic peroxides or polymers (Fugger *et al.*, 1951b). It was early realized that the dimers and polymers might be linked directly through carbon–carbon bonds, or might be linked through ether or peroxide groups. Both kinds have been found (Williamson, 1953). O'Neill (1954), using the technique of cleaving ether groups with hydrogen iodide, found that polymers from oleate are linked mostly through ether bonds, while those from linoleate are held together largely by carbon–carbon bonds.

Chang and Kummerow (1953b) found, however, that polymer formed by oxidizing methyl linoleate at 30°C could be cleaved to a large extent by hydrochloric acid, indicating that its fatty acid chains were joined through oxygen links; hydrogenation of their polymer yielded ketohydroxy acids. They also found (Chang and Kummerow, 1954) that when the polymer stood at low temperature in the absence of air it decomposed to form volatile aldehydes, suggesting that it contained unstable peroxides.

Dimers and polymers formed by conjugation and auto-oxidation of methyl docosahexenoate have been studied by Fukuzumi *et al.* (1963), Fukuzumi and Miyakawa (1963), Fukuzumi and Ishida (1964), and Fukuzumi and Maruyama (1965). The formation of these polymers is accompanied by a decrease in the level of α-methylene groups and of double bonds along with increases in the levels of conjugated double bonds and α,β-unsaturated carbonyl groups. The polymers contained substantial amounts of hydroperoxy groups, and it was concluded that they were linked together partly through 1,2-dioxane rings, thus being linked through both carbon and oxygen bonds.

Kartha (1960) oxidized oleate at 25°C, and subjected the products formed to oxidative degradation with acidic permanganate. His results indicated that the polymer was partly ether-linked, and must therefore have arisen through attack of a hydroperoxide or alkoxy radical on the double bond of an oleate molecule. The polymers formed at 60°C were, in contrast, principally linked together through carbon–carbon bonds, and must have arisen by a different mechanism. He also found substantial differences between the polymers from methyl oleate and those from triolein. Some of the discrepancies among the reports of earlier workers may be explained by Kartha's suggestion that the course taken by a polymerization reaction depends in part on whether the fatty acid chains are free to move about as methyl esters or have their mobility restricted by incorporation in triglyceride molecules.

A key property of many of the oxidation products of fats is their oxidizability. Details have been worked out for some of the compounds involved. The hydroperoxides themselves readily undergo further oxidation to diperoxides; the rate constant for oxidation of methyl linoleate hydroperoxide is twice as great as the rate constant for oxidation of methyl linoleate, and the activation energy is only 80% as great (Dulog *et al.*, 1961; Dulog and Burg, 1963). Chang and Kummerow (1953a) found that the polymers isolated from oxidized linoleate could readily be oxidized further to yield the volatile aldehydes typical of linoleate oxidation. They, as well as Evans *et al.* (1960), attributed the flavor instability of partially oxidized oils to these oxidizable polymers.

Lillard and Day (1964) found that the saturated aldehydes produced by oxidation of fats can be further oxidized to carboxylic acids. The unsaturated aldehydes undergo a similar reaction at a rate faster than the rate of oxidation of linolenate, and both classes of aldehydes are also oxidized to shorter-chained acids. Oxidation of the dienals affords malonaldehyde. Anderson and Huntley (1964) also reported that unsaturated carbonyl compounds act as pro-oxidants in unsaturated fats.

These observations make it evident that a fatty material which has already suffered some degree of oxidative abuse is likely to be more susceptible to further oxidation than the original fatty material — a susceptibility which is even further enhanced by the exhaustion of antioxidants from the material during the preliminary oxidation.

D. BIOLOGICAL PROPERTIES OF OXIDIZED FATS

Fats oxidized at low or moderate temperatures contain free hydroperoxides, and feeding studies with such fats are probably influenced by the presence of peroxides. Their effects have already been mentioned. The other oxidation products and polymers can hardly be without effect, however. The response to the consumption of oxidized fats presumably represents the sum of the effects produced by the intake of many such substances simultaneously.

All of the feeding experiments to be described here employed fats that had been oxidized to a much greater extent than would ever be encountered in culinary practice. Fats become unpalatable at low peroxide levels, but the fats used in these experiments had peroxide values of several hundred. Such high values were usually attained by prolonged bubbling of air through the fat. While experiments of this kind lead toward a better understanding of the metabolism of fat oxidation products, the results from such experiments are not necessarily applicable to practical dietary conditions. The levels, and probably even the kinds, of transformation products are not representative of those encountered in the preparation of food for human consumption.

In spite of the rigorous conditions used in preparing the test materials, the effects of consuming highly oxidized fats are generally mild. The inclusion of highly oxidized vegetable fat at levels of 10-20% in the diet of rats resulted in loss of appetite and growth reduction (Greenberg *et al.*, 1953; Kaunitz, 1953) with enlargement of livers and kidneys (Kaunitz *et al.*, 1961). Swine reacted similarly (Oldfield *et al.*, 1963). The growth depression could be overcome in part by increasing the protein level of the ration (Kaunitz, 1953; Greenburg *et al.*, 1953) or its content of unheated fat or low-melting fat (Kaunitz *et al.*, 1955, 1960a), or by adding antioxidants. Four possible mechanisms suggest themselves to account for the harmful effects reported, namely: (1) reduced food intake because of decreased palatability, (2) destruction of vitamins in the mixed ration prior to feeding or in the gastrointestinal tract, (3) irritation of the intestinal mucosa by peroxides with consequent loss of ability to absorb nutrients, and (4) interference with absorption of fat by the presence of nonabsorbable polymer in the intestinal contents. The relative magnitudes of these effects may be different in different experiments. For instance, in the work of Kaunitz et al. (1960a), the effect of peroxides must have been small, because they found that cottonseed oil oxidized to a peroxide value of 191 meq/kg had only a slight effect, but that when aeration was continued, the peroxide value fell to 141 and the fat became more toxic.

Two long-term experiments by Kaunitz et al. demonstrated the absence of toxicity in oxidized fats. In the first (Kaunitz et al., 1965) they fed fresh cottonseed oil, olive oil, beef fat, and chicken fat, along with the same fats after 40 hours' aeration at 60°C. Peroxide values of the oxidized fats varied among fats and among batches of each fat, but went as high as 324 for one batch. The fats were fed to rats as 20% of a semisynthetic diet for periods up to 2 years. Oxidized olive oil gave the smallest weight gain and the lowest mortality rate; oxidized cottonseed oil gave the greatest weight gain and the highest mortality rate. The other fats, fresh and oxidized, gave values in between these extremes. Histological studies revealed few, if any, abnormalities attributable to the consumption of oxidized fat.

In a later experiment, Kaunitz et al. (1966) fed corn oil, soybean oil, butter oil, and lard, either fresh or oxidized as before. Animals fed the fresh vegetable fats did not live as long, on the average, as those fed fresh animal fats, but the oxidized vegetable fats gave longevity rates comparable to those of the fresh animal fats. From these results it was suggested that fresh vegetable fats contain toxic substances which are detoxified by aeration. Further work with rats on iodine-deficient diets revealed that the animals receiving vegetable oils tended to have larger thyroids than animals receiving animal fats — an effect tentatively attributed to the presence of goitrogenic substances in the vegetable fats. Since there were no differences in thyroid size between rats fed fresh and oxidized vegetable fats, it appeared that the postulated goitrogenic substance was not identical with the substances responsible for reduced longevity (Kaunitz and Johnson, 1967).

The highly unsaturated fish oils, which have been extensively studied in Japan, are more susceptible than plant and animal fats to physiologically undesirable changes during oxidation. The fish oils themselves are not toxic, as was once believed, but can become toxic when oxidized (Matsuo, 1954a, b, 1957a, b, c). The fatty acids and ethyl esters of these highly unsaturated oils also become toxic on oxidation (Higashi *et al.*, 1953; Kaneda *et al.*, 1954a,b; Raulin and Petit, 1962). From the information available, it is not clear how severely the fish oils were oxidized to produce the effects reported, but there is one suggestion (Higashi *et al.*, 1953) that the vitamin levels in the rations may have been so low that oxidation of vitamins in the diet by fatty peroxides may have caused vitamin deficiencies.

There has lately been some concern about diseases induced in animals of economic importance by the consumption of oxidized or readily oxidizable fats. Grant (1966) has reviewed the evidence relating microangiopathy in pigs to oxidative instability of feed fat. Carpenter *et al.* (1966) reviewed the literature dealing with injury to livestock from oxidized feed fat, but they concluded from their own work that if the diet were supplied with vitamins according to standard commercial practice no harm would come from this source unless the peroxide level of the entire diet exceeded 40 meq/kg. To attain this level of peroxide would require adding fat of peroxide value 800 as 5% of the diet, if all of the peroxide were to come from the added fat. Such a peroxide value can be attained only when fats have been deliberately and artificially abused. It was found, in fact (Lea *et al.*, 1966), that fish oil oxidized to high peroxide value, mixed into a ration, and stored until further oxidative deterioration had occurred, was as effective as fresh fat in promoting growth of turkeys. L'Estrange *et al.* (1967) saw no differences among pigs fed rations formulated with 10% of meat meal containing 15-17% of lipid which had either low (3-17) or high (114-150 meq/kg) peroxide values. In experiments with chickens, Lipstein *et al.* (1965) found that oxidation diminished the growth-promoting properties of acidulated soybean soap stock but not that of the crude oil.

III.   Thermal Reactions in the Absence of Air

A. CHEMICAL CHANGES

1. *Volatile and Monomeric Products*

Much of our knowledge of what happens to fatty materials when they are heated without exposure to air relates to the production of stand oil by the paint and varnish industry rather than to edible fats and culinary practice. Almost the only reason for juxtaposing the two technologies is the widespread supposition that fats which have been heated in the absence of air may contain some of the same transformation products as fats which have been heated in cooking, and that the study of such products is easier in the less complex mixtures which result from heating without aeration. This supposition persists despite evidence that fats heated *at frying temperatures* in the absence of air suffer relatively little change even after prolonged heating (Rock and Roth, 1964a,b; Yuki, 1967g; Fuller, 1967). To produce a toxic fat by heating it without exposure to air requires the use of temperatures much higher than those used in frying.

Knowledge applicable to frying fats has, however, grown out of the work of Crampton and his colleagues. Their work, which will be discussed below, followed attempts to make a flavor-stable shortening from linseed oil by thermal polymerization of its linolenate and removal of the polymer by solvent extraction (Privett *et al.*, 1945).

The products formed when fatty materials are heated in the absence of air can be roughly divided into three classes: (1) volatile substances which can readily be distilled out, (2) monomers which still contain about the original number of carbon atoms in the fatty acid chain, and (3) dimers and polymers formed by attaching two or more fatty acid chains together. The nature and amounts of these transformation products depend on the temperature and duration of heating, on the degree of unsaturation of the fatty acid chains, and on whether they are present as free acids, simple esters, or triglycerides.

The volatiles formed under anaerobic heating conditions include products typical of those formed by pyrolysis of most organic matter such as short-chained aldehydes, ketones, olefins, carbon monoxide, carbon dioxide, and water (Axt, 1959; Petit and Bosshard, 1952a,b). Transesterification takes place (Capella *et al.*, 1961; Boelhouwer *et al.*, 1967), and free fatty acids are liberated. Long-chained ketones form, presumably by decarboxylative dimerization of the fatty acids (Chalmers, 1951). Even saturated triglycerides undergo such reactions if heated strongly enough (Crossley *et al.*, 1962), but the extent of transformation increases with increasing unsaturation. Acrolein has been reported as a fat pyrolysis product; it probably comes from the glycerol moiety rather than from the fatty acid chains. Some of these volatile materials, being highly reactive, may take part in the formation of polymers which occurs at the same time as the volatiles are being formed.

Sen Gupta (1966) heated methyl oleate for 65 hours at 280°C under argon. About 70% of the starting material was recovered as methyl octadecenoate. The balance was transformed into C_{36} dimers, methyl decanoate, 9,17-hexacosadiene, methyl 9-octadecen-1,18-dioate, methyl 9,17-hexacosadien-1,26-dioate, methyl 9,17-hexacosadienoate, and unidentified materials, each in quantities representing 0.4–5.5% of the original oleate. The finding of the C_{18} dicarboxylic acid and the several C_{26} species seemed particularly surprising. Sen Gupta explained them by a mechanism involving cleavage of the unsaturated oleate chain at positions alpha to the double bond followed by recombination of the radicals with each other or attachment of them to the C_{18} position of oleate. Nawar and Dubravcic (1968) expressed reservations about Sen Gupta's proposed mechanism and suggested an alternative one, which had the virtue of depending on homolytic cleavage of the fatty acid chain at a position beta to the double bond; there is ample precedent in the literature for such cleavage. Their mechanism seems more satisfying than Sen Gupta's as a way of accounting for most of the products which he found, but it does not account for the presence of the C_{26} dibasic acid, nor for Sen Gupta's isolation of methyl 15-tetracosenoate from a mixture of methyl oleate and methyl palmitate after heating.

Double bonds undergo isomerization during heating, changing both from cis to trans and from nonconjugated to conjugated (Ueno and Sakurai, 1949; Kurita, 1958), and these changes may be important preludes to subsequent reactions (Paschke *et al.*, 1952). Prolonged heating causes a decrease in the number of double bonds through their involvement in cyclization and polymerization reactions (Sims, 1957; Mehta and Sharma, 1956).

The cyclic materials formed by heat alone are thought to arise through the attack by a fatty acid radical on a carbon atom elsewhere in its own chain. This process forms a six-membered ring with a hydrocarbon chain and an ester-terminated chain remaining on adjacent carbon atoms of the ring. The double bonds are rearranged from their original positions. Although compounds of this type can be formed from oleate or linoleate in the presence of air (see Section IV,B,3), they appear to form in the absence of air only from trienoic fatty acids unless extreme temperatures (above 300°C) are used (Mehta and Sharma, 1957).

Bradley and Johnston (1941) suggested that thermally polymerized oils might contain cyclic monomers. Waterman *et al.* (1949) found evidence for their presence. The introduction of urea adduction as a separating technique permitted the segregation of cyclic monomers in high concentrations (Wiseblatt *et al.*, 1953; MacDonald, 1956), and finally gas–liquid chromatography made it possible to isolate groups of closely related compounds for structural analysis. McInnes *et al.*

(1961) determined that the cyclic monomers formed during the heating of linseed oil were 1-propyl-2-alkenecarboxycyclohexenes with the double bonds in several different positions. Hutchison and Alexander (1963), working with material formed in the same way, proposed a similar structure in which the alkyl side chain contained only one, rather than three, carbon atoms. Subsequent work by Friedrich (1967), who reported spectral data on a series of methyl ω-(o-alkylcyclohexyl)alkanoates, casts doubt on the conclusions of Hutchison and Alexander; the material they studied was probably not a single substance.

Friedrich's work had grown out of a different line of study. Paschke and Wheeler (1955) obtained a cyclic compound by thermal treatment of methyl eleostearate. They showed that it could be aromatized to a benzene derivative and that the aromatic compound could be oxidized to phthalic acid. Thus it was established that the conjugated trienoic acid cyclizes to a 1,2-disubstituted six-membered ring compound. Since the double bonds of linolenate can be conjugated by alkali treatment, an extensive program at the Northern Regional Laboratories of the U.S. Department of Agriculture has been carried out for the deliberate preparation of cyclic compounds by alkali treatment and heating of linseed oil and for the proof of structure of the cyclic materials thus formed (Scholfield and Cowan, 1959; Friedrich et al., 1963; Eisenhauer et al., 1963, 1964; Beal et al., 1964; Friedrich, 1967).

Lange and Mikusch (1967) have recently proposed that part of the cyclic material formed by treating linseed oil with alkali may have structures like (8) with an exocyclic double bond. It has not been suggested that such structures might be present in the thermally cyclized fat. The possibility that five-membered, as well as six-membered, rings might be present in heat-bodied linseed oil was put forward by Gast et al. (1963).

$$\text{CH}-(\text{CH}_2)_n-\text{CH}_3$$
$$(\text{CH}_2)_m\text{COOCH}_3$$

(8)

The cyclic fatty acids are not wholly foreign to nature, for 11-cyclohexylundecanoic acid has been isolated from butter fat (Schogt and Begemann, 1965) and from sheep perinephric fat (Hansen and Gerson, 1967).

2. Dimers and Polymers

The increase in viscosity exhibited by a drying oil during the process of heat bodying results from the formation of polymers, and the rate of viscosity increase parallels the rate of polymer formation (Sims, 1957; Taeufel *et al.*, 1958). Dimers formed in the absence of air, unlike those formed by oxidation, are not held together by oxygen bridges but rather by carbon–carbon bonds. Champetier and Petit (1945) offered evidence that these dimers are cyclic Diels–Alder adducts. Clingman *et al.* (1954) showed that the dimeric fractions isolated from strongly heated eleostearate, linoleate, or linolenate contain six-membered rings. Aromatization and oxidation of the dimers yielded prehnitic acid as the sole aromatic product, indicating that the dimers had formed by Diels–Alder reactions. In the case of linoleate and linolenate, the Diels–Alder reactions must have been preceded by conjugation of the double bonds. Since Paschke *et al.* (1964) established definite structures for the various possible isomers formed by adding one molecule of methyl 10,12-octadecadienoate as a dienophile to another molecule of the same ester as diene, the validity of the Diels–Alder mechanism for the polymerization of conjugated polyenoic esters seems well established.

Experiments by Wheeler and White (1967) indicated that the dimer formed by heating methyl linoleate under vacuum for 48 hours at 290°C was a mixture of dimers containing one, two, and three rings. Heating linoleate with di-*tert*-butyl peroxide yielded a predominantly acyclic dimer, which could be cyclized by further heating into a mixture of molecules containing one and two rings. It can be concluded that unless the double bonds of the linoleate have previously been conjugated, thereby setting the molecule up for a Diels-Alder reaction, a number of pathways are available for dimerization.

Sen Gupta (1967a) reported that thermal polymerization of methyl linoleate at 280°C with rigorous exclusion of air gave very little of the Diels–Alder adduct, and he suggested that traces of oxygen are required to initiate the conjugation of double bonds. Under his operating conditions a series of dimers formed. They contained one, two, or three rings, and correspondingly, three, two, or one double bond. He proposed structures for many of these products and explained them as having resulted from the addition of an allylic radical to the double bond of another fatty acid molecule forming an acyclic dimer, or to a double bond elsewhere in the dimer molecule forming cyclic structures. Structure (9) is suggested for a typical tricyclic dimer.

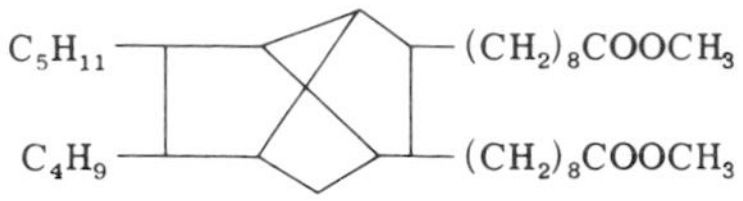

C_5H_{11} — / — $(CH_2)_8COOCH_3$

C_4H_9 — / — $(CH_2)_8COOCH_3$

(9)

Sen Gupta (1967b) has also studied dimers formed from a monounsaturated fatty acid. He heated methyl oleate at 280°C for 65 hours under argon. In addition to the volatile and monomeric products described in his previous publication (Sen Gupta, 1966), he detected dimers by paper chromatography of the free fatty acids. The chromatographic method used permitted separation of saturated from unsaturated dimers. By destruction of the latter with osmium tetroxide, he was able to isolate the saturated dimer for structural investigation by mass and NMR spectroscopy. Since this dimer differed in its refractive index from the dimer formed by a Diels–Alder reaction of conjugated octadecadienoate (followed by hydrogenation), he concluded that its structure must include a five-membered ring (10). To account for this

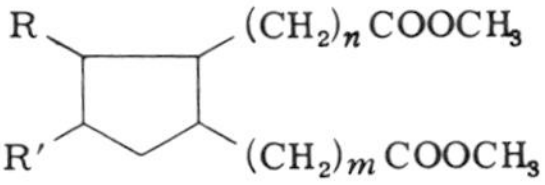

R — $(CH_2)_n COOCH_3$

R′ — $(CH_2)_m COOCH_3$

(10)

R — CH — $(CH_2)_n COOCH_3$

R′ — CH = CH — $(CH_2)_m COOCH_3$

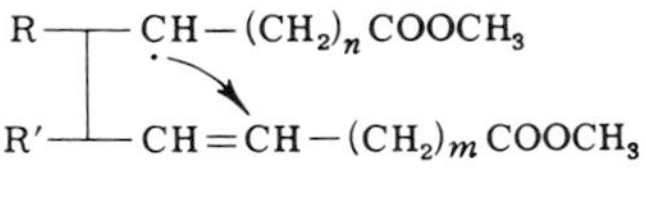

(11)

structure, he invoked the mechanism proposed by Whitmore and Gerecht (1950) for dimerization of methyl undecylenate or one-octene, namely, cyclization of the radical (11). Radical (11) would be expected as the initial product from the addition to oleate of the allylic radical derived from another oleate molecule. But, since only traces of oxygen are sufficient to trigger double bond conjugation (Martinenghi, 1967) and the Diels–Alder reaction, it seems unlikely that dimers such as (10) are present to any appreciable extent in fats which have been heated in the air, as in frying.

    When the fatty acid moieties undergoing dimerization are present as triglycerides, two types of dimerization can take place. One would be a true dimerization, between fatty acid chains attached to different triglycerides; the other would be an "intramolecular dimerization" or cyclization, linking together two fatty acid chains that were attached to the same glycerol. This intramolecular reaction could then be followed by a transesterification with another glyceride molecule to yield a dimerized glyceride essentially indistinguishable from one formed by direct intermolecular dimerization. Boelhouwer *et al.* (1967) showed that in the polymerization of linseed oil this indirect path of intramolecular dimerization followed by transesterification is the major route for the formation of dimers and the resulting increase in viscosity.

Dimerization is, of course, the first step toward polymerization, and much of the viscosity increase that occurs during the production of stand oils depends on the formation of higher polymers, ultimately including those cross-linked in three dimensions (Fedelli *et al.*, 1963a,b). But the conditions required for substantial formation of higher polymers by thermal reactions alone are so drastic as to render any discussion of them inappropriate in a review concerned primarily with edible fats.

B. BIOLOGICAL PROPERTIES OF FATS HEATED IN THE ABSENCE OF AIR

The available evidence indicates that the nutritional properties of fats are not appreciably altered by heat alone unless the heating is extreme or unless the fats contain linolenic or more highly unsaturated acids.

Alfin-Slater *et al.* (1959) heated soybean and cottonseed oils *in vacuo* at 322°C for 70 or 100 minutes and then fed them to rats as 15% of the diet for the lifespan of the animals. Nutritional indices such as growth, feed efficiency, fat absorbability, reproduction and lactation, longevity, and tissue cholesterol were measured. No evidence of impaired nutrition or of harmfulness was observed in any of the groups except those fed the more highly polymerized soybean oil, where an iodine value decrease of 10% and a viscosity increase of 100% were associated with a slight depression in growth and an interference with reproductive performance of the females. This interference was alleviated by supplementation with α-tocopherol. There was no evidence of increased tumor incidence in the groups ingesting the heated oils. Absorbability of the heated oils was only slightly decreased.

Lang *et al.* (1966) carried out extensive experiments to establish the safety of palm oil that had been strongly heated to aid in its decolorization. The oil, before refining, was subjected to anaerobic heat treatments up to 5 hours at 220°C or 15 minutes at 260°C (Becker *et al.*, 1966). The heated oils, and unheated control fats, were given to rats in long-term and generation studies. There were no indications that the heated oils were injurious to health. There were some differences among the groups, generally in favor of the unheated oil, but these were not practically significant, and the groups receiving heated oils were not outside the limits of normalcy. Injection of the heated oils into fertile eggs did not prevent hatching.

The work of Crampton *et al.* (1951a,b,c, 1953, 1956) in this area is most significant and has been a key element in bringing about our present level of understanding of the nature and degree of toxicity in heated fats. These workers found that linseed oil that had been heated under a carbon dioxide atmosphere for 12 hours at 275°C caused weight loss and high mortality among rats receiving it as 20% of the diet. They sought to determine what factors in the heated oil were responsible for such results. By varying the oil used for heating, they established that linolenate was the precursor of the toxic material, since the degree of toxicity seen was proportional to the level of linolenate in the original oil, and fats lacking this trienoic acid did not develop the toxicity. By converting the heated linseed oil to ethyl esters and fractionally distilling the esters, they learned that the toxicity lay in the distillable or monomeric portion. The polymers, while non-nutritious and causing diarrhea for mechanical reasons when fed at high levels, did not appear to be inherently toxic. Urea fractionation of the distilled esters showed that the straight-chained, urea-adductable esters were innocuous and that the toxic component stayed with the nonadductable portion. This distillable, non-urea-adductable fraction was the material later shown by McInnes *et al.* (1961) to contain 1-propyl-2-alkenecarboxycyclohexenes. As successive separation steps increased the concentration of cyclic materials in the fractions being bioassayed, the toxicity also increased. The distillable, non-urea-adductable fraction, which was comparatively rich in cyclic materials, caused poor weight gains, but no deaths, when fed to rats as 2.5% of the diet for 28 days.

Matsuo carried out similar experiments, confirming and extending Crampton's conclusions. He found (Matsuo, 1957a,d,e) that the highly unsaturated oil of cuttlefish became toxic after 10 hours of heating at 225°C under anaerobic conditions, owing, not to peroxides, but to cyclic esters. In order for the toxicity to be demonstrated, the heated fat had to be fed at the 20% level; the 5% level was insufficient (Matsuo, 1957d). Ethyl linolenate gave similar results after it had been heated 40 hours at 250°C (Matsuo, 1959b, 1962). Additional evidence for the toxicity of cyclic compounds was obtained by feeding the di-*n*-butyl esters of 4-cyclohexene-1,2-dicarboxylic acid; rats receiving this ester as 20% of their diets died within 11 days (Matsuo, 1959c). Diethyl phthalate and benzene were much less toxic than the cyclohexene ester. Rapeseed oil and cuttlefish oil ethyl esters were both toxic after strong heating, owing to their content of cyclized esters (Matsuo, 1959a, 1960a, 1965). The cyclic adduct formed by heating ethyl β-eleostearate with acrolein depressed the growth of rats and killed them when fed for 5–7 days as 10% of the diet (Matsuo, 1960b, 1961). A valuable English-language summary of Matsuo's work is included in the Oregon State Symposium publication (Schultz *et al.*, 1962).

It must be concluded that the harmful effects which come about when rats are fed high levels of polyunsaturated fats that have been heated at temperatures above 200°C in the absence of air result more from cyclic monomers than from polymers. Numerous other workers have offered evidence that can be cited in support of this conclusion (Lassen *et al.*, 1949; Raulin and Petit, 1960; Kaneda *et al.*, 1955; Firestone *et al.*, 1961a; Munn *et al.*, 1960; Raulin *et al.*, 1959, 1960; Kato and Sakurai, 1949).

For all the biological evaluations described above the fats were heated in the absence of air. None of the publications indicate, however, that rigorous efforts had been made to exclude all traces of oxygen during the heating. Since Sen Gupta (1967a) and Martinenghi (1967) have pointed out that traces of oxygen are sufficient to cause conjugation of double bonds and therefore to influence profoundly the subsequent nature of the chemical reactions occurring in a hot fat, there is a possibility that even the highly unsaturated fats would not be nutritionally affected by heating in the complete absence of oxygen, at least at temperatures below 280°C.

IV. Oxidation at High Temperatures

A. CHEMICAL REACTIONS

Many observations have been made on fats during or after thermal oxidation processes. Different kinds of fat and fatty materials have been treated under a wide range of temperatures, times, time-temperature cycles, and degrees of aeration. Although the results from some of these experiments have been interpreted as relevant to used frying fat, the differences between actual frying conditions and conditions used for thermal oxidations in the laboratory suggest that it is unjustified to apply results from laboratory heating to practical frying without careful discrimination. Information derived from thermal treatments in the laboratory should be kept as a separate category of information from that based on actual frying experiments or near approximations to them. A fat's nutritive properties can readily be destroyed by artificial heating and oxidation, but most nutritional evaluations of actual used frying fats have shown little or no nutritional impairment. It is, of course, perfectly valid to study thermal oxidations of fats in simplified systems and under exaggerated conditions if the results are used as a guide toward the much more complex study of fats that have actually been used for frying. The remainder of this section deals with thermally oxidized fats; frying fats will be discussed in Section VI.

The wide range of conditions used by different workers who have studied thermal oxidations has led to some disparities in the results reported, but it is possible to make some generalizations which are supported by the bulk of the evidence available (Banu et al., 1967; Candea and Manughevici, 1944; Chahine et al., 1967a; Fukuzumi, 1961; Johnson and Kummerow, 1957; Kritchevsky et al., 1962b; Larsen and Morris, 1943; LeClerc et al., 1966; Mariam and Pochetti, 1965; Michael et al., 1966; Mukai et al., 1966; Ota and Yamamoto, 1964; Ota et al., 1963a, 1964a,b; Ondreicka et al., 1963; Pathak and Mathur, 1954; Pokorny, 1957, 1966; Ramel et al., 1965a; Rock and Roth, 1964a; Sedlacek, 1964, 1966a,b; Simko et al., 1961; Steibert and Sliwiok, 1966; Taeufel et al., 1959).

Oxidation of a fat at high temperature differs from oxidation of the same fat at low temperature. Not only are the reactions speeded up at higher temperature but also quite different reactions take place. This is because the initial oxidation products which form at low temperatures are too unstable to exist more than transiently at high temperatures. The thermal instability of peroxides was discussed above (Section II,C). Thus, when a fat is heated in air, it first shows a gain in weight as oxygen is absorbed, and its peroxide value may increase. But as heating continues, the peroxides decompose, and scission products start to distill off, leading to a net loss in weight. The refractive index and ultraviolet absorption of the fat increase owing to conjugation of the double bonds and to the accumulation of oxygenated products. These oxygenated products include carbonyl, hydroxy, and epoxy derivatives. They may be detected spectroscopically or by chemical methods. Eventually the fat turns brown in color. The color has been attributed to α,β- and α,α'-unsaturated carbonyl compounds (Mukai et al., 1965).

The iodine value of the fat may rise during the early stages of thermal oxidation because of the formation of new unsaturated linkages, but it later falls as the double bonds are consumed in various reactions. Polymers form, increasing the viscosity of the fat and its tendency to foam. Water forms in the fat, and not only distills off, carrying other volatiles with it, but also brings about hydrolysis of the fat, with liberation of free fatty acids. The temperature and duration of heating, the extent of aeration (including the surface-volume ratio of the fat), the degree of unsaturation of the fat, and the presence of catalysts all influence the extent to which these changes take place, and their sequence. Extensive deterioration of a fat can be effected if sufficiently abusive conditions are used.

Even completely saturated compounds have been oxidized in the presence of catalysts (Paquot and de Goursac, 1950), or with sufficiently vigorous high-temperature oxidation (Endres *et al.*, 1962a,b). When catalysts were used, the products were short-chained fatty acids resulting from successive β-oxidations of the original fatty acid chains. Oxidation without catalyst at 150°C gave saturated fatty ester chains randomly substituted with hydroperoxy groups (Brodnitz, 1967; Brodnitz *et al.*, 1968a,b). Yuki (1968) found that coconut oil readily undergoes thermal oxidation despite its low iodine value. Auto-oxidations of saturated fatty materials were reviewed by Brodnitz (1968); the products formed during such oxidations were studied by Franzke *et al.* (1968).

There is evidence that the fatty acids on the 1 and 3 positions of a triglyceride molecule are more susceptible to oxidative attack than are the ones in the 2 position (Sahasrabudhe and Farn, 1964; Endres *et al.*, 1962a,b).

It is generally supposed that the changes brought about in a fat during thermal oxidation result from the formation and rapid decomposition of hydroperoxides. Similar changes result when a fat is first oxidized at low temperature and then heated in an inert atmosphere (Evans *et al.*, 1965, Kumazawa, 1965; Uzzan and Lobry, 1958; Izumi and Yamada, 1964). There is no clear evidence, however, that all of the changes reported to occur during thermal oxidation take place through the intermediacy of hydroperoxides; it seems quite possible that the free radicals might form more directly and react with each other or with oxygen to form the final products. It is clear from the work referred to above and from experiments in our own laboratories that for a given total duration of heating at a specified temperature continuous heating is less destructive than intermittent heating. Apparently, during intermittent heating, substantial concentrations of hydroperoxides form while the fat is at the lower temperatures. Later, when the fat is reheated, these hydroperoxides decompose to give, all at once, a higher concentration of radicals than is achieved by the slow and steady attack of oxygen at a fixed high temperature. Thus, when a fat is held at high temperature, decomposition of the hydroperoxides will be purely thermal, but under conditions of temperature cycling many peroxide molecules will be attacked by radicals that formed from other peroxide molecules. The two mechanisms of peroxide decomposition, thermal and induced, can be expected to give different products (Hiatt and Irwin, 1968; Hiatt *et al.*, 1968a,b,c,d).

B. PRODUCTS OF THERMAL OXIDATION

1. *Volatiles*

The volatile substances produced when a fat is heated in air appear to be generally like those formed in air at lower temperatures (Section II,C), although they have not been studied so extensively. Products found include free fatty acids, the lower alkanes, saturated and unsaturated aldehydes, ketones, alcohols, half esters of dibasic acids, methylcyclopentane, cyclohexane, benzene, acrolein, crotonaldehyde, carbon monoxide, carbon dioxide, and water. Of these compounds various ones have been reported by Akiya (1965), Hrdlicka and Pokorny (1962, 1963), Ota *et al.* (1963a), Sedlacek (1966c), Toi *et al.* (1961, 1962a,b), Lueck *et al.* (1967), and Fuller (1967).

2. *Monomeric Oxygenated Products*

During the oxidation of fats at high temperatures, there is considerable isomerization of double bonds, as mentioned above, with the result that after oxidation the fat contains substantial levels of trans double bonds and of conjugated double bond systems.

The cleavage processes which give rise to short-chained fatty acids also produce fatty acids containing only slightly fewer carbon atoms than the original fatty acid chains, with the result that these products may be classed somewhat arbitrarily as "monomeric" rather than as "volatile." They have been reported by Paquot and de Goursac (1950), Skellon (1963), and Toi *et al.* (1962b). Toi *et al.* also mentioned the aldehydoesters produced by chain cleavage, and their oxidation products, the dibasic acids. Endres *et al.* (1962a,b) observed the formation of several dicarboxylic acids from 1-oleoyl dipalmitin but not from 2-oleoyl dipalmitin or from saturated triglycerides.

The hydroxyl number of a fat increases during thermal oxidation. Part of the increase might be attributed to the liberation of partial glycerides by hydrolysis, but Deatherage and Mattill (1939) isolated dihydroxystearic acid from thermally oxidized oleate after saponification, while later workers (Ota *et al.*, 1963b; Barrett and Henry, 1966) have detected hydroxyl-containing fatty chains by chromatographic methods. Both γ- and δ-lactones have been found in thermally oxidized fatty esters (Paquot and de Goursac, 1950; Fioriti *et al.*, 1967); these presumably arise through the intermediacy of hydroxy esters.

We have found (Artman and Alexander, 1968) alkoxy-substituted unsaturated esters in thermally oxidized fatty materials. Methyl methoxyoleate was obtained from methyl oleate, while ethyl oleate yielded ethyl ethoxyoleate. Ethyl ethoxyoctadecenoates were also isolated from a sample of partially hydrogenated soybean oil that was thermally oxidized and then subjected to saponification and acid-catalyzed esterification with ethanol. In each case the alkoxy group was allylic to the double bond. The compounds presumably were formed when an allylic hydroperoxy group decomposed in the presence of an ester or alcohol, from which the alkyl group could be abstracted to form the alkoxy group. These unsaturated ethers were the most abundant single class of compound in the distillable non-urea-adducting fraction of the thermally oxidized fats that we studied. Vioque and Maza (1967) have also reported that when hydroxy acids having the hydroxyl group alpha to a double bond are esterified with methanol and acid, the hydroxyl groups are converted to methyl ethers.

Epoxides are key components among the oxidation products of unsaturated fatty materials because of the ease with which they are transformed into other substances. Much has been written about the deliberate production of oxirane groups in fats by treatment with peroxy acids; the oxirane derivatives are useful for industrial purposes. Epoxides also can be found in fats treated with air at high temperatures (Deatherage and Mattill, 1939; Ellis, 1950; Krull, 1959; Ota *et al.*, 1963b; Ney, 1965). In some studies the epoxides were detected and measured by chemical methods; in other studies their presence was inferred by the isolation of the dihydroxy acids which resulted from their hydrolysis. In our laboratories (J. C. Alexander, unpublished work) pure ethyl epoxystearate was isolated in 1–2% yield from ethyl oleate which had been heated in an open beaker for 40 hours at 180°C. Isolation was achieved by distillation, urea adduction, and column chromatography of the urea-adduct-forming fraction. The structure of the isolated epoxide was established by derivative formation and by mass spectroscopy.

Deatherage and Mattill (1939) proposed that the epoxides are formed by oxidation of double bonds with peroxy acids which result from auto-oxidation of aldehydes. However, it was later found by Swift and Dollear (1948) that epoxides can be formed by interaction of oleic acid with methyl oleate hydroperoxide at 90°C. Ney (1965) observed epoxide in methyl oleate which had been first oxidized, then heated; he postulated that the epoxide formed by interaction of double bonds with hydroperoxides. Brill and Barone (1964) showed that substantial yields of both *cis*- and *trans*-epoxybutenes can be obtained by treatment of either *cis*- or *trans*-2-butene with oxygen. They proposed a mechanism involving addition of an oxygen atom from a peroxy radical across the double bond. This mechanism was supported by the later finding (Brill and Indictor, 1964) that decomposition of *tert*-butyl hydroperoxide in the presence of olefins gives the olefin epoxides.

Epoxides are sensitive both to nucleophilic attack and to heat. Krull (1959) observed rapid decreases in the oxirane content of epoxidized oils when they were held at 200°C or above. The knowledge that epoxides are present in thermally oxidized fats makes it easy to account for some of the other oxygenated products which have been reported. Vicinal dihydroxy esters can be formed by treating epoxy esters with acid at low temperature (Maerker *et al.*, 1964), while treatment with acid at higher temperatures gives conjugated dienes or keto esters (Crowder and Elm, 1949; Ney, 1965; Walens *et al.*, 1965). Acid-catalyzed alcoholysis of epoxide probably produced the alkoxyhydroxystearate reported by Artman and Alexander (1968) in thermally oxidized soybean oil. Ellis (1950) recognized the acyloxyhydroxystearate which he found in oxidizing oleate as a secondary product derived from epoxide. Artman and Alexander (1968) isolated both ketostearate and ketooleate from thermally oxidized soybean oil and attributed them to rearrangement of epoxides.

3. *Cyclic Compounds*

Knowledge of the cyclic compounds found in fats that had been heated in the absence of air (Section III,A) directed attention toward the possible occurrence of similar compounds in fats that had been heated in the presence of air. Firestone *et al.* (1961a) and Friedman *et al.* (1961) heated cottonseed oil in air, and from the heated oil they obtained fractions which did not adduct with urea. They presumed these to be cyclic compounds similar to the ones previously isolated from heated linseed oil by Crampton's group. Mukai *et al.* (1966) have made similar observations.

Michael *et al.* (1966) heated methyl linoleate in air at 200°C for 200 hours, and isolated the distillable, non-urea-adductable fraction from it. By subjecting this fraction to column and gas–liquid chromatography, Michael (1966a,b) isolated both aromatic and alicyclic compounds. The aromatic compounds were a mixture of isomers having the general structure (12). The alicyclic compounds had basically the

$$n = 2 - 4$$
$$n + m = 11$$

(12)

same structures but contained only one or two double bonds. The double bonds occupied various positions in the ring and in the side chains. These compounds are, of course, quite similar to those from heated linseed oil whose structures had been established by McInnes *et al.* (1961). In Michael's work the structures were deduced from mass spectra and confirmed by syntheses.

Artman and Alexander (1968) reported similar compounds, aromatic, unsaturated, and saturated, as well as cyclic compounds containing hydroxyl groups. These compounds were isolated from partially hydrogenated soybean oil that had been heated in air, converted to ethyl esters, distilled, urea adducted, and subjected to chromatographic separation.

4. Dimers and Polymers

Dimers and polymers can be formed by thermal oxidation, as well as by aeration at low temperature. They form also when previously oxidized fat is strongly heated (Izumi and Yamada, 1964; Evans *et al.*, 1965; Harrison and Wheeler, 1952). Unlike the dimers produced by oxidation at low temperature, those that form during high-temperature oxidation are not held together by oxygen bridges. Frankel *et al.* (1960) and Ramanathan *et al.* (1959) concluded that the dimers that they prepared were joined through carbon–carbon bonds. Frankel *et al.* were unable to obtain aromatic derivatives from their dimer and concluded that it probably did not contain six-membered rings. Perkins and Kummerow (1959a) indicated that their dimer fraction might be acyclic in structure.

Several workers have recognized that dimers produced by thermal oxidation are highly polar in nature, containing hydroxyl or other oxygen functions (Sahasrabudhe and Farn, 1964; Perkins and Kummerow, 1959a; Ota *et al.*, 1964a,c; Frankel *et al.*, 1960). In many cases they are highly colored, and account for much of the dark color of heated fat, even though they are present at only low levels.

Others have reported the presence of both polar and nonpolar dimers (Michael *et al.*, 1966; Mukai *et al.*, 1966), which can be separated from each other by column chromatography. The nonpolar dimers apparently are very much like those produced by heating in the absence of air being Diels–Alder adducts with six-membered rings (W. R. Michael, this laboratory, unpublished work). The more polar types are the ones responsible not only for the color but also for the foaming tendencies of heated oils (Mukai *et al.*, 1966; Ota *et al.*, 1964d).

5. *Unsaponifiables*

During thermal oxidation of fats the sterols decrease in quantity, presumably because they are partly converted to either volatile or polymeric products (Torres *et al.*, 1956; Kajimoto and Mukai, 1965). Cholesterol in lard, after being heated to 350°C, will no longer form a precipitate with digitonin (Larsen and Morris, 1943). The unsaponifiables of fresh and heated oils differ considerably in their behavior on thin-layer chromatography. The precise nature of the changes is not known, but they are probably similar to the changes documented by Fioriti and Sims (1967) for cholesterol that had been oxidized for 9 weeks at 82°C; epoxides, ketones, and polyhydroxy compounds were found among the oxidation products.

6. *Oxidative Susceptibility*

Fats that have been subjected to thermal oxidation are much more sensitive to further oxidation than are the fresh fats from which they were prepared (Uzzan and Lobry, 1958; Taeufel *et al.*, 1959). This fact must be stressed because of its significance in feeding studies with thermally oxidized fats. Fats oxidized at low temperatures contain high levels of peroxides, and the peroxides alone are sufficient to account for their enhanced oxidizability. Peroxides are seldom present at high levels in fats that have been oxidized at high temperatures, so the oxidative susceptibility of these fats must be attributed to other factors such as the presence of conjugated dienes and aldehydes or the depletion of their antioxidants.

C. BIOLOGICAL PROPERTIES OF THERMALLY OXIDIZED FATS

Many experiments have been reported in which thermally oxidized fats were administered to experimental animals, often with detrimental results. Such findings cannot be applied indiscriminately to all heated or oxidized fats. As will be seen in the following detailed discussion, the adverse effects reported by one laboratory could not be reproduced by another in some cases. In other cases the results can be attributed to auto-oxidation of the heated fat after it was mixed into the animals' ration, with concomitant destruction of vitamins and other nutrients. Many of the studies used fats which had been much more extensively abused than any that might be found in the normal, human diet. From these studies, the generalization can be drawn that as the conditions used for preparing a thermally oxidized fat in the laboratory approach the conditions used for the frying of food there is a corresponding decrease in the appearance of symptoms attributable to the heated fat. The chief value of work with badly abused fats has been in stimulating work with more realistically heated fats and in guiding those who experimented with practically heated fats as to the kinds of effects they should look for.

1. Specific Compounds

Since several components of thermally oxidized fats have been chemically characterized, it seems useful to consider first the biological effects that have been recorded for these compounds. Then in Section IV,C,2 the results obtained by various workers who fed unfractionated heated fats will be examined.

a. Hydrocarbons. The toxicity of hydrocarbons found in the volatiles from heated fat was investigated by Akiya and Shimizu (1965). They found that the hydrocarbons having less than 9 carbon atoms had no nutritive value but were not toxic, while those having more than 9 carbon atoms were toxic to rats. The level of toxicity which they reported is noteworthy because it is so low. They found that the addition of 1 ml of decene to 5 gm of basal ration caused the death of all rats consuming it, while the addition of 0.25 ml did not.

b. Hydroxy Fatty Acids. Lang *et al.* (1963) extensively studied hydroxylated fatty acids. They fed rats for 8 weeks with diets containing up to 20% of the fatty acids formed by hydrolysis of epoxidized soybean oil. The hydroxylated oil was well absorbed except at the highest level of hydroxylation, where decreased feed efficiency and high mortality appeared. The hydroxylated oils caused an impairment of liver function, an increase in blood lipids and cholesterol, and an impairment of spermatogenesis, but no other histological changes.

The same group (Kieckebusch *et al.*, 1963b) also fed methyl ricinoleate to rats for 4 weeks. When the hydroxy ester comprised 5% of the diet they observed a slight growth depression, decreased protein efficiency, elevated respiratory quotient, and an increased level of plasma triglycerides. Ricinoleate accumulated in the depot fat. With higher doses, there was an increase in the rate of peristalsis, but no influence on temperature, pulse, liver function, plasma proteins, organ weights, or histological structure of tissues.

Hydroxy acids isolated from oxidized corn oil (Perkins *et al.*, 1961) or from castor oil (Risser *et al.*, 1966) are absorbed into the lymph and deposited in the body tissues. In contrast, Kaunitz and Johnson (1964) found that dihydroxystearic acid was poorly absorbed by the rat and was not deposited in the tissues.

c. Epoxides. Chalvardjian *et al.* (1962) demonstrated that although epoxy acids survive gastric acidity and are absorbed and deposited in the body, they are not toxic. Specifically, rats showed no abnormalities of either growth or tissue structure after 28 days on a diet which included 7% of Vernonia oil containing 69% of *cis*-12,13-epoxy-9-*cis*-octadecenoic acid. On the other hand, Kieckebusch *et al.* (1963a) and Lang and Fricker (1964) reported that epoxidized soybean oil was toxic. For their work, the oil had been oxidized with peracetic acid. Weanling rats were dosed each day with 50 mg of diepoxystearic acid, which caused growth inhibition. Daily doses nine times higher killed 80% of the rats within 8 days. Unlike the relatively innocuous Vernonia oil, the epoxidized soybean oil contained diepoxides, and these may have been responsible for its toxicity.

d. Cyclic Compounds. When Crampton and Matsuo, in their several works cited above (Section III), attributed the toxicity of thermally polymerized drying oils to the cyclic monomers which they contained, attention was directed to the possibility that the nutritional impairment brought about in fats by thermal oxidation might also be caused partly by their content of cyclic compounds. Firestone *et al.* (1961a,b), Munn *et al.* (1960), and Michael *et al.* (1966) isolated non-urea-adductable fractions from thermally oxidized fats. They found the fractions to be toxic to rats and attributed this to cyclic compounds. The work of Michael *et al.* eliminated any possible effects from polymers for they studied the distillable, non-urea-adductable fraction rather than the total urea filtrate fraction. In an extension of this work, Michael (1966a) synthesized the aromatic compound, methyl 9-(2'-propyl)phenylnonanoate, and found it to be toxic in the weanling rat test described below.

J. C. Alexander, G. A. Nolen, D. E. Smith, and N. R. Artman of this laboratory (unpublished work) compared the toxicities of distillable non-urea-adductable fractions from fats heated in different ways with the hope of ascribing the toxicity to specific components. The bioassay procedure originally used by Crampton *et al.* (1953) involved feeding substantial amounts of material for several weeks and consumed so much of the material that it could not reasonably be used for assaying concentrated fractions. A procedure described by Firestone *et al.* (1961a,b) offered quicker results with less expenditure of material, and this was adapted to our purposes. For this test, 5 50-gm weanling rats were dosed by stomach tube with 0.5 ml of the substance being tested on each of three successive days. The animals were observed and weighed for 10 days. Samples were judged to be toxic when their administration was followed by abnormally low weight gain, diarrhea, premature involution of the thymus, or death; the degree of toxicity could be judged subjectively on the basis of the severity of the symptoms and the fraction of the animals affected. The method gave a measure of toxicity which was comparable to that obtained by feeding the test substance to weanling rats for 30 days as 10% of the diet.

In this bioassay procedure, the distillable, non-urea-adductable fraction of unheated soybean oil was used as a negative control; it caused no impairment of weight gain or other untoward effect. The distillable, non-urea-adductable fraction from linseed oil which had been heated for 12 hours under carbon dioxide at 275°C was used as the positive control. This is equivalent to the material fed by Crampton *et al.* (1953) and usually caused death in about half of the animals receiving it. The distillable, non urea-adductable fractions from soybean oil that had been heated in air for 40 hours at 180°C, or from methyl linoleate heated in air for 200 hours at 200°C were about equivalent to Crampton's material in toxicity. However, when olive oil or pure methyl oleate were heated in air for 40 hours at 180°C, the distillable, non-urea-adducting fractions were decidedly more toxic than the positive control, suggesting that oleate is more important than linoleate or linolenate as a precursor of toxic substances when fats are heated in air. This is in contrast to results from the anaerobic heating of fats, where, as noted above, oleate does not produce toxic materials. It is supposed that the polyunsaturated fatty acid chains, being more reactive toward oxygen than oleate is, are more readily converted to inert polymers or to volatile scission products, and thus they are unavailable for ring formation.

It is instructive to compare these results with those of Potteau and Cluzan (1966), who heated linseed oil in both the presence and the absence of air at 220° and 275°C, respectively. The oil heated in the absence of air was much more toxic than the oil heated with exposure to air. Their work suggests that this highly unsaturated oil tends to polymerize, rather than cyclize, during thermal oxidation.

Evidence regarding the toxicity of the cyclic compounds is still only presumptive. Michael (1966b) showed that the aromatic compounds which he synthesized were toxic, but the alicyclic compounds have been administered only as highly concentrated isolates rather than as pure compounds. There remains a slight possibility that the effects resulted from traces of other materials.

Michael, using the weanling rat bioassay technique, demonstrated that the aromatics can cause an acute toxicity response when administered in large doses (30 ml/kg of body weight during 48 hours). Gottenbos and Thomasson (1965) related the toxic response to the level of feeding; they fed lower levels of aromatized fatty acids for a longer period. Their rats initially showed some appetite depression and growth inhibition, but later they adapted to the aromatics and resumed growth. The aromatic compounds had been prepared by cyclization of fish oil to give a product containing 7% aromatic fatty acids; fractionation procedures raised this level to 60%. When the fatty material containing 60% aromatics was fed as 14.7% of the ration, the rats receiving it survived and adapted during the 18-week study, whereas rats fed the same material as 29.4% of the diet died within 5 weeks. When fed at the lower level, the aromatic compounds were absorbed from the intestine and excreted in the urine, indicating that a detoxification mechanism exists and that its activity can be increased with prolonged exposure.

Other substances which are present in the distillable, non-urea-adductable fraction of esters made from thermally oxidized fats, namely, ethoxyoleate, ethoxyhydroxystearate, and ketostearate, do not elicit a toxic response in the weanling rat acute bioassay (J. C. Alexander and G. A. Nolen, this laboratory, unpublished experiments).

   e.   Polymers. The literature concerning the toxicity of dimers and polymers in thermally oxidized fats is confused. Many workers, having observed a coincidence between polymer content and toxicity, have attributed the toxicity to the polymer without having established that the polymers themselves were actually responsible. The term "polymer" has been used very loosely in the heated fat literature.

There have been several reports attributing toxicity to the polymers produced during thermal oxidation of fats. Perkins and Kummerow (1959b) heated corn oil at 200°C for 48 hours. They isolated the non-distillable residue from the non-urea-adducting fraction of the fatty acids. This residue, which amounted to about 30% of the original oil, killed all of the rats to which it was fed as 12% of the diet for 7 days. Dilution of the polymer with fresh corn oil assured survival of the rats for 21 days, but only partially counteracted the growth-depressing effects of the polymer. (It is curious that, in this work, distillable, non-urea-adductable fraction, which others have reported to be toxic, supported growth as well as the fatty acids of fresh corn oil.)

Kaunitz *et al.* (1956b) aerated fats at 95°C for 200 hours, and then subjected them to molecular distillation. Diets containing 20% of the nondistillable residues were fed to rats, which quickly died. The rats gradually developed a tolerance when the residues were fed at the 10% level; at the 4-7% level they caused only growth depression. Later work (Kaunitz *et al.*, 1959) established that animals receiving the growth-depressing fractions had enlarged livers and kidneys, as well as abnormal levels of lipids and cholesterol in the serum and tissues.

In an effort to associate the biological properties of oxidized fats with specific kinds of substances, Kaunitz *et al.* (1960b) oxidized ethyl oleate at 95°-100°C for 240 hours, and then fractionated it by distillation and urea adduction. The distillation temperatures used (up to 168°C) probably caused chemical changes among the fat oxidation products. The various distillation fractions were given to 100 gm rats for 3 weeks as 8% of the diet. The mortality rate was not high, but growth depression and organ weight changes resulted. The distillable, urea-adductable fraction was essentially innocuous, and the polymer fraction (the residue from the molecular distillation) produced only small irregularities in the animals receiving it. The toxic components were concentrated in the nonadductable monomers and the dimers. Similar results were seen with oxidized ethyl linoleate. Among the biological effects observed were increased thirst (hence diuresis), enlargement of individual organs, depression of neutral fat deposition, and lowered values for liver and serum cholesterol—different effects were produced by the different fractions, showing that they contained a variety of physiologically active entities.

Firestone *et al.* (1961a) detected toxicity in dimers isolated from cottonseed oil that had been heated in air, and they attributed the toxicity to the fact that the dimer contained carbonyl groups, hydroxyl groups, and unsaturation difficult to remove by hydrogenation. Parteshko (1962) reported that the dimers isolated from oxidized sunflower seed oil were toxic and growth-depressing when given to rats in doses of 100 mg/rat/day for 12-14 weeks. There was growth depression, along with the development of catarrh, desquamation, and necrosis of the intestinal epithelium. Wholesome fat offered no protection for the dimers were administered as a 5% solution in fresh sunflower seed oil. Although Parteshko did not describe the procedure used for oxidizing the fat or isolating the polymer, the material fed contained 22%

of oxygen and had a peroxide value of 46 meq/kg; thus, the effects seen may have been as much related to the peroxides or other oxidized components as to the polymeric nature of the material.

Raulin and Petit (1962) heated herring oil for 50–60 hours at 185°C with a stream of air bubbling through it. The monomeric fraction isolated by distillation of the ethyl esters supported rat growth better than the distillation residue, which caused 100% mortality among rats receiving it as 20% of the diet for 67 days. This residue was, of course, rich in oxygen-containing substances.

Michael *et al.* (1966), after heating methyl linoleate in the presence of air for 200 hours at 200°C, concentrated monomeric, dimeric, and polymeric fractions by molecular distillation. The dimers were further fractionated by column chromatography into polar and nonpolar fractions. The polymeric material and the nonpolar dimer, like the polymers formed by heating linseed oil in the absence of air, were not toxic in the weanling rat bioassay. The polar dimers were toxic. These results tend to support the view, which was also advanced in Section III, that fatty polymers, being unabsorbable, are innocuous except when fed at quite high levels, and that other, absorbable, substances are responsible for the toxic effects that have been seen when badly abused fats were fed to laboratory animals.

2. *Feeding Experiments with Thermally Oxidized Fats*

In contrast to the work described above, where fractions or components of thermally oxidized fats were studied, the following experiments involved feeding the whole fat, with little or no attempt being made to ascribe the results produced to any particular class of compounds contained in it. There are great variations among the experiments in the kinds of fat used, the heating conditions, the method and level of administering the fat to the animals, and the criterion by which the performance of the animals was measured. Because of these variations, it is difficult to draw any broad conclusions from the experiments, or even to arrange the descriptions of them in any meaningful sequence.

Simko *et al.* (1963) concluded from their experiments that nutritionally harmful substances may develop in fats under ordinary conditions of kitchen use, for guinea pigs to which they gave heated fats for 10 weeks showed fatty necrosis of the liver and fatty or calciferous lesions in the myocardium and aorta. The fats used were sunflower seed oil, hydrogenated vegetable fat, lard, and butter. The fats had been heated for 120 minutes at 170°C. These conditions seem well within the range of culinary practice, but the fats were stirred and aerated continuously during heating, which probably explains the very substantial changes in chemical composition that were seen. For instance, the iodine values fell from 124 to 88 for sunflower seed oil, and from 80 to 51 for hydrogenated vegetable oil. The peroxide values of the lard and butter were 200 and 124, respectively. These values are so unlike those found in numerous other reports on used frying fats as to indicate that the conclusions of Simko *et al.* relate only to fats subjected to the particular conditions that were used and not to practical culinary fats.

The heating conditions used by Esh *et al.* (1960) were more nearly like actual frying conditions. They heated six different fats for 10 minutes, 1 hour, or 10 hours in an iron pan at 180°C and fed them to rats at the 10% level in semisynthetic diets. The rats that received fats heated for 10 minutes or 1 hour showed normal performance, but those receiving fats heated for 10 hours showed poor growth and diminished feed efficiency. It is noteworthy that after 1 hour all the fats showed moderately high peroxide values, from 8 to 35 meq/kg. For most of the fats, the peroxide values decreased during the subsequent 9 hours of heating, showing that the oxidations had gone far along into the stage where peroxides were decomposing to form secondary products. Meanwhile the iodine values of the fats had dropped as much as 31%. These figures indicate that the degree of chemical change suffered by the fats was relatively severe compared to most samples of frying fats (see Section VI,A). It is noteworthy that in this experiment, where the degree of abuse to which the fats were subjected was not nearly so unrealistic as in some other experiments, the physiological effects were the mild ones of poor growth and feed efficiency, which may be attributable to poor absorbability of the polymeric material in the fat.

Quite a different heating regimen was employed by Raju *et al.* (1965), who heated fats in open iron pans for 8 hours at 270°C. The heated fats were fed to rats, and produced growth depression, fatty livers, and elevated blood glucose and cholesterol values. Although these authors state that their heating conditions are typical of those used in India, Western culinary practice would not normally resort to such high temperatures. By our standards, these fats must be considered to have been artificially abused. No analyses of the fats were given, nor is there any indication that steps were taken to avoid dietary rancidity during the feeding study.

Johnson *et al.* (1956) in Kummerow's laboratory compared the susceptibility of different kinds of fat to thermal damage. They heated corn oil, margarine fat, and butter at 200°C for 24 hours while blowing with air at the rate of 100 ml/minute. The fats had moderately high peroxide values (18-21) and painty odors; they would likely have been unacceptable in a human diet. The oxidized corn oil caused diarrhea and growth depression in rats; the oxidized margarine oil had a similar, but slighter effect, and the butter oil, none. The affected animals recovered quickly when put on normal rations.

Keane *et al.* (1959) attempted to repeat this work, but they did not find the symptoms reported by Johnson *et al.* when they fed a similar fat in a diet of their own formulation. When they fed their fat in a diet which duplicated that of Johnson *et al.*, they did see the same symptoms of diarrhea and growth depression. On this basis, they proposed that the diet used by Johnson *et al.* had been inadequate in one or more nutrients, and they noted that subsequent experiments in Kummerow's laboratory (Witting *et al.*, 1957) had employed diets enriched in vitamins. Experiments in our own laboratories (J. C. Alexander and G. A. Nolen, unpublished) confirmed that rats consuming oxidized fats need larger quantities of a whole spectrum of vitamins, possibly because these vitamins are destroyed by contact with the oxidized fats in the mixed diet or in the gut. It is possible also that the consumption of oxidized fats represents a stress condition which increases the animals' need for vitamins.

Further investigations by Johnson *et al.* (1957) showed a correlation between the level of linoleate in an oil and its susceptibility to oxidative damage as indicated by growth inhibition in rats. The oxidized fats were absorbed more slowly than fresh fats and were more slowly hydrolyzed by pancreatic lipase *in vitro*, but the magnitude of these changes was not large enough to account fully for the observed growth depression. Animals receiving the oxidized fats had abnormally high liver weight–body weight ratios in this experiment.

Friedman *et al.* (1961) found similar effects when they fed cottonseed oil which had been heated for 190 hours in air at 225°C. The adverse effects of this oil were attributed to its content of nonadductable substances, i.e., cyclic, branched, or polymeric materials.

Kieckebusch *et al.* (1962) studied the toxicity of oxidized soybean oil as a function of heating time and degree of aeration at 180°C. As criteria of toxicity they measured primarily the growth and feed efficiency of young rats, but they also made numerous physiological observations in an attempt to understand the mechanism of the toxicity. From their series of time-aeration studies it can be seen that a long heating time (10-20 hours) and a low degree of aeration (0.06-0.2 m³ of air per kilogram of fat) is much less harmful than shorter times (2-7 hours) with more vigorous aeration (0.7-5 m³/kg). The mildest of their treatments produced fats which differed hardly at all from the fresh fat in either chemical or biological properties. The more oxidized fats had high hydroxyl values (8-38) and epoxide numbers (2-8), and their iodine values had decreased from 125 or 130 down to 110 or below. These highly oxidized fats caused extensive mortality in rats, but there was no correlation between toxicity and peroxide value.

In a subsequent experiment from the same laboratory, Degkwitz and Lang (1962) analyzed the body fat of rats receiving either fresh or oxidized soybean oil, with and without vitamin E supplementation. The body fat of animals receiving the oxidized oil contained relatively high levels of fat oxidation products. In this, they resembled rats receiving unsaturated fats with inadequate levels of vitamin E. Rats receiving the oxidized fat also showed relatively low levels of polyunsaturated fatty acids in their tissues. The soybean oils fed in this experiment had been so oxidized that their content of linoleate had decreased by more than 50%.

Akiya found oxidized fats to be toxic only after harsh oxidative treatments. In his first set of experiments (Akiya, 1961), soybean oil, linseed oil, and trilinolein were oxidized in thin layers at 37°-42°C and then kept for 2 hours at 200°C. No adverse effects were seen when these fats were fed to mice as 15% of the diet. In a later study (Akiya *et al.*, 1962), three unsaturated fats that had been heated at 200°C for 12 hours were fed to rats at the level of 1.5 gm/day. Changes in the properties of the oils were only slight during the first 9 hours of heating, but substantial changes were found after 12 hours. The increase in viscosity was especially noteworthy. The nutritive properties of soybean oil and rice bran oil were unchanged by this treatment, but the oxidized rapeseed oil caused some growth reduction on feeding. In a third series of experiments, Akiya (1962) tested some badly abused oils. Linseed oil and trilinolein were heated at 280°-300°C for 24 hours. These oils caused growth inhibition when fed and were lethal when injected intraperitoneally. The greatest toxicity was seen in a fraction separated by molecular distillation at temperatures up to 280°C.

Simko and Bucko (1963) heated fats for 2 hours at 170°C and fed them to guinea pigs for 10 weeks at the rate of 1 ml/day. Fat absorption was measured during the experiment. Heated and unheated sunflower seed oil and heated hydrogenated fat were all absorbed equally well; the unheated hydrogenated fat was absorbed somewhat less well. Food consumption of animals receiving the heated hydrogenated fat was less than for the others, but otherwise the heated fats had no adverse effects.

Selva (1956) compared heated and unheated butter, lard, and olive oil. Each fat was heated to the "bubbling point" for 5 minutes. Diets containing 15% of these fats were offered to rats for 85 days. Rats receiving the heated olive oil diet showed less growth than those on the unheated olive oil diet. The diet containing unheated butter produced only slightly better performance than its heated counterpart, mostly during the first 15 days of the feeding trial. Heated lard produced better growth than unheated lard. It was postulated that toxic substances formed in the olive oil during the heating. This report might have been more meaningful if the temperatures to which the fats were heated had been recorded.

Lea *et al.* (1964) compared the performance of rats fed diets containing 5% of beef fat that had been treated in one of several ways, namely: (1) no heat treatment, (2) oxidation at 100°–110°C for 11.5 hours to a peroxide value of 93, (3) deodorization with steam at 180°C, and (4) heating for 5 hours at 180°C under carbon dioxide. All the diets produced normal growth, and there were no adverse effects as a result of heating. Rats receiving the oxidized fat had lower levels of linoleate in their adipose tissues than did the others, suggesting that the oxidized fat had depressed either the absorption or deposition of linoleate.

The experimental findings of Binet and Wellers (1966) would be most alarming if they were considered alone rather than with reference to the whole body of information cited in this review. These workers heated peanut oil, butter, and margarine to 180°C for 20 minutes and fed them to rats, using the unheated fats as controls. The heated fats produced severe growth inhibition and high mortality. Heated peanut oil was the worst; half of the rats receiving it died within 92 days. No explanation is readily at hand to account for the startling difference between these results and those of many other workers.

Dangoumau *et al.* (1957), in a paper which seems to have been overlooked by many subsequent workers, told about an unsuccessful attempt to repeat the findings of Johnson *et al.* (1956), which were described near the beginning of this section. Dangoumau *et al.* heated peanut oil at 200°C for 24 hours with air bubbling through it at the rate of 100 ml/minute. The oil was fed to rats as 20% of a semisynthetic ration for 4 months. Although the rats grew slightly less than control animals receiving the unheated oil, they showed equal fat deposition and musculature with no abnormalities apparent on histological examination.

A subsequent paper from the same laboratory (Dangoumau *et al.*, 1958) described four experiments. In each experiment fats were oxidized by bubbling air through them for 24 hours at 200°C. The air was finely dispersed through a frit and was passed at the rate of 100 ml/minute through 1500 gm of oil. Analyses showed that the oils had been severely oxidized. They suffered iodine value decreases of 13-25%. The oxidized fats were fed to rats as 19% of a semisynthetic diet. Diets were prepared fresh weekly and were kept refrigerated until the time they were used. The first experiment, which ran for 10 months, compared oxidized and unoxidized peanut oil. The oxidized oil gave slightly poorer growth. Reproduction studies failed with both the heated and the unheated oil. The second experiment also used peanut oil and lasted for 15 months. Five rats of each sex received diets containing oxidized oil, commercial oil, or oil carefully extracted from peanuts at low temperature in the laboratory. The female rats showed no differences in growth. Among the males, those receiving the oxidized oil grew somewhat more slowly than those receiving either of the unheated oils. They also showed transient disorders of the skin and hair. Other isolated incidents and autopsy findings were reported, but their significance cannot be ascertained. The authors concluded that the oxidized oil was not particularly detrimental to the health of the rats consuming it.

The third experiment in this series compared fresh and oxidized cottonseed oil during a 20-week feeding study. The oxidized oil caused some growth inhibition, starting at about the fifth week, among the males, but not among the females. All the animals remained in a good state of health with no diarrhea. Histological examination of the livers suggested pre-cirrhotic changes because of the high level of fat in both diets. A fourth, similar experiment with corn oil showed no weight differences in either sex. Acute, but transient, alopecia appeared among some of the animals receiving the oxidized fat. It is specifically mentioned by these authors that they did not see the diarrhea, the unthrifty appearance, and the mortality reported by Johnson *et al.* (1956).

Lanteaume *et al.* (1966) conducted a 1-year rat feeding study to compare heated and unheated grape-seed oil. The unheated oil, containing 72% linoleic and 17% oleic acids, was fed as 4 or 15% of the diet. The heated oils were fed as 15% of the diet. These had been heated at 200°C, one lot for 2 days, another for 4 days. They were exposed to air during heating, with 500 cm² of exposed surface for 4 liters of oil. The diets used were semisynthetic, containing sugar, starch, casein, vitamins, and minerals. Sixteen male rats received each diet for 1 year, starting at 7 weeks of age. The heated fats were slightly less well absorbed than the unheated, and they gave slightly poorer growth. They also produced some alopecia. Extensive biochemical and histological examinations revealed no effects attributable to the heating of the fat. The heated fat produced no increase in mortality.

The same workers have also carried out a much more comprehensive study (Ramel *et al.*, 1967). Corn oil, peanut oil, hydrogenated palm oil (iodine value 14), and grape-seed oil were heated for 8 days at 200°C with exposure to air. This treatment was recognized as being extremely drastic; iodine values fell to 50-70% of their original values, free fatty acids rose to 0.7-1.27%, and the level of oxidized fatty acids rose to 8-23%. The heated fats were very dark and viscous. For the feeding study these fats were added at the 15% level to a commercial ration, which already contained 5% fat. The diets were fed to rats for 1 year, starting from the time of weaning. Animals receiving the heated fats showed poorer growth and poorer fat absorption than animals receiving the unheated fats, and, in most cases, they had heavier livers. Other irregularities occurred in all groups except the control group, which received the commercial ration without added fat. These irregularities were attributed, not to the heating, but rather to the "richness" of the diet, a term which presumably implies an excessive energy-protein ratio. The rats were bred when they were 9 months old. Reproduction and lactation proceeded normally for all groups, and the pups were placed on their respective diets at weaning so that a multigeneration study could be carried out. This study is still in progress.

The latest communication from the same laboratory (Lanteaume *et al.*, 1968) describes an experiment with dogs, the only such experiment thus far reported. Dogs were fed diets containing 10% of grape-seed oil, either fresh or heated as described in the second paragraph above. Oil that had been heated for 2 days was fed for the first 3 months, then for the next 4 months the dogs were given oil that had been heated for 4 days. Part of the dogs started the experiment at weaning; the others were already 3 months old. For the two groups of dogs, those receiving fresh and those receiving oxidized fat, there were no appreciable differences in weight gain, general state of health, serum lipids, serum protein, serum cholesterol, serum fatty acids, or in histological findings. The only difference observed between the two groups was a hypercoagulability of the blood of the animals receiving the heated fat. The thromboelastographic technique of Harter which was used also showed the coagulability to be markedly influenced by the age of the animals, regardless of the dietary fat.

V. Commercial Processing Conditions

A few workers have wondered whether the thermal and oxidative treatments incidental to the commercial processing of fats and oils — refining, bleaching, and deodorization — adversely affect the nutritional properties of the fats. There are reports of oxidation and degradation during refining (Becker and Niederstebruch, 1966; Wode, 1957) and during bleaching (Dangoumau and Debruyne, 1957a,b; Guillaumin, 1967; Guillaumin and Pertuisot, 1968), but biological tests have, for the most part, failed to show any nutritionally harmful results from those processes.

Dangoumau *et al.* (1957) included in their rat feeding study a comparison of commercially processed peanut oil with oil obtained by careful extraction of peanuts in the laboratory without heating. There was no difference in the biological response to the two oils. Pokorny and Kakac (1959) found that the nutritional values of soybean, peanut, and palm oils, and of lard did not change during the usual refining processes.

Wilding *et al.* (1963) reported that chemical and physical tests showed no undesirable changes during refining, bleaching, and deodorization of soybean and cottonseed oils, and that oils deodorized at 238°C had the same nutritional value as oils deodorized at 160°C. Lea *et al.* (1964) saw no difference in the growth-promoting properties of deodorized and undeodorized beef fat. Lang *et al.* (1966) found that palm oil, which had been heated 5 hours at 220°C to aid in its bleaching, gave no evidence of being injurious to rats in long-term and generation studies.

The only contrary report is by Raulin *et al.* (1959, 1960), who found that herring oil deodorized for 8 hours at 180°-200°C gave poorer growth and was less absorbable than the unheated oil. They also saw an infiltrating myocarditis without vascular injuries. Both the physiological effects and the heating conditions suggest that a substantial degree of polymerization or cyclization may have taken place in this oil during the prolonged deodorization, which, because of its duration and of the highly unsaturated nature of the stock being treated, would not be considered within the range of normal practice in the United States.

VI.   Frying

A. Chemical and Physical Changes during Frying

1. *Frying Conditions*

An understanding of the changes which take place in a fat during frying and a realistic assessment of the possible nutritional hazards associated with these changes requires that we review the conditions actually used for frying. Frying operations fall into two distinct types, namely, pan or griddle frying, and deep fat frying. The latter, which has received much more attention than the former, can be further divided into continuous operations, as in the manufacture of potato chips, and intermittent frying, as in many restaurants or in the home.

In pan frying or griddling operations, there is a high ratio of food to fat, and a very high surface–volume ratio, with, consequently, a large exposure of the fat to air. Temperatures are variable, depending partly on the skill and attention of the cook. For instance, it is recommended that pancakes be cooked at 200°C, but temperatures as high as 230°C may sometimes be attained in practice. Miyakawa (1964) reports that most frying in Japan is carried out at 150°–200°C, except that rice cakes are cooked at 250°C. Although fats used for pan frying undergo extensive deterioration in a short time (Ota *et al.*, 1966), they have received very little attention in the literature, probably because the quantities used in any one frying operation are so small that it would be very time consuming to obtain enough of the used oil for extensive studies. Because the quantity of oil used is small, little is available to be absorbed into the food. Moreover, the frying is accomplished quickly, repeated reuse of the oil is not dictated by economic considerations, and there is no opportunity for degradation products to build up over a long period of time. For these reasons, there has been little concern over the nutritional properties of the fat absorbed into foods during pan frying.

In contrast, a great deal of concern has been expressed over deep fat frying, because here the fat is kept hot for long periods of time, it is used over and over again, and substantial quantities are absorbed into the foodstuff. It is precisely this removal of fat from the frying kettle as part of the fried food that helps maintain the quality of fats used in large-volume continuous frying operations. For instance, it is variously reported that potatoes fried as 12 mm slices contain 7% fat in the finished product (Strock *et al.*, 1966), and that potatoes fried as 1 mm slices contain 30–40% fat (Montefredine, 1965). Watt and Merrill (1963) list the fat contents of typical fried foods as 13–14% for French fried potatoes, 40% for potato chips, and 19-27% for doughnuts. Because so much fat is removed along with the fried food, it is necessary to replenish the frying bath frequently with fresh fat. Through these processes of removal and replenishment, or fat turnover, the fat soon reaches a steady state condition and does not deteriorate further with continued service. Obviously the higher the frying load, the faster the turnover, and the higher the quality of the fat (Perkins and Van Akkeren, 1965; Gooding and Melnick, 1961; Lantz and Carlin, 1938; Robertson, 1966; Yuki, 1967d; Chahine *et al.*, 1967b). For satisfactory frying results, temperatures must be maintained within the range of 200°C or below (Montefredine, 1965). Examination of oils actually being used for the production of potato chips showed them to be only very slightly changed from the corresponding unheated oils (Melnick, 1957a,b; Melnick *et al.*, 1958).

More abusive conditions may be encountered in some restaurants, particularly those that have a relatively small volume of frying business and fail to exercise proper quality control. Here the fat is likely to be kept hot for long periods with only occasional use for frying, and, therefore, with relatively slow turnover of fat. Moreover, the fat may be allowed to cool down overnight so that it is repeatedly cycled through high and low temperatures. There are, of course, all degrees of abusive conditions encountered in actual practice, between the ideal, high-volume, continuous frying situation with careful quality control and the extreme case where no more attention is given to the maintenance of fat quality than is necessary for producing salable foods.

Because of the wide variations possible in the handling of fats, in either a food preparation establishment or in the laboratory, it is not surprising that the different investigators who have examined used frying fats have reported quite different findings. Nevertheless, the general pattern seems clear: There is some degradation of fat during frying, in greater or less degree depending on the conditions, but the extent of degradation is much less than that which has frequently been reported for fats heated under laboratory conditions. This is simply another way of saying that many of the laboratory preparations of heated or oxidized fats have been carried out under conditions incompatible with the preparation of acceptable fried foods.

2. Properties of Used Frying Fats

Fats used for frying show elevated acid values. Bates (1952) mentioned 1% free fatty acid as a typical figure. Custot (1959) reported 1.13%, Goodman and Block (1952) attained 0.74% during frying, and

Montefredine (1965), 0.6%. Only slight changes in free fatty acid level were reported, however, by Janicek *et al.* (1961), Melnick *et al.* (1958), Shil'man (1964), and Silvestre (1960). Any hydrolysis of fat to free fatty acid must be accompanied by liberation of a corresponding amount of mono- and diglycerides or glycerol, which would be measured as polar compounds or hydroxyl compounds.

Use of a fat in frying causes its iodine value to decrease; again the extent of change is variable. Montefredine (1965) reported changes of 1–4%, Becker and Rost (1964) about 10%, Custot (1959) about 20%. We found (Nolen *et al.*, 1967) changes of less than 10% in fats which had been used for intermittent frying until the end of their useful frying lives was attained. Melnick (1957a), Janicek *et al.* (1961), and Kumazawa (1963a) all considered the change of iodine value to be the most important measurement for judging the extent to which a fat had been degraded by frying.

Slight increases in peroxide value were found during frying by Custot (1959), Janicek *et al.* (1961), and Nolen *et al.* (1967), but Montefredine (1965) saw both increases and decreases in peroxide content. Since peroxides are unstable during frying, and since heated fats are quite susceptible to auto-oxidation (Carlin and Lannerud, 1941; Yuki, 1967c), the peroxides that were reported might have formed while the samples of fat which had been removed from the kettle were cooling and awaiting analysis. Rather than peroxides, the high-temperature oxidation process would be expected to form secondary oxidation products such as hydroxy compounds and other polar materials. These have been reported in used frying fats by Becker and Rost (1964), Ramel *et al.* (1965a), Nolen *et al.* (1967), and others. Interestingly, although Becker and Rost (1964) found hydroxyl values as high as 15–20 in linseed oil heated for 30 hours, they did not see increases in epoxide content.

Other changes that have been widely observed during frying are an increase in ultraviolet absorption in the neighborhood of 231 nm (Kumazawa, 1963a; Montefredine, 1965; Ramel *et al.*, 1965a; Rinetti and Giovetti, 1962; Silvestre, 1960), an increase in the refractive index (Carlin and Lannerud, 1941; Custot, 1959; Ramel *et al.*, 1965a), a decrease in the level of polyunsaturated acids (Fleischman *et al.*, 1963; Harvey, 1965; Kilgore and Luker, 1964; Kilgore, 1966; Ramel *et al.*, 1965a; Beare *et al.*, 1968), and darkening in the color of the fat (Bennion and Hanning, 1956b).

All of these changes are those one would expect on the basis of experiments in which fats were merely heated in air without frying. The significance of these many reports is the small degree to which the changes took place compared to the changes reported when fats are heated without frying. The reason these changes are small in a used frying fat, compared to fat heated under conditions reported by many laboratories, is that in frying the temperature must be kept moderate and the fat must be discarded after a time if good frying results are to be achieved. These limits do not apply when fats are heated in the laboratory.

One of the most important changes which takes place in a fat during frying, just as in other heating or oxidizing situations, is the formation of polymers. Little can be said about the absolute levels of polymers which exist in used frying fats since there is no analytical method generally recognized as truly measuring the amount of polymer in a heated fat. The methods which have been worked with are discussed in Section X. It has, however, been recognized that increases in polymer content seem to parallel increases in hydroxyl value (Becker and Rost, 1964), decreases in iodine value (Kotsubo and Ueyanagi, 1955), and increases in viscosity (Rock and Roth, 1966; Ramel *et al.*, 1965a). The correlation between viscosity and polymer content is not only a logical and understandable one but also is an important one, for viscosity can also be related to foaming tendency or the extent to which a fat forms a stable foam during frying. It is foaming which ultimately limits the life of a frying fat (Miyakawa, 1964; Nolen *et al.*, 1967). When the polymer content and viscosity increase up to some critical level, then the fat foams out of the kettle when food is introduced into it, and further frying in that lot of fat becomes impossible.

Miyakawa (1964) found a correlation between carbonyl value and foaming, with stable foams appearing in oils whose carbonyl values corresponded to a 9% content of oxypolymerized fatty acids. He concluded that carbonyl compounds were responsible for the foaming. However, Ota *et al.* (1964a,b) chromatographed foamy oils and found that the most polar fractions, which would be expected to contain hydroxyl groups, were the ones most able to produce foaminess when added to fresh oils. Moreover, they found that the foaming tendency was increased when carbonyl compounds were reduced to hydroxyl compounds by borohydride. For any one oil it is possible to correlate the foaming tendency, the viscosity, and the content of oxidized material, but these measurements do not necessarily correlate between different oils. Foaminess does not correlate with surface tension (Ota, 1964). Several simple methods for measuring the foaming tendency have been published (Miyakawa, 1964; Ota *et al.*, 1964a; Kajimoto, 1964; Becker and Rost, 1964).

Used oils, which show increased viscosity and increased foaming tendency, give poorer quality in the foods fried in them, the poorer quality being mainly manifested as off-flavors, irregular browning, poor appearance, and higher fat content (Ota and Izuyama, 1964; Becker and Rost, 1964; Bates, 1952; Carlin *et al.*, 1954; Miyakawa, 1964; Kajimoto, 1964; Jacobson, 1967; Hall *et al.*, 1962; Goodman and Block, 1952; Stern and Roth, 1959). These observations suggest the existence of a natural mechanism to protect the consumer from exposure to badly abused fats, since badly abused fats, whose high viscosities make them poor heat transfer media, are incapable of producing fried goods of acceptable quality. In extreme cases, used frying fats foam so badly that it becomes impossible to fry in them. In addition, elevated levels of free fatty acid in a fat lower its smoke point, making it unsuitable for frying. The absorption of fat into the foodstuff being fried increases with increasing viscosity. This effect leads to still another protective mechanism, since, for any given rate of frying usage, the rate of fat turnover will increase as the fat grows more viscous.

3. *Effects of Frying Conditions on Fat Properties*

As might be expected, the deterioration of frying fat is strongly influenced by temperature, and by the degree and duration of exposure to oxygen (Yuki, 1967d; Kilgore, 1966; Becker and Rost, 1964; Rock and Roth, 1964a). Kumazawa (1961) found that frying for 3 hours at 200°C produced as much deterioration as frying for 5 hours at 170°C, according to measurements of color, viscosity, refractive index, peroxide value, and conjugated diene formation. And, as mentioned above, alternate heating and cooling are more destructive than continuous heating for the same total number of hours at high temperature (Perkins and Van Akkeren, 1965).

LeClerc *et al.* (1966) found the degree of degradation to be more dependent on duration of heating than on the nature or unsaturation of the starting fat. The kind of fat being heated is of some importance, nevertheless. More highly unsaturated fats are more susceptible to breakdown than less highly unsaturated fats (Bito and Yamamoto, 1960; Becker and Rost, 1964; Janicek and Pokorny, 1961; LeClerc *et al.*, 1966; Ota *et al.*, 1964b). Thus Custot (1959) concluded that the French practice of frying in unhardened sardine oil was undesirable. The condition of the fat before its use for frying is also important, oils that have previously suffered auto-oxidation being more susceptible to deterioration than good quality oils (Mroczkowski and Ziombski, 1962).

The system used for heating can influence the deterioration of the fat, since intense local heating, as from a high-temperature heating element, not only exposes part of the fat to quite high temperature but also promotes agitation of the fat by convection currents. On the other hand, circulation of the hot fat through a heat exchanger avoids local overheating, but greatly increases the agitation, and hence the aeration, of the fat (Rock and Roth, 1964b). Agitation by circulation has been shown to be more thorough than the agitation which results from releasing water within the fat (Strock *et al.*, 1967). Whether the container used for heating the fat is of glass or iron is not important (Kilgore, 1966), but copper is definitely detrimental compared to iron, stainless steel, or aluminum (Ota and Yamamoto, 1964).

The presence of water in a fat while it is being heated increases the extent of oxidation which it suffers. (Lobanov and Brents, 1962; Ota and Yamamoto, 1964; Porter *et al.*, 1932; Bito and Yamamoto, 1960; Dornseifer *et al.*, 1965; Perkins and Van Akkeren, 1965). The subject has been studied extensively by Yuki (1967a,b,c,d) who found that the changes promoted by the addition of water are mostly of a hydrolytic nature, rather than oxidative, although the ratio of oxidative to hydrolytic changes will vary depending on the temperature and the degree of exposure to air. Naturally if the oil is exposed to water but not to air, then hydrolysis will predominate. At higher temperatures, the effect of water is minimized, presumably because it boils away quickly, but the increase in carbonyl compounds is also minimized, because they too are volatile. The presence of surface-active agents accelerates hydrolysis (Yuki, 1967e).

It has often been suggested that the steam blanket produced over a fat by water volatilizing from the food being fried helps protect the fat from oxidation. Yuki (1967g) made an extensive study of the effects of steam blanketing. He found that a steam blanket produced by spraying water onto the fat provided protection against atmospheric oxidation only if the fat was contained within a hood which limited the displacement of the steam blanket by air. In an ordinary frying kettle, the steam blanketing effect is probably not a significant protective factor.

Overall, it appears that the kind and extent of changes which can be expected in the properties of a frying fat will represent a balance between many factors: degree of aeration produced by the agitation resulting from water volatilization, degree of protection afforded by steam blanketing over the fat, degree of hydrolysis (both of the fat itself and of its oxidation products) resulting from the amount and temperature of water addition, the surface to volume ratio of the fat, the temperature, and the extent of local overheating.

An interesting model system was developed by Krishnamurthy *et al.* (1965) to isolate volatiles formed during frying without having their results confounded by the presence of volatiles driven off from food-stuffs during frying. They simply fried wet cotton balls, and, in view of the balance of factors mentioned above, it seems likely that this model is perfectly reasonable, being an arbitrary choice in an area where any choice would be arbitrary.

Owing to the complex interactions of the factors already mentioned, it is not surprising that there are contradictory reports concerning the effects of food components on frying fats. Becker and Rost (1964) found potatoes to have no influence, but Lobanov and Brents (1962) found that potatoes and yeast dough tend to protect the fat in which they are being fried. Kilgore and Luker (1964) reported that the frying of potatoes decreased the linoleic acid level of the oil but frying chicken did not. According to Bito and Yamamoto (1960), foods rich in vitamin C protect the fat in which they are fried. Janicek and Pokorny (1961) and Janicek et al. (1961) reported that carrots, starchy foods, and casein all exert a protective effect. Kajimoto and Kamo (1964) also found a protective action from casein. Silvestre (1960) pointed out the protective action of tocopherols naturally present in vegetable oils, but he reminds us that they become used up in time.

An aspect of the interactions between foods and fats not to be over-looked is the one of possibly extracting lipids from the food being fried into the frying bath, and thereby altering the composition of the frying fat.

Bennion (1967) and Bennion and Park (1968) have studied the components in batter responsible for darkening in fats used for frying the batter. Many of the batter components — flour, sugar, salt, milk, and egg white — had little influence on the darkening of the fat, but egg yolk and baking powder, either alone or together, greatly enhanced both the darkening and the increase in free fatty acid levels. The effect of egg yolk was attributed to leaching of phospholipids from the batter into the fat during frying; the effect of the baking powder was attributed to its increasing the porosity and permeability of the batter. Although the fats used for frying the batters containing egg yolk and baking powder discolored and foamed, neither their viscosity nor their content of non-urea-adductable fatty acids was greater than the levels found for fats used to fry batters not containing those ingredients. Perhaps the extracted phospholipids were themselves responsible for the foaming of the fats, as well as for the color.

The addition of silicones, such as poly(dimethylsiloxane), to a frying fat at levels of a few parts per million is very effective in slowing down the oxidation of the fat (Martin, 1953; Kumazawa, 1963b; Nolen et al., 1967).

Although the addition of water to hot fat accelerates its deterioration, that is not necessarily the case when food is added to hot fat for frying. Several workers directly compared the deterioration resulting from frying with the deterioration resulting from keeping fat at frying temperature, unused, for the same period of time. Perkins and Van Akkeren (1965) found that frying produced more deterioration than heating alone, but less than heating and injecting water. On the other hand, Goodman and Block (1952), Ramel *et al.* (1965a), LeClerc *et al.* (1966), and Chahine *et al.* (1967b) found frying to be less destructive than simple heating.

4. *Surveys of Used Frying Fats*

Examinations of fats actually being used for frying in commercial practice have been carried out. Melnick (1957a) procured samples of oil from the kettles of 89 different potato chip manufacturers and found that they differed only very slightly from the respective unheated oils, having in most cases iodine value changes of less than 1% from the original values. Thompson *et al.* (1967) reported a limited survey of fats and oils which had been used for commercial deep fat frying. The eight samples which they analyzed in detail had all been used until they had either become ready for discard or had reached a steady state of deterioration. These samples represented a variety of fat types, from liquid oils to hydrogenated shortenings, and a variety of usage conditions, from continuous potato chip manufacture to intermittent restaurant usage. The used fats were compared analytically with the respective fresh fats, and, as might be expected, showed wide variations in the degree of change which they had undergone. Fat from a potato chip manufacturing operation was, in confirmation of Melnick's report, little changed, but some of the other fats had free fatty acid values as great as 8.5%, iodine value decreases as great as 6.2 units, and disappearances of linoleate as great as 12%. The viscosity of one fat increased from 9.13 to 10.86 centistokes.

A large-scale survey was made in 1964 by The Procter & Gamble Company (H. L. Lawson, unpublished). Sixty-nine samples of fat were obtained from restaurants and institutions in all parts of the United States. The samples represented many kinds of starting fat and were picked up when they were ready to be thrown away. The reasons for discarding were varied: some were being discarded on the restaurant's regular schedule of fat replacement, others because of color, foam, smoke, or odor, or because they were "broken down." For most, the level of free fatty acid fell in the range of 1–3% but a few went as high as 6–8%. Iodine value decreases could not be determined since

corresponding samples of fresh fat were not available. "Polar triglycerides" were measured by partition chromatography; most of the fats
showed values in the range of 5-20%, with several going into the
range 20-30% and two at 36%. With few exceptions, the fats with
higher levels of "polar triglyceride" showed extreme foaming during
use and had been discarded because of foaming or because they were
"broken down." Many of the samples were deteriorated in flavor, having either rancid or burnt-type flavor notes, or both. It is difficult to
summarize such varied results as these, but perusal of them makes it
clear that although some restaurants discard their fat on a regular
schedule before it is appreciably degraded a great many keep using
their fat until it ceases to perform satisfactorily. These results determined the method for preparing used frying fats for the 2-year feeding
study described in Section VI,B. (Nolen *et al.*, 1967). Those fats were
used for intermittent frying until they foamed excessively, thereby
simulating the most abusive conditions likely to be found in the food
industry.

5. *Components of Used Frying Fats*

Little attention has been given to the components that form in a fat
during frying and remain there. The analytical values mentioned
above make it obvious that the substances formed resemble, at least
grossly, those isolated from artificially heated fats, namely, free fatty
acids, carbonyl compounds, polymers, etc. Most workers probably
have been deterred from attempting to isolate such compounds from
used frying fats by the likelihood of encountering a multitude of other
substances derived from the foodstuffs.

The volatiles that form during frying have been studied in considerable detail, however. Bennion and Hanning (1956a) condensed the
vapors which evolved during frying and found them to contain acids,
aldehydes, and substances that react with thiobarbituric acid.

Wishner and Keeney (1965) fried potatoes in several kinds of fat.
They isolated the carbonyl compounds from the fats, separated them
into classes, and measured the levels of each member in the homolo-
gous series of 2-alkanones, alkanals, 2-alkenals, and 2,4-alkadienals.
In addition they collected the volatiles given off during the frying and
determined the carbonyl compounds contained in them. As might be
expected, the shorter-chained carbonyl compounds tended to concen-
trate in the distillate, and the longer chained ones to remain in the fat.
The compounds identified were much the same as those enumerated

in Section II,C as having been found in fats oxidized at moderate temperatures. The levels of monocarbonyl compounds found totaled from 73μmoles/kg of fat for hydrogenated vegetable fat, through 101 for lard, to 234 for corn oil.

The volatiles given off during simulated frying were studied by a group at Rutgers (Krishnamurthy, 1966; Kawada *et al.*, 1967; Krishnamurthy and Chang, 1967). For these experiments, wet cotton balls were fried in corn oil under conditions closely simulating those prevailing in actual frying conditions, including a moderate rate of fat turnover. The apparatus used permitted the volatiles formed to be condensed for analysis. Some 95 compounds were recognized in the distillate. The compounds were generally similar to those listed in Section II,C for oxidized oils. There were alkanoic and alkenoic acids, dibasic acids, keto and hydroxy acids, δ-lactones, paraffins and olefins, alkanols and alkenols, alkanals, alkenals, and alkadienals, and several saturated and unsaturated ketones. The list also includes some aromatic compounds: toluene, benzaldehyde, benzoic acid, phenol, 2-pentylfuran, propiophenone, 5-phenyl-3-pentanone, 6-phenyl-3-hexanone, 3-phenylpropionaldehyde, and 4-phenylbutyraldehyde. Although the residual oil was not examined, it seems likely that stripping of the volatiles from the oil was less than complete, and that many of these same compounds, or their higher homologs, may have been present in the oil, along with partial glycerides containing similar functional groups on one of their fatty acid chains. In later work from the same laboratory (Yasuda *et al.*, 1968; Reddy *et al.*, 1968; Thompson, 1968) the technique of simulating frying conditions was somewhat altered, and the investigation was extended to include synthetic trilinolein and cottonseed oil. The volatile products isolated were much the same as those found earlier for simulated frying in corn oil.

Many of the same carbonyl compounds reported in the condensed volatiles have been found also in potato chips. where they make contributions to the flavor of the chips (Dornseifer and Powers, 1963; Mookherjee *et al.*, 1965).

Kumazawa (1964) compared the carbonyl compounds present in a frying oil at times early and late in the frying life of the oil and found distinct changes which coincided with the point at which the oil began to show serious deterioration. As deterioration proceeded, the levels of unsaturated and of odd-carbon number carbonyl compounds increased more rapidly than did the levels of saturated carbonyls and of carbonyls containing even numbers of carbon atoms.

B. Biological Properties of Used Frying Fats

There is a striking contrast between the large number of papers that report feeding experiments with artificially heated or oxidized fats and the small number describing work with fats that have actually been used for frying. With a few exceptions, papers describing work with used frying fats are much less alarming than the ones dealing with artificially abused fats. This circumstance reiterates the point made above that the conditions required for frying are milder than the conditions used by many workers when they prepare heated fats in the laboratory.

Mameesh *et al.* (1965) kept cottonseed oil at 195°C for 8 hours daily during 25 days. It was allowed to cool overnight. Each day it was used for frying broad-bean cakes. Portions of the fat were removed at intervals and fed to rats as 10% of a diet otherwise composed of bread, milk, and salt. Unfried bean cakes were included in the diet fed to a control group. Rats receiving the heated fat showed growth impairment compared to controls receiving fresh fat. The poorer growth was associated with lower feed intake and lower fat absorbability. Consumption of the heated fats caused lower levels of fat in the livers but no change in liver size. No mention was made in the paper of any attempt to protect the compounded rations from oxidative rancidity, or of the analytical properties of the used fat.

A later report from the same laboratory (Mameesh *et al.*, 1967) describes autopsy results on rats that had received the used fat. After 8 weeks, animals that had received the fat heated for the longest time (204 hours of heating) showed hyperplastic lymphoid tissue under the serosa and scattered over the small intestine, as well as microscopically visible changes in the nuclei of liver cells. Fat heated for 68 hours produced similar changes but only after 17 weeks of feeding. The authors contrasted the relatively mild changes which they saw with the severe changes reported by previous authors who fed artificially abused fats. They emphasized that the heating regimen that they employed was designed to induce the maximum toxic effects by keeping the frying time to a minimum in relation to the total heating time. They concluded that even a minimum amount of frying largely, although not completely, suppresses the formation of the toxic substances which appear when cottonseed oil is heated without frying.

Kajimoto and Mukai (1964) reported a correlation between the amount of foam formed during frying and the extent of degradation of the frying fat. They further found (Kajimoto *et al.*, 1964) that the used frying fats showing the most severe foaming decreased the rate of growth when fed to weanling rats as 10% of the diet.

Utyumova-Malova and Vershinin (1966) examined oil that had been used for frying fish. Clinical and morphological studies established that mice fed oil with an acid value of less than 4 did not show any adverse effects, whereas oil with an acid value greater than 6 produced changes in appearance, ruffled hair, poor appetite, and liver enlargement.

Kaunitz *et al.* (1956a) fed rats with the distillate obtained by molecular distillation at 280°C of fat that had been used for frying for 80 hours at 190°C. They observed only slight decreases in net dietary energy and growth rate.

Hashimoto *et al.* (1958) compared raw soybean oil with oil used in sautéing or roux preparation of vegetables. No differences in the utilizations of the two fats were apparent.

Thirty-four samples of commercially used fats were obtained from bakeries, restaurants, and manufacturers of potato chips by Poling *et al.* (1960, 1962). The fats were evaluated in a 7-day feeding test with rats. They showed little or no loss in available biological value and caused little or no liver enlargement. These results were in marked contrast to results obtained with fats that had been heated in the laboratory without frying. Lipids extracted from well-done cuts of meat showed no change in available energy as a result of the heating they had received (Warner *et al.*, 1962).

Cottonseed oil used for frying potato chips in the laboratory was fed to rats as 20% of the diet (Rice *et al.*, 1960). Decreased feed intake, decreased growth, and increased liver size were observed only with those fat samples that had been heated for so long that they foamed violently when used for frying.

Nutt (1966) compared three samples of a partially hydrogenated soybean oil. One was the fresh oil, the second had been heated 48 hours at 200°C, and the third had been used for 39 days in a cafeteria frying kettle. Both of the heated fats showed some decrease in their levels of unsaturated fatty acids with corresponding increases in the levels of saturates. When the fats were fed to rats for 6 weeks, the differing fatty acid compositions of the fats were reflected to some extent in the compositions of the rat body lipids, but no growth depression or other manifestation of toxicity was observed.

Deuel *et al.* (1951) saw no adverse effects in either male or female rats over 10-week feeding periods during which their diets contained margarine fat that had been heated for 8 hours at 205°C or had been used for deep fat frying.

Fats that had been used for up to 24 days in commercial frying operations were investigated by Keane *et al.* (1959). These fats were fed to rats as 18% of the diets for 7 weeks. In this experiment, the used fats had higher caloric efficiencies than the fresh fats and gave better growth with no evidence of toxicity.

Several long-term feeding experiments with heated fats have been carried out by Groupe de Recherches du Laboratoire Central des Subsistances in Paris. In the first of these (Ramel et al., 1965b) grape-seed oil was used for frying 10 batches of potatoes at 180°C. The fats were refrigerated between each frying. Analyses showed moderately severe degradation of the oil. The used oil, along with an unheated control, was fed for 16 months to male Wistar rats as 15% of the diet, starting when the rats were 7 weeks old. Growth curves of the two groups were entirely superimposable, and no biochemical or histological changes were noted which could have been attributed to the heating of the fat.

Subsequent work from the same laboratory has been done, for the most part, with artifically heated fats, and has already been discussed in Section IV,C. There it was mentioned that Lanteaume et al. (1966) had fed heated fats to rats for 1 year as 15% of a semisynthetic diet and that slightly decreased utilization of the fat was the only adverse symptom observed. That feeding trial was accompanied by another, in which the fat was grape-seed oil that had been used for frying 60 batches of potatoes, without any addition of fresh oil during the course of the fryings, and with refrigeration of the oil between each group of five fryings. Utilization of this fat was intermediate between the utilizations of the fresh and the artificially heated fats. Results of all the other biochemical examinations carried out were indistinguishable from those produced by the unheated oil.

In our own laboratories we have attempted to assess as realistically as possible the practical hazards of consuming used frying fats. Five fats were used for frying potatoes, onions, and fish at 182°C on an intermittent frying schedule. This schedule provided for keeping the fat hot during long periods without frying in it and for cooling it overnight; these conditions correspond to the most abusive commercial frying operations. Frying was continued in four of the fats until foaming became so severe that further frying would have been impractical and unsafe; this point was reached after 49-116 hours of heating. The fifth fat, which contained methyl silicone, never foamed that badly, so frying in it was discontinued after 216 hours total heating time. Each of these fats, along with unheated controls, was fed to 100 rats as 15% of the diet for 2 years from the time of weaning. The heated fats gave slightly poorer growth and feed efficiency than the controls, owing to their content of nonabsorbable polymers as measured by fat balance studies. They did not cause any increase in mortality, any irregularities detectable by extensive biochemical and histological examinations, or any increase in tumor incidence. These used fats contained low levels of distillable, non-urea-adductable materials which were toxic when separated, concentrated, and administered at exaggerated levels in a bioassay with weanling rats. However, the absence of adverse effects in the 2-year study indicated that such substances offer no hazards in a chronic feeding situation analogous to human consumption of used frying fats (Nolen *et al.*, 1967).

VII. Carcinogenicity Studies

Off and on for many years there has been speculation that heated fats might be carcinogenic. There has been just enough evidence in support of the speculation to keep it alive despite many exculpatory reports. Moreover, it is generally recognized that most organic substances form polycyclic hydrocarbons under pyrolysis conditions, but it is often overlooked that such pyrolyses require temperatures at least 100° above normal cooking temperatures.

The evidences of carcinogenicity have been seen only by those workers who deliberately sought to form carcinogens from fats by extreme heating conditions. Other investigators, who have worked with used frying fats or with fats that had suffered moderately exaggerated abuse, have looked deliberately but unsuccessfully for evidence of carcinogenicity.

The classical reports on this subject were issued by Roffo (1939a,b, 1942, 1944), who found tumors in rats to which he fed strongly heated fats. He attributed the tumors to oxidized cholesterol in the fats. Roffo's work has not been substantiated by later investigators and is no longer taken seriously. Peacock and Kirby (1944) fed heated cholesterol to rats for 2 years without producing tumors. Morris *et al.* (1943), although specifically looking for carcinogenic activity, were unable to produce gastric or hepatic tumors by feeding rats for 27 months with a diet containing 50% of a lard that had been heated to 350°C. Grossman (1950) found no tumors in rats from Roffo's strain that were kept through seven generations on diets containing fats that had been heated to 350°C. Ivy (1955) also did not produce tumors by feeding similarly heated fat for several months. Both Grossman and Ivy did, however, detect weak carcinogenic activity when their fats were painted on mouse skin. It must be emphasized that their fats were heated more than 150°C above the temperatures normally used for frying, and therefore underwent chemical reactions not seen in culinary fats (Morris, 1947).

Lane *et al.* (1950) fed rats of the Roffo strain for 18-24 months with lard that had been "browned" by heating 30 minutes at 350°C. They saw in animals consuming the heated fat a 37% incidence of gastric lesions, either papillomas of the forestomach and hyperplasia of the limiting ridge, or ulceration and petechial hemorrhage in the glandular stomach, or both. They emphasized, however, that they saw no gastric cancer in their animals, and they concluded that the heated lard did not contain a carcinogen capable of causing cancer of the glandular stomach when fed to these rats. A small but significant number of malignant tumors was produced by subcutaneous injection of pyrolyzed (350°C for 30 minutes) fats, but none by fats that had been repeatedly used for frying.

The older literature on carcinogenesis was reviewed by Peacock (1946). He realized that there was no evidence to support the concept that fats that have been heated at temperatures below 300°C might be carcinogenic. He felt that heating above 300°C might produce carcinogenicity. Peacock (1948) found that cholesterol that had been heated to 300°C, or cottonseed oil that had been heated to 350°-400°C caused sarcomas at the site of injection in mice. The heated oil produced tumors in the stomachs of 2 out of 300 mice maintained on it for 15 months.

Later Peacock and Beck (1951) kept mice on a balanced diet supplemented with 1% of heated cottonseed oil. To ensure contact between the heated fat and the mucous membrane of the stomach, the fat was dissolved in 10% aqueous ether soap solution (not further defined). Mice kept on this regimen showed more tumors, of a variety of types, than did animals receiving no supplement or those receiving the heated cottonseed oil dissolved in alcohol. Although the paper catalogs the tumors in detail, it gives no information about the preparation or properties of the heated fat. In view of Peacock's other work, it is likely that the fat was heated to 300°C or above.

In a continuation of this work, Chalmers (1954) found that cottonseed oil heated 4 hours at 350°C produced fewer tumors than did cottonseed oil which had been heated 2.5 hours at 320°C in the presence of iron filings. He interpreted his results to mean that a weak carcinogen was present in the latter sample, which, incidentally, contained 35% unsaponifiable material. Neither of these heated fats produced tumors upon injection. Chalmers looked for, but did not find, evidence of carcinogenicity in used frying fats; he conceded that the chemical changes which had taken place in the fats during frying were very slight.

Arffmann (1964) and Arffmann and Glavind (1967) tested heated and oxidized fats as possible carcinogens in newts. Positive results of varying degree were obtained with peroxidized soybean oil and with the peroxides of ethyl oleate, linoleate, and linolenate. The activities were considered weak in view of the high peroxide values (750-1500) and the extreme sensitivity of the test animals. Reduction of the peroxides by heating or by chemical reactions diminished the activity only slightly. Epoxidized soybean oil produced no reaction, although all the isomers of diepoxybutane gave positive results. Heating of cholesterol at 350°C for 1 hour gave a newt-positive product, while cholesterol heated for 1 hour at 200° was negative. Commercially polymerized soybean oil, as well as soybean oil that had been heated for 1 hour at 350°C, had no effect on the skin of newts. Glavind and Arffmann (1968) offered results supporting the hypothesis that the presence of conjugated double bonds in a lipid brings about newt-positive properties.

Van Duuren and Goldschmidt (1966) generalized that, of epoxides, only the water-soluble ones can be carcinogenic, and that most of the known carcinogenic epoxides are polyfunctional. Van Duuren *et al.* (1966, 1967a,b) established by mouse and rat painting and injection experiments that epoxystearic acid was not carcinogenic under their test conditions.

Highly oxidized sesame oil appeared weakly carcinogenic when injected into mice, according to a report by Bischoff (1957). He also indicted unoxidized sesame oil as cocarcinogenic in the sense that when solutions of known carcinogens in oil were injected beneath the skin of mice the incidence of fibrosarcomas developing in association with the resulting oleoma was higher than the incidence of tumors produced by injecting the same substance in aqueous suspension. Certain oxidation products of cholesterol were shown to be carcinogenic when injected in an oil medium, and it was implied that such substances might be produced by oxidation *in vivo* of cholesterol.

Sugai *et al.* (1962) ran several experiments in which they fed a known carcinogen, acetylaminofluorene, along with fresh fat, artificially heated fat, used frying fat, the non-urea-adductable fraction of oxidized fat, or the non-lipase-digestible fraction of oxidized fat. The latter two materials were fed in admixture with fresh fat. The incidence of tumors was higher among animals receiving any of the heated fat materials than among animals receiving the fresh fat. It was concluded that the oxidized and heated fats contained substances cocarcinogenic with acetylaminofluorene. The mechanisms postulated for this activity involved the presence of oxidatively unstable materials in the heated fats, and it was observed that the diets that contained the heated fats were indeed readily susceptible to rancidity. Despite this, there is no statement in the paper to indicate that precautions were taken in diet handling to ensure that the level of dietary rancidity was no greater than would have been organoleptically acceptable in a human diet. There was no evidence that the heated fats themselves were carcinogenic.

During many of the feeding studies cited elsewhere in this review, the investigators looked for evidence that heated or oxidized fats might be carcinogenic, but no such evidence was found. From all the information available, it can be concluded that used frying fats do not represent a source of dietary carcinogens.

VIII. Metabolic Effects of Heated and Oxidized Fats

Most of the biological effects of abused fats, as recited in the preceding sections, have been of a rather nonspecific nature. Typically the animals receiving badly abused fats showed effects which might include appetite and growth depression, diarrhea, alopecia, premature involution of the thymus, general morbidity, and death. Most of these symptoms seem to reflect a generalized response to stress conditions. More specific effects have been occasionally reported. For instance, Kieckebusch et al. (1962) cataloged the effects produced by feeding rats with polyunsaturated oils that had been blown with air for several hours at 180°C. Among the observations listed were a decrease in the efficiency of protein utilization, disturbance of the liver function, increased response of the central nervous system to stimuli, increased spontaneous moving about of the animals, alterations in kidney function, increased capillary permeability, changes in motor and secretory functions of the intestinal tract, histologically demonstrable changes in the thyroid gland, and deposits in the kidneys. Many workers have reported enlargement of the liver and other organs in rats receiving artificially abused fats. But none of these observations tell much about the mechanisms through which the components of abused fats affect the metabolic process, and few experiments have been designed for this purpose.

Nonabsorbability of heated or oxidized fats is one of the most obvious places to look for evidence of metabolic interference; many reports have cited evidence that abused fats are poorly absorbed and utilized. The nonabsorbable polymers present in these fats probably interfere with the absorption of the unaltered components of the fat and may also interfere with the absorption of other nutrients.

Rinetti and Giovetti (1963) reported that corn oil that had been heated in air was less susceptible to hydrolysis of pancreatic lipase *in vitro* than was unheated oil. In contrast to that finding, Degkwitz and Lang (1963) found that purified preparations of pancreatic lipase or liver esterase effected hydrolysis of epoxidized, hydroxylated, irradiated, or thermally oxidized soybean oil nearly as well as they hydrolyzed fresh soybean oil. These results do not account for the decreased absorbability of oxidized oils. Sasaki *et al.* (1951) had earlier found that oil of plaice was less susceptible to digestion by pancreatin after thermal oxidation than before oxidation; the degree of digestibility was related to the degree of aeration to which the oil had been subjected.

McKay *et al.* (1967) showed that at least certain fractions of oxidized fat can be absorbed into the lymph from the intestine. Freeman and O'Brien (1967) fed and also injected linoleic acid hydroperoxide labeled with carbon-14. In each case the labeled material was metabolized by the animals, and was found partly as free fatty acids and partly as oxidized scission products or polymer but not as peroxide. It was concluded that the peroxide was not reconverted to unoxidized fatty acid *in vivo* but rather was converted to intermediates which could be metabolized by mechanisms similar to those involved in the metabolism of ordinary fatty acids. Bhalerao *et al.* (1963) found that thermally oxidized fats are absorbed into the lymph of lymph-cannulated rats, but the extent of absorption was about 10% less than for fresh fats. Differences in absorption between fresh and oxidized fats were greater for highly unsaturated fats, such as corn and olive oils, than for butter fat and coconut oil. Hydroxylated fats, including ricinoleic acid and triricinolein, were absorbed more slowly than corn oil, and yielded, in the lymph, a lower proportion of triglycerides and a higher proportion of partial glycerides and free fatty acids than corn oil did (Risser *et al.*, 1966).

A very illuminating report was recently published by Shue *et al.* (1968) on the acute physiological effects of feeding rats the non-urea-adductable fraction from fatty acids that had been strongly heated during commercial distillation. The material used was concentrated by urea treatment of the still-pot residue, and, although it was not completely described in the publication, it may have contained substantial levels of cyclized fatty acids. It was lethal when stomach-tubed into rats at sufficiently high levels. The LD_{50} values were approximately 0.6 ml of urea filtrate material per 100 gm of rat body weight, administered in two doses 24 hours apart. The symptoms observed included a rapid reduction in body temperature and the accumulation of fat in the livers. Toxicity could be minimized by simultaneous administration of other foods, such as milk, or aggravated by the simultaneous administration of fat. These observations suggested that the urea filtrate material was inhibiting normal fat catabolism. Additional work confirmed this theory. When the dose of urea filtrate acids was followed by intraperitoneal injection of radio-labeled palmitic acid, excretion of radioactivity was slower than in control animals. But when the radioactivity was administered as glucose, excretion of radioactivity was faster than in control animals. Thus the urea filtrate material seemed to interfere with the normal processes for obtaining energy from fats, and caused the animals receiving it to use carbohydrate as an energy source instead, while fat merely accumulated in the body. This mechanism seems consistent with most of the other observations about the physiological effects of feeding heated fat fractions. Obviously the interference with normal fat metabolism is neither complete nor irreversible; otherwise animals could not become adapted to sublethal levels of fat oxidation products nor survive through their normal lifetimes on high levels of used frying fats.

Glavind and Tryding (1960) reported that the toxic effects of lipid hydroperoxides were manifested at the intestinal wall. Dakhil and Vogt(1961) found that fatty acid hydroperoxides cause contraction of the isolated intestine of the guinea pig; this phenomenon might be related to the diminished absorbability of oxidized fats.

Parteshko (1966) found that rats receiving the dimer fraction of auto-oxidized sunflower seed oil had higher liver cholesterol values and lower liver phospholipid levels than rats receiving either fresh sunflower seed oil or auto-oxidized sunflower seed oil of high peroxide value. Kritchevsky *et al.* (1962a) found that a ration containing cholesterol dissolved in corn oil by heating was more atherogenic to rabbits than a ration in which the cholesterol had merely been suspended in the oil without heating. The difference was attributed to an enhanced absorbability of cholesterol from a medium containing low levels of free fatty acid.

Thus it is apparent that there is little agreement among literature reports concerning which components of a heated or oxidized fat are absorbed, or to what extent. The further actions of oxidized fatty materials after absorption are equally unclear, although gross effects of one kind or another have been observed. Cytochrome oxidase activity is reduced in the liver and heart of rats consuming herring oil polymerized in air but not in those consuming herring oil polymerized under carbon dioxide (Raulin and Terroine, 1962). Liver injury and impairment of liver function have been reported in rats fed secondary oxidation products or dimers of fatty acids but not in those fed oxidized fish oil containing high levels of peroxide and low levels of secondary breakdown products (Czok, 1965).

Kokatnur *et al.* (1966b) found that hemin was decomposed by fatty acid peroxides, while Burlakova *et al.* (1962) and Kudryashov *et al.* (1961) found that oxidized fatty materials exert a destructive action on erythrocytes. McKay *et al.* (1964) reported that an oxidized lipid diet caused blockage of the reticuloendothelial system in pregnant rats. Menzel (1967) studied the reactions of oxidizing lipids with ribonuclease.

Although it is known that the cyclized fatty acids which can be isolated from the distillable, non-urea-adductable fraction of heated fats are absorbed into the lymph (J. C. Alexander, this laboratory, unpublished), nothing is known about their subsequent metabolism. The synthetic route developed by Michael (1966c) offers an attractive way to prepare these cyclic materials labeled with either tritium or carbon-14; thus, the tools are available for further investigations in this area.

From all of the foregoing discussion it should be apparent that detailed knowledge of the mechanisms through which oral ingestion of oxidized fats sometimes causes toxic manifestations is lacking. To obtain the needed information it will be necessary to work with fully defined materials. Differentiation of primary from secondary effects will be required, as well as careful attention to the question of whether the results have meaning with relation to culinary practice and human nutrition.

IX. Interaction of Heated Fats with Other Dietary Components

It has been recognized for many years that incorporation of rancid fats into animal diets results in rapid destruction of vitamins and other dietary components (Quackenbush, 1945; Kennelly and Quackenbush, 1946; Grant, 1966; Clement, 1966). Heated or oxidized fats have been shown to be antagonistic to thiamine (Potteau *et al.*, 1967), to pyridoxine (Emerson and Gilfillan, 1960), to calcium pantothenate (Kummerow *et al.*, 1948), to riboflavin (Kaunitz *et al.*, 1952; Witting *et al.*, 1957), to tocopherol (Payne, 1959; Nishida *et al.*, 1960; Miller *et al.*, 1955; L'Estrange *et al.*, 1966), to vitamin A (Stoerck *et al.*, 1952; Reporter and Harris, 1961), and to protein, methionine, and lysine (Kaunitz, 1953; Carpenter *et al.*, 1963). Barnes (1946) reported that the growth depression caused by the inclusion of rancid lard in a purified diet could be relieved by adding yeast or other crude sources of B vitamins. Most of these reports describe the appearance, in animals receiving oxidized fats, of a variety of symptoms which can be relieved by supplementation with the specified nutrients. In some cases, evidence has been offered that the destruction of essential nutrients by the oxidized fats occurs *in vivo*. It also appears (Alexander, 1966) that serious impairment of nutritional quality can take place during the time that a prepared ration stands about in the laboratory before being consumed, provided that the diet contains a fat that has been rendered more than normally susceptible to autoxidation by having previously received thermal or oxidative abuse. Very few of the papers that report heated fats as being toxic mention that any particular precautions were taken to avoid destruction of essential nutrients in the diets. Alexander's experience indicates that ordinary good diet handling procedure is inadequate in work with abused fats.

The interaction of oxidized fats with proteins has received particular attention, and it is clear that many of the components present in oxidized lipids bind, probably by hydrogen bonds, to proteins or even to synthetic polyamides (Kuroda *et al.*, 1956a,b; Toyomizu, 1961; Narayan *et al.*, 1964; Andrews *et al.*, 1965; Pokorny *et al.*, 1966a,b,c, 1967a; Crawford *et al.*, 1967). These effects should have profound repercussions when oxidized fats are injected intravenously, but their significance in nutrition is not clear. It seems likely that the most serious consequence of this binding would be to decrease somewhat the availability of protein in a diet where the protein and the oxidized fat had been intimately mixed.

X. Analytical Methods

The analytical methods used for examining oxidized and heated fats have been touched on in many of the previous sections of this review, but the subject is important enough to warrant specific discussion. At present there is neither an ideal method for analyzing used fats to tell whether their consumption might be harmful, nor even a basis for developing such a method. What is needed is to recognize the components of heated and oxidized fats that are actually undesirable from a nutritional standpoint and to develop analytical methods for determining them. Then it might be possible to find the levels of those substances present in fats that have been exposed to various abusive conditions, and determine the levels that may safely be tolerated in the diet.

A goal more nearly within our reach would be to learn whether the levels of undesirable components in an abused fat can be correlated with results from some analytical method already in use. The method of choice would be a simple one that could be carried out rapidly by a cook so that he could easily determine when to discard a batch of fat. Although there is ample evidence that the "analytical methods" already available to the cook, namely, the appearance of excessive foam, smoke, color, and poor quality in fried foods, dictate discarding of fat when it still contains only insignificant levels of transformation products, the scientific community would doubtless be pleased to have more precise definitions and measurements.

Many tests do already exist, designed to measure either fat quality, however that may be defined, or the level of certain transformation products in the fat (Werner and Wurziger, 1966). These tests have been essential to the understanding of the chemistry of fat deterioration, and they have been used for the measurement of fat quality despite the lack of evidence indicating that the things they measure are actually relevant to the question of whether or not a fat is suitable for human consumption. We shall review these methods briefly.

The traditional method for measuring the degree of oxidation that a fat has undergone is the determination of peroxide number. Although improvements in this determination have recently been developed (Frankel *et al.*, 1961b; Said *et al.*, 1964; Niederstebruch and Hinsch, 1967), it is not particularly meaningful for heated fats because the peroxides decompose during heating. Alternatives, such as the active oxygen method or oxygen absorption measurements, tell what may happen to a fat during future exposure to oxygen rather than what has happened to it in the past (Arenson and Heyl, 1943; Pohle *et al.*, 1964a,b). In some cases, the results of such measurements correlate with other tests such as the thiobarbituric acid test (Pazlar *et al.*, 1966). The thiobarbituric acid test appears to be a valid measure of rancidity (Tarladgis *et al.*, 1964; Yu and Sinnhuber, 1964; Purr, 1964; Mihelic, 1963), but it depends for its color development on the presence of malonaldehyde, which is volatile at frying temperatures. Therefore it is not a valid measure of fat oxidation under all circumstances, and its use with heated fats has been questioned (Uezumi *et al.*, 1962). All of these methods are of doubtful value for estimating the freshness of a fat because changes in the analytical values become apparent only at about the same time as rancidity becomes obvious (Loury *et al.*, 1966). In fact, Hamm *et al.* (1968) found no correlation of milk fat off-flavors with peroxide or thiobarbituric acid values.

The hydroxyl value of a fat increases during oxidation, and its measurement has served as an index of deterioration (Becker and Rost, 1964). Applewhite (1965) provided a review of the methods available for the determination of hydroxy acids.

Numerous other methods for estimating oxidative deterioration have been proposed, based on such miscellaneous principles as the Tortelli-Jaffe reaction (Murase and Toyama, 1960a,b; Ono, 1960), ultraviolet absorption after treatment with alkali (Wurziger and Junker, 1963), the evolution of pentane (Scholz and Ptak, 1966), fluorescence in hexane solution (Nemets and Nesterova, 1962), or the absorption of bromine by conjugated double bonds (Pokorny, 1961).

Elegant methods for determining the carbonyl content of fats have been developed and are probably more nearly valid than peroxide values for estimating the quality and history of an oxidized fat (Kumazawa, 1965). By first converting the peroxides to carbonyl compounds, a single value can be obtained representing both kinds of oxidation products (Horikx, 1964). Carbonyl determinations almost always involve measurements of the 2,4-dinitrophenylhydrazones derived from the carbonyl compounds. The hydrazones can be measured colorimetrically in the whole oil (Henick *et al.*, 1954; Kumazawa and Oyama, 1965) or in distillates from the oil (Lea and Swoboda, 1962; Rothe *et al.*, 1967). The hydrazones can also be isolated from the fat by chromatography for fractionation into classes (Schwartz *et al.*, 1962a,b, 1963) or can be further examined by gas chromatography (Soukup *et al.*, 1964). When the carbonyl compounds are converted to hydrazones, any hydroperoxides which may be present decompose, yielding additional carbonyl compounds which also form hydrazones. Ways of avoiding this difficulty have been worked out (Fioriti, 1965; Mizuno and Chipault, 1965; Linow *et al.*, 1966).

Several methods are available for determining fatty epoxides, owing to their importance in polymer technology and to their occurrence in certain natural seed oils. Several recent papers have reviewed and compared these different methods (Morris *et al.*, 1961; Morris and Holman, 1961; Hassan and Lea, 1965; Suhara, 1965; Maerker, 1965; Maerker and Haeberer, 1966; Fioriti *et al.*, 1966a,b). None of the procedures appears to be altogether free from possible interferences by other constituents of oxidized fats.

Polymers are among the most conspicuous components of oxidized and heated fats, but direct and accurate measurement of their level is difficult. Indeed, no method is known that gives absolute results. For comparisons between fats it is useful to resort to other methods such as changes in hydroxyl value (Becker and Rost, 1964), iodine value (Kotsubo and Ueyanagi, 1955) or viscosity (Rock and Roth, 1964a); these give values seemingly parallel to polymer content. Partially polymerized fats can be converted to methyl esters, and the methyl esters can be distilled to give a crude separation of monomer, dimer, and polymer (Crampton *et al.*, 1953; Boelhouwer *et al.*, 1967; Michael *et al.*, 1966). Results obtained by this method can hardly be considered quantitative, particularly in view of the possibility that components of an oxidized fat may further polymerize during the distillation. Paper chromatography has been used for the determination of polymer content in thermally treated oils, but the method is not applicable to oxidatively treated fats (Rost, 1963). Partition chromatography and solvent distribution have been used for separating polymers from other fat components. Since these methods are based primarily on differences in polarity, rather than molecular weight, it is not certain that they separate all classes of monomer from all classes of polymer. Prevot (1965) recommended a gas chromatographic method for the determination of polymers in heated fat.

Adduction with urea removes unchanged fatty acids or methyl esters and has been made the basis for a determination of polymer content (Sahasrabudhe and Bhalerao, 1963). Unfortunately, the highly unsaturated fatty acids are only partially removed with a single urea treatment. Moreover, the nonadductable fraction contains cyclic and branched materials as well as polymers.

There are many methods for measuring the total content in a fat of the materials loosely classed together as "oxidized fatty acids" or "polar fraction." Some of these depend on the insolubility of the polar materials in petroleum ether (Rzhekhin and Pogonkina, 1958), or on lowering of the aniline point (Wurziger and Lindemann, 1959), or on differential solubility (Fugger *et al.*, 1951a). More recently, the trend has been toward chromatographic methods, using either adsorption chromatography (Pokorny and Zwain, 1967; Pokorny and Hladik, 1968) or thin-layer chromatography (Steibert and Sliwiok, 1966; Seher, 1967). The methods that have received the most attention, however, are those involving reversed phase partition chromatography (Desnuelle and Burnet, 1956; Burnet and Desnuelle, 1956, 1958; Naudet *et al.*, 1960a,b; Naudet, 1964; Frankel *et al*, 1961b,c).

Since the cyclic compounds formed at low levels during the heating of a fat are among the few components for which reasonably convincing evidence of actual toxicity has been obtained, it would seem most desirable to have a dependable method for their determination. Although the several varieties of cyclic compounds — saturated, unsaturated, aromatic, and oxidized — can be separated from each other and from branched-chain materials by column and gas chromatography (Wieske and Rinke, 1967; Perkins, 1967; Artman and Alexander, 1968), the separation of the whole complex of cyclic and branched compounds from noncyclized fatty acids has always depended on urea adduction. Urea adduction as normally carried out, that is, in a batchwise process, has not been suitable for use as an analytical method since it is neither specific nor complete in the separations it permits. A breakthrough appears to have been made, however, by Sagredos (1967). He resorted to the simple measure of packing urea into a chromatographic column and letting a mixture of fatty esters trickle through it. The cyclic esters came through the column quantitatively, while the straight-chained ones, even the unsaturated ones, were retained almost completely on the column. A similar method has been devised by Coles (1968). This procedure offers much promise as an analytical tool and also as a method for purifying the nonadductable esters before they are separated from each other for further characterization.

XI. Summary

When fats are heated in air, they are partially transformed into volatile chain-scission products, to nonvolatile oxidized derivatives, to cyclic substances, and to dimers and polymers. The dimers and polymers consist of both oxidized and nonoxidized species. The nature and extent of these changes depend very much on the kind of fat and the way it is heated. The changes can be followed by a variety of analytical methods, which have been useful in furthering our understanding of the chemical changes taking place during thermal oxidation of fats.

If the heating or oxidation is severe, the fats lose part of their nutritive value, probably because they contain substantial levels of unabsorbable polymers. Further thermal or oxidative abuse may cause the fats to become toxic. Evidence on this point is subject to question, however, for many workers have failed to see evidences of toxicity in even severely heated or oxidized fats and attribute the toxicity reported by others to vitamin deficiencies caused by oxidative instability of rations containing previously oxidized fat.

If the heating is carried out under practical frying conditions, the extent of the changes is small and is limited by reactions which make the fat unsuitable for further frying service. At this point some of the components which are present at low levels in the fat can be shown to be toxic if they are administered to laboratory animals at levels much higher than the animals could receive by consuming the whole fat. Certain cyclic derivatives and the oxidized dimers are probably among the toxic compounds. The polymers, although their presence is obvious because of viscosity changes, are probably not toxic per se.

Despite the presence of low levels of these transformation products, there is ample evidence to show that used frying fats are harmless when consumed at realistic dietary levels, even over long periods of time.

ACKNOWLEDGMENTS

Thanks are expressed to Drs. P. H. Begemann, S. S. Chang, P. Kamel, and J. A. Thompson, who provided information before its appearance in print, to the members of The Procter & Gamble Company's Technical Information Service, who helped procure much of the literature needed for this review, and to Dr. F. H. Mattson, who offered many valuable suggestions during the preparation of the manuscript.

References

Akiya, T. (1961). *Eiyo To Shokuryo* **14**, 71.
Akiya, T. (1962). *Eiyo To Shokuryo* **15**, 226.
Akiya, T. (1965). *Yukagaku* **14**, 347.
Akiya, T., and Shimizu, T. (1965). *Yukagaku* **14**, 520.
Akiya, T., Ishii, S., Sakai, H., and Arai, K. (1962). *Eiyo To Shokuryo* **14**, 397.
Alexander, J. C. (1966). *Lipids* **1**, 254.
Alfin-Slater, R. B., Auerbach, S., and Aftergood, L. (1959). *J. Am. Oil Chemists' Soc.* **36**, 638.
Anderson, R. H., and Huntley, T. E. (1964). *J. Am. Oil Chemists' Soc.* **41**, 686.
Andrews, F., Bjorksten, J., Trenk, F. B., Henick, A. S., and Koch, R. B. (1965). *J. Am. Oil Chemists' Soc.* **42**, 779.
Andrews, J. S., Griffith, W. H., Mead, J. F., and Stein, R. A. (1960). *J. Nutr.* **70**, 199.
Applewhite, T. H. (1965). *J. Am. Oil Chemists' Soc.* **42**, 321.
Arenson, S. W., and Heyl, E. G. (1943). *Oil Soap* **20**, 149.
Arffmann, E. (1964). *Acta Pathol. Microbiol. Scand.* **61**, 161.
Arffmann, E., and Glavind, J. (1967). *Acta Pathol. Microbiol. Scand.* **70**, 185.
Artman, N. R., and Alexander, J. C. (1968). *J. Am. Oil Chemists' Soc.* **45**, 643.
Axt, J. (1959). *Nahrung* **3**, 18.
Banks, A., Fazakerley, S., Keay, J. N., and Smith, J. G. M. (1961). *J. Sci. Food Agr.* **12**, 724.
Banu, C., Nadelcu, C., Murgeanu, A. and Tudorie, A. (1967). *Tluszcze Jadalne* **11**, 57. (*Chem. Abstr.* **68**, 21024.)
Barnes, R. H. (1946). *Biol. Antioxidants, Trans. 1st Conf.* **1**, 49.
Barrett, C. B., and Henry, C. M. (1966). *Proc. Nutr. Soc.* **25**, 4.
Bates, R. W. (1952). *Food Eng.* **24**(12), 82.
Beal, R. E., Eisenhauer, R. A., and Griffin, E. L., Jr. (1964). *J. Am. Oil Chemists' Soc.* **41**, 683.
Beare, J. L., Kennedy, B. P. C., and Heroux, C. M. A. (1968). *J. Inst. Can. Technol. Aliment.* **1**, 48.
Becker, E., and Niederstebruch, A. (1966). *Fette, Seifen, Anstrichmittel* **68**, 182.
Becker, E., and Rost, H. E. (1964). *Fette, Seifen, Anstrichmittel* **66**, 123.
Becker, E., Mader, I., Rost, H. E., and Vogel, P. (1966). *Z. Ernaehrungswiss.* **7**, 98.
Begemann, P. H., Woestenburg, W. J., and Leer, S. (1968). *J. Agr. Food Chem.* **16**, 679.
Bennion, M. (1967). *Food Technol.* **21**, 1638.
Bennion, M., and Hanning, F. (1956a). *Food Technol.* **10**, 229.

Bennion, M., and Hanning, F. (1956b). *Food Technol.* **10**, 290.

Bennion, M., and Park, R. L. (1968). *J. Am. Dietetic Assoc.* **52**, 308.

Bhalerao, V. R., Inoue, M., and Kummerow, F. A. (1963). *J. Dairy Sci.* **46**, 176.

Binet, L., and Wellers, G. (1966). *Ann. Nutr. Aliment.* **20**, 25.

Bischoff, F. (1957). *J. Natl. Cancer Inst.* **19**, 977.

Bito, T., and Yamamoto, A. (1960). *Yukagaku* **9**, 41.

Boelhouwer, C., Knegtel, J. T., and Tels, M. (1967). *Fette, Seifen, Anstrichmittel* **6**, 432.

Bradley, T. F., and Johnston, W. B. (1941). *Ind. Eng. Chem.* **33**, 86.

Brill, W. F., and Barone, B. J. (1964). *J. Org. Chem.* **29**, 140.

Brill, W. F., and Indictor, N. (1964). *J. Org. Chem.* **29**, 710.

Brodnitz, M. H. (1967). *Dissertation Abstr.* **27**, 2738B.

Brodnitz, M. H. (1968). *J. Agr. Food Chem.* **16**, 994.

Brodnitz, M. H., Nawar, W. W., and Fagerson, I. S. (1968a). *Lipids* **3**, 59.

Brodnitz, M. H., Nawar, W. W., and Fagerson, I. S. (1968b). *Lipids* **3**, 65.

Bunyan, J., Green, J., Murrell, E. A., Diplock, A. T., and Cawthorne, M. A. (1968). *Brit. J. Nutr.* **22**, 97.

Burlakova, E. V., Goncharenko, E. N., and Kudryashov, Y. B. (1962). *Nauchn. Dokl. Vysshei Shkoly, Biol. Nauki* p. 94. (*Chem. Abstr.* **57**, 14109.)

Burnet, M., and Desnuelle, P. (1956). *Rev. Franc. Corps Gras* **3**, 325.

Burnet, M., and Desnuelle, P. (1958). *Rev. Franc. Corps Gras* **5**, 194.

Candea, D., and Manughevici, C. (1944). *Bull. Sci. Ecole Polytech. Timisoara* **11**, 292. (*Chem. Abstr.* **41**, 2592.)

Cannon, J. A., Zilch, K. T., Burket, S. C., and Dutton, H. J. (1952). *J. Am. Oil Chemists' Soc.* **29**, 447.

Capella, I. P., De Zotti, G., Arpino, A., Valentini, A. F., Ricca, G. S., and Jacini, G. (1961). *Chim. Ind. (Milan)* **43**, 1004. (*Chem. Abstr.* **56**, 8863.)

Carlin, G. T., and Lannerud, E. (1941). *Oil Soap* **18**, 60.

Carlin, G. T., Hopper, R. P., and Rockwood, B. N. (1954). *Food Technol.* **8**, 161.

Carpenter, K. J., Lea, C. H., and Parr, L. J. (1963). *Brit. J. Nutr.* **17**, 151.

Carpenter, K. J., L'Estrange, J. L., and Lea, C. H. (1966). *Proc. Nutr. Soc.* **25**, 25.

Chahine, M. H., Mameesh, M. S., and El-Hawwary, N. M. (1967a). *Grasas Aceites (Seville, Spain)* **18**, 14.

Chahine, M. H., Mameesh, M. S., and El-Hawwary, N. M. (1967b). *Grasas Aceites (Seville, Spain)* **18**, 149.

Chalmers, J. G. (1951). *Acta Unio Intern. Contra Cancrum* **7**, 595. (*Chem. Abstr.* **48**, 9557.)

Chalmers, J. G. (1954). *Biochem. J.* **56**, 487.

Chalvardjian, A., Morris, L. J., and Holman, R. T. (1962). *J. Nutr.* **76**, 52.

Champetier, G., and Petit, J. (1945). *Bull. Soc. Chim. France* **12**, 680.

Chang, S. S., and Kummerow, F. A. (1953a). *J. Am. Oil Chemists' Soc.* **30**, 251.

Chang, S. S., and Kummerow, F. A. (1953b). *J. Am. Oil Chemists' Soc.* **30**, 403.

Chang, S. S., and Kummerow, F. A. (1954). *J. Am. Oil Chemists' Soc.* **31**, 324.

Chang, S. S., Smouse, T. II., Krishnamurthy, R. G., Mookherjee, B. D., and Reddy, R. B. (1966). *Chem. Ind. (London)* p. 1926.

Chang, S. S., Krishnamurthy, R. G., and Reddy, B. R. (1967). *J. Am. Oil Chemists' Soc.* **44**, 159.

Clement, G. H. (1966). *Proc. Nutr. Soc.* **25**, 31.

Clingman, A. L., Rivett, D. E. A., and Sutton, D. A. (1954). *J. Chem. Soc.* p. 1088.

Cobb, W. Y., and Day, E. A. (1965a). *J. Am. Oil Chemists' Soc.* **42**, 420.

Cobb, W. Y., and Day, E. A. (1965b). *J. Am. Oil Chemists' Soc.* **42**, 1110.

Cobern, D., Hobbs, J. S., Lucas, R. A., and Mackenzie, D. J. (1966). *J. Chem. Soc.* C, 1897.

Coles, L. (1968). *J. Chromatog.* 32, 657.

Corbin, E. A., Schwartz, D. P., and Keeney, M. (1960). *J. Chromatog.* 3, 322.

Crampton, E. W., Farmer, F. A., and Berryhill, F. M. (1951a). *J. Nutr.* 43, 431.

Crampton, E. W., Common, R. H., Farmer, F. A., Berryhill, F. M., and Wiseblatt, L. (1951b). *J. Nutr.* 43, 533.

Crampton, E. W., Common, R. H., Farmer, F. A., Berryhill, F. M., and Wiseblatt, L. (1951c). *J. Nutr.* 44, 177.

Crampton, E. W., Common, R. H., Farmer, F. A., Wells, A. F., and Crawford, D. (1953). *J. Nutr.* 49, 333.

Crampton, E. W., Common, R. H., Pritchard, E. T., and Farmer, F. A. (1956). *J. Nutr.* 60, 13.

Crawford, D. L., Yu, T. C., and Sinnhuber, R. O. (1967). *J. Food Sci.* 32, 332.

Crossley, A., and Thomas, A. (1964). *J. Am. Oil Chemists' Soc.* 41, 95.

Crossley, A., Heyes, T. D., and Hudson, B. J. F. (1962). *J. Am. Oil Chemists' Soc.* 39, 9.

Crowder, J. A., and Elm, A. C. (1949). *Ind. Eng. Chem.* 41, 1771.

Cruz, J. R., and Gonzales-Quijano, R. G. (1965). *Grasas Aceites (Seville, Spain)* 16, 167.

Custot, F. (1959). *Ann. Nutr. Aliment.* 13, A417.

Czok, G. (1965). *Ernaehr.-Umsch.* 12, 164.

Dakhil, T., and Vogt, W. (1961). *Naturwissenschaften* 48, 625.

Dangoumau, A., and Debruyne, H. (1957a). *Rev. Franc. Corps Gras* 4, 478.

Dangoumau, A., and Debruyne, H. (1957b). *Rev. Franc. Corps Gras* 4, 600.

Dangoumau, A., Berlureau, F., and Debruyne, H. (1957). *Rev. Franc. Corps Gras* 4, 541.

Dangoumau, A., Boussagol, and Debruyne, H. (1958). *Rev. Franc. Corps Gras* 5, 613.

Deatherage, F. E., and Mattill, H. A. (1939). *Ind. Eng. Chem.* 31, 1425.

Degkwitz, E., and Lang, K. (1962). *Fette, Seifen, Anstrichmittel* 64, 893.

Degkwitz, E., and Lang, K. (1963). *Z. Ernaehrungswiss.* 3, 170.

Desnuelle, P., and Burnet, M. (1956). *Bull. Soc. Chim. France* p. 268.

Deuel, H. J., Jr., Greenberg, S. M., Calbert, C. E., Baker, R., and Fisher, H. R. (1951). *Food Res.* 16, 258.

Dornseifer, T. P., and Powers, J. J. (1963). *Food Technol.* 17, 1330.

Dornseifer, T. P., Kim, S. C., Keith, E. S., and Powers, J. J. (1965). *J. Am. Oil Chemists' Soc.* 42, 1073.

Dulog, L., and Burg, K. H. (1963). *Deut. Farben-Z.* 17, 21.

Dulog, L., and Kern, W. (1960). *Deut. Farben-Z.* 14, 10.

Dulog, L., Selz, G., and Kern, W. (1961). *Makromol. Chem.* 50, 179.

Eisenhauer, R. A., Beal, R. E., and Griffin, E. L. (1963). *J. Am. Oil Chemists' Soc.* 40, 129.

Eisenhauer, R. A., Beal, R. E., and Griffin, E. L. (1964). *J. Am. Oil Chemists' Soc.* 41, 60.

Ellis, G. W. (1950). *Biochem. J.* 46, 129.

Ellis, R., Gaddis, A. M., and Currie, G. T. (1961). *J. Food Sci.* 26, 131.

Ellis, R., Gaddis, A. M., and Currie, G. T. (1966). *J. Food Sci.* 31, 191.

Emerson, G. A., and Gilfillan, E. W. (1960). *Biochem. Lipids, Proc. 5th Intern. Conf., Vienna, 1958* p. 225.

Endres, J. G., Bhalerao, V. R., and Kummerow, F. A. (1962a). *J. Am. Oil Chemists' Soc.* 39, 118.

Endres, J. G., Bhalerao, V. R., and Kummerow, F. A. (1962b). *J. Am. Oil Chemists' Soc.* 39, 159.

Esh, G. C., Sen Gupta, M. L., Bhattacharya, S., and Som, J. M. (1960). *Ann. Biochem. Exptl. Med. (Calcutta)* 20, 41.

Esterbauer, H. (1968). *Fette, Seifen, Anstrichmittel* **70**, 1.

Evans, C. D., Frankel, E. N., Cooney, P. M., and Moser, H. A. (1960). *J. Am. Oil Chemists' Soc.* **37**, 452.

Evans, C. D., McConnell, D. G., Frankel, E. N., and Cowan, J. C. (1965). *J. Am. Oil Chemists' Soc.* **42**, 764.

Evans, C. D., List, G. R., Dolev, A., McConnell, D. G., and Hoffmann, R. L. (1967). *Lipids* **2**, 432.

Farmer, E. H., Bloomfield, G. F., Sundralingam, A., and Sutton, D. A. (1942). *Trans. Faraday Soc.* **38**, 348.

Farmer, E. H., Koch, H. P., and Sutton, D. A. (1943). *J. Chem. Soc.* p. 541.

Fedeli, E., Capella, I. P., and Valentini, A. (1963a). *Riv. Ital. Sostanze Grasse* **40**, 321.

Fedeli, E., Valentini, A., and Jacini, G. (1963b). *Fette, Seifen, Anstrichmittel* **65**, 402.

Fioriti, J. A. (1965). *J. Am. Oil Chemists' Soc.* **42**, 743.

Fioriti, J. A., and Sims, R. J. (1967). *J. Am. Oil Chemists' Soc.* **44**, 221.

Fioriti, J. A., Bentz, A. P., and Sims, R. J. (1966a). *J. Am. Oil Chemists' Soc.* **43**, 37.

Fioriti, J. A., Bentz, A. P., and Sims, R. J. (1966b). *J. Am. Oil Chemists' Soc.* **43**, 487.

Fioriti, J. A., Krampl, V., and Sims, R. J. (1967). *J. Am. Oil Chemists' Soc.* **44**, 534.

Firestone, D., Horwitz, W., Friedman, L., and Shue, G. M. (1961a). *J. Am. Oil Chemists' Soc.* **38**, 253.

Firestone, D., Horwitz, W., Friedman, L., and Shue, G. M. (1961b). *J. Am. Oil Chemists' Soc.* **38**, 418.

Fleischman, A. I., Florin, A., Fitzgerald, J., Caldwell, A. B., and Eastwood, G. (1963). *J. Am. Dietetic Assoc.* **42**, 394.

Forss, D. A., Angelini, P., Bazinet, M. L., and Merritt, C., Jr. (1967). *J. Am. Oil Chemists' Soc.* **44**, 141.

Fox, M. R. S., and Mickelsen, O. (1959). *J. Nutr.* **67**, 123.

Francois, R., and Loury, M. (1964). *Chim. Ind. (Paris)* **91**, 650.

Frank, C. E. (1950). *Chem. Rev.* **46**, 155.

Frankel, E. N., Evans, C. D., and Cowan, J. C. (1960). *J. Am. Oil Chemists' Soc.* **37**, 418.

Frankel, E. N., Evans, C. D., McConnell, D. G., Selke, E., and Dutton, H. J. (1961a). *J. Org. Chem.* **26**, 4663.

Frankel, E. N., Evans, C. D., Moser, H. A., McConnell, D. G., and Cowan, J. C. (1961b). *J. Am. Oil Chemists' Soc.* **38**, 130.

Frankel, E. N., Evans, C. D., McConnell, D. G., and Jones, E. P. (1961c) *J. Am. Oil Chemists' Soc.* **38**, 134.

Franks, F., and Roberts, B. (1963). *J. Appl. Chem. (London)* **13**, 302.

Franzke, C., Heder, G., Kaiser, W., and Voetisch, K. (1968). *Lebensm. Ind.* **15**, (2), 65. (*Chem. Abstr.* **69**, 20620.)

Freeman, I. P., and O'Brien, P. J. (1967). *Biochem. J.* **102**, 9P.

Friedman, L., Horwitz, W., Shue, G. M., and Firestone, D. (1961). *J. Nutr.* **73**, 85.

Friedrich, J. P. (1967). *J. Am. Oil Chemists' Soc.* **44**, 244.

Friedrich, J. P., Palmer, J. C., Bell, E. W., and Cowan, J. C. (1963). *J. Am. Oil Chemists' Soc.* **40**, 584.

Fugger, J., Zilch, K. T., Cannon, J. A., and Dutton, H. J. (1951a). *J. Am. Chem. Soc.* **73**, 2861.

Fugger, J., Cannon, J. A., Zilch, K. T., and Dutton, H. J. (1951b). *J. Am. Oil Chemists' Soc.* **28**, 285.

Fukuzumi, K. (1961). *Yukagaku* **10**, 143.

Fukuzumi, K., and Ishida, K. (1964). *Kogyo Kagaku Zasshi* **67**, 324. (*J. Am. Oil Chemists' Soc.* **41**(10), 26A.)

Fukuzumi, K., and Maruyama, T. (1965). *Kogyo Kagaku Zasshi* **68**, 308.

Fukuzumi, K., and Miyakawa, T. (1963). *Kogyo Kagaku Zasshi* **66**, 1320.

Fukuzumi, K., Iwata, Y., and Takada, M. (1963). *Kogyo Kagaku Zasshi* **66**, 1675. (*J. Am. Oil Chemists' Soc.* **41**(10), 26A.)

Fukuzumi, K., Miyakawa, T., and Morohira, H. (1965). *J. Am. Oil Chemists' Soc.* **42**, 717.

Fuller, G. (1967). First Research Conference on Utilization of Safflower, *U.S. Dept. Agr.* ARS 74-43, p. 58.

Gaddis, A. M., Ellis, R., and Currie, G. T. (1960). *Food Res.* **25**, 495.

Gaddis, A. M., Ellis, R., and Currie, G. T. (1961). *J. Am. Oil Chemists' Soc.* **38**, 371.

Gaddis, A. M., Ellis, R., and Currie, G. T. (1964). *J. Food Sci.* **29**, 6.

Gaddis, A. M., Ellis, R., Shamey, J., and Currie, G. T. (1965). *J. Am. Oil Chemists' Soc.* **42**, 620.

Gaddis, A. M., Ellis, R., Currie, G. T., and Thornton, F. E. (1966) *J. Am. Oil Chemists' Soc.* **43**, 242.

Gast, L. E., Schneider, W. J., Forest, C. A., and Cowan, J. C. (1963). *J. Am. Oil Chemists' Soc.* **40**, 287.

Gillam, N. W. (1949). *Roy. Australian Chem. Inst. J. Proc.* **16**, 19.

Glavind, J., and Arffmann, E. (1968). *Experientia* **24**, 829.

Glavind, J., and Tryding, N. (1960). *Acta Physiol. Scand.* **49**, 97.

Glavind, J., Soendergaard, E., and Dam, H. (1961). *Acta Pharmacol. Toxicol.* **18**, 267.

Gooding, C. M., and Melnick, D. (1961). U.S. Patent No. 2,973,268.

Goodman, A. H., and Block, Z. (1952). *J. Am. Oil Chemists' Soc.* **29**, 616.

Gottenbos, J. J., and Thomasson, H. J. (1965). *Bibliotheca "Nutr. Dieta"* **7**, 110.

Grant, C. A. (1966). *Proc. Nutr. Soc.* **25**, 18.

Greenberg, S. M., Frazer, A. C., and Roberts, B. (1953). *J. Nutr.* **50**, 421.

Grossman, M. I. (1950). *Proc. 2nd Conf. Res., Council Res., Am. Meat Inst., Univ. Chicago* p. 28.

Guadagni, D. G., Buttery, R. G., and Okano, S. (1963). *J. Sci. Food Agr.* **14**, 761.

Guillaumin, R. (1967). *Rev. Franc. Corps Gras* **14**, 29.

Guillaumin, R., and Pertuisot, J. F. (1968). *Rev. Franc. Corps Gras* **15**, 27.

Gunstone, F. D., and Hilditch, T. P. (1945). *J. Chem. Soc.* p. 836.

Hall, G. E., and Roberts, D. G. (1966). *J. Chem. Soc.* **B**, 1109.

Hall, J. L., and Mackintosh, D. L. (1964). *J. Food Sci.* **29**, 420.

Hall, J. L., Harrison, D. L., and Mackintosh, D. L. (1962). *J. Agr. Food Chem.* **10**, 96.

Hamm, D. L., Hammond, E. G., and Hotchkiss, D. K. (1968). *J. Dairy Sci.* **51**, 483.

Hammond, E. G., and Hill, F. D. (1964). *J. Am. Oil Chemists' Soc.* **41**, 180.

Hansen, R. P., and Gerson, T. (1967). *J. Sci. Food. Agr.* **18**, 225.

Hanson, N. W. (1964). *Chem. Ind. (London)* p. 1541.

Harrison, S. A., and Wheeler, D. H. (1952). *Minn. Chemist* **4**, 17. (*Chem. Abstr.* **47**, 3583.)

Harvey, M. A. (1965). Ph.D. Thesis, Univ. of Tennessee, Knoxville, Tennessee.

Hashimoto, T., Sakamaki, T., and Matsumuro, H. (1958). *Ann. Rept. Natl. Inst. Nutr. (Tokyo)* p. 86. (*Chem. Abstr.* **53**, 12514.)

Hassan, M. M., and Lea, C. H. (1965). *Chem. Ind. (London)* p. 1760.

Henick, A. S., Benca, M. F., and Mitchell, J. H., Jr. (1954). *J. Am. Oil Chemists' Soc.* **31**, 88.

Hiatt, R., and Irwin, K. C. (1968). *J. Org. Chem.* **33**, 1436.

Hiatt, R., Mill, T., and Mayo, F. R. (1968a). *J. Org. Chem.* **33**, 1416.

Hiatt, R., Mill, T., Irwin, K. C., and Castleman, J. K. (1968b). *J. Org. Chem.* **33**, 1421.

Hiatt, R., Mill, T., Irwin, K. C., and Castleman, J. K. (1968c). *J. Org. Chem.* **33**, 1428.

Hiatt, R., Irwin, K. C., and Gould, C. W. (1968d). *J. Org. Chem.* **33**, 1430.

Higashi, H., Kandea, T., and Nakajima, T. (1953). *Nippon Suisan Gakkaishi* **19**, 171. (*Chem. Abstr.* **48**, 11586.)

Hill, F. D., and Hammond, E. G. (1965a). *J. Am. Oil Chemists' Soc.* **42**, 891.

Hill, F. D., and Hammond, E. G. (1965b). *J. Am. Oil Chemists' Soc.* **42**, 1148.

Hoffmann, G. (1961a). *J. Am. Oil Chemists' Soc.* **38**, 1.

Hoffmann, G. (1961b). *J. Am. Oil Chemists' Soc.* **38**, 31.

Hoffmann, G. (1962). *J. Am. Oil Chemists' Soc.* **39**, 439.

Hoffmann, G., and Keppler, J. G. (1960). *Nature* **185**, 310.

Holman, R. T., and Greenberg, S. I. (1954). *Arch. Biochem. Biophys.* **49**, 49.

Holman, R. T., and Greenberg, S. I. (1958). *J. Am. Oil Chemists' Soc.* **35**, 707.

Horgan, V. J., Philpot, J. St. L., Porter, B. W., and Roodyn, D. B. (1957). *Biochem. J.* **67**, 551.

Horikx, M. M. (1964). *J. Appl. Chem.* (*London*) **14**, 50.

Horikx, M. M. (1965). *J. Appl. Chem.* (*London*) **15**, 237.

Horvat, R. J., Lane, W. G., Ng, H., and Shepherd, A. D. (1964). *Nature* **203**, 523.

Horvat, R. J., McFadden, W. H., Ng, H., Black, D. R., Lane, W. G., and Teeter, R. M. (1965). *J. Am. Oil Chemists' Soc.* **42**, 1112.

Horvat, R. J., McFadden, W. H., Ng, H., Lane, W. G., and Shepherd, A. D. (1966). *J. Am. Oil Chemists' Soc.* **43**, 350.

Howard, J. A., and Ingold, K. U. (1967). *Can. J. Chem.* **45**, 785.

Hrdlicka, J., and Pokorny, J. (1962). *Sb. Vysoke Skoly Chem.-Technol. Praze, Oddil Fak. Potravinareske Technol.* **6**, 161. (*Chem. Abstr.* **62**, 2953.)

Hrdlicka, J., and Pokorny, J. (1963). *Sb. Vysoke Skoly Chem.-Technol. Praze, Oddil Fak. Potravinareske Technol.* **7**, 113. (*J. Am. Oil Chemists' Soc.* **41**(11), 28A.)

Hutchison, R. B., and Alexander, J. C. (1963). *J. Org. Chem.* **28**, 2522.

Ivy, A. C. (1955). *Gastroenterology* **28**, 345.

Iwata, N., Morita, M., and Ota, S. (1965). *Yukagaku* **14**, 241. (*J. Am. Oil Chemists' Soc.* **42**, 478A.)

Iwata, N., Morita, M., and Ota, S. (1967). *Yukagaku* **16**, 113. (*Chem. Abstr.* **66**, 104133.)

Izumi, G., and Yamada, Y. (1964). *Yukagaku* **13**, 418.

Jacini, G., Fedeli, E., and Schaefer, W. C. (1966). *J. Agr. Food Chem.* **14**, 650.

Jacobson, G. A. (1967). *Food Technol.* **21**, 43.

Janicek, G., and Pokorny, J. (1961). *Nahrung* **5**, 387.

Janicek, G., Pokorny, J., and Shupova, I. (1961). *Vopr. Pitaniya* **20**, 12.

Johnson, O. C., and Kummerow, F. A. (1957). *J. Am. Oil Chemists' Soc.* **34**, 407.

Johnson, O. C., Chang, S. S., and Kummerow, F. A. (1953). *J. Am. Oil Chemists' Soc.* **30**, 317.

Johnson, O. C., Sakuragi, T., and Kummerow, F. A. (1956). *J. Am. Oil Chemists' Soc.* **33**, 433.

Johnson, O. C., Perkins, E., Sugai, M., and Kummerow, F. A. (1957). *J. Am. Oil Chemists' Soc.* **34**, 594.

Kadar, R. (1961). *Rappt. Nord. Fettharskningssymp., 3rd, Sandefjord, Norway* p. 49. (*Chem. Abstr.* **58**, 14327.)

Kajimoto, G. (1964). *Eiyo To Shokuryo* **16**, 506.

Kajimoto, G., and Kamo, K. (1964). *Eiyo To Shokuryo* **16**, 510.

Kajimoto, G., and Mukai, K. (1964). *Eiyo To Shokuryo* **16**, 425.

Kajimoto, G., and Mukai, K. (1965). *Yukagaku* **14**, 359.

Kajimoto, G., Tamai, I., Furui, Y., and Mukai, K. (1964). *Eiyo To Shokuryo* **16**, 432.

Kaneda, T., Sakai, H., and Ishii, S. (1954a). *Eiyo To Shokuryo* **7**, 188. (*Chem. Abstr.* **53**, 8333.)

Kaneda, T., Sakurai, H., and Ishii, S. (1954b). *Nippon Suisan Gakkaishi* **20**, 50. (*Chem. Abstr.* **48**, 11586.)
Kaneda, T., Sakai, H., and Ishii, S. (1955). *J. Biochem. (Tokyo)* **42**, 561.
Kartha, A. R. S. (1960). *J. Sci. Ind. Research (India)* **19B**, 438.
Kartha, A. R. S. (1964). *Indian J. Chem.* **2**, 118.
Kato, U., and Sakurai, Y. (1949). *Shokuryo Kenkyusho Kenkyu Hokoku* **2**, 59.
Kaunitz, H. (1953). *Arch. Exptl. Pathol. Pharmakol. Naunyn-Schmiedebergs* **220**, 16. (*Chem. Abstr.* **48**, 1496.)
Kaunitz, H. (1960). *Exptl. Med. Surg.* **18**, 59.
Kaunitz, H. (1967). *Food Technol.* **21**(3), 60.
Kaunitz, H., and Johnson, R. E. (1964). *J. Am. Oil Chemists' Soc.* **41**, 50.
Kaunitz, H., and Johnson, R. E. (1967). *J. Nutr.* **91**, 55.
Kaunitz, H., Johnson, R. E., and Slanetz, C. A. (1952). *J. Nutr.* **46**, 151.
Kaunitz, H., Slanetz, C. A., and Johnson, R. E. (1955). *J. Nutr.* **55**, 577.
Kaunitz, H., Slanetz, C. A., Johnson, R. E., Guilmain, J., Knight, H. B., Saunders, D. H., and Swern, D. (1956a). *J. Nutr.* **60**, 237.
Kaunitz, H., Slanetz, C. A., Johnson, R. E., Knight, H. B., Saunders, D. H., and Swern, D. (1956b). *J. Am. Oil Chemists' Soc.* **33**, 630.
Kaunitz, H., Slanetz, C. A., Johnson, R. E., Knight, H. B., Koos, R. E., and Swern, D. (1959). *J. Am. Oil Chemists' Soc.* **36**, 611.
Kaunitz, H., Slanetz, C. A., Johnson, R. E., and Babayan, V. K. (1960a) *J. Nutr.* **70**, 521.
Kaunitz, H., Slanetz, C. A., Johnson, R. E., Knight, H. B., and Swern, D. (1960b). *Metab. Clin. Exptl.* **9**, 59.
Kaunitz, H., Slanetz, C. A., Johnson, R. E., and Herb, S. F. (1961). *J. Am. Oil Chemists' Soc.* **38**, 301.
Kaunitz, H., Johnson, R. E., and Pegus, L. (1965). *J. Am. Oil Chemists' Soc.* **42**, 770.
Kaunitz, H., Johnson, R. E., and Pegus, L. (1966). *Proc. Soc. Exptl. Biol. Med.* **123**, 204.
Kawada, T., Krishnamurthy, R. G., Mookherjee, B. D., and Chang, S. S. (1967). *J. Am. Oil Chemists' Soc.* **44**, 131.
Keane, K. W., Jacobson, G. A., and Krieger, C. H. (1959). *J. Nutr.* **68**, 57.
Kennelly, B., and Quackenbush, F. W. (1946). *Biol. Antioxidants, Trans. 1st Conf.* p. 56.
Kern, W., and Dulog, L. (1959a). *Makromol. Chem.* **29**, 199.
Kern, W., and Dulog, L. (1959b). *Makromol. Chem.* **29**, 208.
Kern, W., and Schnecko, H. W. (1959). *Makromol. Chem.* **32**, 184.
Kern, W., Dulog, L., and Selz, G. (1959). *Makromol. Chem.* **32**, 191.
Khan, N. A. (1954). *Can. J. Chem.* **32**, 1149.
Khan, N. A. (1964). *Oleagineux* **19**, 397.
Khan, N. A. (1965a). *Oleagineux* **20**, 683.
Khan, N. A. (1965b). *Oleagineux* **20**, 751.
Kieckebusch, W., Jahr, K., Czok, G., Griem, W., Baessler, K. H., Hammar, D. C. H., and Lang, K. (1962). *Fette, Seifen, Anstrichmittel* **64**, 1154.
Kieckebusch, W., Jahr, K., Czok, G., Degkwitz, E., and Lang, K. (1963a). *Fette, Seifen, Anstrichmittel* **65**, 919.
Kieckebusch, W., Griem, W., Czok, G., Baessler, K. H., Degkwitz, E., Schaeffner, E., and Lang, K. (1963b). *Z. Ernaehrungswiss.* **4**, 26.
Kilgore, L. (1966). *J. Am. Oil Chemists' Soc.* **43**, 590.
Kilgore, L., and Luker, W. D. (1964). *J. Am. Oil Chemists' Soc.* **41**, 496.
Kloepffer, W., Esterbauer, H., and Schauenstein, E. (1965). *Fette, Seifen, Anstrichmittel* **67**, 198.
Knight, H. B., Eddy, C. R., and Swern, D. (1951). *J. Am. Oil Chemists' Soc.* **28**, 188.
Kohn, R., and Nahar-Rahman, S. Q. (1966). *Nahrung* **10**, 205.

Kokatnur, M. G., Bergan, J. G., and Draper, H. H. (1965). *Anal. Biochem.* **12**, 325.

Kokatnur, M. G., Bergan, J. G., and Draper, H. H. (1966a). *Proc. Soc. Exptl. Biol. Med.* **123**, 254.

Kokatnur, M. G., Bergan, J. G., and Draper, H. H. (1966b). *Proc. Soc. Exptl. Biol. Med.* **123**, 314.

Kotsubo, M., and Ueyanagi, F. (1955). *Kasiegaku Zasshi* **6**, 5. (*Chem. Abstr.* **50**, 14995.)

Krishnamurthy, R. G. (1966). Ph.D. Thesis, Rutgers Univ., New Brunswick, New Jersey.

Krishnamurthy, R. G., and Chang, S. S. (1967). *J. Am. Oil Chemists' Soc.* **44**, 136.

Krishnamurthy, R. G., Kawada, T., and Chang, S. S. (1965). *J. Am. Oil Chemists' Soc.* **42**, 878.

Kritchevsky, D., Tepper, S. A., and Langan, J. (1962a). *J. Atherosclerosis Res.* **2**, 115.

Kritchevsky, D., Tepper, S. A., and Langan, J. (1962b). *J. Nutr.* **77**, 127.

Krull, L. (1959). *Fette, Seifen, Anstrichmittel* **61**, 223.

Kudryashov, Y. B., Mat'ts, V., Goncharenko, Y. N., Kakushkina, M. L., Lomsadze, B. A., Hsing, W.-T., Hsueh, Y.-H., and Chang, C.-L. (1961). *Radiobiologiya* **1**, 78.

Kumazawa, H. (1961). *Yukagaku* **10**, 531.

Kumazawa, H. (1963a). *Yukagaku* **12**, 214.

Kumazawa, H. (1963b). *Yukagaku* **12**, 288. (*Chem. Abstr.* **60**, 6137.)

Kumazawa, H. (1964). *Yukagaku* **13**, 537. (*Chem. Abstr.* **63**, 18939.)

Kumazawa, H. (1965). *Yukagaku* **14**, 229.

Kumazawa, H., and Oyama, T. (1965). *Yukagaku* **14**, 167. (*Chem. Abstr.* **63**, 18491.)

Kummerow, F. A., Chu, T.-K., and Randolph, P. (1948). *J. Nutr.* **36**, 523.

Kurita, K. (1958). *Yukagaku* **7**, 186.

Kuroda, K., Mishiro, Y., Watanabe, S., and Kai, T. (1956a). *Igaku To Seibutsugaku* **38**, 129. (*Chem. Abstr.* **52**, 6435.)

Kuroda, K., Mishiro, Y., and Inaba, M. (1956b). *Igaku To Seibutsugaku* **39**, 160. (*Chem. Abstr.* **52**, 6435.)

Lane, A., Blickenstaff, D., and Ivy, A. C. (1950). *Cancer* **3**, 1044.

Lang, K., and Fricker, A. (1964). *Z. Lebensm.-Untersuch.-Forsch.* **125**, 390.

Lang, K., Kieckebusch, W., Jahr, K., Czok, G., Griem, W., and Degkwitz, E. (1963). *Helv. Physiol. Acta* **21**, 354.

Lang, K., Henschel, J., Kieckebusch, W., and Griem, W. (1966). *Z. Ernaehrungswiss.* **7**, 109.

Lange, H., and Mikusch, J. D. (1967). *Fette, Seifen, Anstrichmittel* **69**, 752.

Lanteaume, M. T., Ramel, P., LeClerc, A. M., and Rannaud, J. (1966). *Rev. Franc. Corps Gras* **13**, 603.

Lanteaume, M. T., Ramel, P., Acker, P., LeClerc, A. M., and Wirth, C. (1968). *Rev. Franc. Corps Gras* **15**, 71.

Lantz, C. W., and Carlin, G. T. (1938). *Oil Soap* **15**, 38.

Larsen, C. D., and Morris, H. P. (1943). *J. Am. Chem. Soc.* **65**, 2301.

Lassen, S., Bacon, E. K., and Dunn, H. J. (1949). *Arch. Biochem.* **23**, 1.

Lea, C. H. (1965). *Chem. Ind. (London)* p. 244.

Lea, C. H., and Hobson-Frohock, A. (1965). *J. Sci. Food Agr.* **16**, 18.

Lea, C. H., and Jackson, H. A. F. (1964). *Chem. Ind. (London)* p. 1429.

Lea, C. H., and Swoboda, P. A. T. (1962). *J. Sci. Food Agr.* **13**, 148.

Lea, C. H., Parr, L. J., L'Estrange, J. L., and Carpenter, K. J. (1964). *Brit. J. Nutr.* **18**, 369.

Lea, C. H., Parr, L. J., L'Estrange, J. L., and Carpenter, K. J. (1966). *Brit. J. Nutr.* **20**, 123.

LeClerc, A. M., Ramel, P., Dumain, J., and Faucquembergue, D. (1966). *Rev. Franc. Corps Gras* **13**, 175.

L'Estrange, J. L., Carpenter, K. J., Lea, C. H., and Parr, L. J. (1966). *Brit. J. Nutr.* **20**, 113.
L'Estrange, J. L., Carpenter, K. J., Lea, C. H., and Parr, L. J. (1967). *Brit. J. Nutr.* **21**, 377.
Lillard, D. A., and Day, E. A. (1964). *J. Am. Oil Chemists' Soc.* **41**, 549.
Linow, F., Roloff, M., and Taeufel, K. (1966). *Fette, Seifen, Anstrichmittel* **68**, 866.
Lipstein, B., Budowski, P., and Bornstein, S. (1965). *Poultry Sci.* **44**, 1480.
Lobanov, D. I., and Brents, Y. M. (1962). *Izv. Vysshikh Uchebn. Zavedenii, Pishchevaya Tekhnol.* p. 63.
Loury, M. (1957). *Bull. Soc. Sci. Hyg. Aliment.* **45**, 255.
Loury, M. (1961). *Rev. Franc. Corps Gras* **8**, 686.
Loury, M. (1967). *Parfum. Cosmet. Savons* **10**, 424.
Loury, M., Lechartier, G., and Forney, M. (1965). *Rev. Franc. Corps Gras* **12**, 253.
Loury, M., Lechartier, G., and Bloch, C. (1966). *Rev. Franc. Corps Gras* **13**, 395.
Lueck, H., Rahman, Q. N., and Kohn, R. (1967). *Fette, Seifen, Anstrichmittel* **69**, 842.
Lundberg, W. O. (ed.). (1961–1962). "Autoxidation and Antioxidants," Vols. 1 and 2. Wiley, New York.
MacDonald, J. A. (1956). *J. Am. Oil Chemists' Soc.* **33**, 394.
McInnes, A. G., Cooper, F. P., and MacDonald, J. A. (1961). *Can. J. Chem.* **39**, 1906.
McKay, D. G., Margaretten, W., and Rothenberg, J. (1964). *Lab. Invest.* **13**, 54. (*Chem. Abstr.* **61**, 4791.)
McKay, D. G., Kaunitz, H., Csavossy, I., and Johnson, R. E. (1967). *Metab. Clin. Exptl.* **16**, 111.
Maerker, G. (1965). *J. Am. Oil Chemists' Soc.* **42**, 329.
Maerker, G., and Haeberer, E. T. (1966). *J. Am. Oil Chemists' Soc.* **43**, 97.
Maerker, G., Haeberer, E. T., and Ault, W. C., (1964). *J. Am. Oil Chemists' Soc.* **41**, 585.
Mameesh, M. S., Chahine, M. H., and El-Hawwary, N. M. (1965). *Grasas Aceites (Seville, Spain)* **16**, 65.
Mameesh, M. S., Abdin, F. H., Chahine, M. H., and El-Hawwary, N. M. (1967). *Grasas Aceites (Seville, Spain)* **18**, 213.
Marcuse, R. (1967). *Fette, Seifen, Anstrichmittel* **69**, 845.
Marcuse, R., Remi, K., and Goethe, P. O. (1964). *Fette, Seifen, Anstrichmittel* **66**, 992.
Mariam, E., and Pochetti, F. (1965) *Ann. Chim. (Rome)* **55**, 1113. (*J. Am. Oil Chemists' Soc.* **43**, 312A.)
Martin, J. B. (1953). U.S. Patent No. 2,634,213.
Martinenghi, G. B. (1967). *Chem. Ind. (London)* p. 1815.
Matsuo, N. (1954a). *J. Biochem. (Tokyo)* **41**, 481. (*Chem. Abstr.* **48**, 13843.)
Matsuo, N. (1954b). *J. Biochem. (Tokyo)* **41**, 647. (*Chem. Abstr.* **49**, 4098.)
Matsuo, N. (1957a). *Seikagaku* **29**, 769. (*Chem. Abstr.* **53**, 11550.)
Matsuo, N. (1957b). *Seikagaku* **29**, 773. (*Chem. Abstr.* **53**, 11550.)
Matsuo, N. (1957c). *Seikagaku* **29**, 807. (*Chem. Abstr.* **53**, 11550.)
Matsuo, N. (1957d). *Seikagaku* **29**, 885. (*Chem. Abstr.* **53**, 11550.)
Matsuo, N. (1957e). *Eiyo To Shokuryo* **10**, 255. (*Chem. Abstr.* **53**, 11551.)
Matsuo, N. (1959a). *Eiyo To Shokuryo* **12**, 118. (*Chem. Abstr.* **55**, 2825.)
Matsuo, N. (1959b). *Eiyo To Shokuryo* **12**, 206. (*Chem. Abstr.* **55**, 2825.)
Matsuo, N. (1959c). *Eiyo To Shokuryo* **12**, 210. (*Chem. Abstr.* **55**, 2825.)
Matsuo, N. (1960a). *Yukagaku* **9**, 37. (*Chem. Abstr.* **55**, 2825.)
Matsuo, N. (1960b). *Nippon Kagaku Zasshi* **81**, 469. (*Chem. Abstr.* **55**, 2825.)
Matsuo, N. (1961). *J. Biochem. (Tokyo)* **49**, 635. (*Chem. Abstr.* **55**, 27637.)
Matsuo, N. (1962). *Bull. Chem. Soc. Japan* **35**, 105. (*Chem. Abstr.* **57**, 3740.)
Matsuo, N. (1965). *Seikei Daigaku Kogakubu Kogaku Hokoku* **1**, 81. (*Chem. Abstr.* **65**, 15682.)

Mehta, T. N., and Sharma, S. A. (1956). *J. Am. Oil Chemists' Soc.* **33**, 38.
Mehta, T. N., and Sharma, S. A. (1957). *J. Am. Oil Chemists' Soc.* **34**, 448.
Melnick, D. (1957a). *J. Am. Oil Chemists' Soc.* **34**, 351.
Melnick, D. (1957b). *J. Am. Oil Chemists' Soc.* **34**, 578.
Melnick, D., Luckmann, F. H., and Gooding, C. M. (1958). *J. Am. Oil Chemists' Soc.* **35**, 271.
Menzel, D. B. (1967). *Lipids* **2**, 83.
Michael, W. R. (1966a). *Lipids* **1**, 359.
Michael, W. R. (1966b). *Lipids* **1**, 365.
Michael, W. R. (1966c). *J. Chem. Eng. Data* **11**, 134.
Michael, W. R., Alexander, J. C., and Artman, N. R. (1966). *Lipids* **1**, 353.
Mihelic, F. (1963). *Kem. Ind (Zagreb)* **12**, 147. (*Chem. Abstr.* **60**, 6138.)
Miller, R. F., Small, G., and Norris, L. C. (1955). *J. Nutr.* **55**, 81.
Miyakawa, T. (1964). *Fette, Seifen, Anstrichmittel* **66**, 1048.
Mizuno, G. R., and Chipault, J. R. (1965). *J. Am. Oil Chemists' Soc.* **42**, 839.
Montefredine, A. (1965). *Riv. Ital. Sostanze Grasse* **42**, 482.
Mookherjee, B. D., Deck, R. E., and Chang, S. S. (1965). *J. Agr. Food Chem.* **13**, 131.
Morris, H. P. (1947). *Biol. Antioxidants, Trans. 2nd Conf.*, p. 96.
Morris, H. P., Larsen, C. D., and Lippincott, S. W. (1943). *J. Natl. Cancer Inst.* **4**, 285.
Morris, L. J., and Holman, R. T. (1961). *J. Lipid Res.* **2**, 77.
Morris, L. J., Holman, R. T., and Fontell, K. (1961). *J. Lipid Res.* **2**, 68.
Mroczkowski, S., and Ziombski, H. (1962). *Roczniki Panstwowego Zakladu Hig.* **13**, 175.
Mukai, A., Yamamoto, I., and Ota, S. (1965). *Yukagaku* **14**, 292.
Mukai, A., Yamamoto, I., and Ota, S. (1966). *Yukagaku* **15**, 58.
Mukherjee, S. (1951). *Indian Soap J.* **16**, 183. (*Chem. Abstr.* **45**, 10617.)
Munn, J. I., Koch, S. A., and Fitzhugh, O. G. (1960). *Federation Proc.* **19**, 323.
Murase, Y., and Toyama, Y. (1960a). *Nagoya Sangyo Kagaku Kenkyusho Kenkyu Hokoku* **12**, 42.
Murase, Y., and Toyama, Y. (1960b). *Nagoya Sangyo Kagaku Kenkyusho Kenkyu Hokoku* **12**, 45.
Narayan, K. A., Sugai, M., and Kummerow, F. A. (1964). *J. Am. Oil Chemists' Soc.* **41**, 254.
Naudet, M. (1964). *Oleagineux* **19**, 449.
Naudet, M., Perrot, M. J., and Desnuelle, P. (1960a). *Rev. Franc. Corps Gras* **7**, 429.
Naudet, M., Perrot, M. J., and Desnuelle, P. (1960b). *Peintures, Pigments, Vernis* **36**, 634.
Nawar, W. W., and Dubravcic, M. F. (1968). *J. Am. Oil Chemists' Soc.* **45**, 100.
Nemets, S. M., and Nesterova, I. M. (1962). *Konserv. i Ovoshchesushil. Prom.* **17**, 4. (*Chem. Abstr.* **57**, 12968.)
Ney, K. H. (1965). *Fette, Seifen, Anstrichmittel* **67**, 190.
Niederstebruch, A., and Hinsch, I. (1967). *Fette, Seifen, Anstrichmittel* **69**, 637.
Nishida, T., Tsuchiyama, H., Inoue, M., and Kummerow, F. A. (1960). *Proc. Soc. Exptl. Biol. Med.* **105**, 308.
Nolen, G. A., Alexander, J. C., and Artman, N. R. (1967). *J. Nutr.* **93**, 337.
Notevarp, O., and Sellaeg, S. (1961). *Rappt. Nord. Fettharskningssymp., 3rd, Sandefjord, Norway* p. 55. (*Chem. Abstr.* **58**, 14328.)
Nutt, S. M. (1966). *Dissertation Abstr.* **26**, 4621.
Oette, K. (1965). *J. Lipid Res.* **6**, 449.
Olcott, H. S., and Dolev, A. (1963). *Proc. Soc. Exptl. Biol. Med.* **114**, 820.

Oldfield, J. E., Sinnhuber, R. O., and Rasheed, A. A. (1963). *J. Am. Oil Chemists' Soc.* **40**, 357.

Ondreicka, R., Simko, V., and Bucko, A. (1963). *Vopr. Pitaniya* **22**, 43. (*Chem. Abstr.* **60**, 4700.)

O'Neill, L. A. (1954). *Chem. Ind.* (*London*) p. 384.

Ono, F. (1960). *Nagoya Sangyo Kagaku Kenkyusho Kenkyu Hokoku* **12**, 47.

Ota, S. (1964). *Yukagaku* **13**, 269.

Ota, S., and Izuyama, Y. (1964). *Yukagaku* **13**, 328. (*J. Am. Oil Chemists' Soc.* **41**(12), 30A.)

Ota, S., and Yamamoto, I. (1964). *Yukagaku* **13**, 651.

Ota, S., Iwata, N., Mukai, A., and Enei, H. (1963a). *Yukagaku* **12**, 403. (*Chem. Abstr.* **59**, 15863.)

Ota, S., Mukai, A., and Yamamoto, I. (1963b). *Yukagaku* **12**, 409.

Ota, S., Iwata, N., and Morita, M. (1964a). *Yukagaku* **13**, 210.

Ota, S., Mukai, A., and Yamamoto, I. (1964b). *Yukagaku* **13**, 264.

Ota, S., Mukai, A., Iwata, N., Yamamoto, I., and Morita, M. (1964c). *Yukagaku* **13**, 471.

Ota, S., Iwata, N., Mukai, A., and Morita, M. (1964d). *Yukagaku* **13**, 595.

Ota, S., Mega, A., and Shibue, T. (1966). *Yukagaku* **15**, 533. (*Chem. Abstr.* **70**, 20754.)

Paquot, C., and de Goursac, F. (1950). *Bull. Soc. Chim. France* p. 172.

Paquot, C., and Mercier, J. (1962). *Rev. Franc. Corps Gras* **9**, 275.

Paquot, C., Mercier, J., and Reveillon, F. (1967). *Compt. Rend.* **265C**, 831.

Parks, O. W., Keeney, M., and Schwartz, D. P. (1963). *J. Dairy Sci.* **46**, 295.

Parteshko, V. G. (1962). *Cesk. Gastroenterol. Vyziva* **16**, 305.

Parteshko, V. G. (1966). *Byul. Eksperim. Biol. i Med.* **61**, 43. (*Chem. Abstr.* **64**, 18103.)

Paschke, R. F., and Wheeler, D. H. (1955). *J. Am. Oil Chemists' Soc.* **32**, 473.

Paschke, R. F., Jackson, J. E., and Wheeler, D. H. (1952). *Ind. Eng. Chem.* **44**, 1113.

Paschke, R. F., Peterson, L. E., and Wheeler, D. H. (1964). *J. Am. Oil Chemists' Soc.* **41**, 723.

Pathak, S. P., and Mathur, S. S. (1954). *Indian Soap J.* **20**, 41. (*Chem. Abstr.* **49**, 16463.)

Patton, S., Barnes, I. J., and Evans, L. E. (1959). *J. Am. Oil Chemists' Soc.* **36**, 280.

Payne, W. J. A. (1959). *Nature* **183**, 828.

Pazlar, M., Kocova, P., and Pokorny, J. (1966). *Z. Lebensm.-Untersuch.-Forsch.* **131**, 269.

Peacock, P. R. (1946). *Brit. Med. Bull.* **4**, 364.

Peacock, P. R. (1948). *Brit. J. Nutr.* **2**, 201.

Peacock, P. R., and Beck, S. (1951). *Acta Unio Intern. Contra Cancrum* **7**, 612.

Peacock, P. R., and Kirby, A. H. M. (1944). *Cancer Res.* **4**, 94.

Perkins, E. G. (1960). *Food Technol.* **14**, 508.

Perkins, E. G. (1967). *Food Technol.* **21**, 611.

Perkins, E. G., and Kummerow, F. A. (1959a). *J. Am. Oil Chemists' Soc.* **36**, 371.

Perkins, E. G., and Kummerow, F. A. (1959b). *J. Nutr.* **68**, 101.

Perkins, E. G., and Van Akkeren, L. A. (1965). *J. Am. Oil Chemists' Soc.* **42**, 782.

Perkins, E. G., Endres, J. G., and Kummerow, F. A. (1961). *Proc. Soc. Exptl. Biol. Med.* **106**, 370.

Perlstein, T., Eisner, A., and Ault, W. C. (1966). *J. Am. Oil Chemists' Soc.* **43**, 380.

Petit, J., and Bosshard, G. (1952a). *Bull. Soc. Chim. France* p. 293.

Petit, J., and Bosshard, G. (1952b). *Bull. Soc. Chim. France* p. 618.

Pohle, W. D., Gregory, R. L., and Van Giessen, B. (1964a). *J. Am. Oil Chemists' Soc.* **41**, 649.

Pohle, W. D., Gregory, R. L., Weiss, T. J., Van Giessen, B., Taylor, J. R., and Ahern, J. J. (1964b). *J. Am. Oil Chemists' Soc.* **41**, 795.

Pokorny, J. (1957). *Sb. Vysoke Skoly Chem.-Technol. Praze, Oddil Fak. Potravinareske Technol.* p. 215. (*Chem. Abstr.* **53**, 3730.)

Pokorny, J. (1961). *J. Inst. Chem. Tech. Prague* **5**, 51. (*J. Am. Oil Chemists' Soc.* **41**(8), 34A).

Pokorny, J. (1962). *J. Inst. Chem. Tech. Prague* **6**, 267. (*J. Am. Oil Chemists' Soc.* **41**(3), 42A).

Pokorny, J. (1966). *Sb. Vysoke Skoly Chem.-Technol. Praze, Potraviny* **9**, 103. (*Chem. Abstr.* **66**, 20213.)

Pokorny, J., and Hladik, J. (1968). *J. Chromatog.* **33**, 267.

Pokorny, J., and Kakac, B. (1959). *Cesk. Gastroenterol. Vyziva* **13**, 582. (*Chem. Abstr.* **54**, 11323.)

Pokorny, J., and Kondratenko, S. S. (1967). *Oleagineux* **22**, 103. (*Chem. Abstr.* **66**, 106151.)

Pokorny, J., and Zwain, H. (1967). *Fette, Seifen, Anstrichmittel* **69**, 330.

Pokorny, J., Zwain, H., and Janicek, G. (1966a). *Ernaehrungsforschung* **11**, 478. (*Chem. Abstr.* **66**, 75012.)

Pokorny, J., Zwain, H., and Janicek, G. (1966b). *Nahrung* **10**, 315.

Pokorny, J., Klein, S., and Koren, J. (1966c). *Nahrung* **10**, 321.

Pokorny, J., Klein, S., and Zelinkova, M. (1967a). *Nahrung* **11**, 121.

Pokorny, J., Kondratenko, S. S., and Janicek, G. (1967b). *Nahrung* **11**, 657.

Poling, C. E., Warner, W. D., Mone, P. E., and Rice, E. E. (1960). *J. Nutr.* **72**, 109.

Poling, C. E., Warner, W. D., Mone, P. E., and Rice, E. E. (1962). *J. Am. Oil Chemists' Soc.* **39**, 315.

Popov, A., and Yanishlieva, N. (1967). *Nahrung* **11**, 645.

Popov, A., Mizev, I., and Yanishlieva, N. (1967). *Rev. Franc. Corps Gras* **14**, 75.

Porter, F. R., Michaelis, H., and Shay, F. G. (1932). *Ind. Eng. Chem.* **24**, 811.

Potteau, B., and Cluzan, R. (1966). *Ann. Biol. Animale, Biochim., Biophys.* **6**, 47.

Potteau, B., Biette, E., and Lhuissier, M. (1967). *Ann. Biol. Animale, Biochim., Biophys.* **7**, 59.

Powick, W. C. (1923). *J. Agr. Res.* **26**, 323.

Prevot, A. (1965). *Rev. Franc. Corps Gras* **12**, 299.

Privett, O. S., and Nickell, E. C. (1959). *Fette, Seifen, Anstrichmittel* **61**, 842.

Privett, O. S., and Quackenbush, F. W. (1954). *J. Am. Oil Chemists' Soc.* **31**, 281.

Privett, O. S., Pringle, R. B., and McFarlane, W. D. (1945). *Oil Soap* **22**, 287.

Purr, A. (1964). *Deut. Lebensm.-Rundschau* **60**, 269. (*Chem. Abstr.* **62**, 4527.)

Quackenbush, F. W. (1945). *Oil Soap* **22**, 336.

Raju, N. V., Rao, M. N., and Rajagopalan, R. (1965). *J. Am. Oil Chemists' Soc.* **42**, 774.

Ramanathan, V., Sakuragi, T., and Kummerow, F. A. (1959). *J. Am. Oil Chemists' Soc.* **36**, 244.

Ramel, P., LeClerc, A. M., Dumain, J., and Faucquembergue, D. (1965a). *Rev. Franc. Corps Gras* **12**, 153.

Ramel, P., Lanteaume, M. T., LeClerc, A. M., Rannaud, J., and Morel, E. (1965b). *Rev. Franc. Corps Gras* **12**, 517.

Ramel, P., Lanteaume, M. T., LeClerc, A. M., and Rannaud, J. (1967). *Rev. Franc. Corps Gras* **14**, 505.

Rao, B. Y. (1960). *J. Sci. Ind. Res. (India)* **19A**, 430.

Raulin, J., and Petit, J. (1960). *Arch. Sci. Physiol.* **14**, 143. (*Chem. Abstr.* **54**, 21357.)

Raulin, J., and Petit, J. (1962). *Arch. Sci. Physiol.* **16**, 77.

Raulin, J., and Terroine, T. (1962). *Arch. Sci. Physiol.* **16**, 89.

Raulin, J., Richir, C., Escribano, L., and Jacquot, R. (1959). *Compt. Rend.* **248**, 1229.

Raulin, J., Richir, C., and Jacquot, R. (1960). *Symp. Substances Etrangeres Aliments, 5ᵉ, Budapest, 1959*, p. 227.
Reddy, B. R., Yasuda, K., Krishnamurthy, R. G., and Chang, S. S. (1968). *J. Am. Oil Chemists' Soc.* **45**, 629.
Reporter, M. C., and Harris, R. S. (1961). *J. Am. Oil Chemists' Soc.* **38**, 47.
Rice, E. E., Poling, C. E., Mone, P. E., and Warner, W. D. (1960). *J. Am. Oil Chemists' Soc.* **37**, 607.
Rinetti, M., and Giovetti, G. L. (1962). *Minerva Dietol.* **2**, 131.
Rinetti, M., and Giovetti, G. L. (1963). *Minerva Dietol.* **3**, 172.
Risser, N., Kummerow, F. A., and Perkins, E. G. (1966). *Proc. Soc. Exptl. Biol. Med.* **121**, 294.
Robertson, C. J. (1966). *Baker's Dig.* **40**(5), 54.
Rock, S. P., and Roth, H. (1964a). *J. Am. Oil Chemists' Soc.* **41**, 228.
Rock, S. P., and Roth, H. (1964b). *J. Am. Oil Chemists' Soc.* **41**, 531.
Rock, S. P., and Roth, H. (1966). *J. Am. Oil Chemists' Soc.* **43**, 116.
Roffo, A. H. (1939a). *Prensa Med. Arg.* **26**, 619. (*Chem. Abstr.* **37**, 2065.)
Roffo, A. H. (1939b). *Bol. Inst. Med. Exptl. Estud. Cancer* **15**, 407. (*Chem. Abstr.* **33**, 5478.)
Roffo, A. H. (1942). *Bol. Inst. Med. Exptl. Estud. Cancer* **19**, 503. (*Chem. Abstr.* **37**, 6335.)
Roffo, A. H. (1944). *Bol. Inst. Med. Exptl. Estud. Cancer* **21**, 1. (*Chem. Abstr.* **39**, 1456.)
Ross, J., Gebhart, A. I., and Gerecht, J. F. (1949). *J. Am. Chem. Soc.* **71**, 282.
Rost, H. E. (1963). *Fette, Seifen, Anstrichmittel* **65**, 463.
Rothe, M., Woelm, G., and Voigt, I. (1967). *Nahrung* **11**, 149.
Rzhekhin, V. P., and Pogonkina, N. I. (1958). *Maslob.-Zhir. Prom.* **24**, 6.
Sagredos, A. N. (1967). *Fette, Seifen, Anstrichmittel* **69**, 707.
Sahasrabudhe, M. R., and Bhalerao, V. R. (1963). *J. Am. Oil Chemists' Soc.* **40**, 711.
Sahasrabudhe, M. R., and Farn, I. G. (1964). *J. Am. Oil Chemists' Soc.* **41**, 264.
Said, F., Amer, M. M., and Ahmad, A. K. (1964). *Fette, Seifen, Anstrichmittel* **66**, 1000.
Sasaki, R., Otake, Y., and Miyazaki, M. (1951). *Eiyo To Shokuryo* **3**, 139. (*Chem. Abstr.* **47**, 2393.)
Schauenstein, E. (1967). *J. Lipid Res.* **8**, 417.
Schauenstein, E., and Esterbauer, H. (1968). *Fette, Seifen, Anstrichmittel* **70**, 4.
Schoellner, R., and Herzschuh, R. (1966a). *Fette, Seifen, Anstrichmittel* **68**, 469.
Schoellner, R., and Herzschuh, R. (1966b). *Fette, Seifen, Anstrichmittel* **68**, 616.
Schogt, J. C. M., and Begemann, P. H. (1965). *J. Lipid Res.* **6**, 466.
Scholfield, C. R., and Cowan, J. C. (1959). *J. Am. Oil Chemists' Soc.* **36**, 631.
Scholz, R. G., and Ptak, L. R. (1966). *J. Am. Oil Chemists' Soc.* **43**, 596.
Schultz, H. W., Day, E. A., and Sinnhuber, R. O., eds. (1962). "Symposium on Foods: Lipids and Their Oxidation." Avi, Westport, Connecticut.
Schwartz, D. P., Johnson, A. R., and Parks, O. W. (1962a). *Microchem. J.* **6**, 37.
Schwartz, D. P., Parks, O. W., and Keeney, M. (1962b). *Anal. Chem.* **34**, 669.
Schwartz, D. P., Haller, H. S., and Keeney, M. (1963). *Anal. Chem.* **35**, 2191.
Sedlacek, B. A. J. (1964). *Nahrung* **8**, 58.
Sedlacek, B. A. J. (1966a). *Nahrung* **10**, 155.
Sedlacek, B. A. J. (1966b). *Nahrung* **10**, 581.
Sedlacek, B. A. J. (1966c). *Fette, Seifen, Anstrichmittel* **68**, 725.
Seher, A. (1967). *Nahrung* **11**, 825.
Selva, D. (1956). *Boll. Soc. Ital. Biol. Sper.* **32**, 1059.
Sen Gupta, A. K. (1966). *Fette, Seifen, Anstrichmittel* **68**, 475.

Sen Gupta, A. K. (1967a). Abstracts of Papers, Am. Oil Chemists' Soc. Meeting, October, 1967. *J. Am. Oil Chemists' Soc.* **44**(8), 386A.

Sen Gupta, A. K. (1967b). *Fette, Seifen, Anstrichmittel* **69**, 907.

Sephton, H. H., and Sutton, D. A. (1953). *Chem. Ind. (London)* p. 667.

Shil'man, L. Z. (1964). *Izv. Vysshikh Uchebn. Zavedenii, Pishchevaya Tekhnol.* p. 67.

Shue, G. M., Douglass, C. D., Firestone, D., Friedman, Leo, Friedman, Leonard, and Sage, J. S. (1968). *J. Nutr.* **94**, 171.

Silvestre, J. (1960). *Trav. Soc. Pharm. Montpellier* **20**, 182.

Simko, V., and Bucko, A. (1963). *Cesk. Gastroenterol. Vyziva* **17**, 86.

Simko, V., Bucko, A., and Ondreicka, R. (1961). *Cesk. Gastroenterol. Vyziva* **15**, 429. (*Chem. Abstr.* **57**, 7690.)

Simko, V., Bucko, A., Babala, J., and Ondreicka, R. (1963). *Nutr. Dieta* **6**, 91.

Sims, R. P. A. (1957). *J. Am. Oil Chemists' Soc.* **34**, 466.

Skellon, J. H. (1963). *J. Oil Colour Chemists' Assoc.* **46**, 1001.

Skellon, J. H., and Wharry, D. M. (1963). *Chem. Ind. (London)* p. 929.

Slover, H. T., and Dugan, L. R., Jr. (1957). *J. Am. Oil Chemists' Soc.* **34**, 333.

Smouse, T. H., and Chang, S. S. (1967). *J. Am. Oil Chemists' Soc.* **44**, 509.

Smouse, T. H., Mookherjee, B. D., and Chang, S. S. (1965). *Chem. Ind. (London)* p. 1301.

Soukup, R. J., Scarpellino, R. J., and Danielczik, E. (1964). *Anal. Chem.* **36**, 2255.

Stapf, R. J., and Daubert, B. F. (1950). *J. Am. Oil Chemists' Soc.* **27**, 374.

Steibert, E., and Sliwiok, J. (1966). *Przemysl Spozywczy* **20**, 394. (*Chem. Abstr.* **66**, 94062.)

Stern, S., and Roth, H. (1959). *Cereal Sci. Today* **4**, 176.

Stoerk, H. C., Kaunitz, H., and Slanetz, C. A. (1952). *A.M.A. Arch. Pathol.* **53**, 15. (*Chem. Abstr.* **46**, 8208.)

Strock, H., Ball, C. O., Chang, S. S., and Stier, E. F. (1966). *Food Technol.* **20**, 545.

Strock, H., Ball, C. O., and Chang, S. S. (1967). *Food Technol.* **21**, 649.

Sugai, M., Witting, L. A., Tsuchiyama, H., and Kummerow, F. A. (1962). *Cancer Res.* **22**, 510.

Suhara, Y. (1965). *Tokyo Kogyo Shikenso Hokoku* **60**, 264. (*Chem. Abstr.* **64**, 6914.)

Suzuki, Y., and Takeuchi, T. (1964). *Yukagaku* **13**, 431. (*J. Am. Oil Chemists' Soc.* **41** (11), 30A.)

Swift, C. E., and Dollear, F. G. (1948). *J. Am. Oil Chemists' Soc.* **25**, 52.

Swift, C. E., Dollear, F. G., and O'Connor, R. T. (1946). *Oil Soap*, **23**, 355.

Swoboda, P. A. T., and Lea, C. H. (1965). *J. Sci. Food Agr.* **16**, 680.

Taeufel, K., and Heder, G. (1963). *Fette, Seifen, Anstrichmittel* **65**, 85.

Taeufel, K., and Zimmermann, R. (1960). *Nahrung* **4**, 1010. (*Chem. Abstr.* **55**, 13701.)

Taeufel, K., Franzke, C., and Hoppe, H. (1958). *Deut. Lebensm.-Rundschau* **54**, 245.

Taeufel, K., Franzke, C., and Leske, E. (1959). *Nahrung* **3**, 270.

Tarladgis, B. G., Pearson, A. M., and Dugan, L. R., Jr. (1964). *J. Sci. Food Agr.* **15**, 602.

Thompson, J. A. (1968). Ph.D. Thesis, Rutgers Univ., New Brunswick, New Jersey.

Thompson, J. A., Paulose, M. M., Reddy, B. R., Krishnamurthy, R. G., and Chang, S. S. (1967). *Food Technol.* **21**, 405.

Timms, E. (1963). *Australian J. Dairy Technol.* p. 106.

Tobolsky, A. V., Metz, D. J., and Mesrobian, R. B. (1950). *J. Am. Chem. Soc.* **72**, 1942.

Toi, B., Ota, S., and Iwata, N. (1961). *Yukagaku* **10**, 536.

Toi, B., Ota, S., and Iwata, N. (1962a). *Yukagaku* **11**, 504. (*Chem. Abstr.* **58**, 10414.)

Toi, B., Ota, S., and Iwata, N. (1962b). *Yukagaku* **11**, 508. (*Chem. Abstr.* **58**, 10414.)

Torres, D., Trinchese, T., Foley, Sr. E., and Krabinos, J. V. (1956). *Trans. Illinois State Acad. Sci.* 49, 205.
Toyomizu, M. (1961). *Nippon Suisan Gakkaishi* 27, 323. (*Chem. Abstr.* 57, 6043.)
Tsukamoto, T. (1960). *Pharm. Acta Helv.* 35, 431. (*Chem. Abstr.* 55, 4991.)
Ueno, S., and Sakurai, H. (1949). *Kogyo Kagaku Zasshi* 52, 256. (*Chem. Abstr.* 45, 4463.)
Uezumi, N., Yamada, T., and Fukuda, H. (1962). *Eiyo To Shokuryo* 15, 15.
Uri, N. (1967). *Chem. Ind. (London)* p. 2060.
Utyumova-Malova, A. V., and Vershinin, A. A. (1966). *Vopr. Pitaniya* 25, 54. (*Chem. Abstr.* 66, 54355.)
Uzzan, A., and Lobry, R. (1958). *Rev. Franc. Corps Gras* 5, 233.
vander Poel, G. H. (1961). *Neth. Milk Dairy J.* 15, 98. (*Chem. Abstr.* 55, 13701.)
Van Duuren, B. L., and Goldschmidt, B. M. (1966). *J. Med. Chem.* 9, 77.
Van Duuren, B. L., Langseth, L., Orris, L., Teebor, C., Nelson, N., and Kuschner, M. (1966). *J. Natl. Cancer Inst.* 37, 825.
Van Duuren, B. L., Langseth, L., Orris, L., Baden, M., and Kuschner, M. (1967a). *J. Natl. Cancer Inst.* 39, 1213.
Van Duuren, B. L., Langseth, L., Goldschmidt, B. M., and Orris, L. (1967b). *J. Natl. Cancer Inst.* 39, 1217.
Vioque, A., and Maza, M. P. (1967). *Grasas Aceites (Seville, Spain)* 18, 302.
Vioque, A., Albi, M. A., and Villagran, M. P. (1964). *J. Am. Oil Chemists' Soc.* 41, 785.
Vioque, A., Gutierrez, R., Albi, M. A., and Nosti, N. (1965a). *J. Am. Oil Chemists' Soc.* 42, 344.
Vioque, A., Gutierrez, R., Albi, M. A., and Nosti, N. (1965b). *Grasas Aceites (Seville, Spain)* 16, 235.
Walens, H. A., Koob, R. P., Ault, W. C., and Maerker, G. (1965). *J. Am. Oil Chemists' Soc.* 42, 126.
Warner, W. D., Abell, P. N., Mone, P. E., Pulling, C. E., and Rice, E. E. (1962). *J. Am. Dietet. Assoc.* 40, 122.
Watanabe, H., and Toyama, Y. (1958). *Mem. Fac. Eng., Nagoya Univ.* 10, 95.
Waterman, H. I., Cordia, J. P., and Pennekamp, B. (1949). *Research (London)* 2, 483.
Watt, B. K., and Merrill, A. L. (1963). "Composition of Foods," Agr. Handbook No. 8. U.S. Dept. of Agr., Washington, D.C.
Werner, H., and Wurziger, J. (1966). *Fette, Seifen, Anstrichmittel* 68, 441.
Wheeler, D. H., and White, J. (1967). *J. Am. Oil Chemists' Soc.* 44, 298.
Whitmore, W. F., and Gerecht, J. F. (1950). *J. Am. Chem. Soc.* 72, 790.
Wieske, T., and Rinke, H. (1967). *Fette, Seifen, Anstrichmittel* 69, 503.
Wilding, M. D., Rice, E. E., and Mattil, K. F. (1963). *J. Am. Oil Chemists' Soc.* 40, 55.
Wilkinson, R. A., and Stark, W. (1967). *J. Dairy Res.* 34, 89.
Williamson, L. (1953). *J. Appl. Chem. (London)* 3, 301.
Wiseblatt, L., Wells, A. F., and Common, R. H. (1953). *J. Sci. Food Agr.* 4, 227.
Wishner, L. A., and Keeney, M. (1965). *J. Am. Oil Chemists' Soc.* 42, 776.
Witting, L. A., Nishida, T., Johnson, O. C., and Kummerow, F. A. (1957). *J. Am. Oil Chemists' Soc.* 34, 421.
Wode, G. (1957). *Nord. Symposium om Harskning af Fedtstoffer, 2nd Symposium, Helsinki* p. 181. (*Chem. Abstr.* 52, 17757.)
Wurziger, J., and Junker, M. (1963). *Deut. Lebensm.-Rundschau* 59, 133.
Wurziger, J., and Lindemann, E. (1959). *Fette, Seifen, Anstrichmittel* 61, 257.
Yasuda, K., Reddy, B. R., and Chang, S. S. (1968). *J. Am. Oil Chemists' Soc.* 45, 625.
Yu, T. C., and Sinnhuber, R. O. (1964). *J. Am. Oil Chemists' Soc.* 41, 540.

Yuki, E. (1967a). *Yukagaku* **16**, 351. (*Chem. Abstr.* **67**, 42687.)
Yuki, E. (1967b). *Yukagaku* **16**, 410. (*Chem. Abstr.* **67**, 89872.)
Yuki, E. (1967c). *Yukagaku* **16**, 449. (*Chem. Abstr.* **67**, 89873.)
Yuki, E. (1967d). *Yukagaku* **16**, 499. (*Chem. Abstr.* **67**, 115908.)
Yuki, E. (1967e). *Yukagaku* **16**, 545. (*Chem. Abstr.* **68**, 2075.)
Yuki, E. (1967f). *Yukagaku* **16**, 600. (*Chem. Abstr.* **68**, 38322.)
Yuki, E. (1967g). *Yukagaku* **16**, 654. (*Chem. Abstr.* **68**, 38324.)
Yuki, E. (1968). *Yukagaku* **17**, 61. (*Chem. Abstr.* **68**, 86249.)

AUTHOR INDEX

A

Abdelhamid, S., 231, *237*
Abdin, F. H., 300, *323*
Abdulla, Y. H., 4, 15, 16, 19, 21, 25, 32, 36, 47, 48, 49, *56, 57, 62*
Abe, H., 97, *132*
Abell, L. L., 104, *127*
Abell, M. R., 227, *239*
Abell, P. N., 301, *329*
Abraham, S., 74, 85, 86, 108, *124, 125, 130*
Abrams, M. E., 41, *61*
Abramson, W., 222, *237*
Abul-Hay, S. K., 5, *61*
Acker, P., 288, *322*
Ackerman, R. F., 39, *62*
Ada, G. L., 33, *56*
Adams, C. W. M., 4, 5, 6, 7, 8, 9, 11, 14, 15, 16, 17, 19, 21, 22, 24, 25, 26, 27, 28, 29, 30, 31, 32, 33, 35, 36, 39, 40, 41, 46, 47, 48, 49, 50, 51, 52, 53, 54, 56, *56, 57, 58, 60, 61, 62*
Adams Smith, W. N., 14, 57, *61*
Adlersberg, D., 80, 81, *124*
Aftergood, L., 267, *315*
Ahern, J. J., 311, *325*
Ahmad, A. K., 311, *327*
Ahrens, E. H., Jr., 100, 104, 121, 122, *124, 128*
Ailhoud, G. P., 84, *133*
Akiya, T., 272, 277, 285, *315*
Albers, R., 35, *60*
Albert, S., 14, 57 191, *237*
Alberts, A. W., 84, *133*
Albi, M. A., 249, *329*
Albright, F., 228, *237*
Albrink, M. J., 64, 80, 81, 101, 103, 108, 113, 122, *124, 126, 133*

Alexander, J. C., 264, 270, 273, 274, 275, 276, 278, 282, 292, 293, 296, 298, 303, 310, 313, *315, 320, 324*
Alexander, N. M., 107, 109, *124, 132*
Alfin-Slater, R. B., 267, *315*
Algard, F. T., 209, 234, *237, 241*
Allan, J. C., 82, *127*
Allen, E., 194, 205, 206, 207, *237, 240, 243*
Allen, F. M., 94, *124*
Allman, D. W., 107, 109, *124*
Altman, K. I., 72, *124*
Altszuler, N., 76, *124*
Amaral, J. A. P., 82, 96, *125*
Amer, M. M., 311, *327*
Anderson, J. T., 112, *124*
Anderson, R. H., 259, *315*
Andervont, H. B., 193, 198, *243, 244*
Andrews, F., 310, *315*
Andrews, J. S., 253, *315*
Andrus, W. DeW., 221, *240*
Angelini, P., 255, *318*
Antoniades, H. N., 209, 210, *237, 243*
Antonis, A., 64, 104, 118, *124*
Applewhite, T. H., 311, *315*
Arai, K., 285, *315*
Arata, D. A., 112, *127*
Arenson, S. W., 311, *315*
Arffmann, E., 189, *237* 304, 305, *315, 319*
Ariel, I. M., 229, *243*
Arky, R. A., 70, 77, 78, 79, 97, *128*
Armin, J., 86, *124*
Armstrong, D. T., 76, *124*
Arnesjö, B., 102, *132*
Arpels, C., 221, *237*
Arpino, A., 262, *316*
Artman, N. R., 270, 273, 274, 275, 276, 278, 282, 292, 293, 296, 298, 303, 313, *315, 324*
Ashburn, L. L., 6, 56, *60*

Ashmore, J., 71, 73, 76, 82, 83, 86, 87, 89, 124, 129, 131, 132, 133
Askonas, B. A., 33, 56
Athias, M., 198, 237
Auerbach, S., 267, 315
Ault, W. C., 250, 274, 323, 325, 329
Axt, J., 262, 315
Ayres, G. B., 203, 242

B

Baba, N., 191, 192, 237
Babala, J., 282, 328
Babayan, V. K., 259, 260, 321
Babcock, V. I., 221, 237
Bacon, E. K., 269, 322
Bacon, R. L., 208, 237, 241
Baden, M., 305, 329
Badger, G. M., 217, 237
Baer, T., 178, 189, 242
Baessler, K. H., 277, 284, 306, 321
Bagdade, J. D., 94, 95, 97, 112, 124, 131
Bagul, C. D., 14, 59
Bahr, G. F., 16, 57
Bailar, J. C., 227, 237
Bailey, E., 115, 124
Bailey, J. M., 138, 139, 144, 146, 147, 148, 150, 152, 153, 154, 155, 156, 157, 161
Baker, R., 301, 317
Baker, J. R., 5, 15, 21, 49, 50, 57
Baker, N., 65, 66, 78, 79, 83, 101, 102, 103, 108, 114, 115, 124, 127, 128
Baker, W. H., 226, 241
Bálint, Z., 6, 59
Ball, C. O., 290, 295, 328
Ball, E. G., 76, 128
Ball, J. J., 95, 124
Balodimos, M. C., 95, 124
Bang, I., 94, 124
Bangham, A. D., 3, 57
Balodimos, M. C., 124
Banks, A., 249, 315
Banu, C., 270, 315
Barbieri, G., 191, 194, 237, 243
Barnes, I. J., 254, 325
Barnes, R. H., 309, 315
Bar-On, H., 107, 112, 113, 114, 115, 116, 124
Barone, B. J., 274, 316
Barrett, C. B., 273, 315

Barrett, M. K., 188, 242
Barrnett, R. J., 49, 61
Baserga, R., 35, 57, 212, 237
Barsky, R. F., 101, 129
Bartley, W., 115, 124
Barzilai, D., 112, 128
Bassett, D. R., 129
Bates, M. W., 99, 124
Bates, R. W., 291, 294, 315
Batts, A. A., 113, 127
Bayliss, O. B., 4, 15, 16, 19, 21, 24, 25, 27, 28, 29, 30, 31, 32, 33, 35, 36, 39, 40, 41, 47, 48, 49, 51, 52, 53, 54, 57, 58, 62
Bazinet, M. L., 255, 318
Beal, R. E., 264, 315, 317
Beare, J. L., 292, 315
Beaumont, J. L., 101, 102, 133
Beck, S., 304, 325
Becker, E., 248, 268, 289, 292, 293, 294, 296, 311, 312, 315
Begemann, P. H., 249, 252, 264, 315, 327
Belfrage, P., 69, 124
Belknap, B. H., 82, 96, 125
Bell, E. W., 264, 318
Bell, J. T., 11, 61
Bellet, S., 94, 132
Belt, W. D., 15, 48, 58
Benca, M. F., 312, 319
Benedetti, E. L., 207, 244
Bengmark, S., 219, 237
Benjamin, W., 85, 127
Bennett, A., 138, 161
Bennett, M. A., 27, 58
Bennett, L. L., 113, 127
Bennion, M., 292, 296, 298, 315, 316
Bensch, K. G., 146, 152, 161
Benton, D. A., 112, 127
Bentz, A. P., 312, 318
Berenbaum, M. C., 8, 58
Berenblum, I., 168, 237
Bergan, J. G., 249, 254, 309, 322
Bergmann, W., 216, 237
Bergström, S., 176, 237
Berkowitz, D., 94, 124
Berliner, D. L., 152, 161, 232, 237
Berliner, M. L., 232, 237
Berlureau, F., 286, 289, 317
Berman, M., 66, 126
Bern, H. A., 220, 243
Berryhill, F. M., 268, 317

Bersohn, I., 64, 104, 118, *124*
Berwald, Y., 219, *237*
Beuving, L., 204, *237*
Beveridge, J. M. R., 118, *124*
Bewsher, P. D., 73, *124*
Bezman, A., 79, 103, 106, *124, 130*
Bhalerao, V. R., 271, 272, 313, *317, 327*
Bhattacharya, S., 283, *317*
Bhalerao, V. R., 271, 307, *316*
Biegler, R., 64, 81, *132*
Bierman, E. L., 76, 80, 81, 82, 89, 94, 95, 96, 97, 112, 118, 122, *124, 125, 130, 131*
Biette, E., 309, *326*
Binet, L., 286, *316*
Bischoff, F., 166, 169, 170, 171, 174, 175, 176, 177, 178, 179, 180, 181, 184, 185, 189, 195, 197, 198, 200, 202, 203, 206, 209, 210, 211, 212, 213, 215, 218, 219, 222, 224, 225, 226, 228, 229, 230, 232, 234, *237, 238, 244*, 305, *316*
Bishop, J. S., 76, *124*
Biskind, G. R., 202, 208, *238, 242*
Biskind, M. S., 208, *238*
Bito, T., 294, 295, 296, *316*
Bittner, J. J., 198, *238*
Björntorp, P., 90, 97, 121, *125, 131*
Bjorksten, J., 310, *315*
Black, D. R., 255, *320*
Blackwood, W., 40, *58*
Bleisch, V. R., 99, *125*
Blickenstaff, D., 304, *322*
Blix, G., 80, 81, 94, *125*
Bloch, C., 311, *323*
Block, K., 71, *125*
Block, Z., 291, 294, 297, *319*
Blomstrand, R., 104, *124*
Blondheim, S. H., 112, *128*
Bloom, H. J. G., 227, *238*
Bloomfield, G. F., 247, 250, *318*
Bloor, W. R., 94, *125*
Blumenthal, M. D., 74, *125*
Bly, C. G., 72, *124*
Bock, F. G., 203, *238, 239*
Boda, J. M., *125*
Boden, G., 73, 85, *125*
Bodian, M., 40, *58*
Boehle, E., 64, 81, *127, 132*
Boelhouwer, C., 262, 267, 313, *316*

Boelsma-Van Houte, E., 25, 26, 39, *58*
Böttcher, C. J. F., 25, 26, 39, *58*
Bogdonoff, M. D., 66, *127*
Bøhmer, T., 87, 88, 107, *125*
Bole, G. G., Jr., 144, *161*
Bolinger, R. E., 90, *126*
Bollman, J. L., 113, *125*
Bolvard, M. N., 168, *244*
Bolzano, K., 101, 102, 119, 122, 123, *132*
Bonsen, P. P. M., 10, *58*
Bonnet, J., 178, 189, *242*
Bonser, G. M., 176, 193, *238, 239*
Booij, H. L., 16, *61*
Boot, L. M., 200, *238*
Bornstein, S., 261, *323*
Bortz, W. M., 84, 86, 87, 108, *124, 125, 131*
Bosshard, G., 262, *325*
Bourgeois, C., 21, 50, *58*
Boussagol, 287, *317*
Bowman, R. H., 86, *131*
Boxer, G. E., 82, *133*
Boyce, C. R., 197, *243*
Boyland, E., 176, *238*
Boyle, J. J., 138, *161*
Brady, R. O., 71, 83, 85, 86, 87, *125, 131*
Bradley, R. M., 85, 86, 87, *125, 131*
Bradley, T. F., 263, *316*
Bragdon, J. H., 101, 102, 103, 106, 111, *125*
Braithwaite, D. M., 112, *129*
Brander, W., 8, *60*
Braunsteiner, H., 81, 89, 91, 101, 102, 119, 121, 122, 123, *125, 131, 132*
Brech, W. J., 119, *125*
Bremer, J., 86, *125*
Brents, Y. M., 295, 296, *323*
Brill, W. F., 274, *316*
Brockerhoff, H., 4,
Brodnitz, M. H., 271, *316*
Brodoff, B., 76, 77, *131*
Brotz, M., 15, 47, *60*
Brown, D. F., 78, 82, 95, 96, 97, *125*
Brown, J. H., 224, *241*
Brown, N. H., 212, *240*
Brown, R. R., 176, *238*
Brown, S. J., 68, *131*
Brown, T. O., 76, 77, 78, 90, 91, 92, 93, 96, 102, 103, *128, 133*
Bruno, D., 111, *131*

Bryan, G. T., 176, 238
Bryant, J. C., 144, 152, 161
Bryson, G., 169, 170, 171, 174, 175, 177, 178, 180, 181, 184, 189, 197, 202, 206, 209, 210, 211, 213, 218, 219, 222, 225, 226, 229, 230, 232, 234, 238
Bruns, G., 178, 238
Bubis, J. J., 9, 58
Buchsbaum, R., 221, 240
Buchko, M., 148, 162
Bucko, A., 270, 282, 285, 325, 328
Budowski, P., 261, 323
Bulbrook, R. D., 228, 244
Bullock, F. D., 197, 202, 238
Bunyan, J., 254, 316
Burch, H. B., 86, 88, 128
Burg, K. H., 251, 258, 317
Burket, S. C., 250, 316
Burlakova, E. V., 309, 316
Burnet, M., 313, 316, 317
Burns, C. H., 151, 161
Burns, E. L., 193, 194, 200, 238, 242
Burt, R. L., 70, 101, 126
Burtner, H. J., 31, 60
Busby, E. R., 176, 238
Busch, K. A., 202, 239
Butcher, R. W., 76, 92, 125, 126
Butler, A. M., 228, 237
Buttery, R. G., 254, 319
Butterfield, W. J. H., 89, 125
Buu-Hoi, N. P., 218, 242
Byers, S. O., 33, 59

C

Cady, P., 33, 59
Cagan, R. N., 82, 125
Cahill, G. F., Jr., 72, 73, 127, 134
Cain, A. J., 7, 17, 21, 26, 55, 58
Calbert, C. E., 301, 317
Calciano, A., 122, 131
Caldwell, A. B., 292, 318
Campbell, J. A., 232, 239
Cameron, J. S., 73, 125
Candea, D., 270, 316
Candy, J., 227, 239
Cannon, J. A., 250, 257, 316, 318
Cantarow, A., 204, 239
Canzanelli, A., 85, 132

Cape, W. E., 5, 62
Capella, I. P., 262, 267, 316, 318
Carbonaro, L., 81, 94, 128
Carlin, G. T., 291, 292, 294, 316, 322
Carlson, L. A., 64, 68, 69, 76, 82, 89, 98, 110, 125, 127, 128
Carpenter, K. J., 261, 286, 289, 309, 316, 322, 323
Carruthers, C., 144, 146, 161
Carruthers, P. J., 76, 132
Casley-Smith, J. R., 32, 58
Caspersson, T., 2, 58
Cass, A., 4, 59
Castleman, J. K., 272, 319
Castor, C. W., 144, 161
Castro, A. J., 213, 244
Cawthorne, M. A., 254, 316
Chahine, M. H., 270, 291, 297, 300, 316, 323
Chai, B., 119, 126
Chaikoff, I. L., 71, 72, 74, 75, 80, 82, 83, 84, 85, 86, 96, 107, 108, 109, 113, 114, 115, 124, 125, 126, 127, 128, 129, 130, 131, 134
Chalmers, J. G., 262, 304, 316
Chalvardjian, A., 278, 316
Champetier, G., 265, 316
Chang, C. -L., 309, 322
Chang, H. C., 100, 125
Chang, S. S., 255, 257, 258, 290, 295, 297, 299, 316, 320, 321, 322, 324, 327, 328, 329
Charles, D., 193, 239
Chayen, J., 8, 60
Chen, T. T., 219, 239
Cherkes, A., 76, 102, 127
Chernick, S. S., 74, 82, 83, 91, 93, 98, 108, 114, 125, 126, 129, 132
Cherry, C. P., 227, 239
Chevallier, F., 75, 108, 128
Ching, T. T., 78, 101, 131
Chipault, J. R., 312, 324
Christensen, B. C., 189, 237
Christophe, J., 99, 107, 108, 114, 115, 126, 127, 134
Chu, T.-K., 309, 322
Clark, J. R., 35, 60
Clark, P. J., 228, 241
Clarke, G. J., 195, 198, 238
Claude, J. R., 101, 102, 133

Clayson, D. B., 176, *238, 239*
Clement, G. H., 309, *316*
Clifford, R., 228, *244*
Clingman, A. L., 265, *316*
Cluzan, R., 279, *326*
Cobb, W. Y., 255, *316*
Cobern, D., 249, 250, *317*
Cockrell, B., 204, *244*
Codoceo, R., 74, *130*
Cody, R., 122, *131*
Cohen, A. M., 114, *126*
Cohen, N. N., 107, 108, 114, 115, 121, *129*
Cole, L. G., 229, *239*
Cole, W. G., 229, *239*
Coles, L., 314, *317*
Collip, J. B., 191, 202, *242, 243*
Common, R. H., 263, 268, 278, 279, 313, *317, 329*
Connell, W. F., 118, *124*
Connor, W. E., 94, *133*
Conway, H., 221, *240*
Cook, J. W., 217, *237*
Coombs, M. M., 217, *239*
Cooney, P. M., 257, 258, *318*
Cooper, F. P., 263, 268, 275, *323*
Coore, H. G., 113, *126*
Corbett, B. N., 101, 102, *131*
Corbin, E. A., 255, *317*
Cordia, J. P., 263, *329*
Corman, L., 107, *132*
Cornatzer, W. E., 144, 145, *163*
Corvilain, J., 113, *126*
Coval, M., 86, *130*
Cowan, J. C., 264, 271, 275, 311, 313, *318, 319, 327*
Craig, J. M., 148, 150, *163*, 192, *240*
Craig, J. W., 113, 114, *126, 130*
Crampton, E. W., 268, 278, 279, 313, *317*
Crawford, D. L., 268, 278, 279, 310, 313, *317*
Creutzfeldt, W., 90, *132*
Criegie, R., 17, *58*
Cristofalo, V. J., 152, *161*
Croft, C. J., 217, *239*
Crossley, A., 253, 257, 262, *317*
Crouch, S., 203, *239*
Crowder, J. A., 274, *317*
Crowley, L. G., 224, *239*
Cruz, J. R., 255, *317*
Csavossy, I., 309, *323*

Csorba, T. R., 76, 77, 90, *126*
Cumings, J. N., 39, 40, *58*
Currie, G. T., 253, 255, *317, 319*
Curtis, M. R., 190, 197, 202, 221, *238, 239*
Curtis, R. G., 149, 150, *161*
Custof, F., 291, 292, 294, *317*
Cutts, J. H., 194, 202, 203, *239, 243*
Czok, G., 253, 277, 278, 281, 306, 309, *317, 321*

D

Daddi, L., 6, *58*
Dagenais, Y., 99, *126*
Daikuhara, Y., 84, *133*
Dakhil, T., 308, *317*
Dam, H., 31, 59, 254, *319*
Dane, E., 216, *244*
Dangoumau, A., 286, 287, 289, *317*
Danielczik, E., 312, *328*
Dannenberg, II., 178, 180, 181, 213, 216, 217, *239*
Dannenburg, W. N., 70, 101, *126*
Dao, T. L., 202, 203, 204, *238, 239*
Daubert, B. F., 255, *328*
Daunas, J., 76, 77, *131*
Davidson, P. C., 108, 113, 122, *124, 126, 133*
Davis, C. L., 202, *244*
Davis, H. II., 222, *239*
Davis, J. B., 222, 223, *239, 242*
Davis, J. N., 36, *58*
Davis, M. E., 212, *239*
Davis, R. K., 202, *239*
Davis, L. L., 121, *127*
Davison, A. N., 24, 33, 35, 40, 52, *57*
Dawson, A. M., 113, *128*
Day, A. J., 39, 41, 58, 60, 136, *161*
Day, E. A., 246, 255, 259, 269, *316, 323, 327*
Dayan, A. D., 29, 40, 54, *58*
Deatherage, F. E., 273, 274, *317*
Deb, C., 15, *60*
de Bodo, R. C., 76, *124*
Debruyne, H., 286, 287, 289, *317*
Deck, R. E., 299, *324*
Degkwitz, E., 277, 278, 285, 307, *317, 321*
de Goursac, F., 271, 272, 273, *325*
De Haas, G. H., 10, *58*

Deierkauf, F. A., 6, 59
Denborough, M. A., 97, 126
Deringer, M. K., 200, 241
Derrow, A., 85, 132
Derry, D. M., 35, 58
Des Ligneris, M. J. A., 168, 174, 239
Desmond, W., 138, 139, 140, 162
Desnuelle, P., 313, 316, 317, 324
de Trey, M., 178, 189, 242
Dettmer, D., 90, 129
Deuel, H. J., 22, 58
Deuel, H. J., Jr., 113, 126, 301, 317
De Waard, F., 224, 239
DeZotti, G., 262, 316
Diamond, E., 228, 241
Dickie, M. M., 99, 125
Diddle, A. W., 224, 239
Diezel, P. B., 7, 27, 29, 41, 54, 56, 58
Dimel, R., 5, 32, 58
Dimick, M. K., 70, 129
Dingwall, J. A., 221, 240
DiPauli, R., 122, 125
DiPietro, D. L., 74, 126
Diplock, A. T., 254, 316
Dishmon, G., 91, 92, 134
Dixon, K. C., 4, 58
Dnochowski, L., 195, 239
Dobbin, V., 104, 130
Doi, H., 77, 131
Dole, V. P., 65, 75, 76, 89, 102, 125, 126
Dolev, A., 253, 254, 255, 318, 324
Dollear, F. G., 248, 249, 259, 274, 328
Donker, C. H. M., 8, 58
Dormandy, T. L., 113, 132
Dornseifer, T. P., 295, 299, 317
Dougherty, T. F., 152, 161, 195, 196, 232, 237, 239, 240
Douglass, C. D., 307, 328
Drägert, W., 90, 132
Draper, H. H., 249, 254, 309, 322
Drucker, W. R., 113, 114, 126, 130
Drury, D. R., 82, 126
Dubravcic, M. F., 263, 324
Dugan, L. R., Jr., 248, 250, 311, 328
Dulog, L., 248, 249, 251, 258, 317, 321
Dumain, J., 270, 292, 293, 294, 297, 322, 326
Dumenigo, F., 221, 239
Dunkerley, A., 76, 77, 78, 90, 91, 128
Dunlop, W. R., 138, 163

Dunn, A., 76, 124
Dunn, H. J., 269, 322
Dunn, J. A., 174, 181, 239, 241
Dunnigan, M. G., 9, 51, 58
Dunning, W. F., 190, 202, 221, 239, 243
Dury, A., 68, 126
Dutton, H. J., 249, 250, 257, 316, 318

E

Eastwood, G., 292, 318
Eaton, R. P., 66, 126
Eddy, C. R., 250, 321
Eder, H. A., 68, 127, 157, 162
Edgar, G. W. F., 8, 58
Edgren, B., 69, 124
Edson, N. L., 113, 126
Eger-Neufeldt, I., 84, 85, 87, 90, 133, 134
Eigenbrodt, E. H., 65, 127
Eik-Nes, K., 209, 239
Einarson, L., 31, 58
Eisen, M. J., 202, 239
Eisenhauer, R. A., 264, 315, 317
Eisler, L., 80, 81, 124
Eisner, A., 250, 325
Ekelund, L.-G., 110, 125
Eker, P., 221, 243
Elbers, P. F., 5, 16, 32, 58
Elftman, H., 5, 58
El-Hawwary, N. M., 270, 291, 297, 300, 316, 323
Elias, J. J., 220, 239, 243
Elleder, M., 9, 16, 22, 24, 58
Elliott, H., 64, 127
Ellis, G. W., 273, 317
Ellis, R., 253, 255, 257, 274, 317, 319
Elm, A. C., 274, 317
Elvehjem, C. A., 112, 127
Emerson, G. A., 309, 317
Endres, J. G., 271, 272, 278, 317, 325
Enei, H., 270, 272, 325
Engel, F. L., 100, 129
Engle, E. T., 205, 239
Entenman, C., 92, 110, 128
Ernest, I., 94, 126
Ervin, D. M., 94, 126
Escribano, L., 269, 289, 326
Esh, G. C., 283, 317
Eshchar, J., 112, 128
Esterbauer, H., 255, 256, 318, 321, 327
Estes, E. H., 66, 127

Evans, C. D., 249, 250, 255, 257, 258, 271, 275, 311, 313, *318*
Evans, H. M., 190, 191, *241*
Evans, L. E., 254, 325
Evans, V. J., 144, 152, *161*
Evans, W. H., 76, *130*
Exton, J. H., 92, 113, *126*

F

Fagan, V. M., 86, *132*
Fagerson, I. S., 271, *316*
Falk, H. L., 169, *239*
Fallon, H. J., 106, 107, 115, *126*
Fang, M., 87, *126*
Farmer, E. H., 247, 249, 250, *318*
Farmer, F. A., 268, 278, 279, 313, *317*
Farn, I. G., 271, 275, *327*
Farquhar, J. W., 65, 100, 104, 106, 118, 121, 122, 123, *124, 126, 127, 131*
Farr, A. L., 35, *60*
Fauvel, J., 222, 223, *239*
Faucquembergue, D., 270, 292, 293, 294, 297, *322, 326*
Favati, V., 212, *238*
Fazakerley, S., 240, *315*
Fedeli, E., 249, 267, *318, 320*
Feigen, L., 11, *58*
Feinberg, F., 94, *130*
Feinleib, M., 223, *239*
Fekete, E., 198, *239*
Felber, J. P., 122, *126*
Feldman, R., 170, *244*
Felton, L., 33, *59*
Felts, J. M., 65, 66, 79, 83, 92, 93, 102, 103, 106, 108, 110, 111, *124, 126, 128, 130, 131*
Feng, L., 114, 121, *129*
Ferrigno, M., 191, *240*
Feulgen, R., 26, *58*
Feustel, E.-M., 5, *58*
Feyrter, F., 29, *59*
Fieser, L. F., 169, 175, 177, 185, 216, *240*
Fieser, M., 185, *240*
Fine, M. B., 76, 119, *126*
Finkelstein, A., 4, *59*
Fioriti, J. A., 255, 273, 276, 312, *318*
Firestone, D., 269, 274, 278, 279, 281, 284, 307, *318, 328*
Fischer, W., 175, 188, *243*
Fischler, F. J., 14, *59*

Fisher, E. A., 71, 75, 85, *133*
Fisher, H. R., 301, *317*
Fitch, W. M., 84, 109, 115, *126*
Fitts, W. T., Jr., 114, 121, *129*
Fitzgerald, J., 292, *318*
Fitzhugh, O. G., 269, 278, *324*
Fleischman, A. I., 292, *318*
Florin, A., 292, *318*
Folch, J., 8, 16, *60*
Foley, Sr. E., 276, *329*
Fontell, K., 312, *324*
Foote, F. W., 222, *240*
Ford, C. R., 90, *126*
Forney, M., 255, *323*
Forss, D. A., 255, *318*
Foster, D. O., 84, 109, *132*
Foster, D. W., 75, 84, 93, 109, *126*
Fox, M. A., 202, *244*
Fox, M. R. S., 249, *318*
Francois, R., 250, 251, *318*
Frank, A., 104, 118, 123, *126*
Frank, C. E., 247, *318*
Frankel, E. N., 249, 250, 257, 258, 271, 275, 311, 313, *318*
Franks, F., 253, 257, *318*
Franzke, C., 265, 270, 271, 276, *318, 328*
Frazer, A. C., 259, *319*
Fredrickson, D. S., 64, 65, 117, 118, 120, 121, *126, 127, 129*
Freeman, I. P., 307, *318*
Freeman, L., 148, *162*
Fredrickson, D. S., 4, *59*
Freiman, D. G., 26, *60*
French, J. E., 69, 106, 111, *127*
Fricker, A., 278, *322*
Friedberg, S. J., 66, *127*
Friedel, M. G., 81, *59*
Friedman, L., 269, 274, 278, 279, 281, 284, *318*
Friedman, Leo, 307, *328*
Friedman, Leonard, 307, *328*
Friedman, M., 33, *59*
Friedrich, J. P., 264, *318*
Fritsch, S., 188, *240*
Fritz, I. B., 65, 73, 87, *127, 129*
Forest, C. A., 264, *319*
Froeb, H. F., 104, *133*
Froesch, E. R., 113, *127*
Fürst, W., 213, 216, 217, *240*
Fugger, J., 257, *318*

Fukayama, G., 119, *126*
Fukuda, H., 311, *329*
Fukuzumi, K., 249, 251, 258, 270, *318, 319*
Fuller, G., 253, 262, 272, *319*
Furnelle, J., 99, *134*
Furth, J., 196, 203, 208, *240, 241*
Furth, O. B., 196, *240*
Furui, Y., 300, *320*
Furuta, F., 70, *129*

G

Gaddis, A. M., 253, 255, *317, 319*
Gahan, P. B., 8, *60*
Gaillard, P., 219, *240*
Galambos, J. T., 33, *61*
Gallyas, F., 24, 52, *59*
Galvin, M. P., 149, 150, *161*
Garcia, A., 72, 73, *134*
Gardner, W. U., 190, 191, 193, 194, 195, 196, 197, 200, 203, 206, 207, 208, *237, 240, 241, 242, 243*
Garfinkel, A. S., 79, 101, 102, 103, *124, 127*
Garland, P. B., 85, 87, 90, *133*
Gass, G. H., 200, *243*
Gast, L. E., 264, *319*
Gaush, C. R., 144, *161*
Gawlak, D., 204, *239*
Gebbie, T., 102, *127*
Gebhart, A. I., 248, 249, 250, *327*
Geer, J. C., 230, *243*
Geiger, J., 210, 221, *243*
Geiger, R. S., *240*
Gellhorn, A., 85, *127*
Gepts, W., 99, *127*
Gerecht, J. F., 248, 249, 250, 266, *327, 329*
Gerschenson, L. E., 138, 139, 140, *161, 162*
Geschickter, C. F., 202, 205, *240*
Gerson, T., 264, *319*
Gey, G. O., 155, *161*
Gey, M. K., 155, *161*
Geyer, G., 5, *58*
Geyer, R. B., 95, *133*
Geyer, R. P., 138, 139, 140, 141, 142, 143, 144, 154, *161*
Ghiron, V., 218, *240*
Ghose, A., 88, *127*

Gibbs, G. E., 80, 82, *125, 127*
Gibson, D. M., 74, 84, 107, 109, *124, 127*
Gidez, L. I., 68, *127*, 157, *162*
Gilbert, C., 82, *127*
Gilbert, J. B., 223, *240*
Gilfillan, E. W., 309, *317*
Gillam, N. W., 247, *319*
Gillette, R. W., 221, *240*
Gillman, J., 82, *127*
Ginsberg, J. L., 113, *127*
Ginsburg, V., 113, *127*
Giovetti, G. L., 292, 306, *327*
Glass, R. M., 199, *244*
Glavind, J., 189, *237*, 253, 254, 304, 305, 308, *315, 319*
Gleysteen, J., 223, *242*
Glick, D., 2, *59*
Glomset, J. A., 160, *161*
Glucksmann, A., 227, *239*
Goethe, P. O., 249, *323*
Gofman, J. W., 64, 104, *127, 130*
Golberg, L., 231, *240*
Goldfarb, J. L., 97, *130*
Goldfein, S., 169, *239*
Goldman, J. K., 72, *127*
Goldschmidt, B. M., 305, *329*
Goldzieher, J. W., 210, *243*
Goltz, H. L., 193, 194, *242*
Gomori, G., 17, *59*
Gonatas, J., 11, *60*
Goncharenko, E. N., 309, *316*
Goncharenko, Y. N., 309, *322*
Gonzales-Quijano, R. G., 255, *317*
Gooding, C. M., 291, 292, *319, 324*
Goodman, A. H., 291, 294, 297, *319*
Goodman, D. S., 69, *131*
Gordon, E. E., 86, *127*
Gordon, E. S., 119, *125*
Gordon, R. S., Jr., 65, 75, 101, 102, 103, 106, 111, *125, 126, 127*
Gore, I., 33, *60*
Gottenbos, J. J., 280, *319*
Gould, C. W., 272, *320*
Gould, R. G., 157, *163*
Goulian, D., Jr., 221, *240*
Grady, H. G., 193, *244*
Graef, I., 44, *59*
Graham, J. B., 190, *243*
Granados, H., 31, *59*
Grande, F., 112, *124*

Grant, C. A., 261, 309, *319*
Grant, R. T., 86, *124*
Grantham, P. H., 199, *244*
Grasso, P., 231, *240*
Grasso, R., 229, *240*
Gray, C. L., 209, 210, *238*
Green, J., 254, *316*
Greenberg, S. I., 253, *320*
Greenberg, S. M., 259, 301, *317, 319*
Greenblatt, R. B., 212, *240*
Greene, H. S. N., 192, *240*
Greene, R. R., 208, *243*
Gregory, R. L., 311, *325*
Gregson, N. A., 29, *59*
Greiner, M. J., 204, *239*
Griem, W., 267, 277, 284, 289, 306, *321, 322*
Gries, F. A., 96, *127*
Griffin, E. L., Jr., 264, *315, 317*
Griffith, W. H., 253, *315*
Griffith, W. P., 15, *59*
Griffiths, C. J., 192, *240*
Gripe, K., 223, *240*
Grodsky, G. M., 113, 120, 122, *127, 128*
Gross, R. C., 65, 82, 98, 104, 118, 119, 123, *126, 127, 131*
Grossfeld, H., 221, *240*
Grossman, M. I., 303, *319*
Grover, P. L., 176, *238*
Guadagni, D. G., 254, *319*
Gueriguian, J. I., 210, *240*
Guérin, M., 168, *243*
Guérin, P., 168, *243*
Guillaumin, R., 289, *319*
Guilmain, J., 301, *321*
Gunstone, F. D., 248, 250, *319*
Gurd, F. R. N., 160, *161*
Gurin, S., 71, 83, 86, *125*
Gurland, J., 6, *61*
Gusberg, S. B., 226, *240*
Gutierrez, R., 249, *329*
Gutman, A. B., 104, 112, *128, 133*

H

Haagensen, C. D., 200, 205, *239, 240*
Haahti, E., 70, *127*
Hack, M. H., 21, *58*
Haeberer, E. T., 274, 312, *323*

Haft, D. E., 72, 73, 85, 86, 108, *127*, 157, 162
Hagen, J. H., 76, *127*
Haggerty, D. F., 138, 139, 140, *161, 162*
Hake, T., 16, *59*
Hakomori, S.-I., 17, *59*
Hale, A. J., 27, *59*
Halevy, S., 154, *161*
Hall, G. E., 249, 250, *319*
Hall, J. L., 249, 294, *319*
Hall, W. T., 200, *240*
Hallberg, D., 69, *125*
Haller, H. S., 312, *327*
Hallgren, B., 94, *126*
Ham, R. G., 139, *161*
Hamlin, J. T., III, 65, 81, 94, 95, *124, 126*
Hamm, D. L., 311, *319*
Hammar, D. C. H., 284, 306, *321*
Hammes, R., 80, *133*
Hammond, E. C., 255, 311, *319, 320*
Hamosh, M., 89, *127*
Hampton, A. O., 228, *237*
Hanker, J. S., 32, *61*
Hanning, F., 292, 298, *315, 316*
Hansen, R. P., 264, *319*
Hanson, N. W., 247, *319*
Harary, I., 138, 139, 140, *161, 162*
Harmuth, E., 81, *132*
Harper, A. E., 112, *127*
Harris, R. S., 309, *327*
Harrison, D. L., 294, *319*
Harrison, S. A., 275, *319*
Hartman, C. G., 205, *240*
Hartroft, W. S., 31, *59*
Hartwell, J. L., 169, 217, *240*
Hartzell, R. W., Jr., 146, 147, 149, 150, 152, 153, 154, 155, 156, 157, *162*
Harvey, M. A., 292, *319*
Hashimoto, T., 301, *319*
Hassan, M. M., 312, *319*
Hastings, A. B., 71, 83, 107, 113, *129, 131*
Hatch, F. T., 104, 118, 121, *127, 131, 133*
Haugaard, E. S., 107, *127*
Hausberger, F. X., 75, 82, *127, 130*
Hauss, W. H., 64, *127*
Havel, R. J., 65, 66, 76, 79, 89, 101, 102, 103, 106, 111, *124, 125, 127, 128, 130*
Hayes, E. R., 15, 48, 52, 58, *59*
Heald, P. J., 10, *128*

Healy, G. M., 144, 152, *162*
Heder, G., 255, 271, *318*, *328*
Hegsted, D. M., 100, *129*
Heidelberger, C., 219, *239*, *241*
Heimberg, M., 76, 77, 78, 90, 91, 92, 93, 96, 106, 110, 111, *128*, *133*, *134*
Hellman, B., 100, *133*
Hempel, K.-J., 231, *237*
Henick, A. S., 310, 312, *315*, *319*
Hennes, A. R., 88, *128*
Henry, C. M., 273, *315*
Henschel, J., 267, 289, *322*
Henson, J. P. G., 31, *60*
Herb, S. F., 259, *321*
Herbst, M., 121, *132*
Herman, R. H., 107, 109, 110, 112, 113, 114, 115, *128*, *134*
Heroux, C. M. A., 292, *315*
Herrera, M. G., 73, *131*
Herring, V., 64, *127*
Hers, H. G., 113, *127*
Hertig, A. T., 224, *240*
Hertz, R., 192, *240*
Herxheimer, G., 6, *59*
Herzschuh, R., 249, 250, *327*
Heslinga, F. J. M., 6, *59*
Heston, W. E., 197, 200, *240*, *241*
Hestrin-Lerner, S., 8, *62*
Hewett, C. L., 217, *237*
Hewitt, J., 64, *127*
Heyes, T. D., 262, *317*
Heyl, E. G., 311, *315*
Hiatt, R., 272, *319*, *320*
Hieger, I., 168, 169, 174, 178, 179, *241*
Higashi, H., 261, *320*
Higgins, H. L., 112, *128*
Higginson, J., 174, *241*
Higuchi, K., 144, 152, *162*
Hilditch, T. P., 4, *59*, 248, 250, *319*
Hill, D. B., 104, 119, *131*
Hill, F. D., 255, *319*, *320*
Hill, R. J., 75, 83, 108, 114, 115, *128*, *134*
Hinsch, I., 311, *324*
Hird Convery, H. J., 75, *133*
Hirsch, E. F., 81, 94, *128*
Hirsch, E. Z., 104, *130*
Hirsch, J., 100, 104, 121, *124*
Hirsch, R. L., 68, *131*
Hirsch, T. V., 29, 40, 54, *59*, *61*
Hisaw, F. L., 192, *241*

Hladik, J., 313, *326*
Hobbs, J. S., 249, 250, *317*
Hobson-Frohock, A., 253, 255, *322*
Hochberg, R. B., 210, *241*
Hoffmann, G., 250, 255, *320*
Hoffmann, R. L., 255, *318*
Holczinger, L., 6, 14, 21, 48, *59*
Holdsworth, C. D., 113, *128*
Holeman, R., 148, *162*
Hollander, V. P., 197, 232, *244*
Hollenberg, C. H., 79, *128*
Hollander, H., *59*
Hollander, W., 28, 33, *60*
Holman, R. T., 253, 278, 312, *316*, *320*, *324*
Honjo, K., 84, *133*
Hood, B., 97, 121, *131*
Hooker, C. W., 193, *241*
Hoppe, H., 265, *328*
Hopper, R. P., 294, *316*
Horgan, V. J., 254, *320*
Horikx, M. M., 255, 257, 312, *320*
Horland, A. A., 100, *132*
Hornbrook, K. R., 86, 88, *128*
Horning, E. S., 195, 208, *239*, *241*
Horvat, R. J., 255, *320*
Horvath, A., 26, *59*
Hoshi, M., 97, *132*
Hotchkiss, D. K., 311, *319*
Hotchkiss, R. D., 27, *59*
Howard, B. V., 137, 138, 144, 152, *161*, *162*
Howard, C. F., Jr., 87, 88, 99, *128*
Howard, J. A., 248, 249, *320*
Horwitz, W., 269, 274, 278, 279, 281, 284, *318*
Hoyle, R. J., 4, *58*
Hrdlicka, J., 272, *320*
Hsing, W.-T., 309, *322*
Hsu, M. P., 87, *127*
Hsueh, Y.-H., 309, *322*
Hubbard, B., 21, 50, *58*
Hubbard, D. D., 74, 84, 107, 109, *124*, *127*
Hudson, B. J. F., 262, *317*
Hueper, W. C., 230, *241*
Huggins, C., 228, *241*
Humphrey, J. H., 33, *56*
Hunt, R. D., 202, *244*
Huntley, T. E., 259, *315*
Hurst, E. W., 17, *59*
Hurst, L., 218, *242*

Huseby, R. A., 202, *244*
Hutchison, C. F., 99, *128*
Hutchison, R. B., 264, *320*
Hydén, H., 2, *59*

I

Ibrahim, M. Z. M., 24, 25, 27, 28, 33, 35, 39, 40, 41, 52, 53, 57
Idelman, S., 32, *59*
Iglesias, R., 192, 207, 208, *242*
Iliopoulos, M. I., 17, *60*
Inaba, M., 310, *322*
Indictor, N., 274, *316*
Ingemanson, B., 219, *237*
Ingenito, E. F., 148, 150, *163*
Ingersoll, F. M., 210, *237*
Ingold, K. U., 248, *320*
Ingraham, L. P., 195, 198, 224, *238*
Inhoffen, H. H., 216, *241*
Inoue, H., 84, *133*
Inoue, M., 307, 309, *316, 324*
Insull, W. Jr., 104, *124*
Irwin, K. C., 272, *319, 320*
Isaeff, E., 82, 83, *126*
Ishida, K., 258, *318*
Ishii, S., 253, 261, 260, 205, 313, 320, 321
Ivanova, O. J., 170, 206, *244*
Ivy, A. C., 303, 304, *320, 322*
Iwata, N., 255, 270, 276, 293, *320, 325, 328*
Iwata, Y., 251, 258, *319*
Iype, P. T., 219, *241*
Izumi, G., 271, 275, *320*
Izuyama, Y., 294, *325*

J

Jacini, G., 249, 262, 267, *316, 318, 320*
Jackson, H. A. F., 253, 255, *322*
Jackson, J. E., 263, *325*
Jacobson, G. A., 284, 294, 301, *320, 321*
Jacobsohn, G. M., 210, *241*
Jacquot, R., 269, 289, *326, 327*
Jagannathan, S. N., 118, *124*
Jahnke, K., 96, *127*
Jahr, K., 277, 278, 284, 306, *321*
Jakobson, T., 122, *128*
Janicek, G., 249, 292, 294, 296, 310, *320, 326*
Jansen, G. R., 99, *128*
Jeanrenaud, B., 99, *126*

Jefferson, L. S., 92, *126*
Jeffries, M. E., 208, *243*
Jellinck, P. H., 203, *241*
Jenkins, V. K., 196, *241*
Jensen, E. V., 211, *241*
Jobst, C., 26, *59*
Johnson, A. D., 39, *59*
Johnson, A. R., 312, *327*
Johnson, M., 138, *162*
Johnson, O. C., 255, 270, 283, 284, 286, 287, 309, *320, 329*
Johnson, R. E., 259, 260, 278, 281, 301, 307, 309, *321, 323*
Johnston, W. B., 263, *316*
Jones, D. P., 70, 77, 78, 79, 97, *128*
Jones, E. M., 35, *60*
Jones, E. P., 313, *318*
Jones, R., 32, *59*
Joslin, E. P., 94, *128*
Jull, J. W., 175, 176, 213, 219, *238, 239, 241*
Jungas, R. L., 76, *128*
Junker, M., 312, *329*
Juret, P., 222, 223, *239*

K

Kadar, R., 253, 255, *320*
Källén, B., 219, *241*
Kagawa, Y., 138, *162*
Kahanpaä, A., 122, *128*
Kai, T., 310, *322*
Kaier, W., 271, *318*
Kayimoto, G., 276, 293, 294, 296, 300, *320*
Kakac, B., 289, *326*
Kakushkina, M. L., 309, *322*
Kalant, N., 76, 77, 90, *126*
Kalkhoff, R. K., 86, 87, 88, *128*
Kallio, V., 94, *128*
Källén, B., 219, *237*
Kallman, F., 16, *61*
Kamo, K., 296, *320*
Kandea, T., 253, 261, 269, *320, 321*
Kane, J. P., 120, 122, *128*
Kartha, A. R. S., 251, 258, *321*
Katherman, R. E., 209, 210, 212, 213, *238*
Kato, U., 269, *321*
Kauffman, N. A., 112, *128*
Kaunitz, H., 247, 259, 260, 278, 281, 301, 307, 309, *321, 323, 328*
Kawada, T., 295, 299, *321, 322*

Kay, R. E., 92, 110, *128*
Keane, K. W., 284, 301, *321*
Keay, J. N., 249, *315*
Keeney, M., 255, 298, 312, *317*, 325, 327, *329*
Keilig, I., 8, 9, *59*
Keith, E. S., 295, *317*
Kekki, M., 65, 66, 78, 92, 115, *130*
Kelley, R. M., 226, *241*
Kemp, E. L., 106, 107, 115, *126*
Kemperman, J. H., 104, *133*
Kendall, F. E., 104, *127*, 176, *242*
Kennan, A. L., 85, *131*
Kennaway, E. L., 169, 217, *237*, *241*
Kennaway, N. M., 217, *237*
Kennedy, B. J., 224, 226, *241*
Kennedy, B. P. C., 292, *315*
Kennelly, B., 309, *321*
Keppler, J. G., 250, 255, *320*
Kern, W., 248, 249, 253, 258, *317*, *321*
Kerr, H. A., 144, 152, *161*
Kessler, J. I., 95, 97, *128*
Keys, A., 112, *124*
Khan, N. A., 249, 250, *321*
Khanolkar, V. R., 14, *59*
Kieckenbusch, W., 267, 277, 278, 284, 289, 306, *321*, *322*
Kilgore, L., 292, 294, 295, 296, *321*
Kim, M., 97, *132*
Kim, S. C., 295, *317*
Kim, U., 203, *241*
King, D. W., 146, 152, *161*
King, H., 228, *241*
Kinsell, L. W., 70, 119, *126*, *132*
Kinsey, A. C., 228, *241*
Kipnis, D. M., 86, 87, 88, *128*
Kirby, A. H. M., 303, *325*
Kirkman, H., 208, 209, *241*
Kirschbaum, A., 196, *241*
Kistner, R. W., 192, *240*
Kiyasu, J. Y., 113, *128*
Klatskin, G., 107, 109, *124*, *132*
Klausner, H., 106, 110, 111, *128*
Klein, B. V., 74, *133*
Klein, M., 217, 218, *241*
Klein, R. F., 66, *127*
Klein, S., 310, *326*
Kleinenberg, H. E., 168, *241*
Klenk, E., 29, *59*
Kloepffer, W., 255, *321*

Kneer, P., 90, *132*
Knegtel, J. T., 262, 267, 313, *316*
Knight, H. B., 250, 281, 301, *321*
Knittle, J. L., 122, *128*
Koch, H. P., 250, *318*
Koch, R., 180, 181, *241*
Koch, R. B., 310, *315*
Koch, S. A., 269, 278, *324*
Kocova, P., 311, *325*
Kohn, R., 247, 272, *321*, *323*
Kokatnur, M. G., 249, 254, 309, *322*
Komatsu, K., 70, *129*
Kondratenko, S. S., 249, *326*
Konetf, A. A., 190, 191, *241*
Koob, R. P., 274, *329*
Koos, R. E., 281, *321*
Kopaczyk, K. C., 5, *62*
Kopriwa, B. M., 33, *59*
Korchak, H. M., 87, *129*
Koren, J., 310, *326*
Korey, S. R., 15 26, 27, 47, *60*
Korn, E. D., 15, 16, 32, *59*
Kornacker, M. S., 75, 84, 99, 109, 115, *129*
Kotsubo, M., 293, 312, *322*
Krabinos, J. V., 276, *329*
Krakower, C., 205, *239*
Kramer, W., 71, *125*
Krampl, V., 255, 273, *318*
Kramsch, D. M., 33, *60*
Kreisberg, R. A., 96, *129*
Krieger, C. H., 284, 301, *321*
Krishnamurthi, A. S., 14, *59*
Krishnamurthy, R. G., 255, 295, 297, 299, *316*, *321*, *322*, *327*, *328*
Kritchevsky, D., 35, *60*, 144, 146, 147, 148, 149, 150, 152, 153, 154, 155, 156, 157, *161*, *162*, 230, *241*, 270, 308, *322*
Kroms, M., 32, *59*
Krull, L., 273, 274, *322*
Krut, L. H., 101, *129*
Kudryashov, Y. B., 309, *316*, *322*
Kühl, I., 178, *242*
Kuhfahl, E., 90, *129*
Kumazawa, H., 271, 292, 294, 296, 299, 312, *322*
Kummerow, F. A., 255, 257, 258, 270, 271, 272, 275, 278, 280, 283, 284, 286, 287, 305, 307, 309, 310, *316*, *317*, *320*, *322*, *324*, *325*, *326*, *327*, *328*, *329*
Kuo, P. T., 112, 114, 118, 121, *129*

Kurita, K., 263, *322*
Kuroda, K., 310, *322*
Kuschner, M., 305, *329*
Kyllästinen, M. J., 93, *129*

L

Lacassagne, A., 166, 193, 218, *242*
Lake, B. D., 29, 40, 41, 54, *58, 60*
Lambert, A. E., 99, *132*
Landau, B. R., 107, *129*
Landing, B. H., 26, *60*
Lane, A., 304, *322*
Lane, M. D., 100, *125*
Langdon, R. G., 86, *129*
Lane, W. G., 255, *320*
Lang, K., 267, 277, 278, 284, 285, 289, 306, 307, *317, 321, 322*
Langan, J., 270, 308, *322*
Langdon, R. J., 87, *129*
Lange, H., 264, *322*
Lange, H.-J., 231, *237*
Lange, W., 50, *60*
Langerbeins, H., 29, *59*
Langseth, L., 305, *329*
Lannerud, E., 292, *316*
Lanteaume, M. T., 207, 288, 302, *322, 326*
Lantz, C. W., 291, *322*
Lardy, H. A., 84, 109, *132*
Larrabee, A. R., 84, *133*
Larsen, C. D., 270, 276, 303, *322, 324*
Larsson, Y., 80, 81, *133*
Larsen, C. D., 188, *242*
Larson, J. A., 224, *242*
Lasnitzki, I., 219, *242*
Lassen, S., 269, *322*
Last, J. H., 5, *62*
Laurell, S., 89, 92, 102, 106, *129*
Lauris, V., 73, *131*
Lavietes, P. H., 81, *124*
Lawry, E. Y., 104, 111, *131, 133*
Lea, C. H., 247, 253, 255, 261, 286, 289, 309, 312, *316, 319, 322, 328*
Lea, M. A., 71, *133*
LeBaron, F. N., 8, 16, *60*
Leblond, C. P., 14, 33, *57, 59*
Lechartier, G., 255, 311, *323*
LeClerc, A. M., 270, 287, 288, 292, 293, 294, 297, 302, *322, 326*
Ledeen, R., 11, *60*
Lee, M., 203, *242*

Leer, S., 249, 252, *315*
Lees, R. S., 4, *59,* 64, 112, 117, 118, 120, 121, *126, 127, 129*
Lehner, T., 41, *60*
Leiner, K. Y., 35, *60*
Leiter, J., 217, *243*
Lemberg, A., 76, 77, *131*
Lepkovsky, S., 70, *129*
Lequin, H. C., 75, *129*
Lerner, R. L., 104, 106, 119, 122, 123, *131*
Lescure, O. L., 210, *242*
Leske, E., 270, 276, *328*
L'Estrange, J. L., 261, 286, 289, 309, *316, 322, 323*
Levine, R., 73, 76, 77, *129, 131*
Levine, S. A., 104, *133*
Levitz, M., 212, 225, *244*
Levy, R. I., 4, *59,* 64, 117, 121, *127*
Lewis, M., 213, *244*
Lewis, P. R., 11, *60*
Lhuissier, M., 309, *326*
Li, M. H., 208, *242*
Liadsky, C., 36, *60*
Liechty, R. D., 223, *242*
Lilienfeld, A. M., 228, *241*
Liljedahl, S. O., 68, *125*
Lillard, D. A., 259, *323*
Lillie, R. D., 6, 14, 27, 31, 55, 56, *60*
Linazasoro, J. M., 75, 108, *128*
Lindemann, E., 313, *329*
Linderstrøm-Lang, K., 2, 35, *60*
Lindgren, F., 64, *127*
Linow, F., 312, *323*
Lippincott, S. W., 303, *324*
Lipschutz, A., 192, 200, 207, 208, *242*
Lipstein, B., 261, *322*
Lison, L., 1, 17, *60*
List, G. R., 255, *318*
Little, C. C., 198, *239*
Lobanov, D. I., 295, 296, *323*
Lobban, M. C., 11, *60*
Lobry, R., 271, 276, *329*
Loeb, L., 193, 194, *238, 242*
Loewe, L., 82, *125*
Lojda, Z., 9, 16, 22, 24, *58*
Lomsadze, B. A., 309, *322*
Long, M. L., 195, 203, *238*
Long, R. W., 87, *131*
Longcope, C., 120, 122, *128*
Lorrain, Smith J., 7, *60*
Lossow, W. J., 96, *130*

Loury, M., 247, 250, 251, 255, 311, *318*, *323*
Love, D. E., 104, *133*
Lovern, J. A., 4, *60*
Lowden, J. A., 11, *62*
Lowenstein, J. M., 75, 84, 86, 87, 88, 99, 100, 107, 109, 115, *126, 128, 129, 132*
Lowry, D. H., 35, *60*
Lucas, C., 122, *131*
Lucas, R. A., 248, 250, *317*
Luckmann, F. H., 291, 292, *324*
Ludwig, E. H., 138, *161*
Lueck, H., 272, *323*
Lukens, F. D. W., 83, *125*
Luker, W. D., 292, 296, *321*
Lumry, R., 209, *239*
Lundberg, W. O., 246, *323*
Lusky, L. M., 207, *242*
Lyinsky, W., 170, *244*
Lynen, F., 84, 86, 87, *125, 130, 131, 134*
Lyon, I., 71, 72, 107, 108, *129, 130*
Lyon, T. P., 64, *127*

M

McArthur, J. W., 210, *237*
McCandless, E. L., 39, *62*
McCarl, R. L., 145, *162*
McConnell, D. G., 249, 250, 254, 271, 275, 311, 313, *318*
Macdonald, I., 100, 104, 112, 114, 118, *129, 224, 239*
MacDonald, J. A., 263, 268, 275, *323*
McDevitt, H. O., 33, *56*
McDougal, D. B., Jr., 35, *60*
McElroy, W. T., Jr., 68, 76, 90, *129, 132*
McEuen, C. S., 191, 202, *242, 243*
McFadden, W. H., 255, *320*
McFarlane, W. D., 262, *326*
McGandy, R. B., 100, *129*
McGill, H. C., 230, *243*
McInnes, A. G., 263, 268, 275, *323*
McKay, D. G., 307, 309, *323*
Mackenzie, C. G., 137, 141, 142, 143, 147, 149, *162*
Mackenzie, D. J., 249, 250, *317*
Mackenzie, J. B., 137, 141, 142, 143, 146, 149, *162*
Mackintosh, D. L., 249, 294, *319*
McLachlan, P. M., 70, *128*

McManus, J. F. A., 27, *60*
McNabb, A. R., 39, *59*
McWilliams, N. B., 113, *127*
Mader, I., 268, *315*
Maerker, G., 274, 312, *323, 329*
Maggi, V., 8, *60*
Mahler, R., 76, 86, 89, *129, 133*
Majchrowitz, E., 114, *129*
Mayerus, P. W., 84, *133*
Mameesh, M. S., 269, 291, 297, 300, *316, 323*
Man, E. B., 64, 80, 81, 103, *124, 129*
Mandella, P. A., 118, 121, *131*
Manjeshwar, R., 71, *132*
Mann, F. C., 113, *125*
Mann, G. V., 104, *133*
Mantel, N., 231, *242*
Mantz, W., 64, *127*
Manughevic, C., 270, *316*
Marchi, V., 17, *60*
Marcuse, R., 247, 249, *323*
Margaretten, W., 309, *323*
Mariam, E., 270, *323*
Mark, J., 202, *242*
Markscheid, L., 79, 103, *129*
Markwardt, F., 210, *243*
Marsh, P. L., 94, *129*
Marshall, N. B., 100, *129*
Marshall, M. W., 112, *129*
Martin, C. E., 228, *241*
Martin, D. B., 86, *129*
Martin, J. B., 296, *323*
Martin, R. H., 217, *237*
Martinelli, M., 148, 150, *163*
Martinenghi, G. B., 266, 269, *323*
Maruhama, Y., 82, 96, *129*
Maruyama, T., *319*
Masoro, E. J., 82, 83, 85, 87, 108, *126, 129, 130, 132*
Mason, W. B., 197, 232, *244*
Masri, M. S., 71, 72, 107, 108, *129, 130*
Mathur, S. S., 270, *325*
Matschinsky, F., 113, *133*
Matsuda, I., 76, 77, 90, *126*
Matsuhashi, M., 86, *130*
Matsuhashi, S., 86, *130*
Matsumoto, Y., 112, *124*
Matsumuro, H., 301, *319*
Matsuo, N., 261, 268, 269, *323*
Matthes, K. J., 85, 86, *124, 130*

Mattil, K. F., 289, *329*
Mattill, H. A., 273, 274, *317*
Mat'ts, V., 309, *322*
Maxwell, L. C., 166, *238*
Mayer, J., 99, 107, 108, 114, 115, *124, 125, 126, 127, 134*
Mayes, P. A., 65, 92, 93, 106, 110, *126, 130*
Mayo, F. R., 272, *319*
Maza, M. P., 273, *329*
Mead, J. F., 138, 139, 140, *161, 162*, 253, *315*
Medes, G., 71, *130*
Mega, A., 290, *325*
Mehta, T. N., 263, *324*
Meigs, W., 64, *124*
Meissner, W. A., 191, 192, *242*
Melnick, D., 247, 291, 292, 297, *319, 324*
Meng, H. C., 96, 97, 111, *128, 130*
Menter, J., 138, 139, *161*
Menzel, D. B., 309, *324*
Mercier, J., 248, *257, 325*
Merrill, A. L., 290, *329*
Merritt, C., Jr., 255, *318*
Mesrobian, R. B., 248, *328*
Metz, D. J., 248, *328*
Miahle, H., 146, 147, 149, 150, 152, 153, 154, 155, 156, 157, *162*
Michael, W. R., 270, 274, 275, 276, 278, 280, 282, 309, 313, *324*
Michaelis, H., 295, *326*
Michaels, G., 119, *126*
Mickelsen, O., 249, *318*
Miettinen, T. A., 122, *130, 131*
Migeon, C. J., 210, *242, 244*
Migliorini, R. H., 86, *124*
Mihelic, F., 311, *324*
Mikusch, J. D., 264, *322*
Milas, N. A., 17, *60*
Mill, T., 272, *319*
Miller, H. I., 89, 92, 102, *130*
Miller, L. D., 114, 121, *129*
Miller, L. L., 72, 73, 85, *124, 127, 130*
Miller, M., 113, 114, *126, 130*
Miller, R., 122, *131*
Miller, R. F., 309, *324*
Milstein, S. W., 75, 82, *127, 130*
Minesita, T., 201, *242*
Mioduszewaka, O., 220, *242*
Mirand, E. A., 193, 194, *242*
Mishiro, Y., 310, *322*

Mitchell, J. H., Jr., 312, *319*
Mitchley, B. C. V., 227, *238*
Mixer, H. W., 196, *241*
Miyakawa, T., 249, 251, 290, 293, 294, *319, 324*
Miyazaki, M., 307, *327*
Mizev, I., 248, *326*
Mizuno, G. R., 312, *324*
Moloney, P. J., 87, *130*
Mone, P. E., 301, *326, 327, 329*
Monson, W. J., 112, *127*
Montefredine, A., 290, 291, 292, *324*
Mookherjee, B. D., 255, 299, *316, 321, 324, 328*
Moore, D. H., 199, 200, *240, 242*
Moorhouse, J. A., 76, *127*
Mora, P. F., 138, *162*
Morel, E., 302, *326*
Morgan, R. S., 33, 35, 36, 40, 57
Morita, M., 255, 270, 275, 276, 293, 320, *325*
Morohira, H., 249, 251, *319*
Morris, B., 69, 106, *127, 130*
Morris, H. P., 270, 276, 303, *322, 324*
Morris, J. H., 90, 111, *126*
Morris, L. J., 278, 312, *316, 324*
Morrison, E. S., 32, 59
Morrison, L. M., 148, *162*
Mosbach, E. H., 176, *242*
Moser, A. B., 29, 60
Moser, H. A., 257, 258, 311, 313, *318*
Moser, H. W., 29, 60
Moskop, M., 193, *242*
Moskowitz, M. S., 141, 142, 143, *162*
Mroczkowski, S., 294, *324*
Mühlbock, O., 199, 200, 207, *238, 242, 244*
Mueller, G. C., 211, *243*
Mueller, P. S., 76, *130*
Müller, F., 90, *129*
Müller, U., *134*
Mukai, A., 270, 272, 273, 274, 275, 276, 293, 294, *324, 325*
Mukai, K., 276, 300, *320*
Mukherjee, S., 250, *324*
Mukherji, M., 15, *60*
Munn, J. I., 269, 278, *324*
Munske, K., 76, *132*
Muntz, J. A., 113, *130*
Murase, Y., 312, *324*
Murgeanu, A., 270, *315*

Murphy, E. D., 192, *242*
Murrell, E. A., 254, *316*

N

Nadelcu, C., 270, *315*
Nahar-Rahman, S. Q., 247, *321*
Naidoo, S. S., 96, *130*
Nair, P. P., 35, *60*
Nakahara, W., 168, 233, *242*
Nakayima, T., 261, *320*
Nakakuki, K., 196, *242*
Nakamura, K., 97, *132*
Nandi, S., 201, *242*
Napalkov, N. P., 220, *243*
Narayan, K. A., 310, *324*
Narita, N., 70, *129*
Naudet, M., 313, *324*
Nauss, S. F., 99, *124*
Nawar, W. W., 263, 271, *316, 324*
Neirenberg, M., 176, *242*
Nelson, N., 305, *329*
Nelson, A. A., 207, *242*
Nelson, W. O., 190, 202, *242*
Nemeroff, K., 35, *57*
Nemets, S. M., 312, *324*
Nesbett, F. B., 71, 83, 113, *131*
Nestel, P. J., 68, 69, 77, 104, 106, 118, 119, 121, *130*
Nesterova, I. M., 312, *324*
Neufach, S. A., 168, *241*
Neufeld, I., *134*
Neukomm, S., 178, 189, *242*
Neumüller, O.-A., 180, *241*
New, M. I., 80, 81, *130*
Newcomb, A. L., 80, *133*
Newman, H. A. I., 39, *60*
Newman, M. S., 216, *240*
Ney, K. H., 273, 274, *324*
Ng, H., 255, *320*
Nickell, E. C., 250, *326*
Nichols, A. V., 104, *130*
Nichols, R., 82, *125*
Niederstebruch, A., 248, 289, 311, *315, 324*
Niemeyer, H., 74, 85, *130*
Niden, A. H., 41, *60*
Nikkilä, E. A., 65, 66, 68, 77, 78, 79, 88, 89, 92, 93, 97, 101, 102, 104, 107, 112, 113, 114, 115, 116, 119, 122, 123, *128, 130, 131*

Nishida, T., 284, 309, *324, 329*
Nissen, N. I., 101, *131*
Noble, R. L., 190, 202, *239, 243*
Noland, J. T., Jr., 17, *60*
Nolen, G. A., 292, 293, 296, 298, 303, *324*
Nordlie, R. C., 84, 109, *132*
Norris, L. C., 309, *324*
Norton, W. T., 15, 26, 27, 47, *60*
Norum, K. R., 87, *125*
Nossal, G. J. V., 33, *56*
Nosti, N., 249, *329*
Notevarp, O., 249, *324*
Nothdurft, H., 168, 169, 174, *243*
Novak, E., 226, *243*
Novak, E. R., 226, *243*
Numa, S., 84, 86, 87, *130, 131, 134*
Nutt, S. M., 301, *324*
Nye, E. R., 68, *125*
Nyman, M. A., 210, *243*

O

O'Brien, P. J., 307, *318*
O'Connor, R. T., 248, 249, 250, *328*
Odell, T. T., Jr., 196, *241*
Odland, G. F., 39, *60*
Oette, A., 100, 121, *124*
Oette, K., 251, *324*
Ogino, R. E., 77, *131*
Ojala, K., 65, 66, 68, 77, 78, 88, 92, 101, 104, 107, 112, 113, 115, 116, *130*
Okamoto, H., 77, *131*
Okano, S., 254, *319*
Okey, A. B., 200, *243*
Olcott, H. S., 253, 254, *324*
Oldfield, J. E., 259, *325*
Olivercrona, T., 69, 78, 95, 96, 102, *124, 125, 132*
Olivi, M., 191, 194, *237, 243*
Olshevskaja, L. V., 170, 206, *244*
Olson, R. E., 65, *131*
Olsson, Y., 40, 41, *61*
Oncley, J. L., 210, *237*
Ondreicka, R., 270, 282, *325, 328*
O'Neill, L. A., 257, *325*
Ono, K., 121, *127*
Ono, F., 312, *325*
Ontko, J. A., 111, *131*
Ormsby, J. W., 39, *60*
Orö, L., *125*
Orr, J. C., 29, *60*

Orr, J. W., 174, *241*
Orris, L., 305, *329*
Orton, C. C., 35, 36, 40 57
Osborn, M. J., 83, *126, 131*
Östman, J., 81, 82, 89, 100, *125, 131*
Ota, S., 255, 270, 272, 273, 274, 275, 276, 290, 293, 294, 295, *320, 324, 325, 328*
Otake, Y., 307, *327*
Overholser, M. D., 207, *243*
Oyama, T., 312, *322*

P

Pack, G. T., 229, *243*
Palmer, J. C., 264, *318*
Pan, S. C., 206, *240, 243*
Panasevich, V. I., 192, 207, *242*
Paoletti, I., 194, *243*
Paquot, C., 248, 257, 271, 272, 273, *325*
Pardini, R., 107, 109, 110, 112, 113, 114, 115, *134*
Park, C. R., 76, 92, 96, 111, *125, 126, 128*
Park, R., 70, *129*
Park, R. L., 296, *316*
Parker, F., 39, *60*
Parker, R. C., 144, 152, *162*
Parks, O. W., 255, 312, *325, 327*
Parmeggiani, A., 86, *131*
Parr, L. J., 261, 286, 289, 309, *316, 322, 323*
Parteshko, V. G., 281, 308, *325*
Paschke, R. F., 263, 264, 265, *325*
Paschkis, K. E., 204, *239*
Passey, R. F., 76, *133*
Passonneau, J. V., 35, *60*
Paterson, B., 97, *126*
Pathak, S. P., 270, *325*
Patton, S., 254, *325*
Paulose, M. M., 297, *328*
Páv, J., 89, *133*
Pavlatos, F. C., 120, 122, *128*
Payne, W. J. A., 309, *325*
Pazlar, M., 311, *325*
Peacock, P. R., 303, 304, *325*
Pearlman, W. H., 210, *240*
Pearse, A. G. E., 29, 31, 54, *60, 61*
Pearson, A. M., 311, *328*
Peckham, B. M., 208, *243*
Pegus, L., 260, *321*
Peiffer, J., 29, 40, 54, 59, *61*

Pelkonen, R., 89, 101, 102, 113, 122, *130, 131*
Penhos, J. C., 76, 77, *131*
Pennekamp, B., 263, *329*
Pennell, R. B., 210, *237*
Peraino, C., 85, *131*
Perez, N., 74, 85, *130*
Perkins, E. G., 247, 275, 278, 280, 284, 291, 294, 295, 207, 307, 313, *320, 325, 327*
Perlstein, T., 250, *325*
Perrot, M. J., 313, *324*
Perry, W. F., 97, 101, 102, *131*
Perry, R. P., 33, *61*
Persson, B., 80, 81, 97, 121, *131, 132*
Pertuisot, J. F., 289, *319*
Peters, J. P., 80, *129*
Peterson, L. E., 265, *325*
Peterson, M. L., 104, *124*
Peterson, N. F., 39, *60*
Petit, J., 261, 262, 265, 269, 282, *316, 325, 326*
Pfeiffer, C. A., 193, 194, 197, 203, 205, *240, 241, 243*
Phibbs, B. P., 81, 94, *128*
Phillips, M. C., 11, *61*
Philpot, J. St. L., 254, *320*
Philpot, D. E., 141, 142, 149, *162*
Pietra, G., 170, *244*
Pietra, G. G., 40, *62*
Pihl, A., 221, *243*
Pilhorn, H. R., 200, 209, *238*
Pitelka, D. R., 220, *243*
Pitot, H. C., 85, *131*
Plotkin, G. R., 79, 97, *128*
Plotz, E. J., 212, *239*
Pochetti, F., 270, *323*
Poel, W. E., 167, 201, *243*
Pogell, B. M., 87, *133*
Pogonkina, N. I., 313, *327*
Pohle, W. D., 311, *325*
Pokorny, J., 248, 249, 251, 270, 272, 289, 292, 294, 296, 310, 311, 312, 313, *320, 326*
Poling, C. E., 301, *326, 327, 329*
Pomeroy, W. B., 228, *241*
Poon-King, T. M. W., 118, 121, *131*
Popov, A., 248, 253, *326*
Popper, H., 7, *61*
Porte, D. Jr., 94, 95, 97, 112, 118, 122, *124, 125, 131*

Porter, B. W., 254, *320*
Porter, F. R., 295, *326*
Porter, J. W., 87, *131*
Porter, K. R., 16, *61*
Portius, H. J., 210, 211, *243*
Portman, O. W., 111, *131*
Potteau, B., 279, 309, *326*
Potter, M., 197, *243*
Potthoff, S., 96, *127*
Powers, J. J., 295, 299, *317*
Powick, W. C., 255, *326*
Poznanski, R., 112, *128*
Prevot, A., 313, *326*
Price, J. M., 176, *238*
Pries, N., 85, *131*
Pringle, R. B., 262, *326*
Pritchord, E. T., 268, *317*
Privett, O. S., 250, 253, 262, *326*
Przeworska-Kaniewicz, D., 219, *244*
Ptak, L. R., 312, *327*
Purr, A., 311, *326*
Pykälistö, O., 79, 97, *130, 131*

Q

Quackenbush, F. W., 253, 309, *321, 326*
Quarfordt, H. S., 69, *131*
Quastel, J. H., 114, *129*
Quilligan, J. J. Jr., 148, *162*

R

Rabajille, E., 74, 85, *130*
Ragan, C., 221, *240*
Raha, C. R., 170, *244*
Rahman, Q. N., 272, *323*
Raikhlin, N. T., 170, 206, *244*
Rajagopalan, R., 283, *326*
Rajagopalan, S., 185, *240*
Raju, N. V., 283, *326*
Ramalie, H., 170, *244*
Ramanathan, V., 275, *326*
Ramel, P., 270, 287, 288, 292, 293, 294, 297, 302, *322, 326*
Randall, H. T., 200, *240*
Randle, P. J., 113, *126*
Randolph, P., 309, *322*
Rannaud, J., 287, 288, 302, *322, 326*
Rao, B. Y., 247, *326*
Rao, M. N., 283, *326*
Rappaport, H., 170, *244*

Rasheed, A. A., 259, *325*
Raulin, J., 261, 269, 282, 289, 308, *326, 327*
Ravetto, C., 29, 54, *61*
Reader, G. G., 80, 81, *130*
Reaven, G. M., 65, 75, 104, 106, 118, 119, 122, 123, *126, 131, 132*
Redding, T. W., 88, *128*
Reddy, B. R., 255, 297, 299, *316, 327, 328, 329*
Reid, J. D., 102, *127*
Reinhard, M. C., 193, 194, *242*
Reiss, O. K., 137, 141, 142, 143, 147, 149, *162*
Reissell, P. K., 118, 121, *131*
Reissert, K., 96, *131*
Reisner, E. H., Jr., 221, *243*
Remi, K., 249, *323*
Renold, A. E., 71, 72, 73, 83, 99, 113, *126, 131, 132, 134*
Repke, K., 210, 211, *243*
Reporter, M. C., 309, *327*
Reshef, L., 68, *131*
Reveillon, F., 257, *325*
Reynolds, E. O. R., 41, *61*
Reynolds, M., 35, *60*
Ricca, G. S., 262, *316*
Rice, E. E., 289, 301, *326, 327, 329*
Richir, C., 269, 289, *326, 327*
Riegel, I. L., 211, *243*
Riemersma, J. C., 16, *61*
Riley, V., 199, *243*
Rinehart, J. F., 5, *61*
Rinetti, M., 292, 306, *327*
Rinke, H., 313, *329*
Risser, N., 278, 307, *327*
Rivera, E. M., 220, 239, *243*
Rivett, D. E. A., 265, *316*
Roberts, B., 253, 257, 259, *318, 319*
Roberts, D. G., 249, 259, *319*
Roberts, J. B., 114, *129*
Roberts, N. R., 35, *60*
Roberts, S., 108, *133*, 209, 211, *243*
Roberts, T. N., 80, 81, 89, *125, 130, 131*
Robertson, A. L., Jr., 149, 150, 152, 156, 157, *162*
Robertson, C. J., 291, *327*
Robertson, W. B., 230, *243*
Robinson, A. M., 217, *237*
Robinson, D. S., 79, *132*
Robinson, J. D., 87, *131*
Robson, J. M., 193, *238*

Rock, S. P., 262, 270, 293, 294, 295, 312, 327
Rockwood, B. N., 294, 316
Rodbell, M., 103, 111, 131
Roe, F. J. C., 227, 238
Röhl, L., 219, 241
Rössle, R., 229, 243
Roffo, A. H., 303, 327
Rogers, G. E., 16, 61
Roheim, P, S., 68, 127, 157, 162
Rohr, A., 138, 161
Roloff, M., 312, 323
Rony, H. R., 78, 101, 131
Roodyn, D. B., 254, 320
Rookledge, K. A., 70, 128
Roozemond, R. C., 5, 61
Rose, A. S., 9, 17, 62
Rose, G., 178, 238
Ross, J., 248, 249, 250, 327
Ross, R., 33, 62
Rossiter, R. J., 4, 39, 59, 61
Rost, H. E., 268, 292, 293, 294, 296, 311, 312, 313, 315, 327
Rostgaard, J., 49, 61
Roth, H., 262, 270, 293, 294, 295, 312, 327, 328
Roth, L. J., 33, 61
Rothblat, G. H., 146, 147, 148, 149, 150, 151, 152, 153, 154, 155, 156, 157, 161, 162
Rothe, M., 255, 312, 327
Rothenberg, J., 309, 323
Rubenstein, B., 77, 131
Rubin, B. A., 243
Rubinstein, D., 77, 131
Rudas, B., 82, 96, 131
Ruderman, N. B., 73, 131
Rudman, D., 68, 131
Rupp, J. J., 169, 176, 195, 238
Rutman, R. J., 82, 127
Rutstein, D. D., 148, 150, 163
Ryan, W. G., 69, 105, 119, 131
Rygaard, J., 194, 240
Rzhekhin, V. P., 313, 327

S

Sacco, O., 191, 237
Sachs, L., 219, 237
Saffioti, U., 170, 244
Sage, J. S., 307, 328

Sagredos, A. N., 314, 327
Sahasrabudhe, M. B., 14, 59
Sahasrabudhe, M. R., 271, 275, 313, 327
Said, F., 311, 327
Sailer, S., 81, 89, 91, 101, 102, 119, 121, 122, 123, 125, 131, 132
Sakai, H., 253, 261, 269, 285, 315, 320
Sakamaki, T., 301, 319
Sakuragi, T, 275, 283, 286, 287, 320, 326
Sakurai, H., 261, 263, 269, 321, 329
Sakurai, Y., 269, 321
Salaman, M. R., 79, 132
Salans, L. B., 75, 132
Salas, M., 71, 110, 133
Salinas, S., 192, 207, 208, 242
Salsman, K., 11, 60
Salyamon, L. S., 232, 243
Samols, E., 113, 132
Samuels, L. T. 209, 239
Sandberg, A. A., 209, 243
Sandberg, H., 94, 132
Sandhofer, F., 81, 89, 91, 101, 102, 119, 121, 122, 123, 125, 131, 132
Sanford, K. K., 219, 243
Saunlé, C., 168, 243
Sasaki, R., 307, 327
Sauberlich, H. E., 107, 109, 110, 112, 113, 114, 115, 134
Saunders, D. H., 281, 301, 321
Saxton, J. A., Jr., 190, 243
Scarpellino, R. J., 312, 328
Schabad, L. M., 168, 241, 243
Schaefer, W. C., 249, 320
Schaeffner, E., 277, 321
Schauenstein, E., 255, 256, 321, 327
Scheid, A., 139, 145, 148, 163
Scheig, R., 107, 109, 124, 132
Scheiner, S., 212, 225, 244
Schellman, J. A., 209, 239
Schenck, G. O., 180, 181, 241
Schenken, J. R., 200, 238
Schilling, E. L., 144, 152, 161
Schimke, R. J., 35, 60
Schjeide, O. A., 162
Schlant, R. C., 33, 61
Schless, G., 89, 125
Schlierf, G., 70, 132
Schmidt, W. J., 8, 61
Schnatz, J. D., 82, 97, 132
Schnecko, H. W., 248, 249, 253, 321
Schneider, W. J., 264, 319
Schnur, J., 6, 61

Schoellner, R., 249, 250, *327*
Schogt, J. C. M., 264, *327*
Scholfield, C. R., 264, *327*
Scholz, R. G., 312, *327*
Schoner, W., 7, *61*
Schott, H. J., 7, *61*
Schotz, M. C., 65, 66, 78, 79, 101, 102, 103, *124, 127, 132*
Schrade, W., 64, 81, *132*
Schreier, K., 114, *132*
Schubert, K., 175, 178, 188, *238, 242, 243*
Schulman, M., 76, *132*
Schultz, A., 11, *61*
Schultz, G., 76, *132*
Schultz, H. W., 246, 269, *327*
Schulz, D. W., 35, *60*
Schusdek, A., 83, 108, *124*
Schwartz, D. P., 255, 312, *317, 325, 327*
Schwartz, I. C., 76, *125*
Schwartz, I. L., 88, *127*
Schwartz, T. B., 69, 105, 119, *131*
Scott, R. F., 32, *59*
Scow, R. O., 82, 85, 86, 91, 93, 98, 103, 111, 114, *125, 126, 131, 132*
Sedallian, J., 233, *243*
Sedlacek, B. A. J., 270, *327*
Segaloff, A., 190, *239, 243*
Seher, A., 313, *327*
Seidman, F., 68, *131*
Seidman, I., 100, *125, 132*
Seligman, A. M., 32, *61*
Selke, E., 249, 250, *318*
Sellaeg, S., 249, *324*
Selva, D., 286, *327*
Selye, H., 191, *237, 242, 243*
Selz, G., 248, 258, *317, 321*
Sen, P. B., 15, *60*
Senft, G., 76, *132*
Sen Gupta, A. K., 262, 265, 266, 269, *327, 328*
Sen Gupta, M. L., 283, *317*
Sephton, H. H., 249, *328*
Sever, J. L., 80, *133*
Shafrir, E., 68, 79, 103, *127, 129, 132*
Shah, S., 119, *126*
Shamey, J., 253, 255, *319*
Shamoian, C. A., 85, *132*
Shapiro, B., 39, *61*, 68, 88, 107, *131*
Shapiro, I. L., 35, *60*
Sharma, C., 71, *132*
Sharma, S. A., 263, *324*

Shay, F. G., 295, *326*
Shear, M., 29, *61*
Shear, M. J., 217, *243*
Shepherd, A. D., 255, *320*
Sherman, G., 191, 192, *242*
Shibue, T., 290, *325*
Shigeta, Y., 88, 97, 99, *127, 132*
Shil'man, L. Z., 292, *328*
Shimizu, T., 277, *315*
Shimkin, M. B., 175, 193, 195, 197, 198, 200, *243, 244*
Shin, S.-I., 221, *244*
Shklar, G., 234, *244*
Shoemaker, W. C., 76, *132*
Shore, M. L., 39, *62*
Shoshan, S., 31, *62*
Shrago, E., 84, 109, *132*
Shreeve, W. W., 88, 99, *127, 128, 132*
Shubik, P., 170, 213, *237, 244*
Shue, G. M., 269, 274, 278, 279, 281, 284, 307, *318, 328*
Shull, K. H., 114, *133*
Shupova, I., 292, 296, *320*
Sidbury, J. B., Jr., 210, *242*
Sidman, R. L., 33, *61*
Siefert, W. L., 68, *129*
Silberberg, M., 195, *244*
Silberberg, R., 195, *244*
Silvestre, J., 292, 296, *328*
Simko, V., 270, 282, 285, *325, 328*
Simons, M., 222, *239*
Simpson, M. E., 190, 191, *241*
Sims, R. J., 255, 263, 265, 273, 276, 312, *318*
Sims, R. P. A., *328*
Singhal, R. L., *133*
Sinnhuber, R. O., 246, 259, 269, 310, 311, *317, 325, 327, 329*
Siperstein, M. D., 86, *132*
Sirtori, C., 223, 229, *244*
Skellon, J. H., 247, 272, *328*
Slanetz, C. A., 259, 260, 281, 301, 309, *321, 328*
Slaunwhite, W. R., Jr., 209, *243*
Sliwiok, J., 270, 313, *328*
Slover, H. T., 248, 250, *328*
Small, G., 309, *324*
Smith, D. F., 113, *127*
Smith, E. B., 39, *61*
Smith, E. C., 138, *163*
Smith, G. M., 194, *240*

Smith, J. G. M., 249, *315*
Smith, P., 228, *237*
Smith, S. C., 138, *163*
Smouse, T. H., 255, *316*, *328*
Smyth, F. S., 80, *125*
Snapir, N., 70, *129*
Sneyd, J. G. T., 76, *125*
Sobel, H., 208, *240*
Socolow, E. L., 146, 152, *161*
Sodero, A , 76, 77, *131*
Sodhi, H. S., 157, *163*
Söling, H. D., 90, *132*
Soendergaard, E., 254, *319*
Sok Min, B., 94, *132*
Solo, A., 71, *132*
Sols, A., 110, *133*
Som, J. M., 283, *317*
Sommers, S. C., 191, 192, 224, *240*, *242*
Soukup, R. J., 312, *328*
Sourander, P., 40, 41, *61*
Southam, C. M., 221, *237*
Spaeth, A. E., 68, 88, 110, *131*
Spath, P., 122, 123, *132*
Spector, A. A., 156, *163*
Spencer, A. F., 86, 107, *132*
Spencer, H., 229, *244*
Spitzer, J. J., 68, 76, 90, *129*, *132*
Srere, P. A., 75, 84, 109, *121*
Srivanij, P., 31, *61*
Srivastava, S. K., *133*
Stadie, W. C., 107, *127*
Stafford, W. S., 76, *129*
Stamm, N. B., 71, 75, 85, *133*
Stanger, D. W., 168, *244*
Stapf, R. J., 255, *328*
Stare, F. J., 100, 104, *129*, *133*
Stark, W., 255, *329*
Stasney, J., 204, *239*
Stauffacher, W., 99, *132*
Stauffer, M., 228, *238*
Stauffer, R. D., 170, 171, 175, 189, 209, 225, *238*, *244*
Steele, R., 76, *124*
Steibert, E., 270, 313, *328*
Steim, J. M., 28, *61*
Stein, O., 39, *61*
Stein, R. A., 253, *315*
Stein, Y., 39, *61*, 100, 107, 112, 113, 114, 115, 116, 121, *124*, *128*
Steinberg, D., 66, 68, *126*, *130*, *132*, 156, *163*

Steinberg, J., 76, *127*
Steiner, G., 121, *132*
Steiner, P. E., 168, 169, *239*, *244*
Sterky, G., 80, 81, *133*
Stern, M. P., 104, 106, 119, 122, 123, *131*
Stern, S., 294, *328*
Stetten, D., Jr., 74, 82, *133*
Stevens, M. L., 221, *239*
Stevens, R , 90, *126*
Stevenson, G. T., 202, *239*
Stewart, F. W., 222, *240*
Steyn-Parvé, E. P., 75, *129*
Stier, E. F., 290, *328*
Stoeckenius, W., 16, *61*
Stoerk, H. C., 309, *328*
Stoffel, W., 139, 145, *163*
Stone, D. B., 94, *133*
Stormont, J. M., 104, 106, *133*
Stoward, P. J., 14, *57*, *61*
Strang, L. B., 41, *61*
Strich, S. J., 36, *61*
Strickland, K. P., 4, *61*
Strisower, B., 64, *127*
Strock, H., 290, 295, *328*
Strong, L. C., 190, 194, *240*
Strong, J. P., 230, *243*
Strout, R. G., 138, *163*
Stumpf, W. E., 33, *61*
Sugai, M., 284, 305, 310, *320*, *321*, *324*, *328*
Suhara, Y., 312, *328*
Sulkin, N. M., 31, *61*
Sundralingam, A., 247, 250, *318*
Suntzeff, V., 193, 194, *238*, *242*
Sussman, K. E., 68, *132*
Sutherland, E. W., Jr., 76, *125*
Sutton, D. A., 174, *241*, 247, 249, 250, 265, *316*, *318*, *328*
Suzuki, Y., 255, *328*
Svanborg, A., 94, *126*
Svennerholm, L., 11, 29, *61*
Swan, D. C., 108, 113, *133*
Sweeney, M. J., 73, 86, 87, *133*
Swern, D., 250, 281, 301, *321*
Swift, C. E., 248, 249, 250, 274, *328*
Swim, H. E., 152, *161*
Swoboda, P. A. T., 253, 254, 255, 312, *322*, *328*
Swynghedauw, B., 101, 102, *133*
Sydnor, K. L., 204, *244*
Symmers, W. St. C., 223, *244*

Szego, C. M., 209, 211, *243, 244*

T

Taeufel, K., 254, 255, 265, 270, 276, 312, *323, 328*
Taghavy, A., 11, *60*
Tagnon, R., 113, *126*
Takada, M., 251, 258, *319*
Takakura, K., 197, 232, *244*
Takeda, J., 84, *133*
Taketa, K., 87, *133*
Takeuchi, T., 255, *328*
Tal, E., 68, 88, 107, *133*
Tamai, I., 300, *320*
Tanaka, A., 156, *163*
Tanaka, Y., 204, *239*
Tanioka, H., 84, *133*
Tarladgis, B. G., 311, *328*
Tarrant, M. E., 73, 76, 82, 86, 87, 89, *124, 129, 133*
Taskinen, M-R., 89, 102, 122, 123, *130, 131*
Taylor, F. B., Jr., 41, *61*
Taylor, C. B., 115, *124*
Taylor, H. A., 17, *62*
Taylor, J. R., 311, *325*
Teebor, G. W., 100, *125, 132,* 305, *329*
Teeter, R. M., 255, *320*
Teinzer, A., 87, 90, *134*
Teitelbaum, A., 107, 108, 114, 115, *126*
Tels, M., 262, 267, 313, *316*
Tepper, S. A., 270, 308, *322*
Tepperman, H. J., 107, 109, *133*
Tepperman, H. M., 107, *133*
Tepperman, J., 107, 109, *133*
Terner, J. V., 6, *61*
Terroine, T., 308, *326*
Thomas, A., 71, *130,* 253, 257, *317*
Thomas, W. A., 32, *59*
Thomasson, H. J., 280, *319*
Thompson, J. A., 297, 299, *328*
Thompson, R. H. S., 82, 86, 87, 89, *133*
Thompson, S. W., 202, *244*
Thornton, F. E., 255, *319*
Timms, E., 247, *328*
Tobolsky, A. V., 248, *328*
Toi, B., 272, *328*
Torres, D., 276, *329*
Tomatis, L., 170, *244*
Tomic, M., 192, *240*
Toolan, H. W., 234, *244*

Torvik, A., 33, *61*
Toth, B., 170, *244*
Touhill, E., 35, *60*
Toyama, Y., 253, 312, *324, 329*
Toyomizu, M., 310, *329*
Traisman, H. S., 80, *133*
Tranzer, J. P., 32, *61*
Trenk, F. B., 310, *315*
Trentin, J. J., 194, 197, 203, *240*
Trepagnier, J. H., 17, *60*
Triebold, H. O., 145, *162*
Trinchese, T., 276, *329*
Trout, D. L., 66, *127*
Truhaut, R., 168, *243*
Tryding, N., 253, 308, *319*
Tsaltos, T. T., 104, *124*
Tsao, S. S., 144, 145, *163*
Tsuchiyama, H., 305, 309, *324, 328*
Tsukamoto, T., 250, *329*
Tubbs, P. K., 85, 87, 90, *133*
Tudorie, A., 270, *315*
Tuqan, N. A., 8, 39, 57, *61*
Turner, D. A., 35, *60*
Turner, J. G., Jr., 178, 185, *238*
Twombly, G. H., 212, 225, *244*
Tzur, R., 68, 88, 107, *133*

U

Ueno, S., 263, *329*
Ueyanagi, F., 293, 312, *322*
Uezumi, N., 311, *329*
Ulfelder, H., 210, *237*
Ullmann, H. J., 166, 224, *238*
Upton, A. C., 196, *241*
Urgoiti, E., 85, 86, *125*
Uri, N., 247, *329*
Urich, H., 28, *61*
Utyumova-Malova, A. V., 301, *329*
Uzman, L. L., 26, *60*
Uzzan, A., 271, 276, *329*

V

Vagelos, P. R., 84, 86, *129, 133*
Valentini, A. F., 262, 267, *316, 318*
Van Akkeren, L. A., 291, 294, 295, 297, *325*
Van Deenen, L. L. M., 10, *58*
vander Poel, G. H., 255, *329*
Van Duuren, B. L., 216, *244,* 305, *329*

Van Duyne, C. M., 65, 66, 102, 106, 111, 128
van Eck, W. S., 81, 133
Van Giessen, B., 311, 325
van Harken, D. R., 91, 92, 93, 96, 128, 133
Van Itallie, T. B., 114, 133
Vanko, M., 113, 130
VanNie, R., 207, 244
Vannotti, A., 123, 126
Vasiliev, J. M., 170, 206, 244
Vazquez-Lopez, E., 190, 191, 244
Vcella, C., 113, 127
Vecchio, D., 99, 132
Veronesi, U., 223, 229, 244
Vershinin, A. A., 301, 329
Ververgaert, P. H. J. T., 5, 32, 58
Vesenne, M.-R., 122, 130
Vester, J. W., 65, 131
Villagran, M. P., 249, 329
Viñuela, E., 70, 110, 132, 133
Vioque, A., 249, 273, 329
Virag, S., 35, 36, 40, 57
Voetisch, K., 271, 318
Vogel, P., 268, 315
Vogt, W., 308, 317
Voigt, I., 255, 312, 327
Voit, K., 26, 58
von Haam, E., 191, 192, 237
Von Hedenberg, C., 223, 240

W

Waddell, W. R., 95, 133
Wagenseil, F., 219, 244
Wagner, R. M., 65, 126
Waite, M., 86, 133
Wakil, S. J., 86, 133
Walens, H. A., 274, 329
Walker, W. J., 104, 133
Wall, P. E., 210, 244
Waller, H. G., 94, 129
Walton, K. W., 6, 61
Wang, C.-I., 81, 124
Wang, D. Y., 220, 244
Warner, W. D., 301, 326, 327, 329
Warren, S., 222, 244
Warshawsky, H., 222, 237
Wasserkrug, H. L., 32, 61
Watanabe, H., 253, 329
Watanabe, S., 310, 322
Waterhouse, C., 104, 106, 133

Waterman, H. I., 263, 329
Watkin, D. M., 104, 133
Watkins, M. L., 106, 110, 111, 128
Watt, B. K., 290, 329
Weast, R-C., 44, 61
Weber, A. F., 11, 61
Weber, G., 71, 75, 85, 133
Webster, W. W., 108, 128
Wegmann, R., 14, 61
Weinhouse, S., 71, 74, 126, 130, 132
Weinstein, D. B., 137, 144, 150, 163
Weinstein, I., 106, 110, 111, 128
Weisburger, E. K., 199, 244
Weisburger, J. H., 199, 244
Weisman, R. A., 32, 59
Weiss, L., 85, 87, 90, 133, 134
Weiss, T. J., 311, 325
Weller, R. O., 8, 11, 19, 21, 32, 39, 48, 49, 57, 61, 62
Wellers, G., 286, 316
Wells, A. F., 263, 268, 278, 279, 313, 317, 329
Wenkeová, J., 89, 133
Werner, H., 311, 329
Wertheimer, E., 89, 127
Werthessen, N. T., 35, 60
West, C. E., 76, 133
Westermann, B., 87, 90, 134
Westman, S., 99, 100, 133
Westphal, U., 209, 244
Wharry, D. M., 247, 328
Wheeler, D. H., 263, 264, 265, 275, 319, 325, 329
Wherrett, J. R., 11, 62
Whipple, A., 26, 60
White, A., 157, 162, 232, 239
White, J., 265, 329
Whitmore, W. F., 266, 329
Whitney, J. E., 108, 133
Wieder, R., 175, 244
Wiedersheim, V., 216, 244
Wieland, H., 216, 244
Wieland, O., 84, 85, 87, 90, 113, 133, 134
Wiener, H., 5, 62
Wieske, T., 313, 329
Wigglesworth, V. B., 5, 15, 62
Wilcox, H. G., 91, 92, 134
Wilding, M. D., 289, 329
Wilkinson, R. A., 255, 329
Williams, P. N., 4, 59
Williams, R. H., 39, 60, 76, 82, 83, 95, 97, 124, 126, 132

Williams, W. L., 195, 196, *240*
Williams, W. R., *134*
Williamson, J. R., 72, 73, *134*
Williamson, L., 250, 257, *329*
Willms, B., 72, 85, *125*
Wilske, K. R., 33, *62*
Winand, J., 99, *134*
Windmueller, H. G., 68, 89, 110, *134*
Wingfield, H. C., 19, *62*
Wintersteiner, O., 176, *237*
Wirsen, C., 68, *125*
Wirth, C., 288, *322*
Wiseblatt, L., 263, *317, 329*
Wishner, L. A., 298, *329*
Witting, L. A., 284, 305, 309, *328, 329*
Wode, G., 289, *329*
Woelm, G., 255, 312, *327*
Woestenburg, W. J., 249, 252, *315*
Wojewski, A., 219, *244*
Wolfe, H. J., 40, *62*
Wolfe, L. S., 11, 35, 58, *62*
Wolfgram, F., 9, 17, *62*
Wolman, M., 5, 8, 9, 14, 16, 27, 31, 38, 41, 43, 44, *62*
Wolmark, N., 4, *58*
Woolf, N., 36, *60*
Woolley, G., 198, *239*
Womack, N. A., 222, *244*
Wong, T.-W., 213, *244*
Wood, H. N., 234, *244*
Woodward, H., Jr., 113, *130*
Wormack, M., 112, *129*
Wright, P. H., 82, 86, 87, 89, *124, 133*
Wu, C. H., 76, 77, *131*
Wu, M. I., 35, *60*
Wurziger, J., 311, 312, 313, *329*
Wyman, R. S., 195, *244*

Y

Yamaguchi, K., 201, *242*
Yamada, T., 311, *329*
Yamada, Y., 271, 275, *320*
Yamamoto, A., 294, 295, 296, *316*
Yamamoto, I., 270, 273, 274, 275, 276, 293, 294, 295, *324, 325*
Yamamoto, R. S., 199, *244*
Yang, N. C., 213, *244*
Yanishlieva, N., 248, 253, *326*
Yannopoulos, K., *241*
Yasuda, K., 299, *327, 329*
Yee, Y. S., 210, *238*
Yoe, J. H., 19, *62*
Youngner, J. S., 144, *161*
Yu, T. C., 310, 311, *317, 329*
Yudkin, J., *134*
Yuki, E., 262, 271, 291, 292, 294, 295, *330*

Z

Zaidel, L., 31, *62*
Zakim, D., 107, 109, 110, 112, 113, 114, 115, *128, 134*
Zanetti, M. E., 99, *128*
Zelikoff, M., 17, *62*
Zelinkova, M., 310, *326*
Zilch, K. T., 250, 257, *316, 318*
Zilversmit, D. B., 39, *60, 62,* 111, *131*
Zimmermann, R., 254, *328*
Zinkham, W. H., 210, *242*
Ziombski, H., 294, *324*
Zomzely, C., 99, *134*
Zottu, S., 107, *129*
Zschiesche, W., 178, *238*
Zugibe, F. T., 5, *62*
Zwain, H., 310, 313, *326*

SUBJECT INDEX

A

Acetyl CoA, 70, 109, 110, 115
Acetyl-CoA carboxylase, 84, 87, 100, 108, 109, 110
Acid hematein technique for phospholipids, 49-50
Acids, as volatile oxidation products, 256
Acrolein, as lipid fixative, 5
Acyl carnitine, 87
Acyl-CoA, 70
  fatty, 66, 67, 72, 73, 87
Acyl CoA synthetase, 67
Adenomas, see also Carcinomas, Neoplasms, Tumors, Sarcomas
  anterior-lobe chromophobe, 190-191
  pituitary, 190-191
Adenosine monophosphate, 76, 92
  steroid synthesis and, 220-221
Adenosine triphosphate, 67, 71
Adenyl cyclase, 76
Adipose tissue, 66, 67, 97, 98, 103, 111, 113, 121
Albright's syndrome, 228
Albumin, as vehicle for carcinogens, 186
Alcohols, as volatile oxidation products, 256
Aldehydes, as volatile oxidation products, 255
Aldehydoglycerides, as nonvolatile oxidation products, 257
Aldosterone, as carcinogen, 220
Alloxan, carcinomas and, 191
Amaurtic idiocy, 41, 42
AMP, see Adenosine monophosphate
Androgens, see also specific compounds
  as carcinogens, 191, 201, 208, 209, 221
Androstenediol, as carcinogen, 201
Androsterone, as carcinogen, 219
Apolipoprotein, 67
Arachidonic acid, in tissue culture cells, 138, 139

Aromatic compounds, as volatile oxidation products, 256
Arteriosclerosis and cholesterol, 231
Atheroma, cholesterol laden, 230-231
Atherosclerosis, 100
  cholesterol and, 230-231
  diabetes and, 81
  histochemical studies of, 39-40
    lipid transport, 39-40
    phospholipids, 39
ATP, see Adenosine triphosphate
Auto-oxidation of fats
  chemistry of peroxides, 247-252, see also Peroxides
  to peroxides, 247-254
  previous reviews on, 247
  reaction steps in, 247-248
    kinetics, 248-249
  secondary oxidation products, 254-259
    nonvolatile, 257-259, see also general categories
    volatile, 254-256, see also general categories
Autoradiography of lipids, 33-35

B

Benzpyrene, as carcinogen, 205
Birefringence of lipids, 7-8
Blocking theories, as related to tumorigenic phenomena, 212-215
  binding to DNA, 213
Breast, fibrocystic disease of, 222
Breast carcinoma, see Carcinomas, breast
Bromine-silver nitrate technique for lipids, 47

C

Calcium-formalin, as lipid fixative, 5
Calcium-formol, as lipid fixative, 5

Carbohydrate metabolism, control of
    plasma and liver triglyceride kinetics
    by, 63-123
Carbohydrates
    dietary, long-term effects on triglycer-
        ide kinetics, 103-117
    influence on triglyceride metabolism,
        100-117
Carboxylic acids, as nonvolatile oxidation
    products, 258-259
Carboxymethyl cellulose, as carcinogen,
    207
Carcinogenesis
    discussion, 231-235
    solid state, 167
        cholesterol, 170-174
    summary, 235-237
Carcinogenic mechanisms, 167-168
    autoimmune theory, 168
    two-step vs summation theory, 168
    unitary theory, 167-168
Carcinogens
    chemical, 167
    cholesterol as, see Cholesterol
    definition, 166-167
    fats as, see Fats
    mechanisms for, see Carcinogenic
        mechanisms
Carcinomas, see also Neoplasms, Tumors,
    Sarcomas, Adenomas
    adrenal cortex, estrone-dependent, 190
    breast
        estrogens and, 222-223
        hormone treatment of, 224
    cervical, 226-227
    endometrial, 224-226
    estrogen-linked, 191-192
    in humans, 222-231, see also specific
        types
    mammary, 197-206
        in mice, 197-202
            spontaneous occurrence, 198, 199
        in monkeys, 205-206
        in rats
            with estrogen, 202-204
            with progesterone, 204-205
    prostate, 227-228
    renal, 227
        estrogen-dependent, 208
Cell permeability, as related to tumori-
    genic phenomena, 211-212

    of fat-cell membrane, 212
    at target site, 211-212
Cerebroside
    modified PAS technique for, 53-54
    staining method for, 27-28
3,5-Cholestadiene, as carcinogen, 175,
    188-189
3,5-Cholestadien-7-one, 176
Cholestane-3β,5α,6β-triol, 176
6-Cholestene-3β,5α-diol, 176
4-Cholestene-3,6-dione, as carcinogen,
    178-179
4-Cholesten-3-one, 176
5-Cholesten-3-one, as carcinogen,
    177-178
Cholesterol
    as carcinogen, 168-189, 207, 225
        Bantu liver extracts, 174-175
        historical background, 168-170
        oxidation products, 176-189, see also
            specific compounds
            historical background, 177
            newt test, 189
            oily vehicle, 177
        pellets
            biological use of, 175
            in bladder, 175-176
        solid state carcinogenesis, 170-174
        in humans, 229-231
    perchloric acid-naphthoquinone tech-
        nique for, 46-47
    staining methods for, 11-14
    in tissue culture cells, 145-155
        cellular sterol excretion, 150
        free, content and incorporation in,
            145-150
        incorporation of labeled, 148
        intracellular location of, 149-150
        synthesis, 151-153
        utilization of esterified, 153-155
Cholesterol dibromide, 176
Cholesterol α-oxide, as carcinogen,
    184-188, 213-215
Cholesteryl ester, in tissue culture cells,
    146-155
Cholesteryl palmitate, solid state carcino-
    genesis, 171-173
Chylomicrons, 69, 78, 94-99, 102, 103,
    106, 111
Cirrhosis of liver, 229

Citrate cleavage enzyme, 75, 84, 99, 109, 115
CoA, 67
Cocarcinogens, definition, 167
Copper rubeanic acid technique for fatty acids, 48
Corticoids, as carcinogens, 221
Corticosterone, as carcinogen, 220
Cortisol, as carcinogen, 197, 220
Cortisone, as carcinogen, 220, 221
Cottonseed oil, as vehicle for carcinogens, 186
Cresyl violet, technique for sulfatide, 54
Cyclic compounds from thermally oxidized fats, biological properties of, 278-280
Cystic disease of breast, see Breast

D

Deoxycholic acid, as carcinogen, 216-218
Deoxycorticosterone, as carcinogen, 193, 208, 220
Deoxycorticosterone acetate, as carcinogen, 194
Dextran sulfate, 97
Diabetes, 80-100
  alloxan-induced, 82, 84, 87, 89-91
  fatty acid and triglyceride metabolism in, with hyperinsulinism, 99-100
  hepatic fatty acid synthesis in, 82-89
  juvenile-type, 80, 82
  plasma triglyceride concentration in diabetes, 80-82
  removal of triglycerides from plasma in, 94-99
  synthesis and release of liver triglycerides in, 89-94
Diabetic ketosis, 120
Dialkyl peroxides, see Peroxides
Dibenzanthrene, as carcinogen, 205
Diels–Alder reaction, 265, 266
Diethylstilbestrol, as carcinogen, 190, 192, 200, 208, 227
Dihydrocholesterol, 176
Dimerization of fatty acid moieties, 266-267
Dimers
  formed in absence of air, 265-267
  as nonvolatile oxidation products, 257, 258

7,12-Dimethylbenz[a] anthracene, as carcinogen, 203, 205
Dyes, lipid-soluble, 6-7, see also specific dyes

E

Electrophoresis, starch-block, of fat particles, 94
Enzymes, see specific enzymes
Epinephrine, 85, 103
Epiperoxides, see Peroxides
Epoxides
  as nonvolatile oxidation products, 257
  from thermally oxidized fats, biological properties of, 278
Esters, as volatile oxidation products, 256
Estradiol, as carcinogen, 190, 193, 195, 196, 198, 200, 203, 205, 206, 208, 219, 220, 225
Estradiol benzoate, as carcinogen, 194-196, 200, 206
Estrogens, see also specific compounds
  as carcinogens, 190-193, 195, 198, 200, 202, 203, 206-209, 221, 222, 224-229
  stimulation with pathological fibrosis, 228-229
Estrone, as carcinogen, 190, 194, 196, 199, 202, 220, 225
Estrone benzoate, as carcinogen, 200
Ethinyl estradiol, as carcinogens, 208
17α-Ethinyl-19-nortestosterone, see Norethindrone
17α-Ethinyl $\Delta^{5,\,10}$-19-nortestosterone, see Norethynodrel

F

Fabry's disease, 41, 42
Fat metabolism, see Triglyceride metabolism, Fatty acids
Fats
  auto-oxidation of, see Auto-oxidation
  bleaching of, 289
  as carcinogens, 303-306
  commercial processing of, 289
  deodorization of, 289
  flavor properties of, 254-255
  frying of, see Frying

Fats (*continued*)
  heated
    in absence of air, biological proper-
      ties of, 267-269
    interaction of with other dietary com-
      ponents, 309-310
  heated and oxidized
    analytical methods for, 310-314
    chemical and biological properties of,
      245-315
    metabolic effects of, 306-309
  oxidation of, *see* Oxidation of fats
  oxidized, *see also* Fats, heated and oxi-
    dized
    biological properties of, 259-261
  refining of, 289
  thermal reaction of, *see* Thermal re-
    actions
  thermally oxidized
    biological properties of, 276-289
    feeding experiments with, 282-289
  used frying
    biological properties of, 300-303
    components of, 298-299
    properties of, 291-294
    surveys of, 297-298
Fatty acid metabolism, in diabetes with
  hyperinsulinism, 99-100
Fatty acid synthesis
  effect of insulin on, 70-75
  hepatic, 107-110
  in diabetes, 82-89
Fatty acid synthetase, 84, 100
Fatty acids
  copper rubeanic acid technique for, 48
  free, 66 ff.
    hepatic uptake and esterification of,
      in diabetes, 90-94
    metabolism of, 63
  hydroxy, from thermally oxidized fats,
    biological properties of, 277-278
  metabolism of, *see* Fatty acid metabo-
    lism
  polyunsaturated, 138-140, *see also* spe-
    cific acids
  as products of thermal oxidation, 272
  staining methods for, 14
  synthesis of, *see* Fatty acid synthesis
  in tissue culture cells, 137-145
    polyunsaturated, 138-140
    source and cellular content, 137-138
    utilization of, 140-144

FFA, *see* Fatty acids, free
Fibrosis, pathological, estrogen stimulation and, 228-229
Flotation of fat particles, 94
Formaldehyde, as lipid fixative, 5
Fixation of lipids, *see* Lipids
Fructose
  diabetes and, 83-85, 91
  effect on triglyceride metabolism,
    113-116
  fatty acid synthesis and, 107, 108, 109
  hyperglyceridemic effect of, 112-113
Frying
  biological properties of used frying fats,
    300-303
  chemical and physical changes during,
    290-299
  conditions, 290-291
    effects of, on fat properties, 294-297

G

Gangliosides
  protein-bound, modified PAS tech-
    nique for, 53-54
  staining methods for, 29
  Svennerholm-Bial reagent for, 54-55
Gaucher's and Krabbe's disease, 41
Glucagon, 85
Glucokinase, 73-75, 85, 89, 100, 110
Glucose, 72, 75
  acute effects of, on plasma triglycerides,
    101-103
  diabetes and, 83, 85, 91, 97
  effect on triglycerides, 105
    metabolism, 113-116
  fatty acid synthesis and, 107-110
  hyperglyceridemic effects of, 111-112,
    121-122
Glucose metabolism, *see* Carbohydrate
  metabolism
Glucose-6-phosphate dehydrogenase, 75,
  109
Glycerol, 121
  diabetes and, 84, 85, 91
  triglyceride turnover rate and, 104
Glycerol phosphate, 74-76, 87, 88, 107,
  110, 113
Glycerol phosphate dehydrogenase, 107,
  115
Glycerophosphate acyltransferase, 66, 67,
  106

Glyceryl palmitate, solid state carcinogenesis, 171-173
Glycosphingosides, 10-11
  staining methods for, 27-29
Gold-hydroxamic acid reaction for phosphoglycerides, 52
Growth hormone, as carcinogen, 203

H

Hamsters, golden, tumors, 208-209
HeLa cells, *see* Tissue culture cells
Hexose monophosphate shunt, 85
HMP, *see* Hexose monophosphate shunt
Hydrocarbons
  carcinogenic, from steroids, 216-218
  from thermally oxidized fats, biological properties of, 277
  as volatile oxidation products, 256
Hydrocortisone
  as carcinogen, 221
  tumor growth and, 202
Hydroperoxides, *see* Peroxides
5α-Hydroperoxy-6-cholesten-3β-ol, as carcinogen, 180-181
6β-Hydroperoxy-4-cholesten-3-one, as carcinogen, 181-184
6β-Hydroxy-4-cholesten-3-one, as carcinogen, 179-180
7α-Hydroxycholesterol, 176
7β-Hydroxycholesterol, 176
17-Hydroxy-11-deoxycorticosterone, as carcinogen, 221
2-Hydroxymethylene-17α-methyldihydrotestosterone, as carcinogen, 201
Hyperglycemia, 70, 82
Hyperglyceridemia, 68, 69, 80, 81, 82, 94, 96-99, 101, 104, 106
  "carbohydrate-induced" metabolic error of, 117-123
  comparison with normal, 117-123
Hyperinsulinemia, 69, 70, 71, 82, 123
Hyperinsulinism, 74, 75, 99-100
Hyperlipemia, 80-82, 94-99, 105, 117-123
Hypoglycemia, 74
Hypothyroidism, pituitary adenomas and, 190-191

I

Idiopathic hyperinsulinism, 123

Insulin
  action on triglyceride metabolism, 69-80
  control of plasma and liver triglyceride kinetics by, 63-123
  effect of, on hepatic fatty acid synthesis, 70-75
    on plasma triglyceride concentration, 70, 71
    on plasma triglyceride outflow, 78-80
    on triglycerides, 105
    on synthesis of, 75-78
  response to dietary carbohydrates, 113
  secretion rate in hyperglyceridemia, 123
Intestine, plasma triglycerides of, *see* Plasma triglycerides

K

Ketoacidosis, 80, 97
Ketoglycerides, as nonvolatile oxidation products, 257
Ketones, as volatile oxidation products, 255-256

L

L cells, *see* Tissue culture cells
Lactones, as volatile oxidation products, 256
Lecithin, in tissue culture cells, 144, 145
Leukemia, 196
  acute lymphatic and chronic lymphocytic, 229
  estrogen-inhibiting mouse virus, 196
  transplantable, tissue cultures of, 221
Leukodystrophy, metachromatic, 40-41
Linoleate, oxidation of, 250
Linoleic acid, in tissue culture cells, 138, 139, 142
Linolenate, oxidation of, 250
Lipase, 67, 80, 103, 121
Lipase-lead sulfide technique for triglycerides, 48-49
Lipid fixation, 5-6, 45, 46, *see also* specific fixatives
Lipid metabolism
  in tissue culture cells, 135-161
    molecular theory, 155-161
    particulate theory, 155-161

Lipid storage diseases, histochemical studies of, 40-41
Lipids, *see also* specific substances
  autoradiography of, *see* Autoradiography
  chemical properties of, 9-11
  conjugated, 10-11
    complex esters or amides, 10-11
    simple esters, 10
  differential solubility of, 8-9
  electron histochemical methods for, 32-33
  enzymic digestive methods for, 31-32
  fixation of, *see* Lipid fixation
  histochemical methods, "slide," 46-56, *see also* specific type of lipid
  histochemistry of, 1-56
    biological and pathological applications, 36-44
    quantitative, 35-36
    slides, 36-38
      limitations, 36-37
      localization vs quantitation, 38
  hydrophilic, 2, 3, 17
  hydrophobic, 3, 4, 17
  metabolism of, *see* Lipid metabolism
  microtomy techniques for, 45-46
  physical properties of, 2-4
    melting points, 4
    surface properties, 2-4
  staining methods, 11-32, *see also* specific lipids
    for unsaturated groups, 14-19
  unconjugated, 9-10
  unsaturated
    bromine-silver nitrate technique for, 47
    Oil Red O technique for, 56
    osmium tetroxide technique for, 47
    Sudan black technique for, 55-56
    ultraviolet-Schiff technique for, 48
Lipofuscins, staining methods for, 31
Liver, plasma triglycerides of, *see* Plasma triglycerides
Liver triglycerides
  alterations in, in insulin deficiency, 98
  effect of insulin on synthesis of, 75-78
  formation and breakdown of, 65-69
  kinetic control of, by carbohydrate metabolism and insulin, 63-123
  secretion of, 110

synthesis and release of, in diabetes, 89-94
Lymphomas, 195, 196
  adrenal steroid hormones in treatment of, 229
Lysolecithin, in tissue culture cells, 144

M

Malate dehydrogenase, 115
Malic enzyme, 84, 115
Malonyl CoA, 109
Mammary carcinoma, *see* Carcinoma
Mammary gland, tissue culture and cancer, 220
Mammotropin, as carcinogen, 220
Mannoheptulose and insulin deficiency, 83
Marchi reaction, 17-19
Methylbisdehydrodoisynolic acid, as carcinogen, 208
3-Methylcholanthrene, as carcinogen, 192, 201, 203, 205, 216, 217, 219
3-Methyl-1,2-di-3-pyridyl-1-propane, as carcinogen, 205
Methyl linoleate, auto-oxidation of, 256
Methyl oleate, oxidation of, 249
Mice
  estrogen-induced tumors in, 195-196
  mammary carcinoma, in, 197-202
  as test animals, *see* specific compounds
Microtomy techniques for lipids, *see* Lipids
Monkeys, mammary carcinomas in, 205-206
Myelin buds, 3

N

NADPH, 71
Neoplasms, *see also* Adenomas, Carcinomas, Sarcomas, Tumors
  endocrine-linked, etiology and treatment of, 222-229
  sarcomas, 192-193
    estrogen-linked, 191-192
    endometrial, in rodents, 191-193
  induced by steroid hormones, 190-209
  uterine-vaginal, 206-207
Nicotinic acid, 79, 121
  effect of, on hepatic lipogenesis, 72-73

Niemann-Pick's disease, 41
Nile blue sulfate, 7
  technique for phospholipids, 55
Norandrostenolone, as carcinogen, 201
Norepinephrine, 121
  effect on plasma triglycerides, 102
Norethindrone, as carcinogen, 192, 207
Norethynodrel, as carcinogen, 207, 208
Norprogesterone, as carcinogen, 207

O

Obesity and diabetes, 80, 81, 90, 93, 99
Oleic acid
  labeling triglycerides with, 115
  in tissue culture cells, 138, 141
Oil Red O technique for lipids, 56
Osmium tetroxide, as lipid fixative, 5, 47
Osmium tetroxide-α-naphthylamine tech-
    nique (OTAN) for phospholipids,
    50-51
Oxidation of fats, *see also* Auto-oxidation
    of fats
  at high temperatures, 269-289
    chemical reactions, 269-272
    products of, 272-276
      cyclic, 274-275
      dimers, 275-276
      monomeric oxygenated, 272-274
      oxidative susceptibility, 276
      polymers, 275-276
      unsaponifiables, 276
      volatiles, 272
  previous reviews on, 246-247
7-Oxocholesterol, 176

P

Palmitic acid
  labeling triglycerides with, 115
  in tissue culture cells, 138, 142
Palmitic acid-1-C^{14}, plasma triglycerides
    and, 71, 76, 77, 90, 91
Palmitic acid-H^3, labeling of plasma tri-
    glycerides, 104
Perchloric acid-naphthoquinone tech-
    nique for cholesterol, 46-47
Periodic acid-Schiff technique for lipids,
    53-54
Peroxides
  absorbability of, 254

biological properties of, 253-254
  chemistry of, 247-252
    formation, 247-249
    structures of hydroperoxides,
      249-251
    polarity of, 251, 252
    reaction steps in auto-oxidation,
      247-248
    toxicity of, 254
Phosphatidate phosphohydrolase, 67
Phosphatidic acid, 67
  in tissue culture cells, 144
Phosphatidylethanolamine, in tissue cul-
    ture cells, 144
Phosphatidylinositol, in tissue culture
    cells, 144
Phosphatidylserine, in tissue culture
    cells, 144
Phosphine 3R, 7
Phosphodiesterase, 76
Phosphofructokinase, 75
Phosphoglycerides, 10
  gold-hydroxamic acid reaction for, 52
  staining methods for, 21-26
    acid hematein, 21
    gold-hydroxamic acid, 24-25
    OTAN, 21-24
Phospholipids
  atherosclerosis and, 39
  choline-containing, acid hematein tech-
    nique for, 49-50
  Nile blue sulfate technique for, 55
  osmium tetroxide-α-naphthylamine
    technique for, 50-51
  as polar lipids, 2, 3
  in tissue culture cells, 137-145
    cellular content and synthesis,
      144-145
    fatty acid incorporation, 145
    specific activity of P^{32} in, 145
Phosphosphingosides, 10
  staining methods for, 30-31
Phytodienes, as carcinogens, 184
Plasma triglycerides
  acute effects of glucose on, 101-103
  alterations in, in insulin deficiency, 98
  concentration in diabetes, 80-82
  effect of insulin on concentration, 70, 71
    on outflow, 78-80
    on synthesis of, 75-78
  fluxes, 104-106

Plasma triglycerides (*continued*)
  formation and breakdown of, 65-69
  kinetic control of, by carbohydrate me-
    tabolism and insulin, 63-123
Plasmalogen phospholipids
  plasmal reaction for, 52-53
  staining methods for, 26-27
Polymers
  formed in absence of air, 265-267
  as nonvolatile oxidation products,
    257-258
  from thermally oxidized fats, biological
    properties of, 280-282
Polyperoxides, *see* Peroxides
Polyvinylpyrrolidone flocculation of fat
  particles, 94
Potassium dichromate, as lipid fixative, 5
Prednisolone, as carcinogen, 221
Prednisone, as carcinogen, 229
4-Pregnen-21-hydroxy-3,20-dione, as carcinogen, 205
Progesterone, as carcinogen, 191, 201,
    204, 205, 207, 208, 220, 224, 225, 227
Progestins
  as carcinogens, 221
  granulosa-cell ovarian tumors and,
    207-208
Prolactin, as carcinogen, 203
Prostate
  carcinomas of, 227-228
  tissue culture and cancer, 219-220
Pulmonary physiology and pathology
  histochemical studies of, 41-44
    paraffin granuloma, 41-44
    pulmonary "surfactant," 41
Pyruvate kinase, 75, 115

R

Rats
  adrenal cortex carcinoma, 190
  mammary carcinomas in, 202-205
  as test animals, *see* specific compounds
Rodents, *see also* specific animals
  anterior-lobe chromophobe adenomas,
    190-191
  endometrial neoplasms in, 191-193

S

Saline, as vehicle for carcinogens, 186,
  187

Sarcomas, *see also* Adenomas, Carci-
    nomas, Neoplasms, Tumors
  endometrial, 192-193
  local, 193-194
Serum
  anti-insulin, 83, 89, 92
  influence on tissue culture cells,
    137-155
  as vehicle for carcinogens, 182, 186, 187
Sesame oil, as vehicle for carcinogens,
    182-183, 187
Silicone, liquid, as carcinogen, 225, 226
Slide histochemical methods for lipids,
    see Lipids, specific methods
Sodium hydroxide-acid hematein tech-
    nique for sphingomyelin, 50
Sodium hydroxide-OTAN technique for
    sphingomyelin, 51-52
Somatropin, as carcinogen, 220
Sphingomyelin
  sodium hydroxide-acid hematein tech-
    nique for, 50
  sodium hydroxide-osmium tetroxide-α-
    naphthylamine technique for,
    51-52
  in tissue culture cells, 144
Squalene, as carcinogen, 184
Staining methods for lipids, *see* specific
    lipids
Stearic acid, in tissue culture cells, 138
Steroid hormone transport as related to
    tumorigenic phenomena, 209-211
Steroid hormones
  adrenal
    in treatment of lymphomas, 229
    neoplasms induced by, 190-209
Steroids, carcinogenic effects of, 165-237
Stilbestrol, as carcinogen, 193, 207, 219,
    227
Sucrose
  fatty acid synthesis and, 107
  hyperglyceridemic effect of, 112
Sudan black, 6-7
  technique for lipids, 55-56
Sudan red dyes, 6
Sulfa drugs, as blocking agents, 212-213
Sulfatide
  cresyl violet technique for, 54
  staining method for, 28-29
Sulfatide lipidosis, 40, 41
Svennerholm-Bial reagent, 54-55

T

Testes, interstitial cell tumors of, 193
Testosterone, as carcinogen, 196, 201,
    206, 208, 219, 221, 225, 227
Testosterone propionate, as carcinogen,
    207
Thermal reactions of fats in absence of air,
    261-269
  chemical changes, 261-267
    of dimers and polymers, 265-267
    of volatile and monomeric products,
      261-264
Tissue culture, as related to tumorigenic
    phenomena, 218-221
Tissue culture cells, lipid metabolism in,
    135-161
Tolbutamide, control of diabetes, 82
Tri-p-anisylchloroethylene, as carcino-
    gen, 193
Tricaprylin, as vehicle for carcinogens,
    183
Triglyceride metabolism
  action of insulin on, 69-80
  control of, by carbohydrate metabolism
    and insulin, 63-123
  in diabetes, 80-100, see also Diabetes
    with hyperinsulinism, 99-100
  influence of exogenous carbohydrates
    on, 100-117
  long-term effects of dietary carbohy-
    drates on, 103-117
Triglyceride synthesis, hepatic, 106-107
Triglycerides
  hepatic uptake, 110-111
  levels and flux rates, 65-69
  lipase-lead sulfide technique for, 48-49
  liver, see Liver triglycerides
  metabolism of, see Triglyceride metab-
    olism
  secretion from liver, 110
  plasma, see Plasma triglycerides
  removal of, from plasma in diabetes,
    94-99
  staining methods for, 10 21
  in tissue culture cells, 137-145
Triolein, as vehicle for carcinogens, 182
Triolein-I^{131}, in diabetes, 95
Tripalmitin-C^{14}, in diabetes, 95
Triphenylethylene, as carcinogen, 193
Triphenylphosphine, as reducing agent,
    251
Tumors, see also Adenomas, Carcinomas,
    Neoplasms, Sarcomas
  androgen-estrogen-induced, 208-209
  granulosa-cell ovarian tumors and
    progestins, 207-208
  interstitial cell, 193
  of lymphocyte, monocyte, and myeloid
    cell origin, 195-197
  plasma cell, 197
  testicular, tissue culture of, 220-221

U

Ultraviolet-Schiff technique for lipids, 48
Uterine-vaginal neoplasms, see Neo-
    plasms

W

Wallerian degeneration, histochemical
    studies of, 38-39
Whole-body radiation, 196